ANNUAL PROGRESS IN CHILD PSYCHIATRY AND CHILD DEVELOPMENT 1978

ANNUAL PROGRESS IN CHILD PSYCHIATRY AND CHILD DEVELOPMENT 1978

Edited by

STELLA CHESS, M.D.

Professor of Child Psychiatry
New York University Medical Center

and

ALEXANDER THOMAS, M.D.

Professor of Psychiatry
New York University Medical Center

BRUNNER/MAZEL, *Publishers* ● **New York**

Library of Congress Catalog Card No. 68-23452
SBN 87630-180-4
ISSN 0066-4030

MANUFACTURED IN THE UNITED STATES OF AMERICA

CONTENTS

ANNUAL PROGRESS IN CHILD PSYCHIATRY AND CHILD DEVELOPMENT 1978

Part I

DEVELOPMENTAL ISSUES

Recent years have witnessed a truly exciting burgeoning of research in child developmental issues. The concept of the newborn infant as a *tabula rasa,* a passive responder to environmental influences, has been discredited. Ideas of "imprinting," "critical periods," the "primacy" of the first five years of life, all of which would freeze basic development sequences in early childhood, have been increasingly challenged by research data which indicate that development is a constantly evolving process of child-environment interaction.

Previous volumes of this Annual Progress series have reprinted many of the research reports which have begun to spell out in detail these new approaches and concepts. Rutter has recently summarized these trends as regards early infancy research: "First, it is evident that, although limited in many ways, the young infant has a surprisingly sophisticated response to his environment and quite substantial learning skills. Second, these skills and capacities have a marked influence on the process of parent-child interaction. In many instances it is the baby who shows initiative and the parent who responds by following. Third, even in the early months of life there are striking temperamental differences between infants which influence both their response to the environment and also how other people react to them" (Rutter, in *Child Alive,* ed. by R. Lewin, London: Temple Smith, 1975, p. 208).

With this perspective in mind, the article by McCall takes on special significance. He challenges the field to face certain crucial issues if progress is to continue and a true science of developmental psychology is to evolve. As he puts it most succinctly and cogently, "My thesis is that we lack a substantial science of naturalistic developmental processes. Furthermore, we will not have such inquiry until we alter a value system that excludes or disparages questions that cannot be studied experimentally, until we correct the attitude that most lon-

1

gitudinal research is so fraught with methodological problems as to be hopelessly confounded or beyond the financial and professional commitment of most psychologists, and until we begin to use methods sufficiently sensitive to the variety of possible developmental progressions that they will reveal the multivariate transformations most of us presume to characterize development."

McCall challenges the researcher using standardized experimental techniques to prove not only that a finding or correlation *can* occur, but also that it *does* occur in real life. "Adults can learn nonsense syllables, but they rarely do; children can be classically conditioned, but this may not be the process by which they learn most or even many behaviors. . . ."

Sroufe, in his review of studies of wariness of strangers, does show this concern for the functional developmental significance of this phenomenon as he summarizes and analyses the data from experimental research. As his review shows, the original characterization of the infant's reaction to strangers as "eighth-month anxiety" is simplistic, one-sided, and interpretive well beyond the data. Positive responses coexist with negative ones, marked individual differences occur, and the infant's response is highly sensitive to contextual variation. The term "anxiety," which gives a highly interpretive meaning to the negative reaction, is replaced by Sroufe and others by the descriptive term "wariness." As Sroufe emphasizes, when properly studied, the investigation of the infant's reaction to strangers, as with the related phenomenon of attachment behaviors, can play a significant role in evolving an integrated, organized view of infancy. The ultimate test, of course, will be the correspondence of any such integrated view with the facts of the infant's actual development.

The report by Belmont examines a specific issue, namely the influence of birth order on psychological development. Her report is of special interest because it is based on a unique body of data—records from the Dutch military pre-induction examination of approximately 400,000 young men. Systematic physical, psychological and sociological information was available. The findings on intellectual competence and psychiatric status are clear-cut, and raise a number of intriguing questions and possibilities for further study.

Mednick utilizes a large birth cohort of 9,006 consecutive deliveries to evaluate the consequences of various transient neonatal symptoms on intellectual and behavioral development, as determined at 10 to 12 years of age. This carefully conducted study adds to our knowledge of the predictive significance or lack of significance of neonatal distress for later development—an issue of both theoretical and practical importance.

PART I: DEVELOPMENTAL ISSUES

1

CHALLENGES TO A SCIENCE OF DEVELOPMENTAL PSYCHOLOGY

Robert B. McCall

Center for the Study of Youth Development, Boystown, Nebraska

This paper explores some conceptual and methodological issues in contemporary developmental psychology. It is suggested that, at present, we essentially lack a science of natural developmental processes because few studies are concerned with development as it transpires in naturalistic environments and because we rarely actually collect or analyze truly developmental data. This problem is believed to derive from the veneration of manipulative experimental methods, which have come to dictate rather than serve research questions. The wholesale denigration of nearly all longitudinal methods as either hopelessly confounded or beyond the financial and time commitments of our discipline and a lack of experience with methods of analysis that might reveal the diverse forms of on-

Reprinted with permission from *Child Development*, 1977, **48**, 333–344. Copyright 1977 by the Society for Research in Child Development, Inc.

An abbreviated version of this paper was presented at the International Society for the Study of Behavioural Development conference, "Ecological Factors in Human Development," University of Surrey, Guildford, England, July 13–17, 1975. Work on this paper was supported in part by grants from NICHHD (HD-07372-02), NIE (G-00-3-0008), and the Samuel S. Fels Fund. I thank C. Dodds, D. Eichorn, R. A. Hinde, W. E. Jeffrey, C. Kennedy, R. Kavanaugh, P. McGhee, and J. Wohlwill for their helpful comments on earlier drafts or portions of this paper and J. Steinhilber for preparing the manuscript.

togenetic change that probably characterize most development also contribute to this situation. Such attitudes are extreme and unjustified, and alternative strategies are offered.

Even a casual glance at the literature in developmental psychology indicates that the field has blossomed during the last 2 decades. A large portion of this growth is represented by the investigation of the traditional topics of experimental psychology with infants and children as subjects in place of adult humans or other organisms. To transfer the successful and respected attitudes and methods of general psychology to immature organisms was an obvious historical progression which gave birth to the field of "experimental child psychology" (e.g., Reese & Lipsitt 1970). Moreover, this orientation infused developmental psychology with scientific respectability, and these values permeate and substantially influence contemporary research in developmental psychology.

While I do not question the salutary impact of this renaissance, a reappraisal of our goals and strategies is always in order, especially after 2 decades of rapid expansion. Wohlwill (1973; see also a review by McCall [1974]) has presented one such penetrating evaluation; this paper draws heavily on some of Wohlwill's ideas to make a briefer critique of the current status of developmental psychology.

My thesis is that we lack a substantial science of naturalistic developmental processes. Furthermore, we will not have such inquiry until we alter a value system that excludes or disparages questions that cannot be studied experimentally, until we correct the attitude that most longitudinal research is so fraught with methodological problems as to be hopelessly confounded or beyond the financial and professional commitment of most psychologists, and until we begin to use methods sufficiently sensitive to the variety of possible developmental progressions that they will reveal the multivariate transformations most of us presume to characterize development.

THE EXPERIMENTAL METHOD

Most modern psychologists have been taught that it is only by the experimental method that direct cause-effect conclusions can be specified with confidence and that such statements constitute the principal goal of our discipline. The axioms of the experimental method have served general psychology well, and they have provided developmentalists with much useful information. Certainly no one would want to exclude this approach from our discipline. But developmental psychology has embraced this attitude so completely that the experimental method now dictates rather than serves the research questions we value, fund, and pursue; as a result the process of development as it naturally transpires in children growing up in actual life circumstances has been largely ignored. Do we not want to understand naturalistic development? Should this not be at least one of the major goals of our science? What value is our knowledge if it is not relevant to real children growing up in real families and in real neighborhoods? Bronfenbrenner (1974), for example, has charged that our discipline is the science of the influence of one strange environmental factor or one strange person on one isolated behavior of a single child placed in a largely artificial context. I am not requesting an applied science of development, although that may be a worthy pursuit. Rather, our pure scientific inquiry should not be irrelevant to naturalistic development, and we must not become so enamored with a specific methodology that we fail to study important problems of naturalistic development simply because they are less amenable to our traditional experimental, manipulative methods.

Not only is the study of naturalistic development a worthy devotion, but continuing to ignore such pursuits may cost our discipline and us dearly. During the last decade developmental psychology has been nurtured with relatively large infusions of federal money. Today, not only have we apparently reached the limit of this support, but some of our patron agencies now seem to favor other disciplines at our expense. A new commitment to naturalistic development might help resurrect our position in the eyes of these benefactors.

There are straws in the wind that signal a change toward this posture. Recent articles and presidential addresses (e.g., Miller 1969; Willems 1973; Bronfenbrenner, Note 1; Siegel, Note 2), as well as an entire convention (International Society for the Study of Behavioural Development, Guilford, England, 1975), have urged that developmental psychologists adopt a more naturalistic, relevant, or ecological orientation. But Wohlwill (1973) has warned that serious study of these issues will require major modifications in our research attitudes and methods. This paper examines some of these philosophical and methodological issues.

Necessary and Sufficient Causes

A paragon of scientific psychology is the search for necessary and sufficient causes of behavior. Usually we strive for a conclusion of causal sufficiency—if circumstance X is present, behavior Y will occur.

But this is simply not an attainable goal for many important questions. Which issues of sufficient cause can be answered?

Can versus does?—If the issue is the practical question of whether a specific event has a certain effect, then if that event can be experimentally imposed on a random sample and proper control groups assessed, it is possible to determine whether the manipulation is sufficient to cause the specified outcome. For example, one might want to ask if infants can learn a response by operant conditioning, if an experimental curriculum or a program of therapy can have a positive influence, or if children can be made aggressive after watching violent television programming. These questions are basically of the form, "*Can,* under certain circumstances, factor X produce behavior Y?" They are important, and within practical limitations they can potentially be answered by experimental methods.

But suppose the research issue concerns the factors responsible for this behavior as it typically develops in natural life circumstances. Do babies learn by operant conditioning in conventional family environments? To what extent does violent television fare produce the aggressive behavior we observe on school playgrounds? These questions are of the form, "*Does,* under typical natural circumstances, factor X produce behavior Y?"

Note the important difference between knowing if factor X *can* cause Y and whether factor X actually *does* cause Y in naturalistic situations. Adults can learn nonsense syllables, but they rarely do; children can be classically conditioned, but this may not be the process by which they learn most or even many behaviors; and children can be made to display more aggressive actions by viewing violent television programs, but television may play a relatively minor role in producing the aggressive acts we see on the playground or the increase in the crime rate.

During the last 15 years, developmental psychology has preferred to ask the "can" questions rather than the "does" questions, because the former issues are amenable to manipulative, laboratory research methods. I would argue that the "does" questions are at least equally important, and that we should value and respect their pursuit as much as we venerate experimental approaches to "can" questions. But this will require considerable retrenchment of our expectations of what we can hope to learn about such behavior. For example, Wohlwill (1973) has concluded that we will never be able to determine unequivocally the sufficient causes of naturalistic development. Why not? The explanation emerges as we consider what research tactics we would employ to address these questions.

Description.—First, we could describe pertinent relations in the naturalistic environment. For example, we could observe a correlation between the extent to which children watch violent programs and the level of their aggressive behavior. This approach is required to be able to conclude that *X* does cause *Y*, but it alone is not sufficient because causality cannot be inferred from correlation.

Training.—Another approach is to specially train children in a specific behavior (Baer 1970; Bijou & Baer 1963). For example, some writers have suggested that by training children who do not yet display conservation, we may be able to discover one functional process that nature might use in the naturalistic development of conservation. But will we really gain much ground with this approach? I think not. The human organism can learn by many routes, and there is simply no guarantee that the researcher has selected the one that actually operates in naturalistic environments (if nature relies on only one). And if the training fails, we cannot conclude that nature has chosen another way, because procedures that do not work on immature or inexperienced children may nevertheless function for other children. For example, educators often do not teach reading to the average first grader with the same methods that they employ either with preschool children or with third graders who have not yet learned to read. "Training research" has great value for the investigation of educational and therapeutic programs, but its potential for revealing naturalistic developmental processes is considerably more limited.

Experimental intervention in naturalistic contexts.—Perhaps the most direct approach is to experimentally impose the hypothesized factor on a random sample in a naturalistic environment. In principle, this is a valuable strategy which also has the obvious appeal of being "experimental." Thus, if a new educational television program on elementary mathematics is to be introduced, towns could be randomly selected for target and control programs and appropriate pre- and posttesting administered.

Unfortunately, this strategy is only possible if the independent variable is manipulable as in the illustrative case of a new educational television program. However, if every child experiences the factor in question, even a necessary and sufficient cause of development could not be studied in this way. For example, exposure to visual pattern is required for the development of a variety of visual functions, but every child receives adequate patterned light. Certain sensorimotor activities may be propaedeutic to the acquisition of agent-action-object language constructions, but almost all children obtain adequate amounts of these experiences. In these cases, we sometimes suppose that "more is better," so we provide disadvantaged children with experiences typically found in the family life of advantaged youngsters in the hope of closing the gap between these groups. If successful, we would then attribute the original difference between these samples to the hypothesized factor. But one then returns to the issue of generalization—*does* the experimental factor or some other circumstance actually operate in the naturalistic development of advantaged children?

Interpreting experimental results.—Even given perfect intervention into naturalistic circumstances, the interpretation of experimental results is likely to be more complicated when the behavior is developing than when it is ontogenetically static (Wohlwill 1973). Suppose it were possible to nutritionally deprive a developing child. During the period of deprivation the rate of growth would likely slow relative to controls, but afterward the rate of growth would actually *exceed* the normal for a short period of time (Tanner 1963). What shall we say caused this "catch-up growth?" Usually, the observed difference between the experimental and the control group is attributable to the experimental manipulation. Shall we then say that the nutritional deprivation caused the catch-up growth? Or was it the termination of the deprivation condition that produced it? Obviously, something not under experimental control, in addition to the deprivation experience, is required to interpret the phenomenon of catch-up growth. The notions of critical period and the "match" between an environmental event and the nature of the child at that time (Hunt 1961; McCall, Appelbaum, & Hogarty 1973) reflect similar situations with respect to behavioral development.

Necessary causes.—Can necessary, as opposed to sufficient, causes of development be discovered? Logically this is possible, but it is unlikely from a practical standpoint. To determine the necessary causes of development, one must deprive the organism of the hypothesized circumstance. However, when children are the focus of study, ethical considerations obviate experimental deprivation in most cases. Therefore, we are not likely to know the necessary causes of development either.

Implications

There is nothing inherently wrong with manipulative experimental studies in developmental psychology, but this methodology is not the only approach, it is often impossible to execute, and it is sometimes not the appropriate research strategy for many important questions that our discipline should be examining.

We must simply accept the fact from logical and practical standpoints that we will probably never prove the sufficient or necessary causes for the naturalistic development of a host of major behaviors, some of which represent the essence of our discipline. We will never unequivocally demonstrate *(a)* the necessary role that sensorimotor and perceptual-cognitive experiences in the first 18 months of life play in the child's development of language or intelligence in the second and third years, *(b)* whether Piaget's stages are necessarily sequenced as proposed and whether they are functionally related, or *(c)* the mental and experiential factors required for the development of reciprocal, self-initiated social relations.

But I do not conclude that we should abandon these questions. On the contrary, I believe we *must* continue to ask them if our discipline is to achieve social utility. Other sciences face these same realities— consider the problems of epidemiology (e.g., what is causing the increase of cancer in the United States?). Epidemiologists are apparently less frustrated by such logical limitations because they do not have a history of deifying the manipulative experimental method above all others in aspiration of being "a science, like physics." Rather, they approach the problem by marshalling evidence from as many of the above strategies as possible, realizing that each is deficient in itself. Thus, if a laboratory study demonstrates that under certain conditions X can lead to Y, if there is a relationship between X and Y in naturalistic settings, if X can be imposed in a naturalistic or quasi-naturalistic environment and it leads to Y, then these several observations coalesce on the tentative proposition that X does cause Y in naturalistic circumstances. Each approach is inadequate by itself, but each makes a vital contribution to the conclusion.

NEW DIRECTIONS

If developmental psychologists are to adopt this strategy of converging operations (Garner, Hake, & Eriksen 1956), we must place equal value on each individual approach, including those we have maligned or ignored in the past—the description of naturalistic events, the use of longitudinal methods, and the willingness to employ procedures sensitive to diverse types of developmental progressions and multiple causal and moderating factors.

Naturalistic Description

A case can be made that the description of relationships in naturalistic environments, while not sufficient to establish that factor X does cause behavior Y, is necessary for such a conclusion. Yet historically, description is. not one of the psychologist's delights—it is a second-class method of study to be used by default, not by choice, because it does not permit one to infer causality. In fact, we rarely take the time to keep our experimental hands off a behavior long enough to make systematic descriptive observations in naturalistic settings of the several dimensions and circumstances of the behavior we wish to study. Although we are intensely empirical about drawing cause-and-effect conclusions, we are quite nonempirical when it comes to selecting the behavior of interest, the particular measurement variable(s), the ecological context, the age of the subjects, and a host of other parameters. We apparently prefer to make all of these vital decisions a priori, rather than from a base of empirical, descriptive information. As a consequence, much of our research represents a nearly blind run into a forest of behavior to study the growth of a single tree.

We could learn much from a descriptive survey of the environmental and behavioral landscape before charting our experimental expeditions. Detailed multivariate longitudinal descriptive studies could reveal ages at which the variability of a behavior is greatest (presumably when it is most plastic), patterns of correlated factors could suggest causal hypotheses, and the interrelationships among dependent variables, as well as their differential correlation with other factors, might point out the most salient measurements as well as the number of independent manifestations of the behavior.

Developmental psychologists should accord description the esteem other disciplines do because much has been learned at its hand: consider the theory of evolution, the plate theory of continental drift, and our knowledge of the early evolution of *Homo sapiens*. Paleontology, geology, and astronomy seem to be alive and well without manipulating fossils, continents, or heavenly bodies, and we might look into our own backyard at Jean Piaget to observe the impact detailed naturalistic description can have on a discipline even when the maximum number of subjects is only three.

Are We Developmental?

The definition of developmental psychology embodies a focus on change—changes that occur over time within organisms (Wohlwill 1973). I believe developmental psychology has not been sufficiently developmental. At the very least, a developmental study should consist of observations at different ages, but only a modest percentage of our professional papers involve any age comparisons at all. Contemporary developmental psychologists primarily focus on specific behaviors displayed by immature organisms at a single age. Even our textbooks in developmental psychology are characterized by the presentation of developmentally static information on certain behavioral dispositions of infants and children (e.g., attention and habituation in infants, factors in children's imitation, environmental correlates of mental behavior, etc.) We do not often read how these behaviors emerge over age, what developmental events constitute their antecedents, or how developmental changes in one behavior are related to developmental changes in other behaviors. Wohlwill (1973) blames the fact that most developmental psychologists have simply carried over the attitudes and methodologies appropriate for the study of static behavioral events to observations of immature organisms and called such efforts developmental. In large part, our discipline is developmental in name only.

However, even when we do assess subjects of more than one age, this fact alone does not strictly merit the label of developmental research. One must distinguish between age differences and age changes (Wohlwill 1973). If one simply wants to describe how organisms differ in behavior at one age versus another, then cross-sectional assessments may be appropriate. A great deal of our current knowledge of infants and children is borne on the shoulders of this strategy. But, if a primary mission is to discern ontogenetic change within individuals, the sequence and timing of developmental transitions, and the changing social and environmental factors that permit development to occur, then we must use longitudinal, not cross-sectional, approaches to our subject matter.

We routinely acknowledge this as the method of choice when the changes within individuals occur over a very short (convenient?) span of time. Would anyone suggest a cross-sectional approach to the study of learning, habituation, or dark adaptation (except under the unusual circumstance in which the testing event influences performance)? Typically we do not design a learning experiment with independent groups of subjects after one trial, two trials, or three trials of training. Moreover, students of learning are also concerned with change within individual subjects as reflected in their skepticism that the average group learning curve typifies the performance of all or even many of the individual subjects within that group. The difference between research on learning and research on development is primarily the length of time between assessments. If we really want to focus our scientific attention on behavioral development within individual organisms, then we must employ longitudinal approaches and analyses that will reveal individual variation in the profile and qualitative nature of such age changes. This is an old saw, but our failure to act on it compels its repetition.

Studying Developmental Change

Apart from our reliance on experimental procedures, developmental methodology in general has not kept pace with the conceptual questions we sometimes want to, or should, ask. For example, development can proceed in two distinct realms, and in my view our failure to maintain this distinction has retarded our progress.

Developmental function versus individual differences.—A behavior can increase or decrease in frequency or amount across age, or one behavior can replace, supplement, or grow out of another with development. The plot of the amount or frequency of a given behavior or set of behaviors across age for an individual or group of individuals is a *developmental function* (Wohlwill 1973). A growth curve for height or Piaget's sensorimotor stages constitute developmental functions. Depending upon whether the nature of the attribute in question undergoes a fundamental qualitative (as opposed to quantitative) change over age, a developmental function may be continuous (e.g., height) or discontinuous (e.g., Piaget's stages).

But development also may be reflected in *individual differences*. That is, does the relative rank ordering of individual subjects on a given attribute relate to the relative rank ordering of those individuals on the same or another attribute assessed at a subsequent age? Usually we approach this question by correlating scores across the two ages. A significant correlation implies stability rather than instability of individual differences (Emmerich 1964).

The important point is that continuity/discontinuity in developmental function is potentially independent from stability/instability in individual differences. For example, the correlation coefficient is independent of the means of the two distributions entering its calculation; therefore, the stability of individual differences across age is potentially independent of the developmental function represented by a plot of the average values at each age.

I believe progress in developmental psychology has been retarded by the failure to keep this distinction in mind. For example, the statement that 50% of a child's adult intelligence is developed by the age of 4 (Bloom 1964) reflects the statistical fact that the correlation between IQ at 4 and at 17 years is approximately .71. But this claim for the development of intelligence *in general* is based solely on the stability of individual differences and completely ignores the fact that the average child's mental age (i.e., developmental function) will increase by 4½ times during this interval. McCall, Eichorn, and Hogarty (in press) have discussed other examples of the failure to make this distinction.

Individual differences and development.—I detect a tendency for our discipline to emphasize information on the stability of individual differences at the expense of data on the developmental function. For decades the entire area of infant mental development was dominated by the attempt to predict individual differences in later IQ, despite the fact that the patriarch of the field, Jean Piaget, totally ignores individual differences in favor of describing the nature of the developmental function. Nevertheless, the stability of individual differences has almost become the validity criterion for infant tests of mental development. Well-meaning scientists have questioned the validity and utility of infant tests because they do not predict later IQ (the reliability of the tests over shorter periods of time is unquestioned). This attitude ignores the possibility that a test may have contemporary but not predictive validity and still be useful. Pediatricians use birth weight as a valid sign of current health status even though it does not predict childhood weight. Moreover, tests could help us learn about the nature of the developmental function for early infant mental development (e.g., McCall et al., in press). Relying solely on an individual difference approach to establish the validity of infant tests or to learn about mental development is rather like concentrating on predicting a 10-foot height difference in mature giant sequoia trees from the size of seedlings while completely ignoring the issue of how all the trees eventually grow to be over 300 feet tall.

Of course, while it is not the only sphere of inquiry, individual differences represents an important topic. But if we are to be truly developmental, its study should be prosecuted with attitudes and methods that are sensitive to describing change as well as stability over age. Heretofore, this has not often been the case. To illustrate, give a developmental psychologist concerned with individual differences a set of longitudinal mental test data, for example, and the first (and regrettably sometimes the only) analysis is typically the calculation of cross-age correlations. From the standpoint of learning about developmental changes, consider the two possible results of such a strategy—a significant or a non-significant correlation. A substantial correlation would indicate that individuals retain their rank ordering over some age span with respect to mental performance. In short, this correlation reveals stability, not developmental change, in individual differences. Moreover, because the correlation coefficient is totally independent of the means of the distributions entering its calculation, a simple cross-age correlational analysis is not sensitive to changes in the group's average performance over age. Finally, when a significant but modest-sized correlation is found, the interpretive emphasis is often on stability even when the proportion of variability reflecting stability is only a fraction of the proportion associated with change in individual differences.

On the other hand, if the longitudinal correlation does not reach significance, we cannot conclude that developmental change has occurred because this would require accepting the null hypothesis. Consequently, the only scientifically legitimate result from a simple cross-age correlational approach is the demonstration of some degree of longitudinal consistency which, in some sense, represents the absence of developmental change. (This simple cross-age correlational approach is to be distinguished from more complex methods that use correlations which can reveal patterns of change—see below.)

New directions.—The pervasiveness of the above strategy implies that even longitudinal studies have not always been truly developmental because their goal has been the description of stability, not change, in individual differences over age. I am appealing for an equally rigorous attempt to describe and explain developmental change. For example, what would we look for if we seriously adopted Piaget's conception of epigenetic development? The order of behavioral dispositions through infancy has been described, but this is not the only question to be asked of stage sequence models. Do stages replace or supplement one another? Is it possible for two attributes to coalesce to form a third; could one attribute dichotomize to form two new dispositions? Several authors have recently described a variety of possible developmental progressions, and if we assimilate them into our thinking and accommodate our methodology to search for them, developmental psychology may yet become truly developmental. I urge readers to consult these references (e.g., Buss & Royce 1975; Coombs & Smith 1973; Emmerich 1968; Flavell 1972; Van den Daele 1969, 1974; Wohlwill 1973; Maccoby, Note 3).

Longitudinal Methodology

Serious developmental study ultimately requires longitudinal data and analysis, but longitudinal research has just suffered a decade of pejorative "re-evaluation." Baltes (Baltes & Schaie 1973), Nesselroade (Nesselroade & Baltes 1974), and Schaie (1965) have warned the developmental community of the inherent confound between age, the year in which someone is measured, and the year of his/her birth (which establishes the subject's cohort). Since age is defined jointly by birth year and year of measurement, there can be no simple way of assessing age changes independent of one or the other of these factors. Moreover, longitudinal studies repeatedly assess individuals, and the assessment experience itself may alter the subjects so that observed changes over age are a result of the experience of repeated testing and not of genuine developmental processes. Finally, if large age spans are involved, subjects drop out of the sample, and there may be a difference between those subjects who remain and those who depart before the end of the project.

The possibility that age changes might be confounded with extraneous variables is a valid concern. The real issue is what should be done about this possibility. Alternative research designs have been proposed, but they are quite demanding. The extreme case was Schaie's (1965) original proposal of a minimum design that required $2k-1$ cohorts (i.e., samples born in different years) for a longitudinal study at k ages. Applied to the Berkeley Growth Study (assuming yearly assessments between 1 and 40 years of age), this design would require more than 5,500 subjects with no dropouts, the study (which was started in 1928) would not be finished until the year 2008, and the cost would be unconscionable. While more economical designs are available, the impact of assessing all extraneous variables has been to define "proper" longitudinal methodology beyond the time and financial means of our discipline.

Which assumption?—While alternative designs have been suggested—even demanded—it is not obvious that these approaches are always, or even often, unqualifiably better. The fact is that age, secular year of measurement, and birth year are *inevitably* confounded and can *never* be teased apart without making *some* assumptions. The issue for developmental psychology is which assumptions shall we make. The milestone longitudinal studies (e.g., Fels and Berkeley) tacitly assumed that their massive programs of repeated assessments did not change their subject's behavior relative to children not experiencing such intensive testing and that any age changes observed in the data were caused by generalizable developmental processes and were not produced by unusual historical events that children born in other decades do not experience at the same age, if ever (e.g., a world war, permissive attitudes in child rearing, etc.). That is, they assumed no effects for repeated testing or secular change (i.e., cohort differences). The tenability of such assumptions should be debated, but it is not always clear that the assumptions required by some of the suggested alternative research designs are more palatable. For example, in the extreme case, one of Schaie's (1965) proposed models actually requires that all effects for age, cohort, and year of measurement are identically monotonic! That is, the dependent variable must increase (or decrease) monotonically in the same way as a function of age, cohort, and year of measurement. After such a prescription, how many degrees of freedom does nature have left for our research to reveal?

If developmentalists are going to study change within organisms, we will have to use longitudinal approaches, and we must make some assumptions concerning extraneous variables regardless of which design we employ. Moreover, such assumptions will be specific to the independent and dependent variables in each study—a total maligning of one or another longitudinal approach is inappropriate and retards progress in our discipline.

Secular change.—The available literature on the influence of year of birth (also referred to as the cohort or secular effect), time of measurement, repeated testing, and selective dropout indicates that these variables have their primary effect on the average level of intellectual and personality characteristics in a group, but these same data also indicate that the correlational structure among variables within an age or from one age to the next is *not* so susceptible to these factors.

To illustrate, Nesselroade and Baltes (1974) demonstrated rather large secular differences and repeated testing effects for the means of six primary abilities and 10 personality variables during adolescence. That is, there were variations in mean performance level at a given age or across age as a function of the year in which children were born as well as the number of tests they had previously experienced, thereby validating the potential impact of secular change and repeated testing on the developmental function for these behaviors.

However, a totally different impression is gained when the stability of individual differences is considered. The authors presented 102 cross-age correlations for each of two samples which differed in their year of birth, time of measurement, and number of tests preceding the assessments of interest (their tables 13 and 14). I have found that only six of these 102 pairs of correlations were significantly different, just about what one would expect on the basis of chance alone. Thus, in a single data base that showed marked effects for the extraneous variables on the average performance of a variety of personality and mental assessments (i.e., on developmental function), there were no obvious effects of these variables on cross-age correlational patterns (i.e., stability of individual differences).

This argument is also buoyed by the fact that some cross-age correlation matrices look remarkably similar even when derived from different studies. The Berkeley Growth Study and the Fels projects were designed quite differently with respect to secular change. Specifically, the Berkeley study consists of a single cohort born in 1928, whereas the Fels study sampled subjects continuously for more than 40 years beginning in 1930. Nevertheless, the pattern of cross-age correlations for IQ from infancy to adulthood is remarkably similar for these two studies. It is pertinent to note that much traditional longitudinal research has concentrated on correlational data analyses, not on average levels of behavior. Despite the limitations of some types of correlational analyses for describing change, other forms of longitudinal analyses that do yield information on change nevertheless rely on correlations which may be less prone to secular fluctuations than some would have us believe.

Therefore, for studies relying on correlations, the assumption of no effects for secular change or repeated testing may be the most appropriate and economical. But correlational studies are not the only context in which secular effects might be presumed negligible. We do not demand controls for the time of day in studies of learning or habituation, but those time-based phenomena are just as confounded with time of day as age is with secular year. Obviously, we decide a priori that such an extraneous factor is irrelevant. It may be equally justifiable to do so in some longitudinal studies. Will someone propose that the ontogeny of Piaget's sensorimotor stages will differ from one decade to the next? The assumption of no secular change is not always unreasonable or impermissible.

Repeated testing—The possible effects on the child of being repeatedly tested may also be overstated. Two large longitudinal studies have enrolled new subjects in the middle of the assessment schedule and found no effects of repeated testing (Freeman & Flory 1937; Moriarty 1966). Analyses I have made on the data presented by Nesselroade and Baltes (1974) show that the repeated-testing effect they observed was much stronger from the first to the second testing than from the second to the third assessments for each of the six primary mental abilities. Therefore, it is possible that repeated testing has its major influence from the first to the second assessment and relatively less thereafter.

Conclusion

To be clear, there is no question that longitudinal research is methodologically complex and requires certain assumptions for its proper interpretation. There is seldom any justification for sloppy or shortcut methodology, and an awareness of the possible confounds of secular change and repeated testing is a necessary constituent of the current state of the scientific art. However, although there are unassailable empirical demonstrations of secular changes and repeated-testing effects on the average level of many behaviors (i.e., on the developmental function), some of us have inappropriately overgeneralized these results to other aspects of these data (e.g., correlational patterns of individual differences). Indeed, this has gone so far that anything "longitudinal" is often quickly maligned or dogmatically cast into a particular design without regard to the specific behavior, the research question, or the empirical justification for making one set of assumptions as opposed to another. All longitudinal research requires some assumptions about secular change, age, and year of measurement, but let us decide which assumptions are plausible on the basis of each individual research question and analysis. The longitudinal method is the lifeblood of developmental psychology; it deserves a more thorough, objective, and constructive evaluation by all developmentalists.

METHODS OF ANALYSIS

It is to the credit of Baltes, Nesselroade, Schaie, Wohlwill, and their colleagues that they have attempted to wrestle with the design and analysis of research whose primary function is to reveal developmental change. Unfortunately, while many of the suggested analyses possess substantial promise, they have rarely been tried (let alone exploited) by developmentalists. Space considerations permit only a brief citation of references, and the reader is especially encouraged to consult Wohlwill's (1973) comprehensive presentation.

Univariate Approaches

Developmental function.—Baltes and Nesselroade (1973), Coombs and Smith (1973), Horn and Little (1966), Nesselroade (1970), Van den Daele (1969, 1974), and Wohlwill (1973) have described and evaluated a variety of statistical approaches to developmental data, and Buss and Royce (1975), Flavell (1972), Van den Daele (1969, 1974), Wohlwill (1973), and Maccoby (Note 3) have considered a variety of possible conceptions of developmental consistency and change in a single variable as well as the ontogenetic sequence of two or more qualitatively distinct behaviors.

Individual differences in developmental functions.—McCall et al. (1973) described individual differences in the developmental pattern of IQ over a wide developmental span, but their methods could be applied to almost any repeatedly assessed variable. In the case of IQ, their approach yielded groups of subjects that were relatively homogeneous for developmental IQ pattern within groups but heterogeneous between groups. Consequently, they described subgroups of subjects who displayed contrasting developmental patterns in a single variable, and differences between these groups were related to other variables of conceptual interest.

Multivariate Approaches

Contemporary thought concerning the ontogeny of behavior emphasizes a complex and interacting set of environmental and organismic determinants that change over age. Therefore, a multivariate, longitudinal approach may be indicated. For example, Sameroff and Chandler (1975) have proposed a general model for developmental processes which they term "transactional" to emphasize the constant interplay and mutual influence of environmental and organismic factors across developmental time. Reciprocal effects in the parent-infant interaction literature represent one currently popular example of this orientation. Scarr-Salapatek (1976) has called attention to the "canalization" approach to issues of heredity and environment, another multivariate developmental conception of growth.

While these models are appealing, how shall we analyze the multivariate, longitudinal data they demand? If there are only two or three measurement variables, one strategy is to apply the procedures used by McCall et al. (1973) sketched above for describing individual differences in developmental patterns separately for each variable and then observe whether there is a correspondence within individuals for the pattern of change in these several measures. However, if there are many variables, this approach becomes unwieldy and a truly multivariate strategy would be desirable. For example, three-mode factor analysis (Tucker 1963) or a similar approach devised by Jöreskog (Note 4) might be considered.

Essentially, three-mode factor analysis is a multivariate extension of the individual difference approach to developmental patterns described above in which the subjects × variables × repeated testings matrix is factored. The results reveal not only how variables, subjects, or repeated assessments cluster and interrelate over the other two modes, but also how variable and subject dimensions interrelate and change over the repeated assessment mode. While there are problems and limitations to this technique (e.g., the variables must be conceptually identical at each assessment age), if we really believe in the transactional perspective and are vigorous about describing multivariate longitudinal change, we cannot continue to avoid exploring these procedures.

An Attitude

While the search for developmental change may frequently involve new methods of analysis, this is not necessarily so. Fundamentally, a revised attitude toward searching for change rather than stability or continuity is needed. For example, using traditional statistical techniques. McCall et al. (in press) observed that relative breaks in the stability of individual differences occurred at the same ages that discontinuities were observed in the developmental function of infant mental test performance. They subjected the individual items from mental tests given to the Berkeley Growth Study subjects periodically throughout the first 5 years of life to principal components analyses and then correlated component scores across age. The level of the cross-age correlations among first principal components dipped at 8, 13, and 21 months, precisely the ages when major changes in the nature of the item composition of those components occurred. Despite the reliance on traditional methods of statistical analysis, this study was distinctive in its avowed attempt to search for change in developmental function as well as individual differences.

CONCLUSION

The purpose of this paper has been to step back from our discipline and assess our goals, values, and methods. I have argued that (1) we are avoiding major research issues necessary to our discipline's social utility because they do not lend themselves to manipulative experimentation, (2) we must revalue naturalistic description as a necessary method for approaching many important problems, (3) we have seldom been truly developmental in thought or research, (4) contemporary chiding of longitudinal methodology has been overgeneralized and is retarding our progress, and (5) we must exploit methods that are sensitive to a variety of forms of developmental change. It is time for developmental psychology to match methods with the demands of the research question, regardless of its complexity or our penchant for univariate, manipulative research.

REFERENCE NOTES

1. Bronfenbrenner, U. Social change: the challenge to research and policy. Paper presented at the meeting of the Society for Research in Child Development, Denver, April 1975.
2. Siegel, A. E. Communicating with the next generation. Division 7 Presidential Address, American Psychological Association, New Orleans, September 1974.
3. Maccoby, E. E. Tracing individuality within age-related change. Paper presented at the meeting of the Society for Research in Child Development, Santa Monica, Calif., March 1969.
4. Jöreskog, K. G. Factoring the multitest-multi-occasion correlation matrix (Educational Testing Service Research Bulletin 69–62). Princeton, N.J., Educational Testing Service, 1969.

REFERENCES

Baer, D. M. An age-irrelevant concept of development. *Merrill-Palmer Quarterly*, 1970. **16**, 238-245.

Baltes, P. B., & Nesselroade, J. B. The developmental analysis of individual differences on multiple measures. In J. R. Nesselroade & H. W. Reese (Eds.), *Life-span developmental psychology: methodological issues*. New York: Academic Press, 1973.

Baltes, P. B., & Schaie, K. W. On life-span developmental research paradigms: retrospects and prospects. In P. B. Baltes & K. W. Schaie (Eds.), *Life-span developmental psychology: personality and socialization*. New York: Academic Press, 1973.

Bijou, S. W., & Baer, D. M. Some methodological contributions from a functional analysis of child development. In L. P. Lipsitt & C. C. Spiker (Eds.), *Advances in child development and behavior*. Vol. **1**. New York: Academic Press, 1963.

Bloom, B. S. *Stability and change in human characteristics*. New York: Wiley, 1964.

Bronfenbrenner, U. Developmental research, public policy, and the ecology of childhood. *Child Development*, 1974, **45**, 1–5.

Buss, A. R., & Royce, J. R. Ontogenetic change in cognitive structure from a multivariate perspective. *Developmental Psychology*, 1975, **11**, 87–101.

Coombs, C. H., & Smith, J. E. K. On the detection of structure in attitudes and developmental processes. *Psychological Review*, 1973, **80**, 337-351.

Emmerich, W. Continuity and stability in early social development. *Child Development*, 1964, **35**, 311–332.

Emmerich, W. Personality development and concepts of structure. *Child Development*, 1964, **35**, 311–332.

Emmerich, W. Personality development and concepts of structure. *Child Development*, 1968, **39**, 671–690.

Flavell, J. H. An analysis of cognitive-developmental sequences. *Genetic Psychology Monographs*, 1972, **86**, 279–350.

Freeman, F. N., & Flory, C. D. Growth and intellectual ability as measured by repeated tests. *Monographs of the Society for Research in Child Development*, 1937, **2**(2, Serial No. 9).

Garner, W. R.; Hake, H. W.; & Eriksen, C. W. Operationism and the concept of perception. *Psychological Review*, 1956, **63**, 149–159.

Horn, J. L., & Little, K. B. Isolating change and invariance in patterns of behavior. *Multivariate Behavioral Research*, 1966, **1**, 219–228.

Hunt, J. M. *Intelligence and experience*. New York: Ronald, 1961.

McCall, R. B. Critique of a field (review of *The Study of Behavioral Development* by Joachim F. Wohlwill). *Science*, 1974, **184**, 673–674.

McCall, R. B.; Appelbaum, M.; & Hogarty, P. S. Developmental changes in mental performance. *Monographs of the Society for Research in Child Development*, 1973,**38**(3, Serial No. 150).

McCall, R. B.; Eichorn, D. H.; & Hogarty, P. S. Transitions in early mental development. *Monographs of the Society for Research in Child Development*, in press.

Miller, G. A. Psychology as a means of promoting human welfare. *American Psychologist*, 1969, **24**, 1063–1075.

Moriarty, A. D. *Constancy and I.Q. change: a clinical view of relationships between tested intelligence and personality*. Springfield, Ill.: Thomas, 1966.

Nesselroade, J. R. Application of multivariate strategies to problems of measuring and structuring long-term change. In L. R. Goulet & P. B. Baltes (Eds.), *Life-span developmental psychology: research and theory*. New York: Academic Press, 1970.

Nesselroade, J. R., & Bältes, P. B. Adolescent personality development and historical change: 1970–1972. *Monographs of the Society for Research in Child Development,* 1974, **39**(1, Serial No. 154).

Reese, H. W., & Lipsitt, L. P. *Experimental child psychology.* New York: Academic Press, 1970.

Sameroff, A. J., & Chandler, M. J. Reproductive risk and the continuum of caretaking casualty. In F. D. Horowitz, E. M. Hetherington, S. Scarr-Salapatek, & G. M. Siegel (Eds.), *Review of child development research.* Vol. **4.** Chicago: University of Chicago Press, 1975.

Scarr-Salapatek, S. An evolutionary perspective on infant intelligence: species patterns and individual variations. In M. Lewis (Ed.), *Origins of intelligence.* New York: Plenum, 1976.

Schaie, K. W. A general model for the study of developmental problems. *Psychological Bulletin,* 1965, **64**, 94–107.

Tanner, J. M. The regulation of human growth. *Child Development,* 1963, **34**, 817–848.

Tucker, L. R. Implications of factor analysis of three-way matrices for measurement of change. In C. W. Harris (Ed.), *Problems in measuring change.* Madison: University of Wisconsin Press, 1963.

Van den Daele, L. D. Qualitative models in developmental analysis. *Developmental Psychology,* 1969, **1**, 303–310.

Van den Daele, L. D. Infrastructure and transition in developmental analysis. *Human Development,* 1974, **17**, 1–23.

Willems, E. P. Behavioral ecology and experimental analysis: courtship is not enough. In J. R. Nesselroade & H. W. Reese (Eds.), *Life-span developmental psychology: methodological issues.* New York: Academic Press, 1973.

Wohlwill, J. F. *The study of behavioral development.* New York: Academic Press, 1973.

PART I: DEVELOPMENTAL ISSUES

2

WARINESS OF STRANGERS AND THE STUDY OF INFANT DEVELOPMENT

L. Alan Sroufe

Institute of Child Development,
University of Minnesota

The construct of wariness of strangers is sufficiently viable to withstand recent critiques and to have an important place in an integrated view of infant development. Negative reactions to strangers appear to be a general phenomenon, although there is considerable individual variation in age of onset and in developmental course. The manifestation of aversive reactions is highly influenced by context and procedural variations. When procedural and coding variations are taken into account, stranger approach studies reveal consistent developmental trends; negative reactions are rare in the first half year, common by 8 or 9 months, and increasingly frequent throughout the first year. The range of reactions can be reliably coded, and even subtle aversive responses have been validated in a variety of ways. There is evidence of some stability of negative reactions, though consistency of individual differences in type of

Reprinted with permission from *Child Development,* 1977, **48,** 731–746. Copyright 1977 by the Society for Research in Child Development, Inc.

The preparation of this paper was supported in part by a contract grant from the National Institute of Mental Health (278-75-0030[ER]) and by a Program Project Grant from the National Institute of Child Health and Human Development (5 PO1 HD 05-027). The contribution of Patricia Yonas in this project is gratefully acknowledged.

*reaction has not been adequately assessed. The meaning and sig-
nificance of wariness are most clearly seen when examined in interaction with the affiliative, exploratory, and attachment systems
and when its implications for major problems in cognitive, social,
and emotional development are considered.*

Currently, wariness of strangers is in disfavor as a useful concept in
studying infant development. Critical papers and reviews have concluded that negative reactions to strangers are unreliable, unstable, inconsistently observed, and incompatible with unequivocally observed
affiliative reactions (Rheingold & Eckerman 1973; Haviland & Lewis,
Note 1; Shaffran & Décarie, Note 2). In their review Rheingold and
Eckerman point to widespread inconsistencies in reported age of onset
and percentage of infants showing fear at a given age and to a reliance on subjective, unvalidated "wary" responses.[1] Since crying and
frank avoidance are less common than smiling and other affiliative
reactions, these authors question the validity of the construct of wariness of strangers.

In this paper the literature on infants' reactions to strangers will be
reviewed to show: (1) that the data are coherent concerning the onset
and development of wariness of strangers, (2) that existing inconsistencies can be reconciled by consideration of procedures and scoring
criteria, (3) that the use of measures other than crying and frank fear
is both defensible and revealing, and (4) that the existence of wariness
and affiliative reactions can be put together into an organized picture
of infant behavior and development. Issues of assessment, reliability,
and stability will be examined. In short, wariness of strangers will be
treated as a developmental construct, and its validity will be assessed.

There has been a notable failure by researchers to discuss the nature of the construct under study in stranger fear studies and a tendency to study reactions to stranger approach without considering the
complexity of infant development. The type of study done and the interpretation given results greatly depend on whether negative reactions to strangers are viewed in terms of developmental milestones,
traits, pre-potent stimuli, conditioned responses, or cognitive-social
organization. The current presentation will emphasize an organizational perspective (Sroufe, in press).

---

[1]In this paper "wariness" (apprehensiveness) will be used to cover the range of negative reactions to strangers. "Wary responses" will also be used in referring to subtle
negative reactions to be described. Fear will be reserved for rather immediate negative
reactions (compare Bronson 1972).

When wariness is defined as an organizational construct, its significance is not as a developmental milestone or as a trait of the individual. Rather, the tendency to inhibit approach or to avoid novel objects and persons is considered in terms of its adaptive value and in terms of its interaction with other behavioral systems (affiliation, exploration, attachment [Bretherton & Ainsworth 1974]). It is as a balance for the infant's strong approach and exploration tendencies, which are also necessary in man's adaptation, that wariness has significance (e.g., Bronson 1972). Developmental changes in wariness are important for what they reflect and imply in other developmental domains and for the study of developmental reorganization. Important individual differences are cast in terms of the organization of wariness with other systems (e.g., the attachment-exploration balance, declining wariness with familiarization), not overall amount of wariness regardless of context. Thus, rather than seeking correlations between age of onset of wariness or degree of wariness and indices of cognitive or social development, within the organizational perspective predictions are based on the interaction of behavioral systems. For example, the ability to use the caregiver as a source of support in overcoming initial hesitance to approach a stranger would be stable (see the discussion of wariness and attachment below).

Spitz (1965) was the first to emphasize the organizational significance of "stranger anxiety." By this he meant that stranger reactions were most appropriately viewed within the matrix of cognitive, social, and emotional development. His own observations led him to conclude that the mere *sight* of the stranger's face, especially in the absence of mother, would automatically elicit fear once the appropriate developmental level was achieved (presumably because the stranger signified mother absence). Research to be reviewed below discredits Spitz's emphasis on the stranger as signifying maternal loss. Whatever the salience of strangers, it is clear that infants' reactions to them are complexly determined. However, the more basic idea, that stranger reactions reflect developmental organization, becomes even more potent in light of this literature.

Assessing the validity of the construct of wariness includes examining the power of this construct in formulating an integrative perspective on infant development. Wariness is no more and no less significant than affiliation, but it is important that it not be discarded simply because evidence of affiliation has come to the fore. Establishing aversive reactions to strangers as a reliable developmental phenomenon would not in itself be sufficient to justify continued interest in this problem. The view to be developed here is that much more than a developmental "milestone" is lost when wariness of strangers is defined out of existence. In support of this view, the importance of stranger reactions for understanding cognitive and social development in infancy and for evaluating theories of emotion will be illustrated. To the extent that stranger reaction studies are of value for the broader task of comprehending infant development, they are significant.

THE DEVELOPMENT OF WARINESS OF STRANGERS

The Incidence of Wariness of Strangers: Longitudinal Studies

In an early study of wariness of strangers, Schaffer and Emerson (1964) reported that fearful or wary reactions occurred in every infant at some age. Later, using this same sample, Schaffer (1966) reported in more detail on 36 infants seen longitudinally in a standard approach sequence in the home. By 28 weeks, 19% had shown an aversive reaction (cry, screw face, hide face, look or turn away); by 36 weeks (8 months), 69%. All but two of the infants showed a negative reaction by 12 months, and these two were fearful at 18 months. The onset of negative reactions was often "sudden," not observed 1 month, then full blown at the following observation. Positive affect regularly declined just prior to observation of wariness, with a lag in the smile and increased sobriety; 39% were "frozen," "without affect" the month before the onset of wariness.

Schaffer's work can be criticized because the experimenter made all of the observations and there were no checks for reliability, but his findings have recently been corroborated in an independent study by Emde, Gaensbauer, and Harmon (1976). Fourteen infants were observed monthly from 4 to 12 months. The strangers approached in three phases, each lasting 1 min: silent approach to within 3 feet of the infant, greeting, and pickup and hold. Negative reactions were scored from films with 88% agreement. With mother present, the median onset of negative reactions (pronounced frowning, whimpering, or crying) was 8 months, and 11 of 14 babies showed aversive reactions by 9 months. These results are strikingly congruent with Schaffer's data. Also important, 11 of 14 infants showed negative reactions for 2 consecutive months, eight of 14 for 3 months.

These studies have been presented in some detail because they speak to the issues of universality and stability. Gaensbauer (Note 3) has argued, for example, that cross-sectional studies, the basis of the Rheingold and Eckerman critique, underestimate the occurrence of

TABLE 1

INFANTS SHOWING NEGATIVE REACTIONS TO INTRUSIVE STRANGER
APPROACH DURING MOTHER'S PRESENCE (%)

	AGE (Months)									
SOURCE	4	5	6	7	8	9	10	11	12	13–18
Morgan (Note 5)	13	...	6	...	13	...	56	...	81	...
Scarr & Salapatek (1970)	...	0	...	...	46	...	63	...	56	44
Waters, Matas, & Sroufe (1975)	...	11	17	15	22	35	59	...	...	...
Emde et al. (1976)	0	0	14	21	43	43	50	50	71	...
Morgan & Ricciuti (1969)	0	...	6	...	25	...	25	...	50	...

negative reactions to strangers. Some infants will not show wary reactions because they have not yet attained the required developmental level; others will have passed their peak responsiveness. All infants in the Schaffer and Emde et al. studies showed wariness at some point, and most of Emde et al.'s subjects showed it in 2 consecutive months, suggesting its stability in the infant's repertoire once achieved.

Developmental Trends

Results from cross-sectional studies support the age trends presented above. The first three studies summarized in table 1 were selected according to five criteria: (1) they had a clear intrude phase, (2) milder reactions as well as frank distress were scored, (3) the approaches were done with mother present, (4) they were based on reliable observations, and (5) percentages of negative reactions are reported without combining or averaging them with positive reactions. For comparative purposes, the longitudinal study of Emde et al. (1976) and Morgan and Ricciuti's (1969) study are also included (see below). As can be seen, and this is true in a large number of studies, only a small percentage of infants is negative during the first half year in a standard approach situation (see also Morgan & Ricciuti 1969; Rand & Jennings, Note 4). It is also clear that the peak intensity or greatest frequency of negative reactions continues to increase throughout the first year (see Morgan, Note 5). The actual percentage of aversive reactions reported at each age also shows some consistency. Studies that include categories of milder aversive responses find a majority of infants to be wary by 10 months (see also Skarin 1977). Crying is reported in a much smaller percentage; for example, Scarr and Salapatek (Note 6) and Waters, Matas, and Sroufe (1975) report crying in only about 10% of their 9–11-month-olds.

The consistency revealed by this summary is in sharp contrast to the conclusion presented by Rheingold and Eckerman (1973). One reason for the greater consistency in the present analysis is that there is some comparability in the studies selected. Morgan and Ricciuti's (1969) important study, for example, found increased wariness with age, but it was not until 12 months that half the infants were negative. Here, in contrast to Morgan's later report (table 1), positive and negative reactions were combined into an overall affect score, obscuring the percentage of babies showing wariness. A variety of procedural and contextual factors, as well as scoring criteria, affect the amount of wariness reported (see below).

Procedural Variations and Their Consequences

Two factors that have major influence on the incidence and degree of wariness observed in stranger contact studies are the behavior of the stranger and a variety of context effects. One clearly important aspect of the stranger's behavior is whether, how directly, and for how long he or she intrudes on the infant's space (Waters et al. 1975; Rand & Jennings, Note 4; Morgan, Note 5; Klein & Durfee, Note 7). Table 2 illustrates the influence of phase in the approach sequence. Studies that are analyzed in this manner are in complete agreement that infants show little negative reaction to strangers at a distance or even when they approach (with mother present). Physically restrained infants become much more negative when the stranger physically intrudes (even with a reach or pickup gesture) and are most negative when picked up or handled. (Skarin [1977] has recently replicated these step effects.) There also seems to be an influence of duration of contact, with more fear in studies where the intrude phase lasts for some time (e.g., Gaensbauer, Note 3).

Other studies make it clear, however, that the effects of close proximity to the infant and even contact can interact with other aspects of the stranger's behavior and with contextual variables. Studies have shown, for example, that a stranger playing peek-a-boo immediately proximal to the baby does not frighten many babies (Morgan, Note 5), nor does approaching the baby with a toy (Bretherton & Ainsworth 1974; Rheingold & Eckerman 1973; Klein & Durfee, Note 7; Clarke-Stewart, Note 8) or in the context of play (Rafman 1974). Besides providing familiar and positive formats for interaction, such procedures increase the response options available to the infant. That expanded options for coping can moderate emotional response is supported by Bronson's (1972) observation of less crying among 9- (vs. 6-) month-olds, despite their greater uneasiness; the younger infants were

TABLE 2

INFANTS SHOWING NEGATIVE REACTIONS AT VARIOUS POINTS
DURING STRANGER APPROACH, MOTHER PRESENT (%)

Source and Age	At Distance	Move to Near	Reach or Touch	Pickup	Wiggle
10 months:					
Morgan (Note 5)(N=16)................	6	...	50[a]	56	...
Waters, Matas, & Sroufe (1975)(N=16)....	12.5	25	50[b]	56	...
12 months:					
Morgan (Note 5)(N=32)................	13	...	50[a]	81	...
Klein & Durfee (Note 7)(N=32).........	2	...	7[c]	43	...
Rand & Jennings (Note 4)(N=43)........	0[d]	...	6[e]	38	51

[a] Sober-faced touch.
[b] Hands extended for pickup.
[c] Toy touch, playful.
[d] "Very negative."
[e] Smiling pat.

restrained while the older ones were free to crawl away from the stranger and thus maintain their composure.

In addition to the degree of control given the child, familiarization time with the stranger or with the novel environment (Skarin 1977; Sroufe, Waters, & Matas 1974) and presence of mother (e.g., Campos, Emde, Gaensbauer, & Henderson 1975; Ricciuti 1974; Skarin 1977; Gaensbauer, Note 3; Rand & Jennings, Note 4) have been shown to decrease the amount of uneasiness observed. More wariness to approaching strangers is routinely found in the absence of mother or even when the infant is a few feet away from the mother, as opposed to on her lap (Morgan & Ricciuti 1969). In the mother-absent condition, Emde et al. (1976) found considerable evidence for negative reactions even with the stringent criterion of "predominance" (i.e., negative and positive reactions summed across phases). In addition they found a differential phase effect (see table 2): most infants became negative only at pickup with mother present, while negative reactions were common even during the protracted approach phase with mother absent.

Studies done in the home, with mother present and the stranger approaching in a gradual, seminatural manner, still produce negative reactions if and when the stranger is intrusive (Schaffer 1966; Gaensbauer, Note 3). Even so, it would be expected that a rapid approach followed by a protracted intrusion phase and carried out in the laboratory with miminal familiarization time would produce more frequent and more extreme negative reactions. Also, male strangers have been found consistently to elicit more wariness than females, though the effect is small (Goulet 1974; Greenberg, Hillman, & Grice 1973; Lewis & Brooks 1974; Morgan, Lewin, & Harmon 1975; Morgan & Ricciuti 1969; Skarin 1977; Shaffran & Décarie, Note 2; Klein & Durfee, Note 7; Clarke-Stewart, Note 8).

Skarin (1977) has recently replicated the results concerning a number of these contextual factors (home-laboratory, step in approach, male-female experimenter, mother present-absent) and shown that they interact in predictable ways. For example, intrusion produced relatively more fear in the laboratory, and the reaction to the stranger was more immediately negative in the absence of mother. These findings would seem to square with our hypothesis concerning stranger reactions as reflecting the infant's context-based evaluation of the event (Sroufe et al. 1974).

Studies reporting very little wariness can be examined in light of these contextual influences. Campos et al. (1975), for example, found little evidence of negative reactions in their mother-present condition, even when 9-month-olds. Because they were recording heart rate without telemetry (i.e., the babies were wired to the recording equipment), they *excluded the intrusion phase* in their procedure. They still found substantial fear in 9-month-olds with mother absent. Haviland and Lewis (Note 1) report little wariness when their strangers merely walked in, touched the baby's hand, and walked out, all within 12 sec, a period allowing orienting but probably insufficient for response uncertainty or completion of assimilation/accommodation efforts (see Cognitive Development, below). Finally, Rheingold and Eckerman (1973) report virtually no fear when infants were given prolonged exposure to the general situation and to the stranger, the stranger mediated her approach with a toy, and the mother was present, interacting with the stranger. It was also the case that despite the detail of the observations, rather insensitive measures were used in the latter two studies. When subtle reactions are attended rather clear evidence of wariness is found in situations quite similar to that of Rheingold and Eckerman (Bretherton & Ainsworth 1974; see Wariness and the Complex of Infant Behavior, below).

Strangers or Strange Behavior

Laboratory studies of stranger reactions typically utilize segmented approach sequences, with experimenters behaving in an only seminatural manner. While such laboratory procedures have been important for revealing contextual factors and necessary for examining heart rate correlates of stranger reactions, their ecological validity may be questioned. Is it strangers or strange behavior that produce negative reactions? Data discussed below indicate that such "stilted" approach by caregivers does not produce wariness. And some have examined wariness in more naturalistic circumstances (Bretherton &

Ainsworth 1974; Sroufe & Waters 1977). More important, there is clear evidence that quite unusual behavior on the part of the mother (approaching with a mask, walking like a penguin, dangling a cloth in her mouth, sucking the baby's bottle) produces uniformly positive reactions (Sroufe et al. 1974; Sroufe & Wunsch 1972). Strangers approaching with the same mask produce negative reactions. While more naturalistic data are needed, it seems unlikely that wary reactions to strangers are due simply to peculiar behavior.

Summary

The review of the literature thus far is sufficient to speak to several points raised by recent critiques. The findings of various researchers are quite consistent in showing the emergence of negative reactions as a common response in standard stranger approach situations between about 7 and 9 months, with a continued increase in frequency of wariness across the first year. These age trends are clearly supported by studies of two non-Western cultures (Goldberg 1972; Konner 1972). The percentage of infants showing negative reactions at any age can vary considerably, but where results are inconsistent, procedural variations seem largely adequate to account for such discrepancies. Moreover, there are sufficient data now to refute the proposition that wariness is due to maternal absence or to peculiar behavior of the strangers. Not only may negative reactions be observed when strangers behave quite naturally (Bretherton & Ainsworth 1974), the data clearly indicate that aversive reactions are produced by the stranger intruding on the infant's space (see studies below contrasting mother and stranger). All in all, considering the varied formats and scenarios for the stranger and contextual manipulations, the data from these studies add up to a rather coherent picture.

VALIDATION OF THE CONSTRUCT OF WARINESS OF STRANGERS

The construct of wariness of strangers has also been questioned because of the low percentages of babies that actually cry in various studies. In the typical case, a majority of infants are classed as negative only when milder aversive (wary) reactions such as worried face, frown, "wary brow," and gaze aversion are recorded. Rheingold and Eckerman (1973) have questioned the reliability and validity of these mild reactions, arguing that they are subject to rater bias and overinterpretation. Indeed, as Waters et al. (1975) have pointed out, there is reason to question the validity of change from a positive expression to a sober, intent expression as an index of fear. However, there are studies in which mild negative reactions have been defined to exclude the sobering category (e.g., Schaffer 1966; Skarin 1977; Waters et al. 1975; Morgan, Note 5). Inclusion or exclusion of wary reactions, in addition to crying and avoidance, can further reconcile discrepancies in the literature concerning percentage of infants showing aversion (see Waters et al. 1975).

Description, Reliability, and Occurrence of Wary Reactions

It has been possible for investigators to achieve satisfactory reliabilities (in the .80s) when including milder fear reactions. Using detailed descriptions of the infants' reactions from videotapes, Waters et al. (1975) achieved an overall reliability of .93 and a reliability of .83 for *wary reactions considered alone* (wary brow, gaze aversion, and cry face). These coefficients were based on the entire sample of 54 subjects, but they do not take advantage of low frequency of response base rates as is sometimes done. Agreement on wariness, for example, meant that both raters coded the infant as wary. Finally, these reactions were seen primarily during intrude phases, not when the stranger initiated her approach or withdrew. At these other times, the infants watched with rapt attention and neutral affect. Such observations suggest that gaze aversion, for example, does not represent disinterest but a temporary avoidance of a stranger. Skarin (1977) using this same coding system obtained an overall reliability of .89 (.78 for wary reactions).

Validation against Concurrent Heart Rate Changes

Despite the fact that frank fear is rare in stranger approach research, three studies have reported significant relationships between codings of wariness or fear and heart rate (HR) acceleration (Campos et al. 1975; Provost & Décarie 1974; Waters et al. 1975). Skarin (1977) also found HR acceleration to be a sensitive indicator of developmental change in reactions to strangers. In each of these studies, HR was assessed independent of knowledge of wary reaction, and in the Campos and Waters studies the relationship was shown to hold across several ages. When a rare 5-month-old was coded as distressed in the Campos et al. study, for example, it also showed HR acceleration. In the Waters et al. study, wary infants showed greater HR acceleration than nonwary infants, even when *crying infants were excluded from the analysis.* Babies who showed frank avoidance (a group Rheingold & Eckerman would allow as fearful) were not responsible for this relationship; turning completely away early in the approach seemed to prevent the HR acceleration.

In further support of the construct of wariness, the timing of the accelerations suggested that gaze aversion (a common wary response) was *in response to arousal.* The gaze aversion occurred when the HR acceleration was near its peak, and the infant again looked at the stranger when HR returned toward basal level. Independently, HR acceleration has been shown to be sensitive to context manipulation, being more pronounced in laboratory stranger approach than in home approaches (Skarin 1977; Sroufe et al. 1974).

Discriminant Validity: Stranger Compared to Mother

A number of studies have shown differential reactions to mother compared to stranger (Bretherton & Ainsworth 1974; Cohen & Campos 1974; Corter 1973; Lewis & Brooks 1974; Rafman 1974; Waters et al. 1975; Klein & Durfee, Note 7). Waters et al. found neither HR accelerations nor wary reactions to mothers, even among infants who had accelerated during the stranger's approach. Such discrimination again attests to the validity of the milder aversive responses. Moreover, while infants smiled at both mother and stranger at the door, they ceased smiling as the stranger intruded. Babies do not react to approach and pickup by a stranger as they do to mother.

This evidence for discriminant validity of wary reactions, along with other evidence for the sensitivity and reliability of such reactions, makes it clear that researchers relying on crying and frank fear (e.g., Rheingold & Eckerman 1973) have underestimated the occurrence of negative reactions.

Retest Reliability and Stability across Time

Recently, Shaffran and Décarie (Note 2) issued a critique of the stranger fear concept based on their failure to find evidence of short-term stability of negative reactions. A trait view of stranger fear, such as that adopted by Shaffran, would predict stable individual differences. From the more complex conception that negative reactions result from the interaction of the infant, at a particular developmental level and in a particular mood and set on a given day, with the particular experimental situation, strong individual consistency may not be expected except in extreme cases. Rather, one would predict that the *proportion* of infants showing wariness would be stable within a constant format. Still, the question of short-term individual stability can be raised from within either of these viewpoints.

However, there were serious problems with the Shaffran and Décarie study. Videotapes were not utilized, and the data were based on the running description of facial, vocal, and motor behavior by *a single observer* (the stranger). Therefore, there were no checks on the reliability of these taxing observations (note procedure below) and subtle negative reactions (e.g., gaze aversion) probably could not have been adequately recorded. The most serious problem, however, concerns data treatment. The procedure lasted 2.75 min and began with the stranger greeting the infant at a distance and engaging in toy-mediated contact. After a minute the stranger did touch the baby and offer pickup, and after 2 min she did pick up the baby. The infant was classed as negative or positive (or undeclared) depending on the *number* of 15-sec intervals in which it was totally positive or totally negative, regardless of when these occurred. An infant that was positive throughout the first 2 min, then clearly distressed at pickup, still would be classed as positive. A stringent criterion of stability was employed, namely, agreement across three testings. Thus, an infant showing frank distress on two occasions and then a negative reaction in combination with affiliative responses (i.e., undifferentiated or positive) would not be judged as stable. Not surprisingly, little evidence of stability was found, and most of this was due to infants reacting totally positively on all three occasions (38% positive vs. 12% negative). It simply should not be expected that infants would consistently show *only* negative reactions to strangers in this situation, given their obvious curiosity and affiliative tendencies. Infants are likely to smile or show other signs of affiliation when the stranger is at a distance and when engaged in toy play, whether they ultimately become distressed or not (see Wariness and the Complex of Infant Behavior, below). Also, one would expect adaptation to this stranger and this procedure across 3 days, and evidence for this was found (23, 18, and 14 infants were classed as negative over the 3 days). The question of whether infants who are wary, especially during intrusion, are likely to be wary on another occasion, is simply not addressed by this study.

Other studies have provided evidence of both test-retest reliability within a session (Bronson 1972; Moss, Robson, & Pedersen 1969; Rand & Jennings, Note 4; Morgan, Note 5) and stability across days, weeks, or months (Bronson 1972; Moss et al. 1969; Scarr & Salapatek 1970). Bronson, for example, found that infants who showed negative reactions at 4 months were more likely to be negative at 6 and 9 months ($r's$ = .75 and .49, respectively, vs. .43 and .46 for the total sample). Moss et al. (1969) report an overall correlation of .69 across 1½ months, but negative reactions were not treated separately. Finally, the longitudinal studies discussed earlier also imply considerable stability of negative reactions (Schaffer 1966; Emde et al. 1976). More information is clearly needed on this problem. The available data on stability are quite limited. Also, it is not clear whether infants show temporal consistency in the type of negative reaction they exhibit (e.g., momentary gaze aversion in contrast to completely turning from the stranger) and whether such individual differences have developmental consequences of significance.

The Developmental Course of Wariness

One aspect of construct validation involves examining the contribution of wariness to an integrated view of infant development. It is clear that such a complex emotional phenomenon is not well suited to serve as a developmental milestone (see Rheingold & Eckerman 1973) in the manner of certain motor accomplishments (e.g., lifting the head). Still, there must be cognitive prerequisites for such a phenomenon and its appearance and development must convey information about developmental level.

The developmental course of negative stranger reactions in the second half year is suggestive. Emde et al. (1976) present considerable evidence of a general developmental shift in the fear system at this time (data from looming and visual cliff studies, as well as stranger fear). Such a shift is supported by comparative and physiological data, including maturational changes in the EEG and a shift to HR acceleration in response to events with negative meaning. The emergence of negative reactions to stranger approach by about 9 months is also consistent with Schaffer's longitudinal study of hesitancy to reach for novel objects (Schaffer, Greenwood, & Parry 1972). His careful work has revealed a clear break between 8 and 9 months, with older infants being much slower to reach, suggesting a qualitatively different treatment of novel objects. Qualitative changes in the domain of positive affect have been found during this same age period, with younger infants laughing at physically intrusive stimulation and older infants laughing in response to cognitive incongruity (Sroufe & Wunsch 1972). The period in question also is a time of rapid social and cognitive development, including advances in memory, object concept, categorical judgment, and differentiation of persons (see Schaffer 1974; Sroufe et al. 1974 for reviews). And it is the period when attachment becomes clearly established (Ainsworth 1973). However, tying wariness of strangers to development in the second half year in a specific way (e.g., relationships with object permanence) has proved difficult (Brossard 1974; Paradise & Curcio 1974; Scarr & Salapatek 1970). It is a principal task for researchers in this area. The crucial question from the emergence of wariness and contextual influences on reactions to strangers are coordinated with other advances in cognitive development, not whether amount of wariness is correlated with cognitive level.

WARINESS AND THE COMPLEX OF INFANT BEHAVIOR

A major criticism of the wariness concept concerns an assumed incompatibility of negative reactions with infants' strong affiliative tendencies toward strangers (Rheingold & Eckerman 1973; Haviland & Lewis, Note 1). If infants are affiliative, if they smile at, look at, or interact with strangers, then, so the logic goes, they must not be wary. If positive responses dominate under certain circumstances, then negative reactions are of little developmental significance. This is a puzzling criticism, given the obvious complexity of infant behavior and development.

Clearly, infants in the second half year of life do show strong affiliative tendencies toward strangers. They watch them, they smile at them, gesture toward them, offer them toys, and accept toys from them. They may even raise their arms when being picked up. A number of studies have shown that under certain circumstances some of these behaviors may even be more frequently directed at strangers than at mothers and may be much more common than signs of frank distress (e.g., Bretherton & Ainsworth 1974; Rheingold & Eckerman 1973; Waters et al. 1975; Morgan, Note 5). To the extent that researchers have been preoccupied with negative reactions to strangers and proximity seeking to mother, *as opposed to* affiliation and exploration, and to the extent that researchers have collapsed negative and positive reactions into an overall affect score, Rheingold and Eckerman's (1973) critique has served a valuable purpose. Exploration and affiliative reactions to strangers are an important part of development in the first year. Positive reactions, as well as wary behaviors, should be recorded and analyzed.

However, it is equally inappropriate to focus on affiliative reactions to the exclusion of wary behavior or to report only the dominant tendency in a particular situation. Recently, a number of studies have looked at both positive and negative reactions. Routinely these studies find evidence for both affiliative and wary tendencies (Bretherton & Ainsworth 1974; Emde et al. 1976; Waters et al. 1975; Shaffran & Décarie, Note 2; Rand & Jennings, Note 4; Morgan, Note 5; Klein & Durfee, Note 7). Most important, there is evidence for differences in timing or contextual base of these reactions, differences in the *quality* of positive reactions to mothers compared to strangers, and evidence for the simultaneous elicitation of positive and negative reactions. Researchers have found, for example, that positive reactions tend to dominate when the stranger is at a distance, while negative reactions become prominent when the stranger physically intrudes on the infant's space (Emde et al. 1976; Skarin 1977; Waters et al. 1975; Klein & Durfee, Note 7). Waters et al. (1975) report that 37% of their 10-month-old infants smiled at the stranger across the room, but only 6% smiled at reach, and no infant smiled at the stranger during pickup. Rand and Jennings (Note 4) present similar results, with the decline in positive reactions and the increase in negative reactions becoming even more prominent with their older group (12 months) when the stranger handled (wiggled) them after pickup (see phase effects, table 2). Infants generally do not manifest affiliative behaviors when strangers touch them or pick them up, nor are they typically comforted by contact with strangers when distressed by mother separation (Ainsworth 1973). These observations are not compatible with the interpretation that they are solely affiliative with respect to strangers. Babies will, for example, smile at their own mothers during pickup episodes (Waters et al. 1975).

Contrary to the notion that presence of affiliative behavior contraindicates wariness, there is even some evidence that infants are more likely to exhibit wariness during an approach in which they smile or show other positive response to the stranger early in the sequence (Waters et al. 1975). Such findings suggest that affiliation and wariness, which may both reflect developments in attentiveness to, involvement with, and reactivity to strangers, are under the control of different aspects of the situation. With infants in the second half year, smiles or looks away when the stranger is at the door do not have the same meaning as similar behavior when the stranger intrudes (nor does the stranger at the door have the same meaning as the intruding stranger for the infant). Babies that smile at "reach" will not cry at "pickup," whereas babies that smile at a distance may. And early looks away are not temporally associated with arousal (HR acceleration) as is gaze aversion when the stranger intrudes on the infant (Waters et al. 1975). Bretherton and Ainsworth's (1974) observation that smiles to mother are of larger magnitude than smiles to strangers also argues against simple frequency counts, independent of context and quality of the response.

The Bretherton and Ainsworth (1974) study is exemplary in its detail of behavior analysis. As such, it provides clear examples of the interplay between wariness, affiliation, attachment, and exploration. Their 106 12-month-old subjects smiled and looked at the stranger more than the mother, and more than half accepted a toy when it was offered—signs of a clear affiliative tendency. But *vocalization decreased* during the stranger's presence, the babies tended to look without approaching when the stranger initially was seated (in contrast to their behavior with novel toys), and half of the infants averted gaze when the stranger approached. Some withdrew from and none touched the stranger. These are all signs of wariness. Some made intention movements toward offered toys (start to reach, then pull back) or exhibited coy behavior (smiling with gaze aversion), which were interpreted as a simultaneous activation of affiliation and wariness. Most interesting, of the 10 babies who spontaneously approached the stranger, nine immediately retreated to the mother, a rather clear indication that expression of the affiliative tendency activated the wariness and attachment systems. Without their appreciation of the complexity of infant behavior, Bretherton and Ainsworth might well have classified these infants as *either* affiliative, because they approached the stranger, *or* wary, because they retreated to the mother. Clearly, neither interpretation does justice to the 12-month-old infant.

Bischof (1975) has proposed a formal analysis and model of the basic behavioral systems discussed by Bretherton and Ainsworth. Rather than seeking to determine whether infants are better characterized by wary or affiliative tendencies with respect to strangers (or by attachment or exploratory tendencies), Bischof's model specifies circumstances in which one tendency or the other will more likely be expressed. Factors such as proximity to the mother, security of the attachment relationship, and general and specific aspects of the context influence the interaction of these basic systems. Such a model of dynamic balance between wariness and approach is at a level of complexity commensurate with infant behavior and development. Several authors have commented that wariness, an initial hesitance, serves a protective function, countering the strong approach tendency also necessary for human development (e.g., Bronson 1972; Schaffer 1974; Sroufe & Waters 1976).

WARINESS OF STRANGERS AND THE STUDY OF
INFANT DEVELOPMENT

Establishing wariness of strangers as a developmental milestone is of secondary importance to understanding the contribution of this phenomenon to the study of early development. Some implications of stranger studies for major problems in development are described below. Segmenting the discussion into cognitive, emotional and social topics is for convenience only; a major concern is to illustrate the place of wariness of strangers within a view of infant development as organized and integrated. The discussion is meant to be illustrative rather than exhaustive.

Cognitive Development

The study of wariness is relevant for attempts to understand the nature of infant cognition. Following Piaget (1952), a number of writers have emphasized scheme formation and assimilation and accommodation in the face of novel stimulation (e.g., Kagan 1971; McCall & McGhee, in press). With repeated exposure, infants form mental representations (models) of their experience. It is hypothesized that by the second half year they have rather ready access to these models for comparison with immediate experience (in contrast to earlier recognition memory). In brief, the "discrepancy hypothesis" (Kagan 1971; McCall & McGhee, in press; Zelazo 1972) states that an event which activates existing structures but which cannot be assimilated to them creates a state of arousal. Moderate discrepancy will produce interest and probably accommodation (altering structures to incorporate the novel event). Somewhat greater discrepancy may lead to positive affect when it is resolved. But at some point, it is argued, the amount of discrepancy (arousal) will be too great, and with the failure of assimilation and accommodation, negative affect will occur.

The discrepancy hypothesis has been stated in very general form (McCall & McGhee, in press); yet, infants' reactions to strangers represent perhaps the most relevant case. With development infants clearly react differently to what is externally the same event—the approach of the stranger. It is reasonable to assume with Piaget that there is basically one structure and therefore that it must be reflected in these changes. It is the cognitive structure that is reflected when the 3-month-old smiles at all faces, caregivers and visitors alike. Faces apparently are assimilated with some effort to a general face scheme. Later, smiling in the immobile face declines; the general face scheme is well developed and there is no discrepancy. Differential smiling to caregivers appears as the scheme becomes differentiated. (The literature supporting these statements is reviewed by Sroufe & Waters [1976]). Then, in the second half year, it is the cognitive structure that is reflected when wariness of strangers becomes prominent. One interpretation of the phenomenon is that schemes for familiar faces are well articulated; the stranger's face is discrepant from the well-formed schemes, and assimilation and accommodation cannot resolve the discrepancy. The ready access to the differentiated scheme underlies wariness of strangers in brief encounters (see also Spitz 1965).

This general model can also be applied within the literature on stranger fear. One clear interpretation of the effects of stranger behavior and context centers on ease of assimilation (e.g., Décarie 1974; McCall & McGhee, in press; Sroufe & Waters 1976). As the infant can assimilate parts of the situation at a given age, fear, as a result of the failure of assimilation and accommodation (Mandler 1975), becomes less likely. Familiarization time, a gradual approach, mediation with a toy or familiar game, presence of the mother, or familiar surroundings all promote assimilation of portions of the situation and reduce the likelihood of negative reactions; for example, the stranger is novel, but her use of a toy can be assimilated to existing structures.

The discrepancy explanation is robust, but it is not completely adequate to explain stranger reactions. It does not explain why intrusion is so crucial in eliciting fear or how familiarization, mother presence, and other factors influence the reaction when the child's attention is so focused on the stranger. Infants typically do not exhibit wariness on mere sight of the stranger; nor do they when mother reappears from behind a screen wearing a mask, discrepant as this event would be.[2] Also, the importance of response options for the infant is not well handled by discrepancy. And it seems to stretch the discrepancy notion considerably to argue that strangers are more discrepant in the lab than in the home (Kagan [1971] predicted otherwise), are less discrepant when the baby is on mother's lap compared to 4 feet away, or are more discrepant following a mother separation than before it.

We have argued previously (Sroufe & Waters 1976) that discrepancy produces arousal, perhaps in the inverted-U-shaped function hypothesized, but that whether arousal will lead to positive or negative

[2]We have seen 60 infants ages 8–16 months in a situation where, following playing peek-a-boo from behind a screen, the mother calls the baby, then appears wearing a mask. Affect is rather uniformly neutral or positive.

affect is determined by the infant's *evaluation* of the event in context. Within broad limits there is not a fixed threshold for the amount of arousal (tension) required for negative affect. The ability to maintain a positive orientation in the face of increasingly complex or discrepant stimulation is in part a function of the security of the infant in the situation (see also Bischof 1975). The stranger, for example, is just as discrepant in the lap condition as in the 4-feet condition, but the infant can better tolerate the discrepancy-produced arousal in the former condition. In some contexts (e.g., playing with mother at home) a great deal of tension can be experienced with the resultant affect being positive. An alternative interpretation is that discrepancy-produced arousal adds to arousal from mother separation, novelty of the situation, and so forth. This would account for much of the fear data; it would not seem to account for laughter in arousing circumstances.

Finally, it is debatable that strangers become increasingly discrepant over the last quarter of the first year and beyond; yet stranger fear appears to intensify. While in part this may relate to the more complete differentiation of persons and more complete formation of attachment, Bronson (1972, Note 9) provides an alternative. Fear of strangers in the last quarter may not result from the failure to assimilate at all. It may result from a categorical recognition of the (intruding) stranger as something "I do not like," probably in part determined by specific experiences with strangers. Such categorical and relational abilities are as important for understanding infant cognitive development in the second half year as the development of cognitive structures. Discrepancy and specific experiences may each play a role in stranger fear or, as Bronson and Pankey (1977) persuasively argue, they may underlie two distinct bases of negative reaction to strangers: what they call "wariness" (a response to unfamiliarity) and what they call fear, a categorical negative reaction based on experience. Wariness continues to be present in the second half year when fear makes its appearance. An understanding of the growth of these two systems and their relation to a more general evaluative system will be important for understanding both cognitive and emotional development.

Emotional Development

Major conceptions of emotion center on cognitive processes such as "appraisal" (Arnold 1960) and "meaning analysis" (Mandler 1975). In Mandler's scheme, for example, interruption (disruption) of "plans" produces arousal followed by attempts at assimilation and accommodation. The particular emotional reaction depends on factors such as the subject's set and the context of the interruption (i.e., the interpretation of the arousal). Arnold's appraisal position would also predict the setting, familiarization time, and other situation effects found in stranger fear studies.

Developmental findings in stranger fear studies also fit well into these theoretical contexts. According to Mandler's notion, for example, one would predict a qualitative change in stranger reactions when the infant has the capacity for plans and some capacity for meaning analysis (e.g., memory, relational abilities). In the first half year, one can think of ongoing *action* being stopped by an arresting event. And if the infant remains captivated for an extended period, it may become distressed. Bronson (1972) indeed reports such distress (what he calls "wariness") as early as 3–4 months. In this case, no intended act or plan is interrupted; rather, the infant's distress results from the inability to release from this engaging event, to behave within it. Such an inability to assimilate/accommodate requires considerable time for its effect (10–30 sec in Bronson's study).

But the disruption of "plans" in Mandler's sense really would not be expected until the second half year, when the infant has rather well-articulated cognitive structures. By this time, the infant has had, and can draw upon, considerable experience with strangers, both positive and negative. The infant also has what may be called intentions with respect to strangers, ways it wants them to behave. Strangers are rather immediately recognized as such, but interpreting a particular contact as positive, negative, or innocuous is generally dependent on the stranger's behavior. If the infant can assimilate the stranger to its "plans" (e.g., go on playing while the stranger chats with mother) or accommodate its plans to the stranger (e.g., engage in toy play), there is no fear. But when the stranger intrudes uninvited on the infant's space, this is disrupting. A fear reaction can be immediate because this is a cognitive disruption, an interruption of the infant's "plan." There is general agreement in the literature that such a rapidly occurring fear reaction emerges during the second half year.

A purely cognitive position such as Mandler's can account for the context effects, phase of approach effects, and the notion of response options. Fear results when the increasingly capable infant cannot exercise an acceptable plan. But this position is difficult to reconcile with the finding of occasional negative reactions which are very rapid on encounters with strangers, or with changing thresholds for negative reactions (e.g., the lap versus mother at a distance effect). It may be that, sometimes, strangers are assimilated to a negative category (see Bronson, Note 10), rather than producing a failure of assimilation/accommodation. Strangers may be perceived as threatening. It is here that Arnold's notion of appraisal, or what we refer (Sroufe et al. 1974) to as evaluation, is germane (see Sroufe, in press, for further discussion).

The infant's evaluation is synthetic. It incorporates set, setting, the behavior of the stranger, and response options available. It also includes the infant's mood, state, and felt security prior to and during the encounter. It reflects the infant's threshold for threat as well as cognitive incongruity and the infant's accommodative skills. The literature supports the position that evaluation (appraisal of threat), in addition to arousal, is important in eliciting fear. Waters et al. (1975) and Campos (Note 11) found that infants extremely distressed on a first approach showed distress sooner on a second encounter. This reflects a categorical reaction, based on evaluation, rather than a faster failure of assimilation/accommodation (see Bronson, Note 10). Moreover, in the Rand and Jennings (Note 4) study, it was the babies who were negative at pickup who were extremely negative at "wiggles" (Jennings, Note 12). Babies reacting positively did not become negative at "wiggles," though one would expect that concurrent autonomic measures would show an increase in arousal.

A developmental theory of fear (and of emotion) will include both concepts like interruption of plans, discrepancy, and failure of assimilation/accommodation and concepts such as appraisal (Sroufe & Mitchell, in press). Evaluative ability, like intentionality, is assumed to advance qualitatively in the second half year of life (Sroufe et al. 1974). Such conceptual breadth seems necessary to account for the emergence and development in the first year of the two negative reaction systems described by Bronson (Note 10): the wariness-novelty system and the fear system.

An understanding of the factors underlying the waning of stranger fear will also be relevant for a developmental theory of emotion. There are few data here, but several factors which may be important can be noted. They all relate in a general way to the infant's developing ability to control emotional experience and expression. Cognitively, it would be expected that with more articulated structures infants would be better able to differentiate threatening from non-threatening encounters. Similarly, they would have an increased ability to appraise and evaluate (and be influenced by) the context of the encounter. They would have a broader array of coping strategies at their command and be better able to maintain a sense of control. Finally, an increased ability to maintain a positive orientation in the face of high arousal (tension) might also be expected (Sroufe & Mitchell, in press).

Social Development: Attachment

The relationship between attachment and stranger fear is certain to be complex. Critics of the stranger fear concept (Rheingold & Eckerman 1973) seem to demand a simple one-to-one correspondence between attachment and stranger fear—the more attachment, the more (or less) stranger fear. Appropriately complex models are available, however (e.g., Bischof 1975; Bretherton & Ainsworth 1974). As discussed earlier, attachment and wariness are interacting systems that influence and are influenced by each other and by affiliative and exploratory tendencies as well. All are under the influence of contextual factors. Such a model makes room for the *quality* of the attachment relationship in understanding wariness of strangers.

Ontogenetically, wariness of strangers and attachment should be clearly related. By definition, each involves the differentiation of persons and the articulation of structures concerning the familiar and the novel; that is, they depend on common cognitive processes.[3] But early or intense wariness of strangers would not necessarily indicate a *good* attachment relationship. Similarly, intensity of separation protest or transiently intense stranger fear would not necessarily indicate a poor attachment relationship. Yet, attachment, separation protest, and wariness of strangers must be related.

Drawing from ethological theory, Ainsworth and her colleagues (Ainsworth 1973; Ainsworth & Witting 1969; Bretherton & Ainsworth 1974) have provided a meaningful conceptualization of the relationships between attachment and wariness of strangers. Central to the definition of attachment in this system are the attachment-exploration balance (caregiver as a secure base for exploration) and the specificity of need for contact with the caregiver *when distressed.* Thus, in mother's presence, with adequate familiarization time, most 12-month-old babies would be expected to engage in toy play with a stranger (even including eye contact, after a time). Such play would not indicate failure of attachment, since it is predicted from the secure-base position. Nor would it *necessarily* indicate a good-quality at-

---

[3]As Paradise and Curcio (1974) did with stranger fear, Bell (1970) found a relationship between quality of attachment and a decalage between person permanence and object permanence.

tachment relationship, because the issue of preferential treatment under stress remains open. However, some babies are completely preoccupied with the mother at virtually all times, hovering near her and avoiding, without warming up to, the stranger. This suggests a maladaptive attachment relationship, not because of the preferential treatment but because, with only mild stress, the mother's presence should be sufficient for the dominance of the infant's exploratory and affiliative tendencies. This degree of wariness suggests insecurity of attachment.

On the other hand, following the distress of being left alone, infants would be expected to specifically require contact with mother. Contact with the stranger may even be persistently resisted, with the baby only becoming fully settled when contact with mother is reestablished. In this instance, it is the infants who are readily settled by the stranger, who appear as comfortable with her as with the mother, who show the maladaptive pattern. These babies, who did not show wariness of the stranger in mother's presence, tend to *avoid* the mother on reunion, confirming that they are not simply placid and contented. Note that there are specific predictions here: for example, infants defined as insecurely attached because of their inability to be settled by the caregiver following a brief separation will be wary of and slow to warm up to a stranger prior to separation and in the caregiver's presence. Infants who do not exhibit preferential treatment following separation will avoid the caregiver on reunion. It is not magnitudes of correlations that are at issue but patterns (organizations) of behavior.

This discussion illustrates both that the relationship between attachment and wariness is complex and that understanding one of these systems is relevant for understanding the other. Securely attached infants may in certain contexts be less wary of a stranger than some babies; in other circumstances they may be more resistant to contact with strangers than another group of babies. The quality of the attachment is defined by this patterning of behavior, not by amount of stranger aversion regardless of context. These statements are more than speculative; we have recently validated Ainsworth's characterization of individual differences in quality of attachment with a large sample. The patterns of secure and insecure attachment she describes, including responses to strangers, are stable across a 6-month period (Sroufe & Waters 1977).

SUMMARY AND CONCLUSION

The literature on the infant's reaction to strangers more than withstands the criticisms that have been leveled against the concept of wariness. When procedural and scoring variations are taken into account, very coherent developmental trends emerge. While some infants exhibit aversive responses earlier, there is general agreement that a significant proportion are negative in a standard approach situation only after 7 or 8 months. Negative reactions continue to become more frequent and intense at least through the first year, even though affiliative reactions are also prominent. The data on the reliability and validity of measures underlying these conclusions are substantial.

Only occasionally is the sight of the stranger sufficient to produce a negative reaction, though if a baby reacts extremely negatively on one exposure it is more likely to be immediately negative on a second trial. Typically infants are negative only when the stranger is intrusive, reaching for them, touching them, picking them up. If the approach is delayed or gradual, or if mediated by toys or play, the infant can tolerate substantial contact with strangers. In concert with other data, this is *not* best interpreted in terms of unusual behavior of the stranger producing negative reactions. When mothers engage in the step-wise approach (very unusual for them) or crawl on the floor, suck a baby bottle, or walk like a penguin (Sroufe et al. 1974), affect is uniformly positive. Rather, it seems that the infant's curiosity and affiliative tendencies, and the ability to assimilate portions of the event, counteract the tendency toward wariness of the unfamiliar person. Strangers with masks are more frightening than strangers without masks; mothers with masks produce positive affect (Sroufe et al. 1974).

When a concept such as stranger fear is discarded much more is lost than a phenomenon amenable to developmental study. The sensitivity of this phenomenon to contextual variation and its potential relation to major problems in cognitive, social, and emotional development show it to have a vital role in evolving an integrated, organized view of infancy. Like attachment, the power of wariness of strangers in evolving such a view can be illustrated when it is treated as a developmental/organizational construct, rather than as a trait or milestone (Sroufe, in press). Integrating infant development is perhaps the most challenging task facing the field. An understanding of the development of wary and affiliative tendencies toward strangers will play a role in this synthesis.

REFERENCE NOTES

1. Haviland, J., & Lewis, M. Infants' greeting patterns to strangers. Paper presented at the human ethology session of the Animal Behavior Society, Wilmington, N.C., May 1975.
2. Shaffran, R., & Décarie, T. Short-term stability of infants' responses to strangers.

Paper presented at the biennial meeting of the Society for Research in Child Development, Philadelphia, April 1973.
3. Gaensbauer. T. Stranger distress as an expectable developmental event. Paper presented at the biennial meeting of the Society for Research in Child Development, Denver, April 1975.
4. Rand, C., & Jennings, K. Reactions of infants and young children to a stranger in an unfamiliar setting. Paper presented at the biennial meeting of the Society for Research in Child Development, Denver, April 1975.
5. Morgan, G. Determinants of infants' reactions to strangers. Revised version of a paper presented at the biennial meeting of the Society for Research in Child Development, Philadelphia, April 1973.
6. Scarr, S. Personal communication, October 1975.
7. Klein, R., & Durfee, J. Infants' reactions to unfamiliar adults versus mothers. Revised version of a paper presented at the biennial meeting of the Society for Research in Child Development, Denver, April 1975.
8. Clarke-Stewart, K. A. Sociability and social sensitivity: characteristics of the stranger. Paper presented at the annual meeting of the Eastern Psychological Association, New York, May 1975.
9. Bronson, G. Personal communication, February 1976.
10. Bronson, G. Aversive stranger reactions: a dual process interpretation. Unpublished manuscript, 1977.
11. Campos, J. Personal communication, February 1976.
12. Jennings, K. Personal communication, April 1976.

REFERENCES

Ainsworth, M. The development of infant-mother attachment. In B. Caldwell & H. Ricciuti (Eds.), *Review of child development research.* Vol. **3.** Chicago: University of Chicago Press, 1973.

Ainsworth, M., & Wittig, B. Attachment and exploratory behavior of one-year-olds in a strange situation. In B. Foss (Ed.), *Determinants of infant behaviour.* Vol. **4.** London: Methuen, 1969.

Arnold, M. *Emotion and personality.* New York: Columbia University Press, 1960.

Bell, S. The development of the concept of object as related to infant-mother attachment. *Child Development,* 1970, **41,** 291–311.

Bischof, N. A systems approach toward the functional connections of fear and attachment. *Child Development,* 1975, **46,** 801–817.

Bretherton, I., & Ainsworth, M. Responses of one-year-olds to a stranger in a strange situation. In M. Lewis & L. Rosenblum (Eds.), *The origins of fear.* New York: Wiley, 1974.

Bronson, G. Infants' reactions to unfamiliar persons and novel objects. *Monographs of the Society for Research in Child Development,* 1972, **37**(3, Serial No. 148).

Bronson, G., & Pankey, W. On the distinction between fear and wariness. *Child Development,* 1977, **48,** in press.

Brossard, M. The infant's conception of object permanence and his reactions to strangers. In T. Décarie (Ed.), *The infant's reaction to strangers.* New York: International Universities Press, 1974.

Campos, J.; Emde, R.; Gaensbauer, T.; & Henderson, C. Cardiac and behavioral interrelationships in the reactions of infants to strangers. *Developmental Psychology,* 1975, **11,** 589–601.

Cohen, L., & Campos, J. Father, mother and stranger as elicitors of attachment behaviors in infancy. *Developmental Psychology*, 1974, **10**, 146–154.

Corter, M. A comparison of the mother's and a stranger's control over the behavior of infants. *Child Development*, 1973, **44**, 705–713.

Décarie, T. *The infant's reaction to strangers*. New York: International Universities Press, 1974.

Emde, R.; Gaensbauer, T.; & Harmon, R. Emotional expression in infancy: a biobehavioral study. *Psychological Issues*, 1976, **10**(1, Whole No. 37).

Goldberg, S. Infant care and growth in urban Zambia. *Human Development*, 1972, **15**, 77–89.

Goulet, J. The infant's conception of causality and his reactions to strangers. In T. Décarie (Ed.), *The infant's reaction to strangers*. New York: International Universities Press, 1974.

Greenberg, N.; Hillman, D.; & Grice, D. Infant and stranger variables related to stranger anxiety in the first year of life. *Developmental Psychology*, 1973, **9**, 207–212.

Kagan, J. *Change and continuity in infancy*. New York: Wiley, 1971.

Konner, M. Aspects of the developmental ethology of a foraging people. In N. Blurton-Jones (Ed.), *Ethological studies of child behavior*. Cambridge: Cambridge University Press, 1972.

Lewis, M., & Brooks, J. Self, other and fear: infants' reactions to people. In M. Lewis & L. Rosenblum (Eds.), *The origins of fear*. New York: Wiley, 1974.

McCall, R., & McGhee, P. The discrepancy hypothesis of attention and affect. In F. Weizmann & I. Uzgiris (Eds.), *The structuring of experience*. New York: Plenum, in press.

Mandler, G. *Mind and emotion*. New York: Wiley, 1975.

Morgan, G.; Lewin, B.; & Harmon, R. Determinants of individual differences in infants' reactions to unfamiliar adults. JSAS *Catalog of Selected Documents in Psychology*, 1975, **5**, 277. (Ms. No. 1006)

Morgan, G., & Ricciuti, H. Infants' responses to strangers during the first year. In B. Foss (Ed.), *Determinants of infant behaviour*. Vol. 4. London: Methuen, 1969.

Moss, H.; Robson, K.; & Pedersen, F. Determinants of maternal stimulation of infants and consequences of treatment for later reactions to strangers. *Developmental Psychology*, 1969. **1**, 239–247.

Paradise, E., & Curcio, F. The relationship of cognitive and affective behaviors to fear of strangers in male infants. *Developmental Psychology*, 1974, **10**, 476–483.

Piaget, J. *The origins of intelligence in children*. New York: International Universities Press, 1952.

Provost, M., & Décarie, T. Modifications du rhythme cardiaque chez des enfants de 9–12 mois au cours de la rencontre avec la personne étrangère. *Canadian Journal of Behavioral Science*, 1974, **6**, 154–168.

Rafman, S. The infant's reaction to imitation of the mother's behavior by the stranger. In T. Décarie (Ed.), *The infant's reaction to strangers*. New York: International Universities Press, 1974.

Rheingold, H., & Eckerman, C. Fear of the stranger: a critical examination. In H. Reese (Ed.), *Advances in Child Development and Behavior*. Vol. 8. New York: Academic Press, 1973.

Ricciuti, H. Fear and the development of social attachments in the first year of life. In M. Lewis & L. Rosenblum (Eds.), *The origins of fear*. New York: Wiley, 1974.

Scarr, S., & Salapatek, P. Patterns of fear development during infancy. *Merrill-Palmer*

Quarterly, 1970, **16,** 53–90.

Schaffer, H. The onset of fear of strangers and the incongruity hypothesis. *Journal of Child Psychology and Psychiatry,* 1966, **7,** 95–106.

Schaffer, H. Cognitive components of the infant's response to strangeness. In M. Lewis & L. Rosenblum (Eds.), *The origins of fear.* New York: Wiley, 1974.

Schaffer, H., & Emerson, P. The development of social attachments in infancy. *Monographs of the Society for Research in Child Development,* 1964, **29**(3, Serial No. 94).

Schaffer, H.; Greenwood, A.; & Parry, M. The onset of wariness. *Child Development,* 1972, **43,** 164–175.

Skarin, K. Cognitive and contextual determinants of stranger fear in six- and eleven-month-old infants. *Child Development,* 1977, **48,** 537–544.

Spitz, R. *The first year of life.* New York: International Universities Press, 1965.

Sroufe, L. A. The ontogenesis of the emotions. In J. Osofsky (Ed.), *Handbook of infant development.* New York: Wiley, in press.

Sroufe, L. A., & Mitchell, P. Emotional development. In J. Osofsky (Ed.), *Handbook of infant development.* New York: Wiley, in press.

Sroufe, L. A., & Waters, E. The ontogenesis of smiling and laughter: a perspective on the organization of development in infancy. *Psychological Review,* 1976, **83,** 173–189.

Sroufe, L. A., & Waters, E. Attachment as an organizational construct. *Child Development,* 1977, **48,** in press.

Sroufe, L. A.; Waters, E.; & Matas, L. Contextual determinants of infant affective response. In M. Lewis & L. Rosenblum (Eds.), *The origins of fear,* New York: Wiley, 1974.

Sroufe, L. A., & Wunsch, J. P. The development of laughter in the first year of life. *Child Development,* 1972, **43,** 1326–1344.

Waters, E.; Matas, L.; & Sroufe, L. A. Infants' reactions to an approaching stranger: description, validation, and functional significance of wariness. *Child Development,* 1975, **46,** 348–356.

Zelazo, P. Smiling and vocalizing: a cognitive emphasis. *Merrill-Palmer Quarterly,* 1972, **18,** 349–366.

3

BIRTH ORDER, INTELLECTUAL COMPETENCE, AND PSYCHIATRIC STATUS

Lillian Belmont

New York State Psychiatric Institute
Columbia University School of Public Health

A commonly held belief is that birth order is one factor which makes a difference to an individual's development. In this paper we present an overview of the results of a series of birth order studies which lend empirical support to this belief.

BACKGROUND OF STUDIES

Our Research Unit has been concerned with birth order associations and personal characteristics, such as intellectual competence, school performance, height, and psychological disorders.

We have been able to conduct such studies because we had available a unique body of data, records from the Dutch military pre-induction examination, containing systematic physical, psychological and sociological information for approximately 400,000 young men born

Reprinted with permission from *Journal of Individual Psychology,* vol. 33, 97-103, 1977.

We thank the Department of Defense of the Netherlands for permission to use the military preinduction examination. This study was supported in part by NICHD Grant No. 06808.

between 1944 and 1947.[1] In the Dutch military examination procedure all young men are processed for military service before a decision is reached on whether they will be required to serve in the army.

The examination consisted of three parts: (1) the young men were given a physical examination, including measures of height and weight; (2) they were examined with a battery of five psychometric tests (Raven Progressive Matrices, a test of arithmetic and mathematics achievement, a test of grammar and language achievement, a clerical aptitude test, and the Bennett Test of Mechanical Comprehension). The raw scores on each test were converted to a 6-point rating scale, with 1 representing the best performance and 6 the poorest performance; and (3) other information was obtained by interview, including father's occupation (used to develop our social class index), the young men's educational status, birth order, and the size of family of origin. (For a fuller description of the data see Belmont & Marolla, 1973; and Stein, Susser, Saenger, & Marolla, 1975.)

The data made it possible for us to study certain characteristics of these young men, who were categorized according to their family size and birth order position. We studied the relation of birth order and family size to test score, school failure, height and psychiatric state. These variables differ in several respects. Test scores and our index of school failure are presumed to reflect intellectual competence, height is presumed to reflect physical development, and the presence of a psychiatric diagnosis is presumed to reflect psychological disorder. With one exception, the variables reflect adult status; school failure, however, reflects functioning during childhood. School failure and test score differ, too, in that the test score represents childhood performance. Further, three of the variables are "objective" (test scores, school failure, height) whereas psychiatric diagnosis represents a clinical judgment.

In addition to the large N, a strength of these studies is that we analyzed birth order effects within specific family sizes. Birth order and family size are not independent of each other (one cannot be fourthborn in a 3-child family).

---

[1]These data were originally supplied to our Research Unit for the study of the mental and physical consequences of the Dutch Famine of 1944-45 (Stein, Susser, Saenger, & Marolla, 1975). Stein and her colleagues found that intra-uterine exposure to the famine produced no measurable adverse effects on survivors at military age.

SUMMARY OF RESULTS

Intellectual Competence

We found that birth order is related to intellectual performance. Using the Raven Progressive Matrices, a non-verbal test of intelligence, we demonstrated that a birth order effect was present even when family size and social class were controlled. Thus, for men of each given family size and of each social class the average test score was inversely related to birth order: firstborn had a better score on the average than did secondborn, etc. The birth order effect was most consistent in family sizes of 2 through 4. We also found that for men of any given birth order, test score on the average was inversely related to family size, so that members of smaller families scored better than members of larger families. The family size effect, however, was not completely consistent for the non-manual social class (Belmont & Marolla, 1973). In a subsequent paper (Belmont, Wittes & Stein, submitted for publication) we reported that this pattern was consistent across a variety of different psychological functions, as measured by the entire test battery. In this study we limited ourselves to young men born between 1944 and 1946 who were members of 1- through 6-child families.[2] Figure 1 illustrates the nature of our findings for intellectual competence using the total score (a sum of standard scores for the five tests, each rated on a scale of 1 to 6, converted back to a 1-6 scale). The figure shows a downward gradient in average test score with increasing birth order, for all family sizes. Average test score becomes poorer as birth order increases. This gradient is consistent for 2- to 4-child families. There is one reversal in the pattern for family size 5 and one for family size 6. With one exception (F.S.1), mean scores within any given birth order become poorer as family size becomes larger. Members of 1-child families do not fit the otherwise consistent family size gradient (see below).

School Failure

It had previously been reported (Schachter, 1963) that firstborns are over-represented among those who are academically successful.

---

[2]Young men could claim exemption from military service if two or three older brothers had already served in the armed forces. This resulted in an estimated loss of only 2% of the total population but a larger percentage loss for the later birth orders and larger family sizes. We therefore excluded individuals from families with seven or more children.

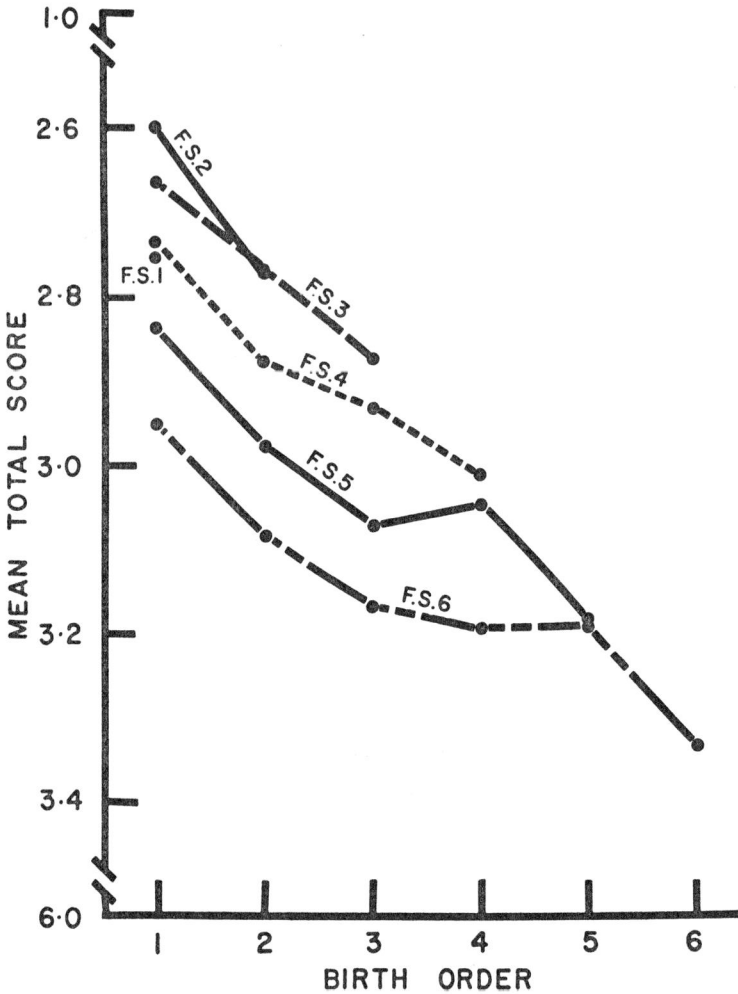

Figure 1: Mean total score by birth order within family size (F.S.) across the population (N=233,654).

We examined a related question of whether lastborn are over-represented among those at the other end of the educational spectrum (Belmont, Stein, & Wittes, 1976). We found that lastborn at each family size are at greater risk than are first- and middleborn of experiencing school failure as measured by (a) attendance at special schools for the mentally retarded, and (b) failure to graduate from lower school (first 6 years of school). In the Netherlands at that time 8 years of schooling was compulsory. Those who "failed lower school" were children who probably repeated grades before reaching school-leaving age and thus did not successfully complete lower school. We examined the rates of school failure for over 200,000 young men born between 1944 and 1946 whose fathers were in the manual and non-manual social classes (85% of the study population). We found that (a) there was a difference in rates for the two social classes (the manual social class showed the higher rate); (b) the larger the family size the higher the rate; and (c) lastborn of each family size had significantly higher rates than did first- and middleborn. These findings suggested to us that childhood school performance reflects a birth order/family size relationship similar to that found in adulthood, as measured on psychometric indices. The birth order effect appears to persist through a long period in the course of development.

Height

We studied the distributions of mean height and mean IQ (Raven) test scores, contrasting the birth order/family size gradients for the two indices in order to determine the environmental effects which underlie somatic development (height) and intellectual development (IQ test score). Height and IQ score both showed a family size effect: members of smaller families were taller and had better IQ scores. However, birth order was not related to height but was related to IQ score (Belmont, Stein, & Susser, 1975). Since height is assumed to reflect physical and biological environmental effects, the birth order relationship with IQ score but not with height suggests that intellectual development, in addition to nutritional adequacy and good physical health, is related to the satisfactory social and family environment.

Psychiatric Status

Only and lastborn children were at greater risk of being diagnosed as psychiatrically disordered than were firstborn. In the course of their physical examination, young men were rated on a 4-point rating scale for physical health and psychiatric status. For any unfit ratings an International Classification of Diseases code was assigned on the basis of clinical interview and review. Neuroses and personality disorders were diagnosed most frequently; for the present paper we report on the combined psychiatric diagnoses.

We studied psychiatric diagnoses with particular emphasis on only children (men from 1-child families). We noted previously that only

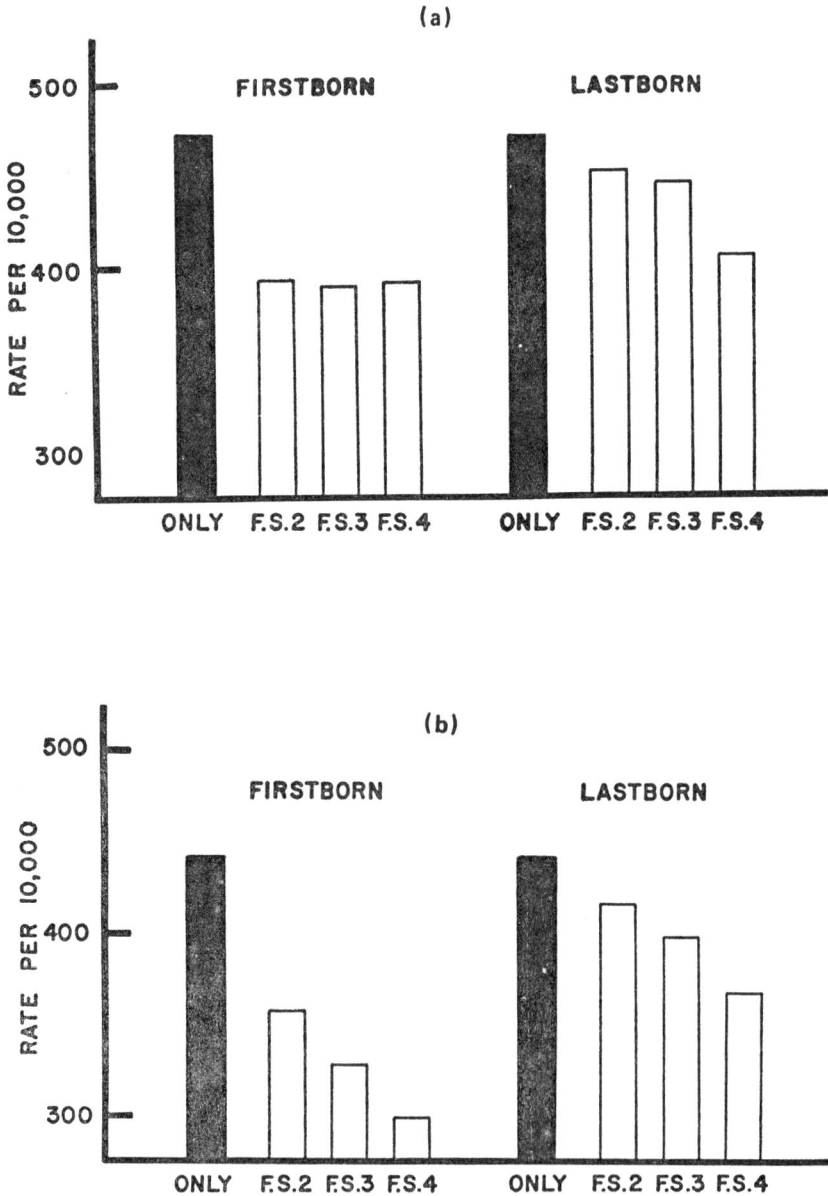

Figure 2: Overall rate per 10,000 population for psychiatric disorder for only children, firstborn and lastborn of F.S. 2 through 4 in the (a) manual and (b) non-manual social classes.

children made a poorer showing than expected (see Figure 1). In the present study of psychiatric status (Belmont, Wittes, & Stein, 1976) we found that only children were at greater risk of receiving a psychiatric diagnosis that were firstborn or lastborn. This trend was particularly marked for only children of the non-manual social class (see Figure 2). Also, firstborn and lastborn from 2- to 4-child families showed an inverse relationship with family size in their risk of obtaining a psychiatric diagnosis. Thus, rates were higher for men from 2-child families than for men from 4-child families. Within specific family sizes, lastborn had higher rates of psychiatric disorder than did firstborn.

LIMITATIONS

In interpreting the significance of our results, it should be recalled that these findings refer to males only; they represent findings for 19-year olds born and resident in the Netherlands at the age of military induction. However, the findings on intellectual competence are in accord with those from a U.S. population of high school juniors in which a birth order effect was found for both females and males (Breland, 1974).

IMPLICATIONS

Our various epidemiologic studies add support to a number of notions and contradict others concerning birth order.

(1) Firstborn at a given family size enjoy a number of advantages: they are at less risk of school failure and tend to demonstrate greater intellectual competence than do lastborn. They tend to have lower risks than lastborn of being psychiatrically disturbed.

(2) Lastborn tend to enjoy no advantages: they are least capable intellectually at any given family size. Their risk of being diagnosed as psychiatrically impaired is greatest.

(3) Members of smaller families tend to be more capable intellectually, tend to experience less school failure and tend to be taller. However, only children do not share these advantages. Yet smaller family size tended to increase the risk of psychiatric disorder.

Our findings tend to be coherent: firstborn have the advantage of intellectual competence and psychological well-being. Lastborn are at greater risk of lowered intellectual competence and of more psychological difficulties. However, only children, contrary to popular thought, tend not to be as intellectually competent as firstborn. Further, they tend to have the greatest risk of psychiatric disorder.

REFERENCES

Belmont, L., & Marolla, F. A. Birth order, family size, and intelligence. *Science,* 1973, *182,* 1096-1101.

Belmont, L., Stein, Z. A., & Susser, M. W. Comparison of associations of height with intelligence test score. *Nature,* 1975, *255,* 54-56.

Belmont, L., Stein, Z. A., & Wittes, J. Birth order, family size and school failure. *Developmental Medicine and Child Neurology,* 1976, *18,* 421-430.

Belmont, L., Wittes, J., & Stein, Z. A. The relation of birth order, family size and social class to psychological functions. Submitted for publication.

Belmont, L., Wittes, J., & Stein, Z. A. The only child syndrome: Myth or reality. Paper presented at the annual meeting of the Society for Life History Research in Psychopathology, Fort Worth, Texas, 1976.

Breland, H. M. Birth order, family configuration, and verbal achievement. *Child Development,* 1974, *45,* 1011-1019.

Schachter, S. Birth order, eminence and higher education. *American Sociological Review,* 1963, *28,* 757-768.

Stein, Z., Susser, M., Saenger, G., & Marolla, F. *Famine and human development: The Dutch hunger winter of 1944-1945.* New York: Oxford University Press, 1975.

4

INTELLECTUAL AND BEHAVIORAL FUNCTIONING OF TEN- TO TWELVE-YEAR-OLD CHILDREN WHO SHOWED CERTAIN TRANSIENT SYMPTOMS IN THE NEONATAL PERIOD

Birgitte R. Mednick

University of Southern California

This study concerns itself with the intellectual and behavioral functioning of 11-year-old children who neonatally presented a variety of short-lived or transient symptoms. These symptoms, while short-lived, are similar in nature to symptoms which other authors have shown to be correlated with later increased rate of brain damage symptoms. By using data from a birth cohort of 9,006 consecutive deliveries we attempted to discover whether such symptoms, when only transiently present in the newborn, are correlated with later intellectual and behavioral functioning. Results indicated that chil-

Reprinted with permission from *Child Development*, 1977, **48**, 844–853. Copyright 1977 by the Society for Research in Child Development, Inc.

This research was supported by grant 19255 from National Institute of Mental Health, USPHS. The author wishes to thank the Pediatric Department of Rigshospitalet, Copenhagen, for the foresight and wisdom in initiating the Danish Perinatal Sample which was the subject population for this study. Special thanks are extended to Professor B. Zachau-Christiansen for his advice and encouragement.

*dren age 10–12 who showed transient neonatal symptoms presented
more intellectual impairment than matched controls.*

In previously published papers (Amiel-Tison 1969; Craig 1950, 1960; Prechtl 1965; Thorn 1968) it has been shown that, if persistent and severe, certain symptoms in the neonate are correlated with a higher than normal rate of brain damage signs later in childhood. These neonatal symptoms include: convulsions, cyanosis, respiratory distress, shivering or jitteriness, irritability, restlessness, rigidity, limpness, apathy, and reflex anomalies. If, on the other hand, these neonatal symptoms are mild or transient, it is common clinical practice (at least in Denmark) to hypothesize that there are no important sequelae and to discharge the child to the home with no further comments to the parents. It is the purpose of the present study to test empirically whether the hypothesis that these transient symptoms are benign can be supported. As part of a longitudinal prospective project, this study examines the intellectual and social functioning of pre-adolescents who as neonates were observed to evidence one or more of these symptoms transiently. In the following, the abbreviation TNS will be used to signify transient neonatal symptoms of the types which if *longer lasting* are known to be correlated with later impaired neurological functioning.

Most of the studies cited above investigated the later *neurological* correlates of persistent neonatal symptoms. Thorn (1968) reports the development of *intellectual* and *social* problems. Indirectly supporting these findings are projects which have observed such developmental problems as afthermaths of perinatal difficulties (Benaron, Tucker, Andrews, Boshes, Cohen, Fromm, & Yacorzynsky 1960; Graham, Ernhart, Thurstone, & Crafft 1962; Honzik, Hutchings, & Burnip 1965; Prechtl 1967; Rosenfeld & Bradley 1948; Schacter & Apgar 1959; Stechler 1964). In addition, retrospective studies suggest that children who have intellectual and/or social impairments have a history of having suffered elevated levels of perinatal difficulties (Lilienfeld, Pasamanick, & Rogers 1955; McNeil & Wiegerink 1971; McNeil, Wiegerink, & Dozier 1970; Pasamanick 1954). The intellectual difficulties which have been observed include perceptual-motor impairment, disorder of speech, memory, and thinking, and general failure to achieve academically. Further disorders of attention, tendency to perseveration, and intellectual immaturity have been reported to occur more frequently. The behavioral impairment characteristically includes hyperactivity, impulsiveness, sensitivity to stress, immaturity, and a wide range of other more or less disruptive behavior disorders.

All of these symptoms may occur individually or in any possible combination.

The subjects of the present study were drawn from the subject pool of a Danish perinatal study. The mean age at follow-up was 11 years (range was 10.0–12.2). This age was chosen because it was considered important that the subjects at follow-up could be expected to have passed the major developmental milestones and to be functioning intellectually as well as behaviorally at an advanced level (Feffer 1959; Piaget 1950). As Windle (1969) points out, the growth process is such that only gross deficits or deficits belonging to certain categories will show up on tests administered to children while still in their early childhood. Some deficits may not become detectable until more highly organized behavior patterns can be demanded and the subjects' performance on these can be evaluated by the examiner.

It was hypothesized that the experimental subjects of this study who neonatally presented TNS at follow-up would show higher incidence of intellectual and personality-social deviance than would matched controls.

METHOD

Subjects

The 48 subjects (24 experimentals, 24 controls) of the present study were drawn from the subject pool of a large Danish perinatal study. This study has largely the same theoretical background and the same research aims as the American Collaborative Perinatal Research Project (Ballow, Andersen, Reynolds, & Rubin, Note 1). The Danish study was begun in 1959 at the University Hospital (Rigshopitalet) in Copenhagen. Between September 1959 and December 1961, 9,006 women delivered in this hospital. For all of these births careful and precoded data were collected on the mother's prepregnancy history, the pregnancy, the delivery process, and the neonatal period (Villumsen 1970; Zachau-Christiansen 1972; Zachau-Christiansen & Ross 1975). Of the 9,125 births included in the Danish perinatal study, 7,407 had birth weight over 2,500 grams. For purposes of the present study, it was decided to draw subjects only from among those with birth weight over 2,500 grams, so as not to be faced with the problem of having to consider the effects of prematurity.

Of the 7,407 maturely born infants, 305 (4.12%) showed one or more of a group of symptoms which have been shown by Amiel-Tison (1969), Craig (1950, 1960), and Thorn (1968) to be correlated with a

TABLE 1

FREQUENCIES OF NEONATAL SYSTEMS
IN EXPERIMENTAL GROUP

Symptom	N Cases
Shivering or jitteriness....................	9
Restlessness..............................	8
Cyanosis, respiratory distress............	8
Convulsions..............................	5
Frog position............................	5
Limpness................................	3

NOTE.—This listing is restricted to symptoms evidenced by the
subjects which have been shown to be related to later signs of brain
damage in previous research. A symptom is listed if it appeared on
either day 1 or 5 or both.

higher than normal rate of brain damage symptomatology later in life.
In 215 of these 305 cases, the signs were of a transient nature and
had disappeared by the eighth day after birth at which time the infants were discharged from the hospital. The experimental group of
this study was drawn from these 215 infants with TNS. This group
was first divided according to sex (130 males, 85 females). Then from
each of the sex groups the first 12 consecutive births (beginning
January 1960) were included in the experimentals group in the case
that the infant (1) had no congenital malformation, and (2) at the time
of follow-up was living in the vicinity of Copenhagen. The latter condition was instituted for practical purposes. The same time span (from
the birthdate of the first to the twelfth subject) was covered in order
to select the male and female subjects. Table 1 describes the neonatal
symptoms and their frequencies in the experimental group.

The experimental subjects were matched one to one with control
subjects for age, sex, and social class (see table 2). The experimental
subjects and controls were invited in for a day of intensive examination by a social worker who visited them in their homes. No invited
subjects refused to participate.

The Follow-up Examination

The following data from the intensive examination were used to test
the hypothesis of higher degree of intellectual impairment in the experimental group.

1. Memory for Designs Test (MFD) (Graham & Kendall 1960). On
this test, widely used for diagnosing possible brain damage, a score of

TABLE 2

CHARACTERISTICS OF EXPERIMENTAL
AND CONTROL GROUPS

	Experi-mental	Control
N females...............	12	12
N males..................	12	12
Mean age (in years).........	11.25	11.02
Mean social class[a].........	2.33	2.66
Age range.................	10–11.90	10–12.20

[a] Social class was determined by Svalastoga's Scale (Svalastoga 1959). This scale runs from 0 (low) to 6 (high). It was developed specifically for use in Denmark.

101 or below is normal; scores between 102 and 106 indicate border-line conditions, and scores of 107 or above indicate brain damage. The score is corrected for IQ.

2. Feffer's Role Taking Test (RTT) (Feffer 1959). The RTT measures the ability to decenter or to change perspective. It has been shown to be a reliable measure of the developmental level of a subject's cognitive functioning. Besides being dependent on higher cognitive processes, adequate performance on the test also depends on verbal competence and requires a certain degree of memory functioning. (Possible range of scores is 0–20.)

3. Selected subtests from the Wechsler Intelligence Scale for Children—similarity, vocabulary, block design, object assembly, mazes.

4. The "Teachers' Judgment of Intellectual Functioning." This measure was obtained from a questionnaire which was filled out in each case by the teacher who knew the subject best. Only the relevant subset of the data obtained from this questionnaire was included in the present paper. Of the questionnaire items, 13 were judged to be relevant to the child's intellectual functioning. These items are concerned with the child's ability to concentrate; reading, arithmetic, and language performance; memory functioning; and whether or not he evidenced perseveration in his thinking. An overall score for intellectual functioning was developed by determining for each of the 13 relevant items whether the teacher's answer indicated no disturbance (score of 0), moderate disturbance (score of 1), or severe disturbance (score of 2). ("Don't Know" answers were regarded as "no disturbance" answers. The disturbance scores for each individual's 13 items were then summed. The sum of these scores constitutes the score for Teachers' Judgment of Intellectual Functioning (range 0–26). It was decided to

use this type of overall score in the analyses of the questionnaire data because item by item analyses were found to be difficult to interpret due to the varying number of "don't know" answers given by the teachers to the individual items.

The following data from the follow-up examination were used to test the hypothesis of more impairment in the personality and social functioning on the part of our experimental subjects: (1) Vineland Social Maturity Scale (Doll 1953); (2) "Teachers' Judgment of Personality and Social Functioning"; and (3) relevant information obtained from interviews carried out with the subjects themselves and with their parents. Only the latter two categories need further comments.

Teachers' Judgment of Personality and Social Functioning.—This score was obtained by the same procedures as were described under Teachers' Judgment of Intellectual Functioning. The individual items contributing to this score are concerned with whether or not the child seems hyperactive and further describe the child in terms of impulse control, maturity, independence, aggressivity, and success in peer relations.

Interview data.—The parent interview, developed at the Psykologisk Instiut, is designed to provide a detailed description of the child and the atmosphere of his home. Information dealing with the child's temperamental characteristics, peer relations, maturity, psychosomatic symptoms, and whether or not he ever had been referred to a psychologist were included in the analyses relevant to the personality and social functioning of our subjects. The child interview was also originally developed as a general information-gathering tool to be used in different types of subject populations. Answers to questions dealing with adaptation in school, social relations, aggressivity, anxiety, and perseveration in emotions were employed in the analyses of the personality and social functioning of the subjects.

Apart from analyses of the data described above which bear directly on the main hypotheses of the study, some additional categories of data were collected and analyzed.

Life history data.—The design of the present study should not be understood as suggesting that a simple cause-effect relationship exists between the neonatal and the follow-up data. Clearly a variety of intermediary variables will have been influencing the development of the subjects during the time passed between the neonatal observations and the follow-up. Consequently, we can at best expect the neonatal symptoms in question to account for a limited proportion of the variance of the follow-up scores—if any. Caregiving patterns, SES, maturational rates, sibling position, physical health, intactness of family, temperamental factors, genetic endowment, and differential life experience are some of the possible intermediating variables influencing the results of the follow-up examination. The importance of many of these variables may only be adequately estimated through data obtained by continuous observation of the subjects. Unfortunately, we have no such observational data available. Other intermediary variables could not be taken into account due to insufficient sample size (i.e., sibling position). However, from the interviews, retrospective information was available concerning family constellation patterns, mother's work patterns, day-care experiences, and types of family stress (marital, economic, poor health, etc.). In addition, data on the biological development and constitution of the subjects stemming from a 1½-hour neurological examination to which all subjects were exposed at follow-up were analyzed.

In view of the fact that other studies have reported differential long-term outcome after perinatal problems as a function of social class differences (Drillien 1964), the possible intermediary influence of SES in our data was assessed.

Pregnancy, Delivery, Neonatal, and One-Year Data

All information relevant to the pregnancy, delivery, neonatal, and 1-year status of each subject was extracted from the files of the Danish Perinatal Project and scored according to a scoring system which yields an estimate of the severity of complication or deviance within each of six categories of data. In this manner, the several hundred data items available for each subject were reduced to the following six scores (serious attempts at factor and cluster analysis proved unsatisfactory): (1) pregnancy score, (2) delivery score, (3) neonatal physical status score, (4) 1-year neurological examination score, (5) 1-year physical examination score, and (6) 1-year motoric development score. This scoring system was developed at the Psykologisk Institut in Copenhagen by collaboration of American and Danish obstetricians and pediatric neurologists. It assigns a weight (1–5) relative to the judged seriousness of every indication of deviance or complication within a given category of data. A subject's score for each data category is the sum of the total number of weights assigned to the relevant symptoms or complications. A more detailed description of these pre-, peri-, neonatal, and early developmental scales may be found in Mednick, Mura, Schulsinger, and Mednick (1971). Data on the pregnancies and deliveries were included in the data analysis due to the etiological relationship which might exist between these variables and the TNS. The three groups of data from the 1-year examination provide us with a chance to examine how well the experimental subjects had succeeded in recovering from or compensating for any neonatal disability. Further, the 1-year data contribute toward filling the gap which exists in our knowledge about our subjects' development between the neonatal period and the follow-up at age 11.

Coding and Data Analyses

All the data collection done in this study as well as all scoring and coding of the collected data was done blindly. In the data analyses 2× 2 factorial analyses of variance by group and sex were employed. In the analyses estimating the intermediating effect of social class, 2× 2 factorial analyses of variance by group and SES were used.

RESULTS

Intellectual Functioning

Table 3 provides the means and standard deviations by group and sex for the data relevant to the intellectual functioning of the subjects. The MFD, the RTT, and the Teachers' Judgment of Intellectual Functioning showed significant group differences. On the MFD the experimental group performed, as predicted, significantly worse than the control group, $F(1,44) = 4.76, p < .05$. The same pattern of results emerged from the analyses of the role-taking test (RTT), $F(1,44)=5.07, p<.05$. The analyses of the Teachers' Judgment of Intellectual Functioning yielded in addition to the significant group difference, $F(1,44) = 7.29, p < .01$, a significant interaction effect, $F(1,44) = 4.09, p < .05$. The teachers' judgments indicate that the experimental females are having more problems within the area of intellectual functioning than either the experimental males or both sexes of the control group. The subjects' scores on Teachers' Judgment of Intellectual Functioning were examined individually in order to ascertain whether only one or two very extreme cases among the experimental females would be responsible for the very elevated mean score presented by this group. It was, however, discovered that six experimental females or half the group had obtained scores of 9 or above

TABLE 3

MEANS AND STANDARD DEVIATIONS BY GROUP AND SEX
ON VARIABLES RELATING TO THE INTELLECTUAL
FUNCTIONING OF THE SUBJECTS

	EXPERIMENTAL		CONTROL	
	Mean	SD	Mean	SD
MFD:				
Males..........	102.58	4.06	101.75	3.57
Females........	104.75	6.57	100.08	1.98
Total..........	103.67	5.45	100.92	2.95
RTT:				
Males..........	8.92	4.54	10.75	4.63
Females........	8.25	4.85	12.63	4.88
Total..........	8.58	4.61	11.65	4.74
IQ verbal:				
Males..........	106.83	8.96	111.92	12.29
Females........	102.75	12.41	98.17	12.86
Total..........	104.79	10.79	105.04	14.17
IQ performance:				
Males..........	108.67	11.87	110.67	16.34
Females........	96.42	20.62	102.67	14.88
Total..........	102.54	17.60	106.67	15.82
IQ full scale:				
Males..........	108.41	10.59	112.23	13.76
Females........	99.75	15.12	100.53	13.66
Total..........	104.08	13.51	106.33	14.74
Teachers' Judgment of Intellectual Functioning:				
Males........	3.92	3.16	3.08	2.24
Females......	8.09	5.61	2.27	2.22
Total........	6.00	4.56	2.69	2.23

(possible range 0–26) whereas only two experimental males and no
control subjects had obtained scores indicating this high degree of abnormality. Analyses of the results obtained on the WISC revealed no
group differences, either on the three scale scores or on any of the
subtests. However, significant sex differences were found on all three
scales. The females scored lower than the males (verbal scale:
$F[1,44] = 6.92, p < .025$; performance scale: $F[1,44] = 4.66, p < .05$; full
scale: $F[1,44] = 7.15, p < .025$). Within the experimental group no difference was found between the scores on the verbal and the performance scales. The same was true for the control group. It should be
emphasized that the means for both groups on all three IQ scales
show that the groups are of average IQ. The experimental females
obtained the lowest mean IQ score, 99.75, and the control males the
highest, 112.33.

Attempts were made to relate specific neonatal symptoms with the scores obtained on the follow-up examination. No significant relationships were disclosed.

Conclusion.—In light of the fact that three group comparisons relevant to intellectual functioning yielded results in the predicted direction, one might consider the hypotheses of higher frequency of intellectual problems within the experimental group to be supported by the data.

Personality and Social Functioning

The analyses of the data relevant to the subjects' personality and social functioning yielded only two significant results. The experimental group was found to show a lower degree of social maturity or independence on the Vineland Social Maturity Test, $F(1,44) = 5.30$, $p <.05$. On an item from the child interview dealing with whether or not the child felt lonely, the experimental subjects admitted to significantly more loneliness than the controls, $F(1,44) = 6.07, p < .025$. Table 4 shows the means and standard deviations for the two variables described above which significantly distinguished the experimental group within the area of personality and social functioning. None of the other 17 analyzed interview items showed any significant group or sex differences. The Teachers' Judgment of Personality–Social Functioning showed an almost significant group difference in the predicted direction, $F(1,44) = 3.92$.

Conclusion.—Of the 20 comparisons made on the data relevant to the subjects' personality and social functioning, only two yielded significant group differences (of .05 and .025 levels, respectively). Maintaining 95% confidence limits, one of these results is likely to have been significant by chance. In view of these considerations we must consider the support given to the hypothesis of more personality-social problems among our experimental subjects to be weak.

Life History Variable

Neither the biological development nor the environmental conditions of the subjects as mirrored by our data showed any significant differences in the group × sex analyses of variance. In the analyses by group and SES by which we attempted to evaluate the intermediating influence of SES on the follow-up data, only the MFD was signifi-

TABLE 4

MEANS AND STANDARD DEVIATIONS FOR THE TWO
VARIABLES WHICH SIGNIFICANTLY DIFFERENTIATED
BETWEEN THE GROUPS ON THE PERSONALITY-SOCIAL
DIMENSION

	EXPERIMENTAL		CONTROL	
	Mean	SD	Mean	SD
Vineland Social Maturity Test:				
Males........	104.25	9.10	114.92	16.40
Females......	104.08	12.25	109.91	9.70
Total........	104.17	10.56	112.52	13.56
Child: I often play alone[a]				
Males........	0.67	0.65	0.42	0.67
Females......	1.00	0.74	0.33	0.49
Total........	0.83	0.70	0.38	0.58

[a] Range of scores, 0–2.

cantly related to the SES of the subjects, $F(1,44) = 5.72$, $p < .05$. Children from lower SES background scored lower on the MFD. No interaction term proved significant.

Pregnancy, Delivery, and Neonatal Physical Status

Table 5 presents the means and standard deviations of the two groups on the scores describing the pregnancies, the delivery, and the neonatal physical examination. As can be seen from table 5, the group difference on the pregnancy score was not significant. The experimental females, however, present a score which is noticeably higher than that of the experimental males, though this difference did not reach significance. With regard to delivery complications, a significant group effect was found. The experimental group suffered more delivery complications than the control group, $F(1,44) = 5.26$, $p < .05$.

As expected, the experimental group received a higher average abnormality score than the controls on the neonatal physical examination. The ANOVA for group difference on this variable yielded a highly significant F value, $F(1,44) = 23.36$, $p < .001$. On this variable the experimental females again presented a higher degree of abnormality than the males. A test between the means of the experimental males and the experimental females yielded a t value of 2.11 (46 *df*, $p < .05$).

TABLE 5

MEANS AND STANDARD DEVIATIONS BY GROUP AND SEX
FOR THE WEIGHTED PREGNANCY-DELIVERY
AND NEONATAL PHYSICAL SCORE

	EXPERIMENTAL		CONTROL	
	Mean	SD	Mean	SD
Pregnancy compli-cations:				
Males........	4.50	3.40	4.40	2.94
Females......	6.42	4.80	4.17	3.35
Total........	5.46	4.18	4.29	3.09
Delivery:				
Males..........	8.92	3.87	4.92	2.99
Females........	7.83	4.50	6.33	4.96
Total..........	8.38	4.15	5.63	4.07
Neonatal physical:				
Males..........	8.92	4.96	4.25	2.30
Females........	12.75	3.77	5.67	5.18
Total..........	10.83	4.73	4.96	3.98

The One-Year Examination

The 1-year examination included a physical and a neurological examination. A questionnaire which the mothers had been asked to fill out during the child's first year of life was also collected. This questionnaire, along with a few items from the physical examination, provided data for the score for 1-year motor development. Table 6 presents the means and standard deviations for the groups on the 1-year variables. The 1-year motor development variable is the only one of the three variables in this category which presents significant differences between the groups. The experimental group performed worse on this measure, $F(1,44) = 16.26, p < .001$.

DISCUSSION

Intellectual Functioning

Of the variables relevant to the intellectual functioning of the two groups, the MFD and the RTT yielded the most straightforward support for the hypothesis. Children with TNS evidenced poorer performance. With regard to the Teachers' Judgment of Intellectual Functioning a more complicated picture presents itself. In view of the fact that the total scale score differentiated between the groups, it was

TABLE 6

MEANS AND STANDARD DEVIATIONS BY GROUP AND SEX
FOR THE ONE-YEAR EXAMINATION

	EXPERIMENTAL		CONTROL	
	Mean	SD	Mean	SD
1-year physical:				
Males.........	8.17	5.02	7.42	4.50
Females........	8.67	4.94	8.67	4.94
Total..........	8.42	4.88	5.95	4.28
1-year neurological:				
Males.........	0.92	1.24	0.92	1.31
Females........	1.83	3.35	0.42	0.67
Total..........	1.38	2.52	0.67	1.05
1-year motor development:				
Males........	3.09	2.98	0.73	1.00
Females......	5.00	3.30	1.40	1.50
Total........	4.09	3.23	1.04	1.28

deemed of interest to investigate which of the individual items of the scale were making the major contributions to this difference. Fisher's Exact Test was used for group comparisons on the individual items constituting the scale. The item-by-item analysis revealed that only items concerning distractibility or lack of concentration significantly differentiated between the groups. The rest of the items (difficulties with reading, arithmetic, language or memory, and perseveration) did not yield significant group differences when analyzed individually. The results uniformly tended to be in the direction of the experimental subjects performing worse.

With respect to IQ scores, the results of the present paper clearly seem to demonstrate that, though some kind of later intellectual impairment may be correlated with TNS, an overall decrease in tested IQ is not to be counted among the reliable later correlates.

The reported findings of the males of both groups receiving higher scores on the WISC than the females is a puzzling result which the author is most tempted to explain as a sampling artifact. However, the author is familiar with a parallel result obtained on another, large sample of same-aged Danish subjects. In a yet-unpublished study of 250 11-year-olds, Mednick and Schulsinger found that the males obtained significantly higher scores on the WISC. In view of this, an alternative explanation of the sex difference on the WISC may be that the Danish edition of this test tends to favor males when applied to this particular age group.

Personality and Social Functioning

As mentioned above, the support is weak for the hypothesis that personality-social problems are among the preadolescent correlates of TNS. The experimental group in this study was found to be a little immature and somewhat lonely. However, the behavior disorders which are much more commonly cited as signs of brain damage in school-aged children, such as hyperactivity, impulsivity, unpredictability, and sensitivity to stress, etc., did not occur significantly more frequently in our experimental group. There are different ways one might try to explain this finding. (1) It is possible that the initial trauma suffered by the experimental subjects in this study was too light or transient to be correlated with the types of sequelae mentioned above. (2) Another related explanation is based on a rather common notion in the field (Bender 1949; Birch 1964; Bradley 1955; Ernhart, Graham, Eichman, Marshall, & Thurstone 1963; Hanvik, Nelson, Hanson, Andersen, Dressler, & Zarling 1961; Willerman 1973). These researchers view the manifestation of brain damage in a child as resulting from a more or less unfortunate interaction between an organism which has suffered some degree of primary damage to the brain and the surrounding environment. The quality of the latter will heavily influence the outcome for the patient. The effects of a primary lesion may be successfully compensated for or significantly extenuated by the individual-environment interaction. It follows that the less severe the primary trauma was, the more unfortunate environmental agents must be involved in producing a symptom picture of a certain severity. With regard to the relative absence of personality social deviances found in the present study, one could imagine that very unfortunate combinations of strength of primary symptoms and unfortunate interactive agents were not present in our experimental groups. (3) Finally, it should be added that many of the earlier studies examining the psychological and behavioral functioning of children diagnosed as having brain damage were done with subjects who were actually initially selected on the basis of behavior disturbance. The subjects were often clinic populations referred for such disturbance. Despite the fact that such studies may provide a somewhat unrepresentative picture of the range of symptoms which might be observed in children with brain damage, our expectations with regard to the experimental group were to some extent based on such studies. It seems obvious that children whose personality and social problems go in the direction of increased loneliness and immaturity (such as our experimental group) will have a smaller chance of being referred to a clinic than children with disruptive behavior disorders, unless their intellectual functioning is profoundly disturbed.

With regard to the absence of the hyperactivity syndrome among the experimental group, a few remarks may be in order. Hyperactivity is often cited as one of the cardinal symptoms of brain damage in children, though it has been demonstrated (Birch 1964) that the frequency of hyperactivity among children with *known* brain damage has been vastly overestimated. We would, however, have expected a somewhat higher incidence rate of this disorder among our experimental group. One reason for the lack of this finding may be ascribed to another bias which has been influencing the results of earlier research on clinic populations. The subjects of these studies have been predominantly males. Wender (1971) cites the incidence rate of hyperactivity as four to 10 times as high for males as for females. Since the number of males and females in the present study was predetermined to be equal and it further turned out that the females showed more signs of impairment at follow-up, the deviances observed in this study would naturally be different from deviances observed in male-dominated samples. The impairments found in the present study may be more characteristic of female subjects. Again, it is also possible that the neonatal symptoms in our experimental group were too short lived to be correlated with later hyperactivity. Only more research which employs severity ratings of peri- and neonatal factors can illuminate this question.

Sex Differences

The data of the present study tend to show the experimental females to be in a worse condition than the males. The females had (according to their teachers) significantly more intellectual problems and showed on several other follow-up variables a tendency to score lower than the males. On the early life variables a similar pattern of results emerges. On the score for neonatal physical status the experimental females scored significantly worse than the males, and with regard to pregnancy complications and 1-year motor development, there was a noticeable—though nonsignificant—tendency in the same direction. At first sight this pattern of results seems surprising in the light of the well-established greater vulnerability on the part of male fetuses, infants, and older children (Maccoby & Jacklin 1974). However, when one considers the sampling method applied in this study together with this increased male vulnerability, a probable explanation of the sex differences in our data suggests itself. The 215 infants from among whom our experimental group was chosen consisted of 130 males and 85 females. From previous research (Maccoby & Jacklin 1974; Mednick et al. 1971) we know that males in general have a lower tolerance of pre- and perinatal stress than do females. It is therefore likely that the 85 females would have to have been more severely traumatized or affected than the males in order to be detected as showing symptoms in the newborn period. Most likely some of the 130 males were as severely traumatized as the average of the 85 females, but the variance in degree of traumatization is likely to have been much greater in the male group as compared with the females. Since we deliberately chose an equal number of subjects from each sex group, we should, according to this line of thinking, expect our female subjects to have been exposed to more traumatizing pre- or perinatal events. The tendency of the female experimental subjects to have had worse prenatal periods and to do worse on the neonatal physical examination point in this direction. The poorer performance of the females on the follow-up measures may then be seen as a correlate of more severe early traumatization.

CONCLUSION

Certain neonatal symptoms which when persistent in the newborn period have been shown to be correlated with presence of brain damage signs later in life have measurable negative correlates in intellectual (and maybe to a lesser degree social) functioning even when only transiently present in the newborn. In the interpretation of the data one should, however, bear in mind that we have not been able to control for many of the important mediating variables which may potentially be influencing the results of the follow-up examination. One might also mention one strength of this study residing in the fact that the subjects stem from a well-defined birth cohort. The experimental group was chosen so as to be representative of maturely born infants with the transient symptoms in question. This fact increases our confidence in the generalizability of the reported findings.

REFERENCE NOTE

1. Ballow, B.; Andersen, J. A.; Reynolds, M.; & Rubin, R. A. Educational and behavioral sequelae of prenatal and perinatal conditions (Interim Report No. 3). U.S. Department of Health, Education, and Welfare, 1969.

REFERENCES

Amiel-Tison, C. Cerebral damage in full-term new-borns: aetiological factors, neonatal factors and long term follow-up. *Biologica Neonatorium,* 1969, **14,** 234.

Benaron, H. B. W.; Tucker, B. E.; Andrews, J. P., Boshes, B.; Cohen, J.; Fromm, E.; & Yacorzynsky, G. K. Effect of anoxia during labor and immediately after birth on subsequent development of the child. *American Journal of Obstetrics and Gynecology,* 1960, **80,** 1129.

Bender, L. Psychological problems of children with organic brain disease. *American Journal of Orthopsychiatry,* 1949, **19,** 404.

Birch, H. G. The problem of brain damage. In H. G. Birch (Ed.), *Brain damage in children.* Baltimore: Williams & Wilkins, 1964.

Bradley, D. Organic factors in the psychopathology of childhood. In P. H. Hoch & J. Zubin (Eds.), *Psychopathology of childhood.* New York: Grune & Stratton, 1955.

Craig, W. S. Intercranial irritation in the newborn: immediate and long-term prognosis. *Archives of Disease in Childhood,* 1950, **25,** 325.

Craig, W. S. Convulsive movements occuring in the first 10 days of life. *Archives of Disease in Childhood,* 1960, **35,** 336.

Doll, E. A. *Vineland Social Maturity Scale.* Psychological Corp., 1953.

Drillien, C. M. *The growth and development of the prematurely born infant.* Edinburgh: Livingstone, 1964.

Ernhart, C. B.; Graham, F. K.; Eichman, P. L.; Marshall, I. M.; & Thurstone, D. Brain injury in the preschool child: some developmental considerations. *Psychological Monographs,* 1963, **77**(11, Whole No. 574).

Feffer, M. H. The cognitive implication of roletaking behavior. *Journal of Personality,* 1959, **27,** 2.

Graham, F. K.; Ernhart, C. B.; Thurstone, D.; & Crafft, M. Development three years after perinatal anoxia and other potentially damaging newborn experiences. *Psychological Monographs,* 1962, **76**(3, Whole No. 522).

Graham, F. K., & Kendall, B.S. *Memory for Designs Test.* Psychological Test Specialists, 1960.

Hanvik, L. J.; Nelson, L. E.; Hanson, H. B.; Andersen, A. S.; Dressler, W. H.; & Zarling, V. R. Diagnosis of cerebral dysfunction in children as made in a child guidance clinic. *American Journal of Diseases in Children,* 1961. **101,** 364.

Honzik, M. P.; Hutchings, J. J., & Burnip, S. R. Birth record assessment and test performance at eight months. *American Journal of Diseases in Children,* 1965, **109,** 416.

Lihenfeld, A. M.; Pasamanick, B., & Rogers, M. The relationship between pregnancy experience and the development of certain neuro-psychiatric disorders in childhood. *American Journal of Public Health,* 1955, **45,** 637.

Maccoby, E. E., & Jacklin, C. N. *The psychology of sex differences.* Stanford, Calif.: Stanford University Press, 1974.

McNeil, Th. F., & Wiegerink, R. Behavioral patterns and pregnancy and birth complication histories in psychologically disturbed children. *Journal of Nervous and Mental Disease,* 1971, **152,** 315.

McNeil, Th. F., Wiegerink, R.; & Dozier, J. E. Pregnancy and birth complications in the births of seriously, moderately and mildly behaviorally disturbed children. *Journal of Nervous and Mental Disease,* 1970, **151,** 24–34.

Mednick, S. A.; Mura, E.; Schulsinger, F.; & Mednick, B. Perinatal conditions and infant development in children with schizophrenic parents. *Social Biology,* 1971, **18,** 103.

Pasamanick, B. *Epidemiology of behavior disorders: neurology and psychiatry in childhood.* New York: Williams & Wilkins, 1954.

Pasamanick, B., & Knobloch, H. Brain damage and reproductive casualty. *American Journal of Orthopsychiatry,* 1960, **30,** 298.

Piaget, J. *The psychology of intelligence.* New York: Harcourt, Brace, 1950.

Prechtl, H. F. R. Prognostic value of neurological signs in the newborn infant. *Proceedings of the Royal Society of Medicine,* 1965, **58,** 3.

Prechtl, H. F. R. Neurological sequelae of prenatal and perinatal complications. *British Medical Journal,* 1967, **4,** 763.

Rosenfeld, G. B., & Bradley, C. Childhood behavior sequelae of asphyxia in infancy. *Pediatrics,* 1948, **2,** 74.

Schacter, F. F., & Apgar, V. Perinatal asphyxia and psychological signs of brain damage in childhood. *Pediatrics,* 1959, **24,** 1016.

Stechler, G. A longitudinal follow-up of neonatal apnea. *Child Development,* 1964, **35,** 333–348.

Svalastoga, K. *Prestige, class, and mobility.* Copenhagen: Gyldendal, 1959.

Thorn, I. *Cerebral symptoms in the newborn.* Copenhagen: Munksgard, 1968.

Villumsen, A. L. *Environmental factors in congenital malformations.* Copenhagen: FADL, 1970.

Wender, P. H. *Minimal brain dysfunction in children.* New York: Wiley, 1971.

Willerman, I., Social aspects of minimal brain dysfunction. *Annals of the New York Academy of Sciences,* 1973, **205,** 164.

Windle, W. F. Brain damage by asphyxia at birth. *Scientific American,* 1969, **221,** 76.

Zachau-Christiansen, B. *Development during the first year of life.* Helsing ør Poul A. Andersen, 1972.

Zachau-Christiansen, B., & Ross, E. M. *Babies: human development during the first year.* New York: Wiley, 1975.

Part II

GENETIC AND
BIOCHEMICAL ISSUES

The study of genetic and biochemical influences on the development of psychiatric disorders in childhood is another area of rapidly expanding research. Many of the findings to date are still tentative, but sufficient to indicate that further addition of knowledge in these areas will have an important impact on theory and practice. The two reviews in this section provide authoritative analytic summaries of our present state of knowledge and point up some of the problems and prospects for future investigation.

Hanson, Gottesman and Meehl provide a review of prospective high-risk studies of the children of schizophrenic parents, and summarize the methods, findings and problems arising from this work. As is so often the case with geneticists, Hanson and his co-workers also emphasize the importance of the environmental contributions to pathological outcome. In addition, they point out the dilemmas and problems in utilizing the genetic knowledge obtained from high-risk studies.

The review by Cohen and Young of recent basic advances in neurochemistry as related to child psychiatry is comprehensive and authoritative. This is indeed an area in which there has been an explosion of knowledge, concepts, and methodological techniques in the past 10 years. The authors do not minimize the serious methodological problems involved in interpreting biological research in child psychiatry, and discuss a number of these problems carefully. They also emphasize the necessity for integrating biochemical knowledge with endocrine, pharmacological and clinical data. Neurochemistry and basic biologic research in general are here not opposed to the clinician's work, as is so often the case. Cohen and Young rather emphasize the opportunity the clinician has for making careful observa-

77

tions on the long-term effects and the acute impact of psychoactive drugs in children. In their words, the clinicians' offices and clinics can provide "very sensitive research settings for studying brain-behavior relationships."

PART II: GENETIC AND BIOCHEMICAL ISSUES

5

GENETIC THEORIES AND THE VALIDATION OF PSYCHIATRIC DIAGNOSES: IMPLICATIONS FOR THE STUDY OF CHILDREN OF SCHIZOPHRENICS

Daniel R. Hanson, Irving I. Gottesman

and Paul E. Meehl

University of Minnesota

The success of prospective methods for studying the development of schizophrenia in those few offspring of schizophrenics who also become schizophrenic (high-risk method) depends on using valid diagnostic criteria for selecting the parent probands. Data from a high-risk study in which the affected parents were diagnosed by five clinicians are used to illustrate the impact different diagnostic

Reprinted with permission from *Journal of Abnormal Psychology*, Vol. 86, 575–588, 1977. Copyright 1977 by the American Psychological Association.

This research was supported in part by a Mental Health Training Grant in Biological Sciences (MH10679) awarded to S. C. Reed and I. I. Gottesman at the University of Minnesota and the Charles M. Goethe Memorial Fund of the Dight Institute for Human Genetics. Support for the preparation of this article came in part from a grant from the Ontario Mental Health Foundation (OMHF 579-75A) awarded to D. R. Hanson.

We thank Rosalyn Rubin and V. E. Anderson of the University of Minnesota and Roland Peek and other members of the Minnesota Department of Public Welfare and Minnesota State Hospital System for their valuable cooperation and assistance.

standards may have on the composition of high-risk samples and control samples of children of other psychiatric patients. Publicly reporting careful assessments of affected parents will also facilitate comparisons among different high-risk samples and will allow estimates of the risks for individuals within each high-risk sample. Genetic theory and empirical data suggest that children with severely affected parents and children with many affected relatives will have the highest risks, while samples of children with only one mildly affected parent may have risks that approach the population base rates. Genetic theory further suggests that some children of validly diagnosed schizophrenics will have no genetic risk for schizophrenia, and some of those who do have the genetic predisposition will enjoy a lifetime of adequate mental health even without intervention, thus confounding the effort of high-risk research to validate indicators of the high-risk genotype with follow-up status. High-risk researchers are cautioned against premature implementation of intervention strategies based on unvalidated indicators of the risks to individuals.

The omissions and distortions in retrospective accounts of the origins of abnormal behaviors led Pearson and Kley (1975) to propose a plan that would allow prospective investigations of infrequent disorders while maintaining sample sizes within practical limits. For any *familial* disorder, the offspring of affected parents will be affected much more frequently than individuals sampled from the general population; thus, Pearson and Kley argued that these high-risk subjects deserved intensive, longitudinal scrutiny. Subsequent to the pioneering work on schizophrenics' offspring by Fish (Fish & Alpert, 1962; Fish & Hagin, 1973) and Sobel (1961), the major impetus for the rapid expansion in prospective studies of children of schizophrenic patients came in 1968 with two publications by Mednick and his colleagues (Mednick & McNeil, 1968; Mednick & Schulsinger, 1968). Recent tallies (Erlenmeyer-Kimling, 1975; Garmezy, 1974) show that at least 20 high-risk projects are now under way and that the vast majority of these studies utilize the familial model for defining high risk.

All of these investigations are being conducted with the hope that prospective methods will lead to the early (premorbid) detection of the schizophrenic process and will uncover potentiating or protective factors (genetic and environmental). Everyone hopes that the early detection of vulnerable individuals and an understanding of the pathophysiological and pathoenvironmental contributors to schizophrenia will lead to rational methods of treatment and, ultimately, to workable strategies for prevention. So far, these goals have not been realized. Some 20 years after the appearance of the Pearson and Kley (1957) article, it is an appropriate time to examine some of the data, logic, and assumptions that form the rationale for studying children of schizophrenic parents (also see Garmezy, 1977; Shields, 1977).

HIGH-RISK RESEARCH AND THE VALIDITY
OF PSYCHIATRIC DIAGNOSES

In contrast to the majority reports (some might say *ideologies*) of a decade or two ago, current research (cf. Cooper et al., 1972; Endicott & Spitzer, 1972; Fischer, 1974; Shields & Gottesman, 1972; Spitzer, 1975; Wing, Cooper, & Sartorius, 1974; World Health Organization, 1973) shows that the diagnosis of schizophrenia can be made with high reliability when, to paraphrase Meehl (1972, p. 358), competent and motivated diagnosticians have accurate and detailed information with which to work. Even though many different criteria for diagnosing schizophrenia can be applied with high reliability, there are considerable differences of opinion on what constitutes the most valid and useful working definition. For high-risk researchers, the issue of the predictive validity of the diagnoses of schizophrenia is of central importance in two respects. First, fulfillment of the high-risk researchers' hopes for early detection of schizophrenia requires the adoption of definitions of schizophrenia for affected parents that *do* accurately predict schizophrenia in the offspring. A lack of predictive validity will mean that the children studied are not at high risk for schizophrenia, and many years of expensive longitudinal research will come to nought. Second, the high-risk method itself provides a powerful way to test the predictive validity of schizophrenia diagnoses, though few prospective high-risk projects have attempted to capitalize on this aspect of the strategy. The predictive validities of current diagnostic criteria for schizophrenia are not established, and consequently, it seems reasonable to employ a range of alternative criteria for parental probands when assembling a high-risk population. Follow-up results can then be used to evaluate which of the criteria deliver the optimal "yield." Data from our own study of children of schizophrenic mothers or fathers (Hanson, Gottesman, & Heston, 1976) illustrates the impact that different definitions could have on the composition of a high-risk sample.

Hanson, Gottesman, and Heston's
(1976) Schizophrenic Sample

Our sample was ascertained by searching for reports of mental illness in mothers or fathers of the first 2,500 births in the Minnesota subsample of the Collaborative Study of Cerebral Palsy, Mental Retardation, and Other Neurological Disorders of Infancy and Childhood, a prospective study of child health and development sponsored by the Perinatal Branch of the National Institute of Neurological and Communicative Diseases and Stroke (Broman, Nichols, & Kennedy, 1975; Niswander & Gordon, 1972). At the time of the 7-year follow-up, 221 of the 5,000 parents (4.4%) had a history of hospitalization for psychiatric care. We excluded 54 cases who did not meet our sampling requirements, which specified native-born Caucasians with no physical or sensory handicap who had been hospitalized for at least 1 week in a Minnesota hospital. After reviewing the hospital records for the remaining 167 patients, we excluded 97 more cases because there was insufficient information to make a diagnosis (e.g., records lost or sealed by the courts [15 cases]), because the affected parent was unquestionably alcoholic with no indication of psychosis (25 cases), or because the patients' illness appeared very mild and transient (e.g., grief reactions [57 cases]). Full details of the sampling procedures can be found in Hanson et al., (1976) and Hanson (1974).

After these exclusions, there remained 70 patients with a variety of hospital diagnoses who had to be confirmed as schizophrenic or not. For each patient, detailed life histories, usually with results from repeated testing with the Minnesota Multiphasic Personality Inventory (MMPI), were submitted to five senior clinicians[1] who made totally independent blind diagnoses and who rated the patients on an 8-point scale of global pathology (see Gottesman & Shields, 1972, p. 229) and a 5-point scale of anxiety level (1 – extremely low and 5 = extremely high). Twenty-nine of the 70 cases were judged to be schizophrenic by at least three diagnosticians, which constituted our consensus schizophrenic sample. For 83% of these consensus schizophrenic diagnoses,

---

[1]The five judges were (a) I. Gottesman, Professor of Psychology and Psychiatry and Director of the Behavioral Genetics Center, at the University of Minnesota, Minneapolis; (b) L. Heston, Professor of Psychiatry and Director of Psychiatric Research at the University of Minnesota, Minneapolis; (c) P. Meehl, Regents Professor of Psychology, Psychiatry, and Philosophy at the University of Minnesota, Minneapolis; (d) V. Tuason, Chief of Psychiatry at Saint Paul-Ramsey Hospital, Saint Paul, Minnesota; and (e) H. Gilberstadt, Chief Research Clinical Psychologist at Minneapolis (Minnesota) Veterans Hospital.

the five judges agreed unanimously or with one dissenting vote. The 29 consensus schizophrenics represented $13\% \pm 2\%$ of the 221 hospitalized parents and $.6\% \pm .1\%$ of the 5,000 parents in the initial sampling frame. A psychiatric control sample contained 34 parents (from the 70) who were judged to be other than schizophrenic by consensus; these patients comprised a heterogeneous cluster of organic syndromes, affective illnesses, and character disorders. Four additional censensus nonschizophrenics were excluded because of diagnostic disagreement (two votes schizophrenic vs. three votes nonschizophrenic), and three other consensus nonschizophrenics were mates to the schizophrenics. Of the $70 \times 5 = 350$ individual diagnoses, 87% agreed with the consensus diagnosis.

Tellegen's adaptation of the Kuder-Richardson 20 formula (see Gottesman & Shields, 1972, p. 216) provided an interrater reliability coefficient of .89. For diagnoses of schizophrenia versus nonschizophrenia, the average pair-wise agreement among the judges was 77%. However, one judge (Meehl) consistently had the lowest agreement with the other four judges. His average pair-wise agreement with the others was 62%. Whereas consensus opinion (including Mcehl) designated 29 of the 70 cases as schizophrenics, Meehl diagnosed schizophrenia 53 times.

A comparison of Meehl's diagnoses with the consensus diagnoses for the 24 cases called schizophrenic by Meehl but called nonschizophrenic by consensus opinion is shown in Table 1. The majority (17/24, or 71%) of the disagreements occurred when Meehl used a diagnosis of "qualified" schizophrenia (i.e., pseudoneurotic, pseudopsychopathic, and schizoaffective). There is close agreement between Meehl and the other four judges for perceived symptomatology. That is, Meehl often made a diagnosis of pseudopsychopathic schizophrenia when the other judges said psychopath, schizoaffective schizophrenic was often used by Meehl when the others reported an affective psychosis, and cases called pseudoneurotic by Meehl were usually just neuroses in the opinion of others. Most of the apparent diagnostic disagreement appears to reflect a theoretical difference in opinion on what constitutes valid indicators of schizophrenia rather than a lack of reliability in recognizing and rating patients' attributes. However, these differences in opinion between Meehl and the consensus opinion of all five judges cannot be dismissed too easily in light of reports that claim a link between typical schizophrenia and a "spectrum" of possibly genetically related psychopathologies (e.g., Kety, Rosenthal, Wender, Schulsinger, & Jacobsen, 1975; H. Schulsinger, 1976, Note 1).

Table 1
Comparison of the 24 Cases called Schizophrenic by Meehl and Called
Nonschizophrenic by Consensus Opinion

	Meehl's diagnosis of schizophrenia				
Consensus diagnosis of nonschizophrenics	Pseudo-psycho-pathic	Schizo-affective	Pseudo-neurotic	Other	Chronic
Character disorder/psychopath	6	0	1	0	3
Affective psychosis	0	4	0	0	1
Neurotic/inadequate personality	0	1	3	0	3
Other	0	1	0	1	0

Table 2
Indicators of Severity for the Three Diagnostic Groups

Indicator of severity	Consensus schizophrenics	Consensus psychiatric controls	Consensus nonschizo-phrenics called schizophrenic by Meehl
Average age (in years) when first hospitalized	24	23	22
Average age (in years) at follow-up	35	32	31
Average no. psychiatric hospitalizations	4.3	3.0	3.0
% hospitalizations less than 6 months	21	59	63
% hospitalizations 6 months to 1 year	41	26	29
% hospitalizations 1-2 years	10	12	8
% hospitalizations more than 2 years	28	3	0
Average weeks in hospital	95	26	21
% ever in state hospital	76	41	29
% committed by court order	45	32	21
% not working at follow-up	66	44	38
Average severity rating	5.6	5.0	5.0

Note. For consensus schizophrenics, $n = 29$; for consensus psychiatric controls, $n = 34$; and for consensus nonschizophrenics called schizophrenic by Meehl, $n = 24$.

Table 2 details some of the characteristics of our consensus schizo-phrenic parents, the consensus controls, and members of the total sample of consensus nonschizophrenics (including the four excluded cases and the three mates to schizophrenics) who were called schizophrenic by Meehl. The consensus schizophrenics tended to be a severely af-fected, chronically ill group. About three fourths of the consensus schizophrenics were state hospital patients, and nearly half of them had been hospitalized under court order. More than a decade (on the average) had elapsed since first hospitalization, yet two thirds of the consensus schizophrenics were still hospitalized, on welfare, or under the guardianship of relatives. One judge (Gottesman), who regularly applied Kraepelinian subtype descriptors, considered 45% of the consensus schizophrenics to exhibit catatonic or hebephrenic features. The control sample, on the average, is less severely affected in all respects and the consensus nonschizophrenics who were called schizophrenic by Meehl comprised a relatively mildly affected group who have spent only about 5 months (on the average) in the hospital during the 9 years since first hospitalization.

Sixty-six of the 70 diagnosed cases had at some time been administered the MMPI, and their scores provide another way of describing our sample. Marks, Seeman, and Haller (1974) have derived detailed descriptors for 16 MMPI profile types that are frequently seen among adult psychiatric patients. Nine of the 16 Marks et al. MMPI code types are most commonly (though not exclusively) observed in schizophrenic patients (see Gottesman & Shields, 1972, p. 272; Marks et al., 1974, Appendix C), and these 9 profile types characterized 22/27, or 81%, of our consensus schizophrenics. The heterogeneous group of consensus nonschizophrenic controls showed a wide variety of code types as expected. Forty-four percent of the controls had code types that were most commonly (but not exclusively) associated with schizophrenia. Notably, none of the controls had Marks et al. MMPI profile types involving both the Schizophrenia scale (8) and the Paranoia scale (6); instead, they usually had elevations on scales for Depression (2), Psychopathic Deviate (4), or Hypomania (9) in addition to any elevation on 8 or 6.

Throughout this diagnostic exercise, Meehl has remained true to his broad concept of schizotypy (Gottesman & Shields, 1972; Meehl, 1962) and has identified as schizophrenic a number of relatively mildly affected ambulatory patients who did have some of the characteristics of more narrowly defined schizophrenics. Yet, on the whole, the symptom patterns of these patients did not resemble schizophrenia sufficiently in the opinion of the majority of diagnosticians. Which point of view is correct? Shields and Gottesman (1972) argue that diagnostic criteria between very broad and very narrow points of view make the most "genetic sense." However, the controversy over the validity of various definitions of schizophrenia and schizophrenia-related disorders is far from settled (see Gottesman & Shields, 1976a; Kety, Rosenthal, Wender, & Schulsinger, 1976; Shields, Heston, & Gottesman, 1975) and is of vital interest to high-risk researchers.

If, for example, a significant proportion of *presumed* nonschizophrenic psychiatric control parents could transmit a diathesis for schizophrenia to their children (as Meehl's diagnoses indicate for about one half of our psychiatric controls), then the contrasts between high-risk and control samples will be blurred, and the specificity of the genetic contribution to the development of schizophrenia may be questioned (cf. Rosenthal, 1975). However, if the broad point of view should prove to be false, there will be other serious consequences for the high-risk studies that adopt it: Many of the children of presumed schizophrenics will not have an increased risk for schizophrenia, the "yield" from the project will be much less than expected, and the potency of specific genetic factors in schizophrenia will be underestimated. Long-term follow-ups of children born to patients who have been screened through a variety of strict and loose criteria for schizophrenia will provide powerful tests of the predictive validities of the many definitions now in use. The employment of a range of potentially valid diagnostic criteria for schizophrenia will greatly broaden the scope of every high-risk project.

The ways in which high-risk investigators define their samples also have important short-term consequences. Until childhood predictors of adult schizophrenia can be confirmed by the realities of follow-up results, or until a state independent biological endophenotype is discovered, the only major indicator of the validity of preliminary results will be their replicability—although, of course, replicability does not guarantee validity (cf. Herman, Mirsky, Ricks, & Gallant, 1977; Rutschmann, Cornblatt, & Erlenmeyer-Kimling, 1977). Replication of results will require the assembling of similar samples, and without thorough descriptions of the diagnosed schizophrenic parents, replications are likely to fail.

GENETIC THEORIES AND EPIGENETIC REALITIES

A summary of the age-corrected lifetime morbidity risks for the occurrence of schizophrenia in individuals who have one schizophrenic parent is shown in Table 3. Children with schizophrenic mothers have the same risk as children with schizophrenic fathers (Bleuler, 1972; Kallmann, 1938). Individuals who have two schizophrenic parents have risks for schizophrenia that range from about 35% to 50% (Erlenmeyer-Kimling, 1968; Rosenthal, 1966). By comparison, the risks to individuals in the general population are about .85% to 1.0% (Slater & Cowie, 1971) when rather strict European diagnostic criteria are applied and are about 3% when broader North American diagnoses are used (Yolles & Kramer, 1969).

All of these risk values are empirical and therefore atheoretical, but the important genetic contribution to schizophrenia evidenced by twin (Gottesman & Shields, 1972), family (Bleuler, 1972), foster (Heston, 1966), adoption (Kety et al., 1975; Rosenthal, Wender, Kety, Welner,

Table 3

Age-Corrected Morbidity Risk for Schizophrenia in Children with One Schizophrenic Parent

Investigator	Children		Morbidity risk ($\% \pm SE$)
	N^a	Affected	
Hoffman, 1921	85.5	6	7.0 ± 2.8
Oppler, 1932	289.5	28	9.7 ± 1.7
Gengnagel, 1933	96.9	8	8.3 ± 2.8
Kallmann, 1938	678.5	94	13.9 ± 1.3
Garrone, 1962	77.0	13	16.9 ± 4.3
Heston, 1966[b]	30.5	5	16.6 ± 6.8
Reisby, 1967	201.8	7	3.5 ± 1.3^c
Lindelius, 1970	243.0	17	7.0 ± 1.6
Fischer, 1973	31.2	3	9.6 ± 5.2
Bleuler, 1972	115.8	10	8.7 ± 2.6
Rosenthal et al. 1971[b]	69[d]	8	11.6 ± 3.8
Reed et al., 1973	108.0[e]	21	19.4 ± 3.8
Karlsson, 1974	82[d]	2	2.4 ± 1.7^f
	46[d]	1	2.2 ± 2.2^f
Schulsinger, 1976	87	9	10.3 ± 3.3^g

[a] N is corrected for age distribution, except where noted, and is equal to risk lives observed (see Slater & Cowie, 1971).
[b] Children were raised apart from the schizophrenic parent.
[c] Risk for schizophrenia or schizophreniform psychoses was 10.4 ± 2.2.
[d] This datum is not age corrected.
[e] Age correction was not required; only schizophrenic psychoses were included.
[f] Risk for all "functional psychoses" was 8.5 ± 3.1 and 4.6 ± 3.1.
[g] Hospitalized cases only were included; inclusion of six additional diagnosed cases gave 17.2% risk or 23.8% by an alternative method.

& Schulsinger, 1971), and cross-fostering (Wender, Rosenthal, Kety, Schulsinger, & Welner, 1974) studies boosts genetic interpretations (see review by Gottesman & Shields, 1976a). The mode of transmission of schizophrenia is not known, but the patterns of transmission are consistent with polygenic theory:[2] (a) Polygenic traits are more

---

[2]Transmission via a dominant gene with variable expressivity cannot be ruled out; at the population level, such a theory generates predictions that are indistinguishable from polygenic expectations using available data. Two of us (Hanson and Gottesman) prefer polygenic models because they are more general and include monogenic models when the number of polygenes is set equal to one, or when monogenic models specify variable expressivity as a result of modifying genes.

common in the general population than deleterious Mendelian traits with full penetrance, (b) polygenic disorders are found with varying severities, (c) the risks are greater in families with many affected relatives compared to families with few affected members, (d) risks to second- and third-degree relatives of affected individuals drop off more sharply than dominant-gene theory expectations, and (3) the risk to a person increases as a function of the severity of a relative's illness. Curnow and Smith (1975) provide a further guide to multifactorial models for familial diseases.

Kallmann's (1938) data (see Table 4) illustrate some of these patterns in samples of children of schizophrenic parents. As we have seen, children with two affected parents have a greater risk than children with one affected parent. The more severely affected catatonic and hebephrenic parents have more affected children than do parents with less devastating paranoid and simple forms of schizophrenia. Many of the nonschizophrenic parents in Kallmann's sample had some type of possibly schizophrenia-related psychopathology; specifying that the nonschizophrenic parents is normal results in a reduction of the overall risks. These relations between magnitude of risk and number of relatives affected or severity of affected relatives' illnesses have been observed in other family (Hallgren & Sjögren, 1959; Lindelius, 1970; Ødegaard, 1972) and twin studies (Gottesman & Shields, 1972). It is apparent that the risk values to samples of children of schizophrenic parents can range anywhere from a low that approaches the general population risk to a high of about 50% depending on the composition of the parent sample. It also appears that at least half (Heston, 1970) and maybe as many as 75% (Bleuler, 1972) of the children with one schizophrenic parent will grow up to be normal and not eccentric. Every high-risk sample will be genetically heterogeneous; those children who receive the necessary genes for schizophrenia will be the true high-risk individuals, and those children who receive none of the necessary genes for schizophrenia will have *no genetic risk* for schizophrenia, even though they are children of schizophrenic parents.

The situation here is like a problem in "sampling without replacement." If all individuals with the high-risk genotypes for schizophrenia (say 10% to 50% of the subjects) are removed from the sample, there remains a large group of individuals who are not at high risk for schizophrenia unless a completely unprecedented set of stressors is brought to bear, thus making "traditional" risk values inapplicable. Genetic theorizing further suggests that there will be individual differences in the magnitude of the necessary diathesis corresponding to

Table 4
Age-Corrected Morbidity Risks for Schizophrenia for Children of Schizophrenic
Parents as a Function of Mating Type and Severity of Illness
(Data are from Kallmann, 1938)

Schizophrenic parents	N[a]	Children	
		% morbidity risk for definite schizophrenia	% morbidity risk for definite or doubtful schizophrenia
Both schizophrenic	23.5	53.3	68.1
One parent as indicated and second parent not specified			
Hebephrenic	265.5	17.3	20.7
Catatonic	106.5	18.8	21.6
Paranoid	212.0	8.5	10.4
Simple	94.5	10.6	11.6
One parent as indicated and second parent normal			
Hebephrenic	144.5	13.1	17.3
Catatonic	49.5	14.1	16.2
Paranoid	118.0	6.8	8.5
Simple	57.0	1.8	1.8

[a] N is adjusted for age distribution of the sample and is equal to "risk lives" observed, or *Bezugsziffer.*

the number and potency of predisposing genes inherited. Those individuals with a relatively mild diathesis will be resistant to all but the most severe environmental stressors, while individuals with very strong predispositions might be vulnerable to breakdown in the face of even the mild stresses of everyday life. The goals of high-risk research include detecting the high-risk genotypes and specifying the life events that actualize the predisposition to schizophrenia. The net result of a dynamic combination of genetic and environmental sources of liabilities and assets determines whether and when a predisposed individual will become a diagnosible schizophrenic.

The lifetime risk estimates discussed above are useful for estimating the final number of high-risk subjects who will eventually break down by the end of the age risk period for schizophrenia. Traditionally, the period of risk for schizophrenia has been thought to extend from age 15 years to age 45 or 50, though Slater and Cowie (1971) have extended the range upward to age 55; and elsewhere, we (Hanson & Gottesman, 1976) have suggested that a downward extension may also be warranted. In addition to lifetime risk estimates, high-risk researchers will also want to estimate how many individuals will break down within a realistic follow-up time.

Table 5 provides the distribution of ages at first hospitalization for

Table 5
Age Distribution of Risk for Schizophrenia
(Data are from Slater and Cowie, 1971)

By age (in years)	Proportion of total risk up to age 55 (percent)	
	Male	Female
15	0·6	0·8
20	11·4	10·6
25	31·4	25·3
30	50·8	43·5
35	70·2	59·7
40	80·6	71·6
45	91·0	83·4
50	95·5	91·7
55	100·0	100·0

schizophrenia and, in conjunction with Table 3, allows easy calculation of the percentage of high-risk subjects expected to break down before any given age range. For example, by age 20 years, a male has been exposed to 11% of the lifetime risk (i.e., 11.4% of all schizophrenic males break down by age 20), and a female has been exposed to 10.6% of the total risk. If we estimate that 10% of a high-risk sample will break down by age 55, then we would expect (.10× .114× 100=) about 1.1% of the high-risk males and (.10× .106× 100=) about 1.1% of the high-risk females to break down by age 20. By age 30, the respective values are 5.1% and 4.4%. Thus, a researcher who starts with a sample of high-risk infants would expect to ascertain only about one half of the eventual schizophrenics after a 30-year follow-up. Any shorter follow-up may provide a distorted view of the natural history of schizophrenia by focusing on the minority of severely affected early-onset cases. Conversely, investigators who report large percentages of affected individuals after short follow-ups are likely to be beating the odds with atypical, severely affected samples or are over-diagnosing schizophrenia.

Genetic theory *does* suggest that schizophrenics who have one or two schizophrenic parents *will* be more severely affected on the average than schizophrenics who have no schizophrenic parents. A recent follow-up of Mednick's (Mednick & Schulsinger, 1968) Danish high-risk sample (H. Schulsinger, 1976) may illustrate this phenomenon. By the time the sample reached a mean age of only 23 years (range of 18 to 30), 9 of 173 (5.3%; 10.3% with age correction) high-risk subjects had been hospitalized for schizophrenia. Application of CATEGO (Wing et al., 1974) diagnostic criteria obtained a similar rate of 5.8%, uncorrected for age, while application of broader DIAGNO II (Endicott & Spitzer, 1972) criteria boosted the uncorrected rate to 17.3%. Schizophrenics with schizophrenic parents may represent a subgroup of all schizophrenics who have atypically strong genetic and environmental diatheses. This would be especially true if the second parent is also schizophrenic or psychiatrically abnormal, as are some of the fathers in the Danish sample (B. Mednick, 1973). The actualization of these strong diatheses would require relatively mild additional stresses from the environment, and these environmental contributors might be so mild and so much a part of everyday life that they pass by unnoticed. Even if the relevant stressors are recorded, they may occur with similar frequencies in high-risk and control samples and may be discounted by investigators not accustomed to thinking in terms of gene-by-environment interactions (cf. Erlenmeyer-Kimling, 1972; Gottesman & Shields, 1976b).

Table 5 may underestimate the rate of breakdown among children of schizophrenics but can serve, at least, as a check on the minimum number of cases expected to break down at any given age. Table 5 also reminds us that even after extensive follow-ups, there may still be a number of individuals in the high-risk sample who will break down at some later date. The presence or absence of breakdown at follow-up is critical to the high-risk method because, in the absence of biological endophenotypic indicators (Shields & Gottesman, 1973) of the schizophrenic genotype, the only proof that certain childhood characteristics are harbingers of adult psychoses comes when forecasted schizophrenics do break down. When the Mednick and Schulsinger (1968) high-risk sample was followed up in 1972 at a mean age of 23.9 years (H. Schulsinger, 1976, Note 1), more overt schizophrenics were found *outside* of the so-called "sick" high-risk subsample than in it. Of 15 consensus-diagnosed schizophrenics in the 173 reinterviewed high-risk subjects, only 4 had been identified in 1962 as in the high-risk sick group.

Some of the possibilities that a high-risk researcher might face at the time of follow-up are illustrated in Figure 1, which shows the phenotypic and genotypic compositions of a high-risk sample of 100 individuals that have been followed up until about age 30 years. The proportion of individuals who eventually break down has been set at 10%. The high-risk genotypes include all children who have the necessary genes for schizophrenia; those without the necessary genes have no-risk genotypes. In this illustration, the minimum proportion

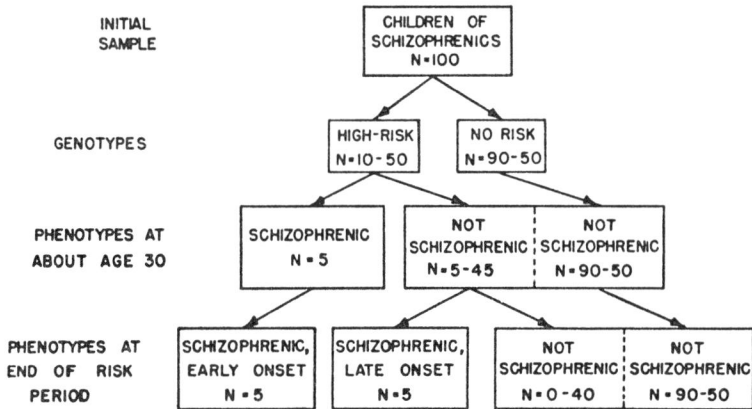

Figure 1. Possible outcomes of a longitudinal study of 100 children with schizophrenic parents.

of high-risk genotypes is 10%, while the maximum has been set at 50% to coincide with Mendelian expectations for dominant inheritance. To keep the graphics simple, we have omitted intermediate-risk genotypes and borderline outcomes. At follow-up, 5 individuals have schizophrenia. Among the 95 who are not schizophrenic, there are 5 more individuals who will develop schizophrenia at a later date, and there are perhaps as many as 40 individuals who have the necessary genotype for schizophrenia but who will never break down. We know there are many individuals with the genetic diathesis for schizophrenia who do not show the trait because only about half of the identical twins of schizophrenics are concordant.[3] Clinical follow-up status, even at the end of the risk period, may not be a sufficient criterion for validating proposed indicators of the high-risk genotype.

Without valid indicators of the high-risk genotypes, high-risk researchers will be hard pressed to fully evaluate the environmental contributors to schizophrenia. Such evaluations require comparisons of those individuals who have the genes and who break down early to those individuals who have the same genetic liability but who break down late; and both of these groups must be compared to the group of individuals who have high-risk genotypes, but who do not break

---

[3]Further evidence that both the affected and discordant twins have the necessary genotype (and therefore are not examples of "environmentally produced" schizophrenia) comes from the observation of a 13% risk to the children ($n=27$) of nonaffected members of the discordant MZ pairs, which is similar to the risk for children of the affected twins (Fischer, 1973).

down at all. Without some heroic "boot-strapping" (Cronbach & Meehl, 1955), the high-risk strategy will have difficulty using fallible indicators to identify either the genetic or the environmental contributors to the development of schizophrenia. The discovery of endophenotypic indicators of the schizophrenic genotype is both a goal of high-risk research and a requirement for the success of the high-risk design.

DISCUSSION

Both Kraepelin (1919) and Bleuler (1911/1950) believed that the first signs of developing schizophrenic illnesses are often present many years before the appearance of psychotic symptoms. Follow-up studies of abnormal children and follow-back studies of schizophrenic adults (for reviews, see Garmezy & Streitman, 1974; Offord & Cross, 1969) support these beliefs, but only about half of all schizophrenics show any retrospective evidence of abnormal prepsychotic behaviors (Slater & Roth, 1969). The known behavioral precursors of schizophrenia are not pathognomonic and include irritability, excitability, anxiety, and unsocialized aggression in addition to apathy and withdrawal. Apparently, normal personalities also precede schizophrenia. Simple shyness alone does not foretell schizophrenia (Michael, Morris, & Soroker, 1957; Morris, Soroker, & Burruss, 1954), and there is little evidence that schizoid behaviors, as they are popularly perceived, are useful predictors (Mellsop, 1973a; Shields, et al., 1975). The fact that some preschizophrenics do have documented histories of abnormal childhood behaviors stands as a warning that the cause-effect ambiguities constantly facing those who study schizophrenia will not be automatically resolved by prospective methodologies. Anytime a high-risk child is identifiable on behavioral measures as a candidate for adult schizophrenia, there is reason to suspect that an important threshold in the disease process has already been passed.

The fact that many schizophrenics do show evidence of abnormality long before psychosis is also the best evidence supporting the contention that prospective studies of children of schizophrenic parents will be able to discern the beginnings of schizophrenia. However, these efforts will be successful only if predictively valid criteria for schizophrenia are used to define the schizophrenic parent sample. Concentrating on severely affected families or families with many affected relatives will increase the chances of including future schizophrenics among presumed high-risk children. Even if the broad definitions of schizophrenia that encompass pseudoneurotic and pseudopsychopathic cases are valid, the relatively milder severity of these varieties reduces their utility for high-risk studies.

There are at least three important realistic goals for high-risk research. The first goal is to define the range and specificity of the childhood characteristics that precede adult schizophrenia. Retrospectively, some preschizophrenics appear behaviorally normal, while some seem "different," and others are markedly disturbed. It does seem clear that childhood psychopathology is often associated with adult psychopathology, but childhood symptomatology is a poor predictor of adult diagnosis (Fish, 1975; Mellsop, 1973b; O'Neal & Robins, 1958a, 1958b; Pritchard & Graham, 1966; Roff, Knight, & Wertheim, 1976). Children of schizophrenic parents must be compared to children at risk for other kinds of psychopathology to resolve the specificity issue.

A second important goal for high-risk researchers is to quantify the relation between predictors and outcomes. The usefulness of predictors will, of course, be directly proportional to the accuracy of the predictions. The predictors' false positive and false negative rates will have to be determined by extensive follow-ups, and the frequency of the predictor traits in high-risk samples will have to be compared to estimates of the population base rates (Meehl & Rosen, 1955) obtained from control samples of children born to normal parents. Base rates may vary as a function of social class or other demographic characteristics, so both matched and unmatched (general-population) comparison groups will be useful.

A third goal of high-risk research is to determine whether valid childhood predictors of adult schizophrenia identify the etiological roots of schizophrenia. At least three possibilities must be considered. First, the predictor variables might be indicators of the high-risk genotype. Such predictors could help elucidate specific neurobiological deficits associated with the development of schizophrenia and would denote individuals with the potential for future schizophrenia, even though some of these individuals will remain behaviorally normal throughout their life. Second, valid childhood predictors of adult schizophrenia might identify potentiators (Meehl, 1973) or correlates of potentiators that lead to breakdown. Such potentiators might be parts of predisposed individuals' environments or general genetic backgrounds (Gottesman & Shields, 1972). For example, let's say school failure in high-risk children often predicts breakdown. Such a school-failure sign might be due to family pathology (or low IQ), and the family pathology (or low IQ) might be a potentiator of schizophrenia in predisposed individuals. Yet, the school-failure sign is neither a consequence of the high-risk genotype nor, by itself, an early sign of schizophrenic behavior. Third, childhood predictors might represent the earliest signs (or effects) of already potentiated schizophrenias. Such predictors would indicate when schizophrenic behaviors begin but would not necessarily shed light on either the genetic or environmental contributors to the development of schizophrenia.

It seems likely that, at least, some early developing schizophrenics will be detected by high-risk researchers. In our own sample (Hanson et al., 1976), 5 out of 30 (17%) 7-year-old children of our consensus schizophrenics were categorized by having poor motor skills, large within-individual inconsistencies in performance on cognitive tasks, and enduring patterns of withdrawal, emotional flatness, irritability, negativism, and emotional instability. None of the 30 children of consensus psychiatric controls and none of 56 children born to normals (see Table 6) had all three "indicators." The 5 children exhibited behaviors found in adult schizophrenics (e.g., loose, bizarre thoughts and extreme anxiety), but none were reported to have delusions or hallucinations, and none fit the syndrome of adult schizophrenia. Most have severely schizophrenic parents, and two children have a second parent with psychiatric problems. If past behavior predicts future behavior, and if a diathesis-stress model of schizophrenia is valid, these 5 children have a higher risk for schizophrenia than all the other children studied. It might be possible to detect some symptoms of the syndrome early in the life of predisposed individuals, but any sample of high-risk children will have to be followed well into adulthood to establish the validity of proposed preschizophrenic traits.

The detection of *some* schizophrenias in childhood will not imply that *all* schizophrenias can be predicted from childhood. Even if a perfect indicator of the high-risk genotype is discovered, prediction of all cases of schizophrenia will be impossible as long as the environmental contributors to schizophrenia are unpredictable. So far, *no* specific environmental source of liability is known; the most likely environmental contributor, stress, may come from many sources and, apparently, may come during any stage of development. Prenatal or birth complications, early deprivations, broken homes, censuring parents, the death of someone close, failures in school, work or social relationships, childbirth, a "bad trip," as well as all kinds of good fortune may have effects on a predisposed individual that are obvious in retrospect. In prospect, it will be impossible to prophesy the events themselves, let alone their effects.

The laudable goal of preventing schizophrenia shares problems with

Table 6
Percentage of Children Who Exhibited Proposed Preschizophrenic Indicators

	% children of parents who are			
Indicator	Consensus schizo- phrenic ($n = 30$)	Other psychiatric patients ($n = 30$)	Normals, matched ($n = 29$)	Normals, not matched ($n = 27$)
Poor motor skills	30	10	21	7
Large within-person test score variance	53	30	28	19
Schizoid behavior at 4 and 7 years	27	3	10	0
Only two indicators	10	10	17	0
All three indicators	17	0	0	0

Note. One sample of children of normal parents was matched to the children of schizophrenics for social class, mother's age when the study child was born, and number of prior live-born children. The other normal comparison sample was selected by taking the next child of normal parents who entered the collaborative study after each high-risk child.

the goal of prediction. Even if a good indicator of the high-risk genotype is discovered and an effective preventative treatment becomes available, the treatment will still have to be applied judiciously, since many individuals with the necessary genetic predisposition for schizophrenia enjoy a lifetime of adequate mental health *without any intervention,* as evidenced by the concordance rate for schizophrenia in identical twins being only about 50%. The accuracy of the predictions, the cost-effectiveness of the treatment, the short-term and long-term risks from side effects of the treatment, and the burden of worry imposed by focusing the targeted individual's attention on a potential problem (cf. the controversy surrounding attempts at early detection of Huntington's disease, Freeman, 1973; Goodman, Ashkenazi, Adam, & Greenfield, 1973; Lyle & Gottesman, 1977) are just a few of the issues that require evaluation. Subjecting otherwise normal individuals to symptomatic but powerful treatments on the basis of theoretical but unvalidated indicators of future schizophrenia is improvident.

It seems unlikely that high-risk research will quickly point the way to cures or preventions for schizophrenia. However, if investigators are wise enough to study the "right" variables, and if they are lucky enough to be on the scene when important events occur, the high-risk method will provide accurate and detailed descriptions of the natural history of schizophrenia. Documenting the age at which the earliest abnormalities (or "oddities") appear and recording the life events that precipitate, exacerbate, or ameliorate these abnormalities are not the same as explaining schizophrenia. In addition, we need to know how these developmental events interact with predisposed individuals' genotypes. If cures or preventions are forthcoming, they will come from an understanding of the joint actions of environmental and apparently specific genetic factors. Claiming specific genetic etiological contributors to the development of schizophrenia does not diminish prospects for treatment; genetics cannot be equated with determinism (Meehl, 1973, 1977). Hopefully, high-risk investigators will incorporate both environmental and genetic theorizing into their research designs and, thus, help bridge the gap between descriptive psychopathology and molecular biology.

REFERENCE NOTE

1. Schulsinger, H. *Clinical outcome of a ten-year follow-up of children of schizophrenic mothers.* Paper presented at the meeting of the Society for Research in Life History and Psychopathology. Fort Worth, Texas, October 1976.

REFERENCES

Bleuler, E. [*Dementia praecox or the group of schizophrenias*] (J. Zinkin, trans.). New York: International Universities Press, 1950. (Originally published in Leipzig, East Germany: Deutiche, 1911).

Bleuler, M. *Die schizophrenen Geistesstörungen im Lichte langjahriger Kranken-und Familiengeschichten.* Stuttgart, West Germany: Thieme, 1972.

Broman, S., Nichols, P., & Kennedy, W. *Pre-school IQ: Prenatal and early developmental correlates.* Hillside, N.J.: Erlbaum, 1975.

Cooper, J. E., Kendell, R. E., Gurland, B. J., Sharpe, L., Copeland, J. R. M., & Simon, R. *Psychiatric diagnoses in New York and London.* London: Oxford University Press, 1972.

Cronbach, L., & Meehl, P. Construct validity in psychological tests. *Psychological Bulletin,* 1955, *52*, 281–302.

Curnow, R. N., & Smith, C. Multifactorial models of familial disease in man. *Journal of the Royal Statistical Society (A),* 1975, *138*, 131–156.

Endicott, J., & Spitzer, R. Current and past psychopathology scales (CAPPS). *Archives of General Psychiatry,* 1972, *27*, 678–687.

Erlenmeyer-Kimling, L. Studies on the offspring of two schizophrenic parents. In D. Rosenthal & S. S. Kety (Eds.), *The transmission of schizophrenia.* Oxford: Pergamon Press, 1968.

Erlenmeyer-Kimling, L. Gene-environment interactions and the variability of behavior. In L. Ehrman, G. S. Omenn, & E. Caspari (Eds.), *Genetics, environment, and behavior.* New York: Academic Press, 1972.

Erlenmeyer-Kimling, L. A prospective study of children at risk for schizophrenia: Methodological considerations and some preliminary findings. In R. Wirt, G. Winokur, & M. Roff (Eds.), *Life history research in psychopathology* (Vol. 4). Minneapolis: University of Minnesota Press, 1975.

Fischer, M. Genetic and environmental factors in schizophrenia. *Acta Psychiatrica Scandinavica,* 1973, Supplement 238.

Fischer, M. Development and validity of a computerized method for diagnoses of functional psychoses (Diax). *Acta Psychiatrica Scandinavica,* 1974, *50*, 243–288.

Fish, B. Biologic antecedents of psychosis in children. In D. X. Freedman (Ed.), *Biology of the major psychoses.* New York: Raven Press, 1975.

Fish, B., & Alpert, M. Abnormal states of consciousness and muscle tone in infants born to schizophrenic mothers. *American Journal of Psychiatry*, 1962, *119*, 439–445.

Fish, B., & Hagin, R. Visual-motor disorders in infants at high risk for schizophrenia. *Archives of General Psychiatry*, 1973, *28*, 900–904.

Freeman, F. R. Pretesting for Huntington's disease. *Hasting Center Report*, 1973, *3*(3), 12–13.

Garmezy, N. Children at risk: The search for the antecedents of schizophrenia, Part II. *Schizophrenia Bulletin*, 1974, *1*(9), 55–125.

Garmezy, N. On some risks in risk research. *Psychological Medicine*, 1977, *7*, 1–6.

Garmezy, N., & Streitman, S. Children at risk: The search for the antecedents of schizophrenia, Part I. *Schizophrenia Bulletin*, 1974, *1*(8), 13–90.

Garrone, G. Etude statistique et génétique de la schizophrenie à Genève de 1901 à 1950. *Journal Génétique Humaine*, 1962, *11*, 89–219.

Gengnagel, E. Beitrag zum Problem der Erbprognosebestimmung. *Zeitschrift für die Gesamte Neurologie und Psychiatrie*, 1933 *145*, 52–61.

Goodman, R. M., Ashkenazi, Y. E., Adam, A., & Greenfield, G. Thoughts on the early detection of Huntington's chorea. In A. Barbeau, T. N. Chase, & G. W. Paulson (Eds.), *Advances in neurology: Huntington's chorea, 1872–1972* (Vol. 1). New York: Raven Press, 1973.

Gottesman, I. I., & Shields, J. *Schizophrenia and genetics: A twin study vantage point*. New York: Academic Press, 1972.

Gottesman, I. I., & Shields, J. A critical review of recent adoption, twin, and family studies of schizophrenia: Behavioral genetics perspectives. *Schizophrenia Bulletin*, 1976, *2*, 360–401. (a)

Gottesman, I. I., & Shields, J. Rejoinder: Toward optimal arousal and away from original din. *Schizophrenia Bulletin*, 1976, *2*, 447–453. (b)

Hallgren, G., & Sjögren, T. A clinical and geneticostatistical study of schizophrenia and low grade mental deficiency in a large Swedish rural population. *Acta Psychiatrica Scandinavica*, 1959, Supplement 140.

Hanson, D. R. *The children of schizophrenic mothers or fathers compared to other psychiatric controls: Their first eight years*. Unpublished doctoral dissertation, University of Minnesota, 1974.

Hanson, D. R., & Gottesman, I. I. The genetics, if any, of infantile autism and childhood schizophrenia. *Journal of Autism and Childhood Schizophrenia*, 1976, *6*, 209–234.

Hanson, D. R., Gottesman, I. I., & Heston, L. L. Some possible childhood indicators of adult schizophrenia inferred from children of schizophrenics. *British Journal of Psychiatry*, 1976, *129*, 142–154.

Herman, J., Mirsky, A. F., Ricks, N. L., Gallant, D. Behavioral and electrographic measures of attention in children at risk for schizophrenia. *Journal of Abnormal Psychology*, 1977, *86*, 27–33.

Heston, L. L. Psychiatric disorders in foster home reared children of schizophrenic mothers. *British Journal of Psychiatry*, 1966, *112*, 819–825.

Heston, L. L. The genetics of schizophrenic and schizoid disease. *Science*, 1970, *167*, 249–256.

Hoffman, H. *Die Nachkommenschaft bei endogenen Psychosen*. Berlin, West Germany: Springer-Verlag, 1921.

Kallmann, F. *The genetics of schizophrenia*. New York: J. J. Augustin, 1938.

Karlsson, J. Inheritance of schizophrenia. *Acta Psychiatrica Scandinavica*, 1974, Supplement 247.

Kety, S. S., Rosenthal, D., Wender, P. H., & Schulsinger, F. Studies based on a total sample of adopted individuals and their relatives: Why they were necessary, what they demonstrated and failed to demonstrate. *Schizophrenia Bulletin,* 1976, *2,* 413–428.

Kety, S. S., Rosenthal, D. Wender, P. H., Schulsinger, F., & Jacobsen, B. Mental illness in the biological and adoptive families of adopted individuals who have become schizophrenic: A preliminary report based on psychiatric interviews. In R. R. Fieve, D. Rosenthal, & H. Brill (Eds.), *Genetic research in psychiatry.* Baltimore, Md.: Johns Hopkins University Press, 1975.

Kraepelin, E. *Dementia praecox and paraphrenia.* Edinburgh, Scotland: E. & S. Livingstone, 1919.

Lindelius, R. A study of schizophrenia. *Acta Psychiatrica Scandinavica,* 1970, Supplement 216.

Lyle, O. E., & Gottesman, I. I. Premorbid psychometric indicators of the gene for Huntington's disease. *Journal of Counsulting and Clinical Psychology,* 1977, *45,* 1011–1022.

Marks, P. A., Seeman, W., & Haller, D. L. *The actuarial use of the MMPI with adolescents and adults.* Baltimore, Md.: Williams & Wilkins, 1974.

Mednick, B. Breakdown in high-risk subjects: Familial and early environmental factors. *Journal of Abnormal Psychology,* 1973, *82,* 469–475.

Mednick, S., & McNeil, T. F. Current methodology in research on the etiology of schizophrenia: Serious difficulties which suggest the use of the high-risk-group method. *Psychological Bulletin,* 1968, *70,* 681–693.

Mednick, S. A., & Schulsinger, F. Some premorbid characteristics related to breakdown in children with schizophrenic mothers. In D. Rosenthal & S. Kety (Eds.), *The transmission of schizophrenia.* Oxford, England: Pergamon Press, 1968.

Meehl, P. E. Schizotaxia, schizotypy, schizophrenia. *American Psychologist,* 1962, *17,* 827–838.

Meehl, P. E. A critical afterward. In I. I. Gottesman & J. Shields, *Schizophrenia and genetics: A twin study vantage point.* New York: Academic Press, 1972.

Meehl, P. E. Specific genetic etiology, psychodynamics, and therapeutic nihilism. In P. E. Meehl (Ed.), *Psychodiagnosis: Selected papers.* Minneapolis: University of Minnesota Press, 1973.

Meehl, P. E. Specific etiology and other forms of strong influence: Some quantitative meanings. *Journal of Medicine and Philosophy,* 1977, *2,* 33–53.

Meehl, P. E. & Rosen, A. Antecedent Probability and the efficiency of psychometric signs, patterns, or cutting scores. *Psychological Bulletin,* 1955, *52,* 194–216.

Mellsop, G. Antecedents of schizophrenia: The "schizoid" myth? *Australian and New Zealand Journal of Psychiatry,* 1973, *7,* 208–211. (a)

Mellsop, G. Adult psychiatric patients on whom information was recorded during childhood. *British Journal of Psychiatry,* 1973, *123,* 703–710. (b)

Michael, C. M., Morris, D. P., & Soroker, E. Follow-up studies of shy, withdrawn children: II. Relative incidence of schizophrenia. *American Journal of Orthopsychiatry,* 1957, *27,* 331–337.

Morris, D. P., Soroker, E., & Burruss, G. Follow-up studies of shy, withdrawn children. I. Evaluation of later adjustment. *American Journal of Orthopsychiatry,* 1954, *24,* 743–754.

Niswander, K., & Gordon, M. *The women and their pregnancies.* Philadelphia, Pa.: Saunders, 1972.

Ødegaard, Ø. The multifactorial theory of inheritance in predisposition to schizophrenia. In A. R. Kaplan (Ed.), *Genetic factors in "schizophrenia."* Springfield, Ill.: Thomas, 1972.

Offord, D. R., & Cross, L. A. Behavioral antecedents of adult schizophrenia. *Archives of General Psychiatry*, 1969, *21*, 267–283.

O'Neal, P., & Robins, L. The relation of childhood behavior problems to adult psychiatric status: A 30-year follow-up study of 150 subjects. *American Journal of Psychiatry*, 1958, *114*, 961–969. (a)

O'Neal, P., & Robins, L. Childhood patterns predictive of adult schizophrenia: A 30-year follow-up study. *American Journal of Psychiatry*, 1958, *115*, 385–391. (b)

Oppler, W. Zum Problem der Erbprognosebestimmung. *Zeitschrift für die Gesamte Neurologie und Psychiatrie*, 1932, *141*, 549–616.

Pearson, J. S., & Kley, I. B. On the application of genetic expectancies as age-specific base ratexs in the study of human behavior disorders. *Psychological Bulletin*, 1957, *54*, 406–420.

Pritchard, M., & Graham, P. An investigation of a group of patients who have attended both the child and adult departments of the same psychiatric hospital. *British Journal of Psychiatry*, 1966, *112*, 603–612.

Reed, S. C., Harley, C., Anderson, V. E., Phillips, V. P., & Johnson, N. A. *The psychoses: Family studies.* Philadelphia, Pa.: Saunders, 1973.

Reisby, N. Psychoses in children of schizophrenic mothers. *Acta Psychiatric Scandinavica*, 1967, *43*, 8–20.

Roff, J. D., Knight, R., & Wertheim, E. A factor-analytic study of childhood symptoms antecedent to schizophrenia. *Journal of Abnormal Psychology*, 1976, *85*, 543–549.

Rosenthal, D. The offspring of schizophrenic couples. *Journal of Psychiatric Research*, 1966, *4*, 169–188.

Rosenthal, D. Discussion: The concept of subschizophrenic disorders. In R. R. Fieve, D. Rosenthal, & H. Brill (Eds.), *Genetic research in psychiatry.* Baltimore, Md.: Johns Hopkins University Press, 1975.

Rosenthal, D., Wender, P., Kety, S., Welner, J., & Schulsinger, F. The adopted-away offspring of schizophrenics. *American Journal of Psychiatry* 1971, *128*, 307–311.

Rutschmann, J., Cornblatt, B., & Erlenmeyer-Kimling, L. Sustained attention in children at risk for schizophrenia. *Archives of General Psychiatry*, 1977, *34*, 571–575.

Schulsinger, H. A ten year follow-up of children of schizophrenic mothers: Clinical assessment. *Acta Psychiatrica Scandinavica*, 1976, *53*, 371–386.

Shields, J. High risk for schizophrenia: Genetic considerations. *Psychological Medicine*, 1977, *7*, 7–10.

Shields, J., & Gottesman. I. I. Cross-national diagnosis of schizophrenia in twins. *Archives of General Psychiatry*, 1972, *27*, 725–730.

Shields, J., & Gottesman. I. I. Genetic studies of schizophrenia as signposts to biochemistry. In L. L. Iversen & S. P. R. Rose (Eds.), *Biochemistry and mental illness* (Special Publication 1). London: Biochemical Society, 1973.

Shields, J., Heston, L. L., & Gottesman, I. I. Schizophrenia and the schizoid: The problem for genetic analysis. In R. R. Fieve, D. Rosenthal, & H. Brill (Eds.), *Genetic research in psychiatry.* Baltimore, Md.: Johns Hopkins University Press, 1975.

Slater, E., & Cowie, V. *The genetics of mental disorders.* London: Oxford University Press, 1971.

Slater, E., & Roth, M. *Mayer-Gross, Slater and Roth Clinical Psychiatry* (3rd ed.). London: Baillière, 1969.

Sobel, D. Children of schizophrenic patients: Preliminary observations on early development. *American Journal of Psychiatry*, 1961, *118*, 512–517.

Spitzer, R. L. On pseudoscience in science, logic in remission, and psychiatric diagnoses: A critique of Rosenhan's "On being sane in insane places." *Journal of Abnormal Psychology*, 1975, *84*, 442–452.

Wender, P. N., Rosenthal, D., Kety, S. S., Schulsinger, F., & Welner, J. Cross fostering: A research strategy for clarifying the role of genetic and experiential factors in the etiology of schizophrenia. *Archives of General Psychiatry*, 1974, *30*, 121–128.

Wing, J. K., Cooper, J. E., & Sartorius, N. *Measurement and classification of psychiatric symptoms*. London: Cambridge University Press, 1974.

World Health Organization. *Report of the international pilot study of schizophrenia* (Vol. 1). Geneva, Switzerland: Author, 1973.

Yolles, S. F., & Kramer, M. Vital statistics. In L. Bellak & L. Loeb (Eds.), *The schizophrenic syndrome*, New York: Grune & Stratton, 1969.

PART II: GENETIC AND BIOCHEMICAL ISSUES

6

NEUROCHEMISTRY AND CHILD PSYCHIATRY

Donald J. Cohen and J. Gerald Young

Yale University School of Medicine

Normal brain function depends on the integration of the synthesis, storage, release, and inactivation of neurotransmitters localized in different brain structures and pathways. Neurotransmitters, such as dopamine, serotonin, and acetylcholine, are implicated in various neurological and psychiatric diseases and in a broad range of normal physiological processes. Neurotransmitters, metabolites, and enzymes can be measured in cerebrospinal fluid, blood, and urine, permitting clinical researchers to study correlations between metabolic and behavioral dimensions. There are serious methodolog-

Reprinted with permission from *Journal of the American Academy of Child Psychiatry*, Vol. 16, No. 3, Summer, 1977, 353–411.

Ms. Barbara Caparulo and Dr. Bennett Shaywitz were essential collaborators in the clinical research. Dr. Malcolm Bowers collaborated in studies of cerebrospinal fluid metabolites, Dr. Jerome Roth and Mary Ellen Kavanagh, in studies of monoamine oxidase, and Warren Johnson and Merilyne Waldo, in various research studies. Virginia Simon provided medical illustrations, and Margrethe Cone provided secretarial assistance.

The clinical studies were made possible by the support of the staff of the Children's Clinical Research Center, Yale-New Haven Hospital, under the direction of Myron Genel, M.D. and Mary Carey, R. N.

The research was supported, in part, by Public Health Service Research Grant HD-03008, the William T. Grant Foundation, NIH Children's Clinical Research Grant RR 00125, the Jean T. Schall Trust, National Research Service Award MH 05223, and by Mr. Leonard Berger.

ical problems which must be considered in interpreting biological research in child psychiatry. However, studies of neurotransmitter metabolism in conjunction with other types of research strategies offer promise for clarifying the basis for some serious developmental disturbances of childhood and the impact of psychoactive medication.

Basic advances in neurochemistry have provided child psychiatrists with biological strategies for investigating severe behavioral disorders and clarifying mechanisms of action of commonly used drugs. The exploitation of new methods and concepts in research on developmental disorders has, however, lagged behind psychobiological research on the adult psychoses and affective disorders. In this review, we will describe the growing field of central nervous system metabolic research and applications in clinical research with psychotic children.

THEORY OF CLINICAL NEUROCHEMISTRY

Neurotransmitters

The brain is not homogeneous but consists of numerous structural subsystems, each containing millions of neurons, with billions of interconnections, and a greater number of glial supportive cells (Iversen and Iversen, 1975). Fortunately, there is a remarkable regularity in chemical processes which occur at points of communication at the cellular level.

Nervous tissue is specialized for the rapid conduction of signals over long distances. This is accomplished by complex electrophysiological and biochemical changes leading to the release of a chemical substance (the neurotransmitter) which crosses a physical space (the synapse) and affects another cell or the signal function of another neuron. The neurotransmitter exerts one of two effects on the postsynaptic cell: excitation (by depolarizing the cell membrane) or inhibition (by hyperpolarizing the membrane). The final membrane state reflects the balance of up to several thousand synaptic inputs acting on this single neuron. Neuronal function may be assessed by measuring excitation, inhibition, or the changing concentrations of neurotransmitters—a goal more easily achieved in animal and peripheral preparations than in the central nervous system of man.

Whatever affects neurotransmitter metabolism can affect the function of the neurons involved. Disease, drugs, or toxins can act on a neurotransmitter at any point along the usual sequence of events:

synthesis of the transmitter; its storage, release, or action at the post-synaptic receptor site; reuptake by the presynaptic neuron; or its catabolism. The precise mode of action of a drug may be clarified by the use of isolated, peripheral, neural tissue; and such studies may, in turn, illuminate the basic functioning of the neuron. These studies have yielded a basic biochemical model of neural functioning involving several known neurotransmitter substances, such as acetylcholine and norepinephrine (Cooper et al., 1974). The extension of this model to the central nervous system introduces a host of technical and conceptual problems—such as differing functions of a neurotransmitter within brain structures and interactions between different neurotransmitter systems. For such reasons, we will first describe the basic model and later discuss the complications involved in extrapolating from peripheral nervous tissue to the human brain.

Catecholamines

Clinically focused researchers have concentrated on two types of biogenic amine neurotransmitters, the catecholamines and the indoleamines (Schildkraut and Kety, 1967). The major indoleamine transmitter is serotonin; common usage limits the term "catecholamine" to three neurotransmitters which follow sequentially in the synthetic pathway illustrated in figure 1: dopamine, norepinephrine, and epinephrine (Axelrod, 1974a; Molinoff and Axelrod, 1971; Moskowitz and Wurtman, 1975).

Dopamine, initially thought to be no more than an intermediate, is now recognized as a brain transmitter centrally involved in a variety of movement and severe behavior disorders (Barbeau, 1974; Hornykiewicz, 1966; Snyder et al., 1970, 1974). Norepinephrine, found in postganglionic sympathetic nerve endings, the adrenal medulla, and the spinal cord and brain, is released along with the enzyme responsible for its formation from dopamine, dopamine-B-hydroxylase (DBH) (Axelrod, 1971; Kaufman and Friedman, 1965). The third catecholamine, epinephrine, is found in the adrenal medulla, from which it is released into the blood to act on several other organs as a stress-related hormone (Axelrod, 1966; Levine and Landsberg. 1974; Pohorecky and Wurtman, 1971). Epinephrine recently has been identified in specific areas of the brain, where it is thought to function as a neurotransmitter (Hökfelt et al., 1974d).

Figure 1
Synthetic Pathway of Catecholamines

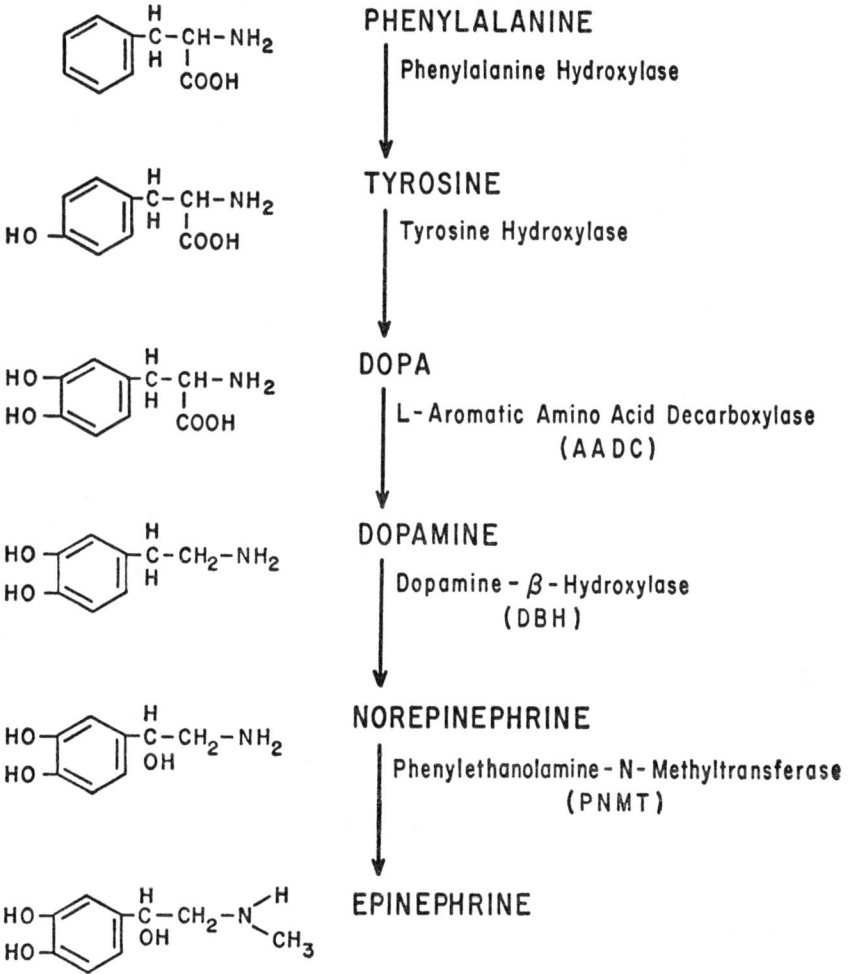

Neuron and Synapse

Figure 2 illustrates a typical nerve cell consisting of cell body, axon (straight or branched), and dendritic tree (varying in size and complexity). Receptors for transmitters released by other neurons are located primarily on the dendrites, as well as on the cell body and a

Figure 2
a. Typical neuron with terminal varicosities at end of long axon
b. Schematic representation of presynaptic varicosity, synaptic cleft, and postsynaptic cell. Modified from Axelrod (1974a)

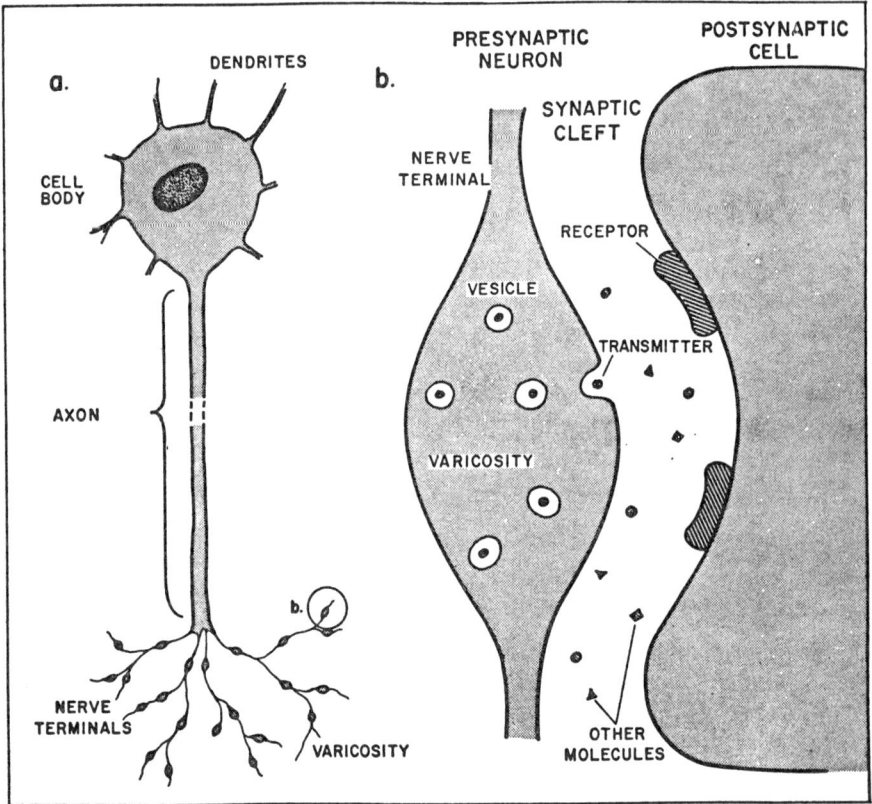

small, proximal area of the axon (the hillock); impulses generated by the neuron are conducted down the axon to its junction with another cell. Axon terminals are specialized for this role by the presence of varicosities in which the transmitter specific to the neuron is manufactured and stored. Enzymes (such as tyrosine hydroxylase) necessary for the synthesis of the transmitter are formed in the cell body and transported down the axon to the varicosity, where the transmitter is synthesized and stored in vesicles or found free in the cytoplasm (Hökfelt, 1973). In the case of norepinephrine, a synthesizing enzyme is also stored in the vesicle with the transmitter and both are released following stimulation of the nerve. Transmitter release appears to be accomplished by the process of exocytosis, through which a vesicle fuses with the cell membrane and an opening forms allowing molecules to move into the synaptic cleft (Smith and Winkler, 1972). The mechanism which couples nerve impulse to secretion of the transmitter is not yet clear, but is of special interest with regard to drug action (Seeman, 1972).

Figure 3 depicts the catecholamine pathway within a varicosity of a noradrenergic neuron. Norepinephrine is synthesized in the storage vesicle through the activity of the DBH present there. Protein and adenosine triphosphate (ATP) apparently bind the amines within the vesicle (Cooper et al., 1974). The rate-limiting step of the synthesis is the point of action of tyrosine hydroxylase (TH), where a feedback mechanism of the transmitter substance on tyrosine hydroxylase appears to inhibit its activity and reduce synthesis (Udenfriend, 1966). Nerve stimulation lowers the level of transmitter in the varicosity, with a resultant decrease in inhibitory feedback (Pletscher, 1972; Weiner, 1970).

Once released, the transmitter diffuses across the synaptic cleft and acts on a receptor, specifically responsive to only this neurotransmitter, located on the membrane of the postsynaptic cell. The interaction of transmitter and receptor initiates sequential events which eventuate in the effector cell performing its particular function or in the modification of some cellular function. The specific molecular events differ from cell to cell. In some dopaminergic and noradrenergic systems the receptor activates an enzyme, adenylate cyclase, which catalyzes the conversion of adenosine triphosphate (ATP) to cyclic adenoisine monophosphate (cyclic AMP). Cyclic AMP is also known as the "second messenger" because of its intracellular role analogous to the extracellular role of messenger compounds such as hormones (fig. 4) (Pastan, 1972; Sutherland, 1972). The cyclic AMP activates specific protein kinases which function in ways specific to the type of cell. Although still hypothetical, the end result appears to be intracellular events such as phosphorylation of membrane proteins (altering electrical properties) or phosphorylation of nuclear histones (affecting the expression of genetically controlled metabolic properties) (Clement-Cormier et al., 1974; Greengard et al., 1972; Rall, 1972). The cell returns to its initial state when (a) cyclic AMP is inactivated by another enzyme, phosphodiesterase, and (b) the mobile phosphate group utilized in phosphorylation is removed through the action of a phosphatase. Xanthine derivatives such as caffeine and theophylline inhibit phosphodiesterase, prolonging the activity of cyclic AMP.

Exquisite control of neuronal function is achieved through a com-

Figure 3

Norepinephrine synthesis, release, and inactivation in schematic presynaptic and postsynaptic cells. Modified from Axelrod (1974a)

TH = tyrosine hydroxylase
DOPA = dihydroxyphenylalanine
AADC = L-aromatic amino acid decarboxylase (DOPA decarboxylase)
DOPAMINE = dihydroxyphenylethylamine (DA)
DBH = dopamine-B-hydroxylase
NE = norepinephrine
ATP = adenosine triphosphate
MAO = monoamine oxidase
COMT = catechol-0-methyltransferase

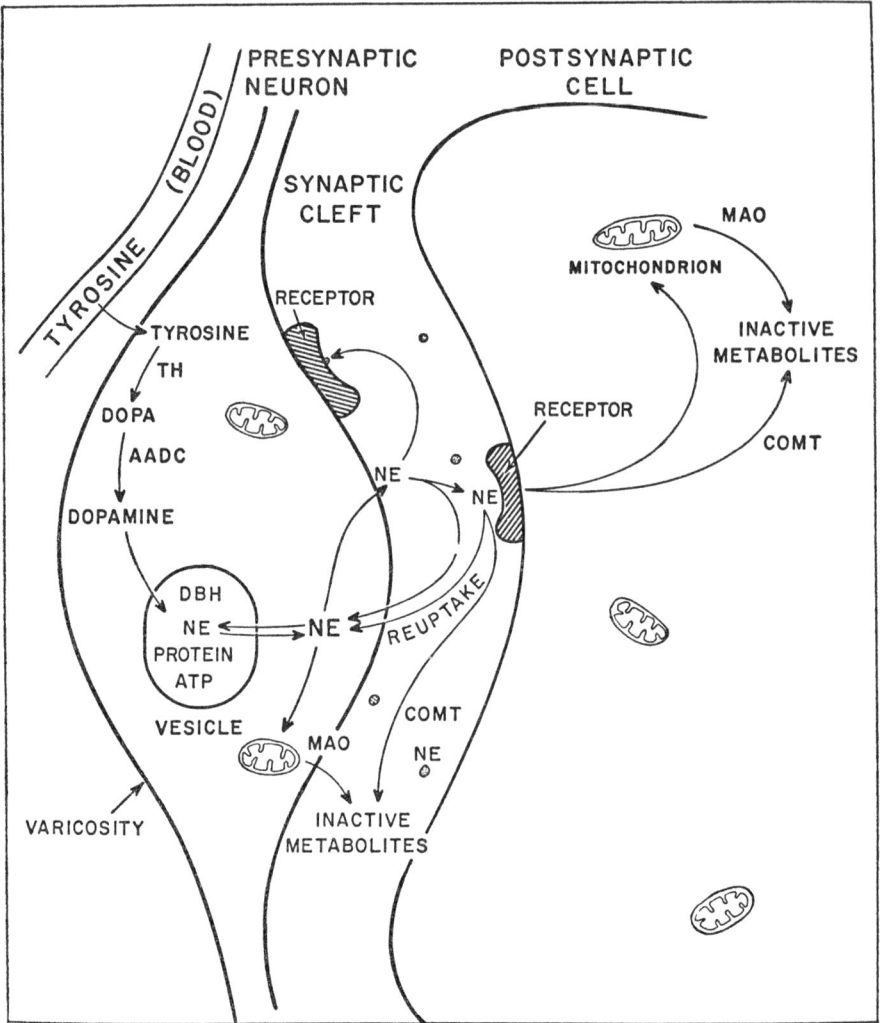

Figure 4
Schematic representation of proposed mechanism for receptor physiology at synapse. Modified from Greengard et al. (1972)

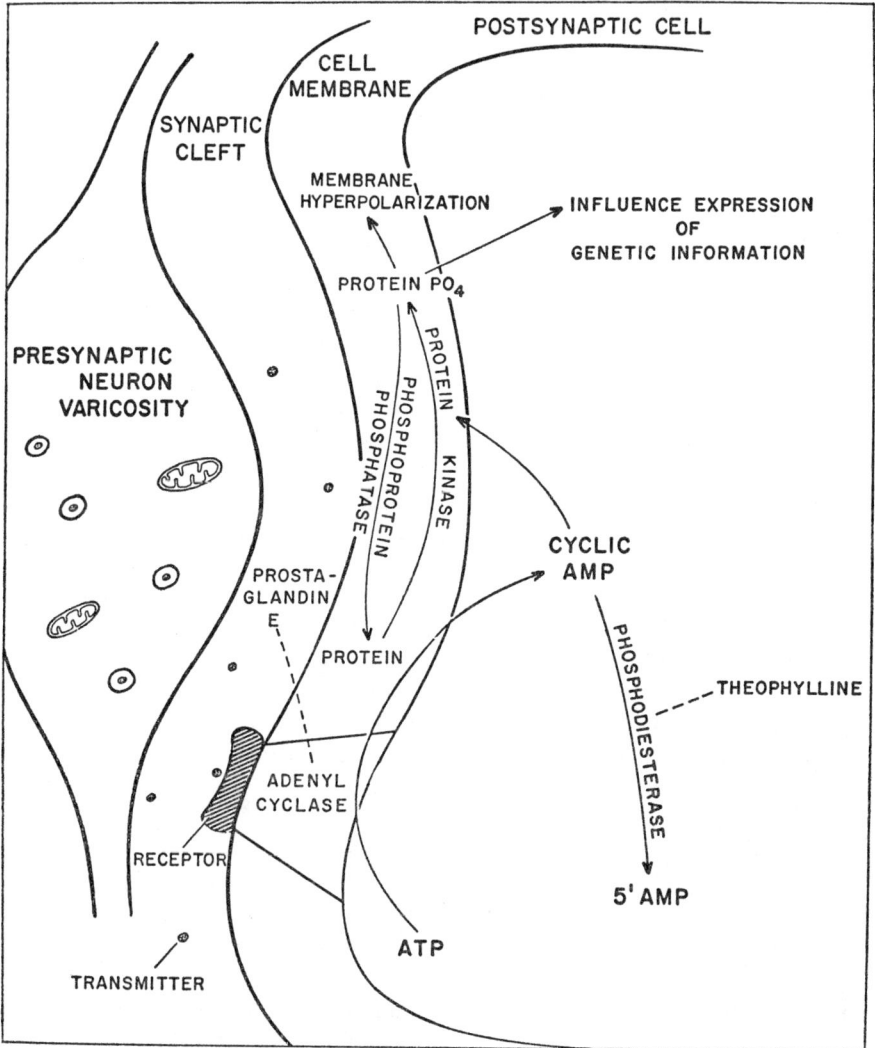

plex system of multiple self-modulatory influences. The following are three examples of control mechanisms. (1) There is evidence for presynaptic receptor sites which become responsive to a critical concentration of transmitter in the synaptic cleft; the transmitter may thus inhibit its own release (Langer, 1973). (2) The "neuronal feedback loop" hypothesis postulates that consecutive neurons form a loop in which increased firing of one neuron leads to an ultimate negative feedback mechanism via the other neurons in the loop (Costa and Meek, 1974). (3) There may be transmitter released not only from the axon terminal, but also from anatomical "specializations" on the dendrites of the same neuron; the released transmitter then acts on its neuron of origin and the overall effect is self-inhibition (Groves et al., 1975).

Metabolism and Reuptake

Duration of transmitter-receptor interaction is regulated by processes of inactivation which must be rapid enough to achieve an adequately responsive fluctuation in signal information. Two general processes regulate the amount of transmitter in the synaptic cleft: active reuptake by the presynaptic neuron, and other adjacent cells, and catabolism by specific enzymes (Trendelenburg, 1972a).

Two enzymes actively degrade catecholamines: monoamine oxidase (MAO) and catechol-O-methyltransferase (COMT) (Sharman, 1973a). MAO, well studied for nearly 50 years, is present in many tissues (Kopin, 1964; Sandler and Youdim, 1974; Zeller, 1959). Intraneuronally, it is localized largely in the outer membrane of mitochondria; it is also abundant extraneuronally. Its activity in the accessible blood platelet has been the object of intensive study in recent years (Collins and Sandler, 1971; Murphy and Donnelly, 1974). Intraneuronal MAO metabolizes the transmitter and other amines free in the cytoplasm, but does not affect vesicle-bound transmitter. It has a regulatory impact on catecholamine synthesis (Neff and Costa, 1966; Weiner and Bjur, 1972), but its contribution to inactivation of the neurotransmitter in the synaptic cleft is apparently slight. COMT, discovered less than 20 years ago, is also found in the cytoplasm of numerous tissues in man (Axelrod and Tomchick, 1958; Axelrod, 1966; Axelrod and Cohn, 1971). Its function in the metabolism of catecholamines appears to be predominantly extraneuronal, where it plays an important role in transmitter inactivation (Guldberg and Marsden, 1975).

Norepinephrine continues to be rapidly inactivated even following the administration of compounds which specifically inhibit the activity of MAO and COMT. This inactivation is accomplished by active reuptake and binding by the presynaptic neuron, the dominant mechanism responsible for rapid inactivation of the transmitter. Less importantly, extraneuronal cells may also take up transmitter ("uptake²"), with subsequent inactivation by COMT (L. L. Iversen, 1967, 1971; Trendelenburg, 1972a).

Figure 5

General pathway for metabolic degradation of catecholamines. R_1 and R_2 are sidechain constituents which distinguish dopamine, norepinephrine and epineprine.

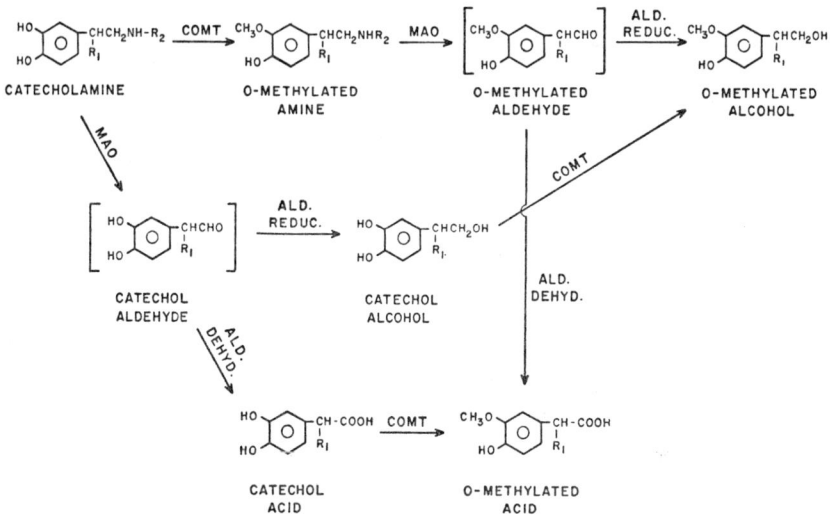

COMT = catechol-0-methyltransferase
MAO = monoamine oxidase
Ald. Reduc. = aldehyde reductase
Ald. Dehyd. = aldehyde dehydrogenase
Aldehyde intermediates, in brackets, exist only transiently.

In the catabolism of catecholamines by MAO and COMT, the intermediate products formed reflect the order in which the enzymes act. A general scheme for the lines of metabolism of a catecholamine (i.e., dopamine, norepinephrine, or epinephrine) is given in figure 5. Deamination by MAO leads to the formation of the corresponding aldehyde. This aldehyde is present only transiently and is rapidly metabolized by one or two reactions: oxidation to an acid by aldehyde dehydrogenase or reduction to an alcohol by aldehyde reductase. Figure 6 depicts the specific metabolic pathways for dopamine, norepinephrine, and epinephrine. For clarity, some transient intermediate aldehydes have been deleted, as well as clinically less significant portions of the pathways (e.g., the catechol alcohol). Because the catecholamines and most of their metabolites are phenols, a common additional form of inactivation (not shown) is their conjugation with glucuronic acid or sulfuric acid (Sharman, 1973a).

Norepinephrine and epinephrine metabolism leads to two major products, VMA and MHPG. The chief products of dopamine in the

Figure 6

Specific pathways for metabolic degradation of dopamine, norepinephrine, and epinephrine, with minor steps and products omitted. Aldehyde intermediates, in brackets, exist only transiently.

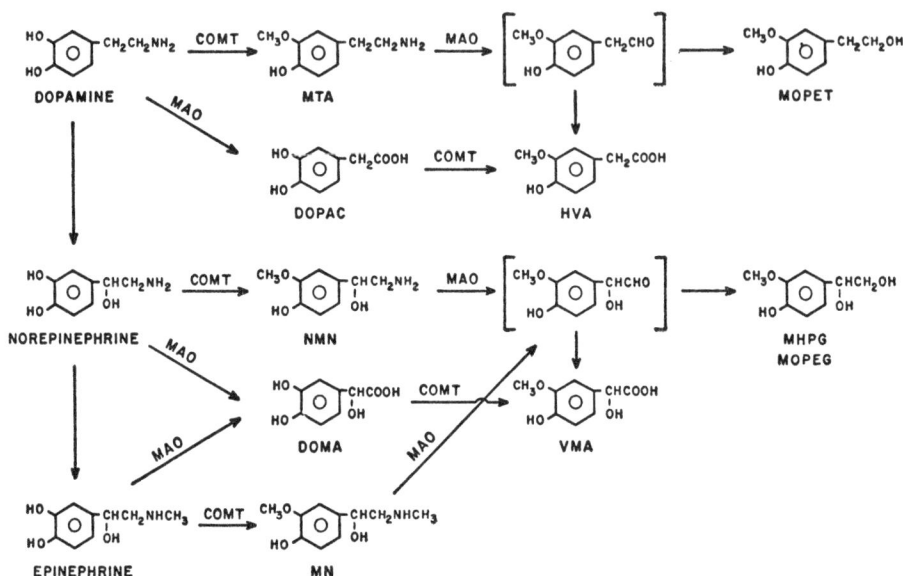

COMT = catechol-0-methyltransferase
MAO = monoamine oxidase
MTA = 3-methoxytyramine
DOPAC = 3,4-dihydoxyphenylacetic acid
NMN = normetanephrine
DOMA = 3,4-dihydroxymandelic acid
MN = metanephrine
HVA = homovanillic acid
VMA = vanillylmandelic acid
MOPET = 3-methoxy-4-hydroxy-phenylethanol (MHPE)
MHPG = 3-methoxy-4-hydroxy-phenylethyleneglycol (MOPEG)

CNS are two acidic metabolites, DOPAC and HVA; HVA is the predominant metabolite in the cerebrospinal fluid and urine. The principal pools of norepinephrine and epinephrine, their manner of inactivation, and their metabolic fate and products are described in table 1.

Indoleamines

Serotonin has been the subject of intensive research in relation to neurological and severe psychiatric disorders of childhood and has been implicated in a wide range of processes and disorders—temperature regulation, sensory perception, movement and seizure

Table 1

Inactivation and Fate of Norepinephrine and Epinephrine

Pool	Inactivation [a]	Metabolic Fate [b]	Excretory Products
NE released from the sympathetic nerve endings	1° Reuptake 2° O-methylation	Excretion unchanged or unconjugated; O-methylation followed in part by deamination	Free or conjugated NE and NMN; VMA
Circulating E (from adrenal medulla) or NE (from adrenergic synapses)	1° O-methylation 2° Uptake	Excretion unchanged or conjugated; O-methylation followed in part by deamination	Free and conjugated catecholamines and metanephrines; VMA
NE stored in nerve endings	Inactive in stored form	Intraneuronal deamination followed by O-methylation	VMA
CNS NE	Reuptake O-methylation Deamination	O-methylation Deamination	MHPG VMA

[a] Termination of biological effects
[b] Principal metabolic pathway
1° = Principal
2° = Subsidiary

Modified from Levine and Landsberg (1974)

disorders, appetite, sleep, and mental retardation—but, in comparison with catecholamines, factors controlling the indoleamine synthetic pathways are less well defined (fig. 7) (Barchas and Usdin, 1973; Breisch et al., 1976; Chase and Murphy, 1973; Coleman, 1973; Freedman et al., 1971; Jouvet, 1969; Sjoerdsma, 1959). The rate-limiting step is the point of activity of tryptophan hydroxylase. Unlike the catecholamines, end-product inhibition is apparently insignificant. Factors that have been demonstrated to have an impact on serotonin synthesis are the level of neuronal activity, the availability of tryptophan in the diet, and the presence of oxygen and pteridine (Fernstrom, 1974; Gál, 1974; Zivkovic et al., 1974). The major mechanism for the metabolism of serotonin is degradation by MAO with subsequent oxidation to 5-hydroxyindoleacetic acid (5HIAA). The neuronal uptake process for serotonin is similar to that for the catecholamines.

Figure 7

Synthesis and Metabolism of Serotonin

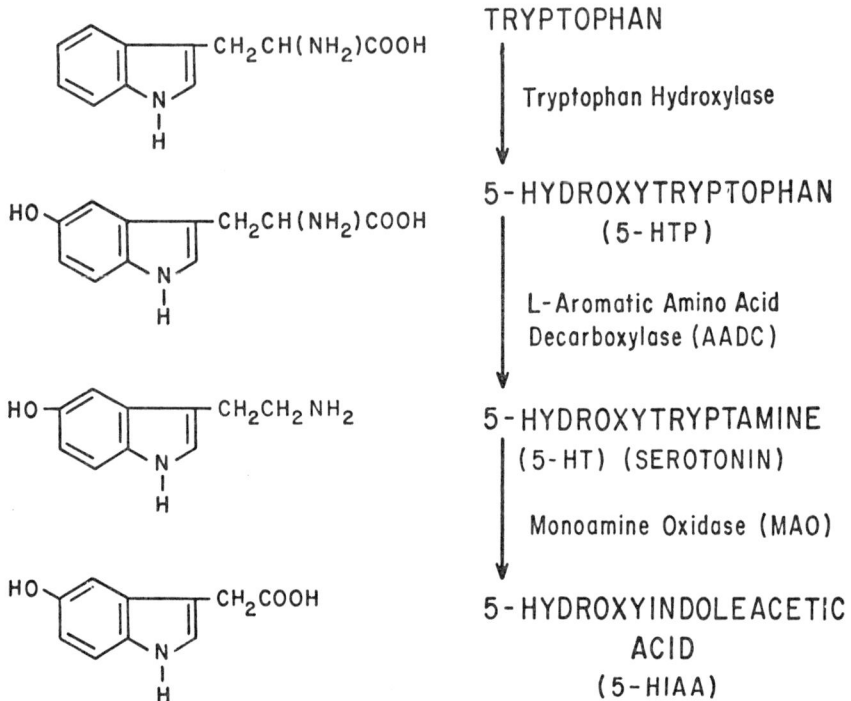

TRYPTOPHAN

↓ Tryptophan Hydroxylase

5-HYDROXYTRYPTOPHAN
(5-HTP)

↓ L-Aromatic Amino Acid
Decarboxylase (AADC)

5-HYDROXYTRYPTAMINE
(5-HT) (SEROTONIN)

↓ Monoamine Oxidase (MAO)

5-HYDROXYINDOLEACETIC
ACID
(5-HIAA)

Acetylcholine

The first neurotransmitter to be studied in the peripheral autonomic nervous system was a relatively simple molecule, acetylcholine: $CH_3COOCH_2CH_2N+(CH_3)_3$. The final step in the synthesis of acetylcholine (ACh), the acetylation of choline with acetyl coenzyme A, is catalyzed by choline acetyltransferase (CAT). When released at the synapse, ACh activity is terminated by a rapid hydrolysis facilitated by the enzyme acetylcholinesterase (AChE). A variety of inhibitors of AChE are used in clinical medicine, all based on their prolongation of the availability of ACh at the receptor. The most familiar of these is physostigmine.

Acetylcholine receptors in the periphery have classically been described as either muscarinic or nicotinic, because the effect of ACh can be mimicked by one or the other of these alkaloids, depending on the receptor site examined. In the *muscarinic* effect, ACh from the postganglionic parasympathetic cell (e.g., the vagus nerve) acts on the autonomic effector cell (e.g., smooth muscle of the intenstine or heart) to produce an action which is slow in onset but relatively sustained. This muscarinic action at the receptor is blocked by atropine and other drugs. In the *nicotinic* effect, ACh is released from two types of presynaptic neurons: the motor nerves (acting on endplates of skeletal muscles) and preganglionic autonomic fibers (acting on autonomic ganglion cells). The ACh initiates two, dose-related effects on nicotinic receptors. At low concentrations, ACh rapidly stimulates the receptors; at higher concentrations, receptors are blocked. Curare, and similar drugs, block all activity at the nicotinic receptors (Koelle, 1975).

Like serotonin, ACh levels in the brain are partially controlled by the availability of its precursor, choline. Another rate-regulatory mechanism in the cholinergic neuron is feedback inhibition on CAT by the end product, ACh (E. L. Cohen and Wurtman, 1976).

Enkephalins and Endorphins

Opioid peptides are the most recently recognized major class of neurotransmitters. While transmitters such as the catecholamines and indoleamines are derived from single amino acids, the more complex peptide transmitters consist of a series of amino acids. Two pentapeptide transmitters have been isolated from the brain, identical except for their terminal amino acid: leucine-enkephalin (consisting of the amino acids tyrosine-glycine-glycine-phenylalanine-leucine) and methionine-enkephalin (consisting of tyrosine-glycine-glycine-phenylalanine-methionine) (Hughes et al., 1975). Three longer opioid peptides, known as endorphins, have been isolated from the pituitary. Endorphins contain the methionine-enkephalin peptide as one segment. The enkephalins and endorphins are all contained as segments of a 91 amino acid pituitary peptide, beta lipotropin. This larger peptide appears to be the inactive prohormone from which the smaller, biologically active peptides are cleaved, under the control of still unknown mechanisms (A. Goldstein, 1976; Guillemin, 1977).

Enkephalins and endorphins were discovered in the search for the endogenous substances which react with the highly specific brain receptors for opiates, such as morphine. Drugs with a spectrum of opiate effects bind to these receptors: opiate agonists with high addictive potential (morphine); opiate antagonists which block narcotic effects (naloxone); and drugs which have mixed, agonist and antagonist effects (nalorphine and pentazocine). The opiate receptor has two conformations, depending on the local concentration of sodium. In the presence of sodium, the receptor equilibrium tends toward the antagonist conformation and the dissociation of morphine, leading to a 60-fold reduction in its potency. Sodium reduces the agonist activity of drugs with mixed, agonist-antagonist properties in direct proportion to their morphinelike effects (the "sodium index"). The binding of antagonist drugs to the receptor is not affected by sodium (Snyder, 1977).

The mechanism of the neurotransmitter action of peptides is not fully understood. Enkephalins and endorphins may decrease neuronal activity by reducing sodium permeability at the ion channel in neuronal membranes. The agonist conformation of the opiate receptor appears to be linked with the inhibition of adenylate cyclase, the enzyme involved in the formation of cyclic AMP.

Neuronal Localization in the Brain

Neurons utilizing a specific transmitter are not evenly distributed throughout the intact brain (Vogt, 1954). Techniques such as fluorescence histochemistry permit localization of discrete transmitter-specific neuronal populations. For example, when freeze-dried brain sections are exposed to formaldehyde vapors, condensation of formaldehyde with catecholamine molecules results in compounds which emit a green fluorescence; this causes a distinctive appearance of catecholamine-containing nerve terminals in the fluorescence micrograph (Falck et al., 1962). These anatomical and biochemical correlations suggest functional hypotheses. For example, a disease presumably involving a neuroanatomical locale might then logically be approached with drugs affecting the relevant specific transmitter system, an approach most vividly illustrated by the findings in Parkinson's disease of anatomical changes in the substantia nigra and biochemical depletion of dopamine in the caudate nucleus (Bloom, 1972; Hillarp et al., 1966).

Dopaminergic Neurons. Figures 8, 9, and 10 schematically map the dopamine and norepinephrine tracts within the rat brain (Ungerstedt, 1971). Cell bodies of dopaminergic neurons lie rostrally and contribute axons to three dopamine systems. The nigrostriatal system, active in motor control, projects from the substantia nigra (A8 and A9 in figs. 8 and 10) to the caudate and amygdaloid nuclei. The mesolimbic projection, possibly involved in emotional responses, arises from the region dorsal to the interpeduncular nucleus (A 10) and terminates in the nucleus accumbens and olfactory tubercle (Matthysse, 1973; Ungerstedt, 1971). Terminals in the cingulate cortex and parts of the

Figure 8

Schematic representation of major dopamine neural tracts in rat brain. Shaded areas indicate principle nerve terminal regions. Nomenclature of cell groups as in Dahlstrom and Fuxe (1965). Modified from Ungerstedt (1971) and Cooper et al. (1974).

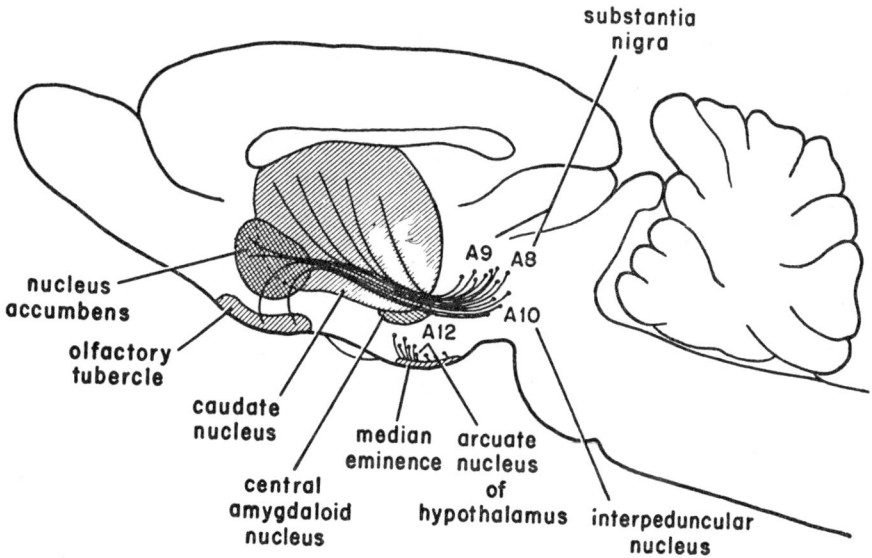

Figure 9

Schematic representation of major ascending norepinephrine neural tracts in rat brain. Shaded areas indicate principal nerve terminal regions. Nomenclature of cell groups as in Dahlström and Fuxe (1965). Modified from Ungerstedt (1971) and Cooper et al. (1974).

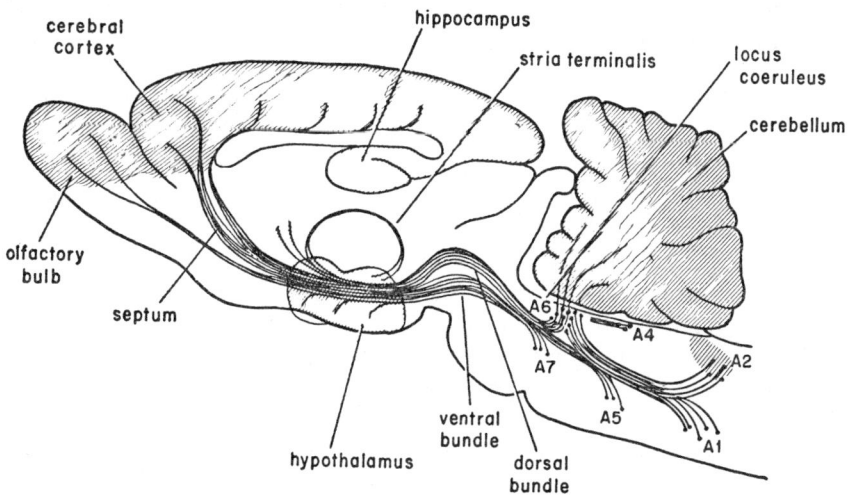

frontal cortex have also been described (Hökfelt et al., 1974b; Thierry et al., 1973). The hypothalamic dopamine system, concerned with hypothalamic-pituitary-endocrine regulation, lies completely within the hypothalamus; cell bodies are found in the arcuate nucleus and innervate the median eminence. Also, there may be dopaminergic projections to the spinal cord.

Noradrenergic Neurons. The pons and medulla oblongata are the locus for the cell bodies of the norepinephrine-containing (or noradrenergic) neurons. Cell bodies are found in compact groups, but the nerve terminals spread diffusely through many brain regions and the spinal cord. The first of two ascending noradrenergic tracts projects from the locus coeruleus (A6 in figs. 9 and 10) via the dorsal bundle to the cerebral cortex, the cerebellar cortex, and the hippocampus. A ventral noradrenergic bundle from other cell groups innervates the lower brainstem and, via the medial forebrain bundle, the hypothalamus and limbic system. Stimulation and lesions of the locus coeruleus have provided direct methods for assessing the impact of noradrenergic pathways on behavior and emotions. Two descending tracts are significant in the control of blood pressure (Chalmers and Wurtman, 1971; Doba and Reis, 1974). The widespread distribution of noradrenergic fibers is consistent with the prominent role this system plays in the modulation of emotional state and mood.

Serotonergic Neurons. Because the yellow fluoresence of serotonin-containing nerve terminals is weak and the serotonin pathways are so diffuse, it has been difficult to clarify all the areas innervated. Figure 11 depicts the major known tracts and terminal regions. Serotonergic cell bodies are found in the nuclei of the raphe system, a midline brainstem structure (fig. 11, B5-B9). Ascending projections reach multiple brain regions, including the hypothalamus, amygdala, forebrain, and cerebral cortex. Fibers also descend (from B1-B3) to the lower brainstem and the spinal cord. There may be another nonserotonergic system of indoleamine-containing neurons in the raphe nuclei (Fuxe and Jonsson, 1974; Harvey et al., 1963). Inhibitory serotonergic neurons have been postulated to play a role in screening or sensory-gating mechanisms and the control of arousal. Their broad distribution would make them suitable for exerting a pervasive influence on CNS function (e.g., in regulation of state) (Aghajanian et al., 1975).

Cholinergic Neurons. Acetylcholine has both muscarinic and nicotinic effects in the brain, as well as a novel inhibitory effect. However, it is unusual for a brain neuron to have a single characteristic response to ACh. Most cells appear to have either a receptor with an intermediate response or more than one type of ACh receptor.

Figure 10

Schematic representation of horizontal projection of ascending dopamine and norepinephrine neural tracts in rat brain. Shaded areas indicate principal nerve terminal regions. Nomenclature of cell groups as in Dahlström and Fuxe (1965). Modified from Ungerstedt (1971).

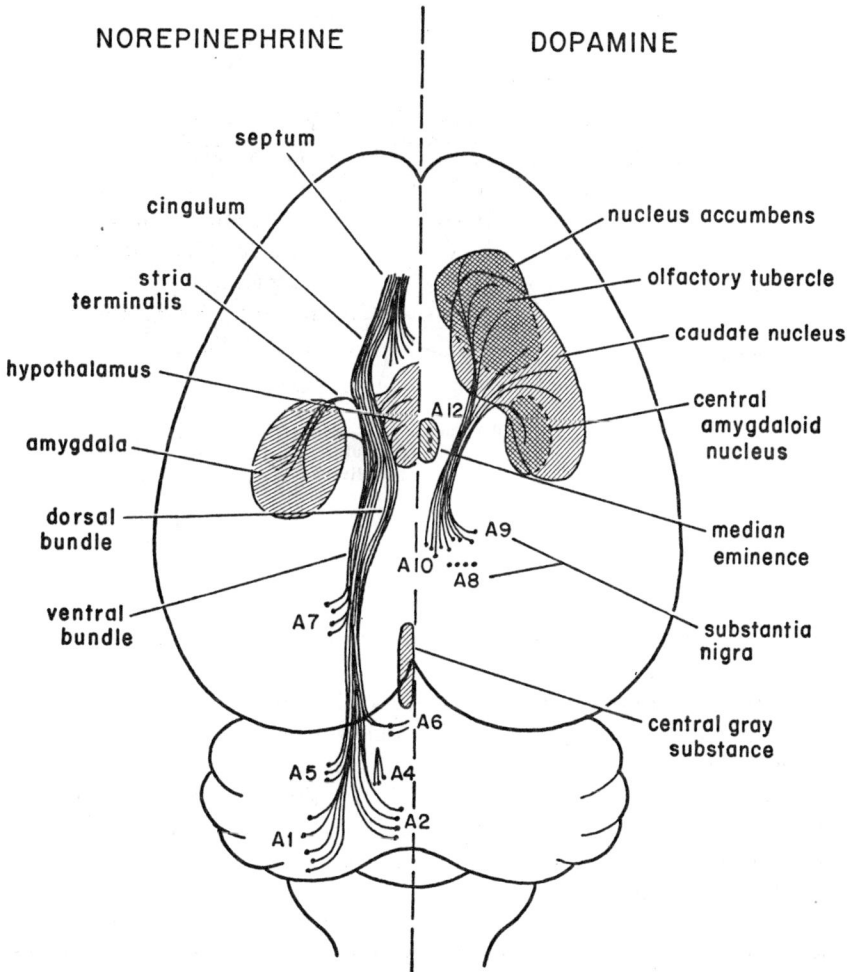

Relatively pure, slow muscarinic excitation occurs only in the deeper neuronal layers of the forebrain. Mixed muscarinic excitation has been found in varying degrees elsewhere in the cortex, in other brain areas, and in the spinal cord. Also, presynaptic muscarinic receptors have been found in several brain areas. Rapid, nicotinic response is

Figure 11

Schematic representation of major serotonin neural tracts in rat brain. Shaded areas indicate principal nerve terminal regions. Nomenclature of cell groups as in Dahlström and Fuxe (1965). Modified from Björklund et al. (1973), Breese (1975), and Fuxe and Jonsson (1974).

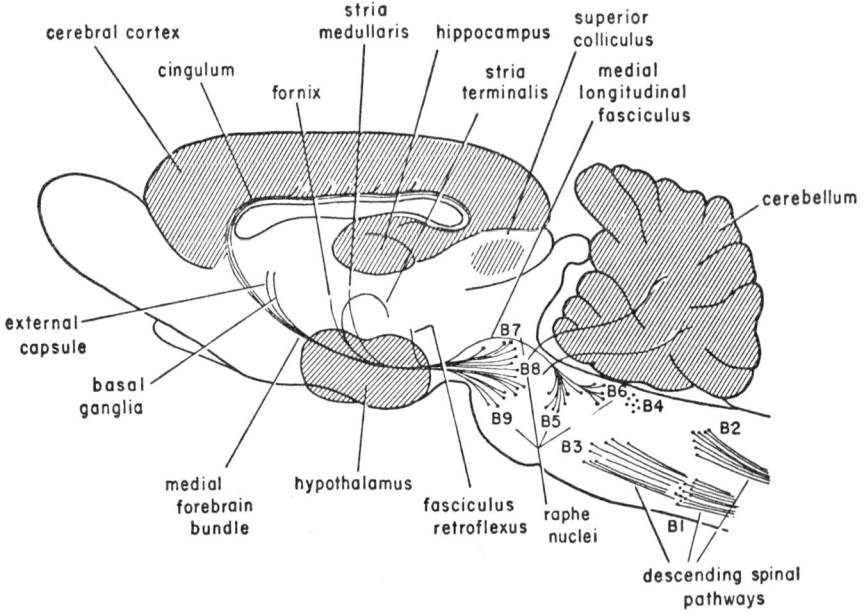

clearly observed only in the Renshaw cells of the spinal cord, innervated by recurrent collateral branches of motor neurons. Inhibitory muscarinic receptors, found in superficial cortical neurons, have a depressant action on single neuronal discharges (Krnjevic, 1975).

The most generally distributed effect of ACh throughout the brain is slow muscarinic excitation, which is unsuited to fast, discrete signal transmission. Stimulation of these ACh receptors leads to decreased potassium conductance at the membrane; neurons become more excitable and responsive and neurotransmission is enhanced (Snyder and Bennett, 1976). This process may have a slowly developing, arousing influence on CNS activity. For example, stimulation of the reticular activating system (RAS) activates the cerebral cortex and leads to the release of cortical ACh, a phenomenon which can be inhibited by muscarinic antagonists. This cortical ACh release has been suggested as a physiological basis for conscious awareness and, at local structural levels, as an aspect of conditioned learning and memory.

Enkephalin and Endorphin Neurons. Immunohistochemical maps have outlined a system of enkephalin nerve terminals and axons which are most highly concentrated in areas of the brain rich in receptors for opiates. The distribution of these drug receptors, determined by binding of isotopically labeled opiates, such as (^{3}H) naloxone (autoradiography), is in good agreement with the classical neuroanatomical understanding of pain. These areas include brain structures subserving deep (but not fine) pain perception (medial thalamic nuclei, substantia gelantinosa of the spinal cord and trigeminal nucleus) and emotional responsivity (amygdala), as well as structures predictable from opiate side effects, such as decreased coughing, blood pressure, and gastric secretion (solitary nucleus of the brainstem) and nausea and vomiting (area postrema and the chemoreceptor trigger zone) (Guillemin, 1977; Snyder, 1977).

The endorphins are found in the pituitary, especially the posterior pituitary, where opiate receptors appear to be involved with hormone release.

In addition to the enkephalins, many other amino acid and peptide neurotransmitters and hormones have been identified, such as glycine and somatostatin. These compounds are broadly distributed in the brain, gastrointestinal tract, and other organs; their interrelations and physiological functions are only in the first stages of clarification (L. L. Iversen et al., 1975).

RESEARCH STRATEGIES

The question faced by clinical researchers is whether an impairment of neurotransmitter metabolism underlies a specific behavioral syndrome or component of such a syndrome. Various problems make this simple question difficult to answer. First, it is not likely that only one transmitter neuronal system would be involved in an illness. Presumably, in syndromes such as the childhood psychoses, many different kinds of cells are involved and a balance between neuronal systems upset, rather than only one impaired (Davis, 1975; Samanin and Garattini, 1975). Second, the types of specimens which can be obtained to test hypotheses about brain transmitters are severely limited. Since biopsy specimens can rarely be obtained from the living human brain, except for therapeutic and diagnostic neurosurgical procedures, researchers are restricted to the use of a variety of indirect techniques involving problematic assumptions. Six indirect clinical research methods will be described.

Blood

Plasma and Whole Blood. Catecholamines in plasma are derived from sympathetic nerve endings and the adrenal medulla, rather than the central nervous system (Levine and Landsberg, 1974). Because of the blood-brain barrier, unmetabolized catecholamines from the brain do not ordinarily reach the peripheral circulation (Oldendorf, 1974). Norepinephrine in the plasma represents the very small amount which escapes inactivation by reuptake or metabolism (at peripheral adrenergic synapses) and which is not metabolized in such organs as the liver and lung (Gillis and Roth, 1976). Plasma epinephrine is the direct product of adrenal chromaffin cells (Vane, 1969). Determination of plasma catecholamine concentrations has, until recent years, involved fluorometric assays with a sensitivity inadequate for the very small amounts present in plasma. Reliability and sensitivity have improved with less complicated radiometric enzymatic assays (Beaven, 1975; Coyle, 1975; Henry et al., 1975; Passon and Peuler, 1973; Weise and Kopin, 1976), which have been used to define sympathetic nervous system function in response to physiological stimuli (e.g., postural change, the cold pressor test, and exercise) and in various disease states (e.g., hypertension) (Cryer and Weiss, 1976; Lake et al., 1976; Lake et al., 1977; Ziegler et al., 1976, 1977).

About 90 percent of the serotonin in the body is in the gastrointestinal tract; another 8 or 9 percent is in the platelets. The remaining 1 or 2 percent is CNS serotonin. Serotonin, like the catecholamines, does not cross the blood-brain barrier. Nearly all of the whole blood serotonin is contained in the platelets, where it is concentrated by an active transport system located in the platelet membrane. Assays are available for whole blood serotonin, platelet serotonin, and whole blood 5-hydroxyindoles (5HI). Of the latter, usually 99 percent is serotonin and 1 percent is 5HIAA, except in the presence of a carcinoid tumor (Coleman and Mahanand, 1973). In sum, catecholamine and serotonin concentrations in blood specimens provide a measure of peripheral metabolism, but not of metabolism in the central nervous system.

The accessibility and convenience of using blood specimens have led to an intensive search for possible abnormalities in central enzyme systems which may be reflected in peripheral enzyme levels. Relevant enzymes in the major synthetic pathways are indicated in figures 1 and 7. The rate-limiting step for the catecholamine pathway is the hydroxylation of tyrosine to form DOPA by tyrosine hydroxylase (TH), an intracellular enzyme which is soluble in the cytoplasm. Tyrosine hydroxylase is present in the adrenal medulla, adrenergic nervous tissue, and brain, but is not ordinarily present in the blood (Udenfriend, 1966). DBH, another intracellular enzyme, is located in the membrane of the storage vesicles of the nerve ending; it catalyzes the final step in the formation of norepinephrine and is released with norepinephrine into the synaptic cleft (Axelrod, 1972). DBH thus has access to the blood stream, and it has been hoped that it might provide an index of sympathetic activity because of its proportional release with the transmitter from neuronal vesicles (M. Goldstein et al., 1971; Weinshilboum and Axelrod, 1971; Weinshilboum et al., 1971). Large differences in serum DBH activity are observed between individuals with apparently equally competent sympathetic function, and genetic control seems to be the predominant influence on serum DBH concentrations (Laduron, 1975; Reid and Kopin, 1974; Schanberg et al., 1974). However, there are some interesting correlations between serum DBH levels and changes in physiological processes under autonomic control, such as blood pressure, which suggest the possible value of DBH determination as a marker of an individual's change of state (Nagatsu et al., 1976; Stone and DeLeo, 1976).

Platelets. The tiny blood platelets of the peripheral circulation appear, at first glance, to be distantly removed from clinical brain research. Yet, fortuitously, blood platelets share several critical features with monoamine neurons and have served as a useful biochemical model in studies of serotonin, dopamine, and MAO. The shared features include an active transport system, located in the cell membrane, for active uptake of biogenic amines; distinctive intracellular vesicles for amine storage; the presence of metabolically relevant enzymes; and similarity in receptor function and response to drugs (Abrams and Solomon, 1969; Born and Gillson, 1959; Pletscher, 1968; Pletscher et al., 1971; Stahl, 1977). Studies of platelet models are more convenient than work with less accessible, and more complex, central or peripheral neurons; yet, these two types of tissue may be fundamentally different in the expression of underlying disturbances in amine metabolism because of the different roles the amines play in brain transmission and blood coagulation. Extrapolations, thus, must be cautious, and even basic questions, such as the relation between platelet and brain MAO levels, are only at the first stage of resolution (Robinson et al., 1977).

Urine

The urine contains a variety of neurotransmitters and metabolites, derived from various sources (table 2) (Goodall, 1959; Kopin, 1972; Levine and Landsberg, 1974). Clearly, free epinephrine and

Table 2

Representative Excretion of Norepinephrine and
Epinephrine and Their Metabolites in Humans

	μg./day [a]	% of Total Excretion	Source
Epinephrine (free)	5	0.1	ADRENAL MEDULLA [b]
NE (free)	30	0.4	SYMPATHETIC NERVE ENDINGS Adrenal medulla
Conjugated catecholamines	100	1.6	SYMPATHETIC NERVE ENDINGS Dietary catecholamines Adrenal medulla
MN (Total)	65	1.0	ADRENAL MEDULLA
NMN (Total)	100	1.6	SYMPATHETIC NERVE ENDINGS Adrenal medulla
VMA	4000	63.5	SYMPATHETIC NERVE ENDINGS (Storage pool) ADRENAL MEDULLA, BRAIN
MHPG	2000	31.8	BRAIN, SYMPATHETIC NERVE ENDINGS (Storage pool) ADRENAL MEDULLA
TOTAL	6300	100	

[a] Average approximate figures from literature; not upper limits.
[b] Major sources in capitals.
Modified from Levine and Landsberg (1974).

norepinephrine comprise only a small percentage of the total excretion, with VMA and MHPG predominating. Peripheral neuronal activity and the adrenal gland contribute minor metabolites in addition to VMA and MHPG. The central nervous system, in contrast, contributes little to the minor metabolites but preferentially metabolizes norepinephrine to MHPG and, less importantly, VMA. MHPG diffuses into the peripheral circulation as well as into the cerebrospinal fluid (CSF). Of the MHPG found in the urine, upward of 30 percent is derived from the brain. Measurement of MHPG in 24-hour urine specimens provides the best available clinical method using urine for determining brain norepinephrine metabolism (Maas and Landis, 1968, 1971; Schanberg et al., 1968). The method has been widely employed in clinical studies of depression and mania. Urinary metabolites of dopamine, primarily HVA, are overwhelmingly the result of peripheral metabolism and their measurement has contributed little to understanding CNS function.

Cerebrospinal Fluid

The brain is bathed by CSF which is constantly produced, circulated within the brain ventricles and spinal canal, and reabsorbed into the peripheral circulation. In addition to various proteins and cells, the CSF contains a variety of compounds related to neural transmission. The neurotransmitters themselves are found in such low concentrations that their measurement has not been feasible until recently. However, the major metabolites of dopamine, serotonin, and norepinephrine (HVA, 5HIAA, and MHPG, respectively) are relatively easily measured by fluorometric and mass spectrometric methods; and the more sensitive, newer methods also permit the study of other metabolites, such as DOPAC (Bowers, 1972; Chase et al., 1973; Sharman, 1973b; Wilk and Watson, 1973). Endorphins can be assayed by radio-immunoassay techniques, but these studies are now only at the first stages.

HVA, 5HIAA, and MHPG are transported into the CSF from which they are actively removed. Measurement of metabolites has been used as an index of "turnover rate" for the parent amines within the brain—the rate at which the amine pool in the brain is replaced. "Turnover rate" is thought to reflect neuronal activity and is not the same as the actual synthesis rate of a neurotransmitter (Brodie et al., 1966; R. H. Roth et al., 1973; Weiner, 1974). In conditions such as Parkinson's, reduced brain synthesis of dopamine is reflected in reduced CSF concentrations of HVA. While measurements of CSF metabolites is the most sensitive method currently available for clinical study of brain biochemistry, there are many methodological and conceptual problems which will be described later.

Postmortem Whole Brain

Problems in the use of postmortem brain specimens include obtaining the specimen, lack of historical information about the subject, concurrent diseases or drug usage, and rapid postmortem decline in activity of the monoamines and related enzymes (Black and Geen, 1975; Hornykiewicz, 1973). These difficulties have been overcome in varying degrees, but with more successful application to neurological than psychiatric diseases. The classical study was the demonstration of reduced dopamine in the basal ganglia of patients with Parkinson's disease. Studies of synthesizing enzymes and amines in the brains of schizophrenics have been suggestive but equivocal (Wise and Stein, 1973; Wise et al., 1974; Wyatt et al., 1975). Since amine concentrations vary widely between brain areas, studies must be performed on discrete regions suggested by theoretical models; this may be particularly important in mental illnesses (Hornykiewicz, 1974). Postmortem fluoresence histochemistry offers the possibility of demonstrating impaired function in specific monoamine systems (Balch et al., 1973; Olson, 1974).

Animal Models

Use of an animal model allows direct access to brain neuronal systems and the possibility of precise, anatomical, biochemical, and functional correlations. These studies can illuminate normal physiology, but are limited by the unavailability of animal models for many psychiatric disorders. While the use of primates is generally desirable, the cost and practical problems in studying a sufficient number of animals have often led to the use of more distant species, generally the rat (L. L. Iversen et al., 1976; Shaywitz et al., 1976a, 1976b). The final problem remains: there is an unbridgeable distinction between man and other species in brain and behavior.

Pharmacological Studies

Drugs may be used as chemical probes in dissecting the various steps in neuronal function and neurotransmitter metabolism. By augmenting or inhibiting enzymatic and neurophysiological processes (e.g., reuptake and release), medications may reveal the relative importance of various neurotransmitter systems, alternative pathways of synthesis and degradation, rate-limiting steps, control mechanisms, and the potential for CNS compensatory changes (Euler, 1972; Pletscher, 1973; Stjärne, 1972). *In vitro* findings may not be applied in a straightforward way to understanding the actual impact of a drug on the CNS. Complications arise because a medication may affect more than one neurotransmitter system or may have differing effects on two different neurotransmitters. For example, tricyclic antidepressants block catecholamine uptake, alter acetylcholine metabolism, and inhibit MAO (J. A. Roth and Gillis, 1975). Because drugs have many different effects, clinical improvement with a medication does not unequivocally point to one specific underlying metabolic dysfunction. Eight major types of pharmacological intervention are relevant to understanding neurotransmitter function (table 3). These interventions augment, inhibit, or specifically block important steps and processes in normal neural activity and have definite behavioral consequences (Aghajanian, 1972; Giarman and Freedman, 1965; Kopin, 1968; Trendelenburg, 1972b).

The modes of action of the antipsychotic (neuroleptic) agents demonstrate some underlying physiological and pharmacological mechanisms.

Phenothiazines, larger and more complex molecules than dopamine, block the functioning of dopaminergic systems. On the basis of X-ray crystallography, the structure of the phenothiazines has been elucidated. Structure-function correlations demonstrate that specific alterations in side-chain configuration and constituents account for varying degrees of clinical effectiveness. When the side chain and adjacent portion can be superimposed over the dopamine or norepinephrine molecule, the phenothiazine effectively blocks the dopamine receptor (Snyder et al., 1974).

On the other hand, the conformation of the receptor might vary, and in this way exert a controlling effect on the overall system. For example, changes in the number of active catecholamine molecules interacting with a pineal gland receptor site lead to the rapid development of receptor subsensitivity or supersensitivity. When a large number of active transmitter molecules are in the vicinity of receptor sites, there appears to be a reduction in the coupling between postsynaptic receptor and adenylate cyclase on the cellular membrane, leading to a decrease in the formation of cyclic AMP (subsensitive response). In the reverse situation, when fewer than normal transmitter molecules are in the pineal receptor locale, there is an increase in receptor-adenylate cyclase coupling and a consequent increase in cyclic AMP formation (supersensitive response). Because these changes to subsensitivity or supersensitivity occur so soon after exposure of the receptor to an excess or deficiency of the transmitter (or agonist drug), it has been suggested that the responsible mechanism is a (reversible) alteration in either the conformation or the availability of the receptor. This provides a useful model for both denervation supersensitivity and drug tolerance (subsensitivity) phenomena (Axelrod, 1974a, 1974b; Mukherjee et al., 1975).

The antipsychotic activity of phenothiazines and butyrophenones is paralleled by their action at extrapyramidal system receptors in the striatum. It might be predicted that if two phenothiazines (e.g., thioridazine and fluphenazine) are given at dosages eliciting comparable antipsychotic effects, they would cause a similar degree of extrapyramidal side effects. Considerable clinical experience, however, indicates that this is not the case, and that antipsychotic and extrapyramidal effects may be dissociated. From a neurochemical perspective, this evidence suggests that drugs do not have a similar effect on all dopamine receptors and that the dopamine-blockage theory of neuroleptic drug action may be in error. However, this apparent discrepancy from the blockade model has been explained by studies of the antimuscarinic effects of various medications.

Anticholingeric agents, such as atropine, are antagonists at muscarinic receptor sites (as discussed earlier). These compounds have long been useful in the treatment of Parkinson's disease, and more recently have been the principal drugs used to minimize the side effects of the neuroleptics. It appears that they compensate for a relative dopamine deficiency in the striatum and restore balance between dopamine and acetylcholine. On the basis of clinical findings, it was hypothesized that phenothiazines with fewer extrapyramidal side effects had an anticholinergic potency. This hypothcsis has been supported by ranking antipsychotic agents by anticholinergic potency. Those with high potency (e.g., thioridazine) have few extrapyramidal side effects because of their built-in anticholinergic activity; those with low potency (e.g., fluphenazine and butyrophenones) have prominent side effects presumably because they fail to balance their strong antidopaminergic effects (L. L. Iversen, 1975; Snyder et al., 1974).

Recent work has indicated that neuroleptics may have a presynaptic effect in addition to the dopamine blockade indicated in table 3. Although the butyrophenones are among the clinically most potent antipsychotic agents, their efficacy as blockers at the dopamine-sensitive adenylate cyclase in animals is not particularly high. One explanatory model for this phenomenon is that haloperidol and related compounds have a particularly strong presynaptic effect. Several types of presynaptic actions have been suggested, but one attractive theory is that haloperidol interferes with the mechanism which couples the neuronal impulses to the neurosecretion of dopamine. This inhibition would then lead to the observed compensatory increase in neuronal firing and dopamine turnover (L. L. Iversen, 1975; Seeman and Lee, 1975).

Pharmacological techniques have been used to characterize properties of the opioid peptides. In classical bioassays and studies of single neuron responses, enkephalins and endorphins behave like morphine and other agonists. Administered to laboratory animals, each of the three types of endorphins elicits replicable behavioral and physiological effects: (1) analgesia, tranquilization, hypothermia (alpha endorphin); (2) catatoniclike stupor, profound analgesia, hypothermia (beta endorphin, by far the most potent); and (3) irritability, hypersensitivity, and hyperthermia (gamma endorphin). These effects subside spontaneously, over a few hours, and can be terminated almost instantaneously with morphine antagonists such as naloxone (Bloom et al., 1976; Jacquet and Marks, 1976; Pert et al., 1976).

The discovery of endorphins and enkephalins has led not only to

Table 3

Neurotransmitter Pharmacology

Type of Action	Drug Effect on Transmitter Physiology	Examples of drugs
1. Inhibition of transmitter synthesis	Interferes with an enzymatic step in the synthesis of a transmitter by interacting with an enzyme or a cofactor	AMPT (inhibits tyrosine hydroxylase), disulfiram (inhibits DBH), fusaric acid (inhibits DBH), PCPA (inhibits tryptophan hydroxylase)
2. Depletion of stored transmitter	Interferes with uptake and storage mechanism of the intraneuronal amine storage vesicle	reserpine (long-lasting depletion of DA, NE, and 5-HT), tetrabenazine (short-duration depletion)
3. False transmitter	"False transmitters" are stored in vesicles with the transmitter, and are released with it, but do not efficiently interact with the receptor. They reduce the effect of the transmitter	octopamine, alpha-methyldopa, metaraminol
4. Enhanced transmitter release	Increases release of the neurotransmitter resulting in its increased availability for interaction with the receptor	Sympathomimetic amphetamine tyramine phenylethylamine Cholinomimetic carbachol
5. Inhibition of reuptake of transmitter	Blocks reuptake resulting in an increase in available transmitter	amphetamine (blocks DA and NE reuptake), cocaine (blocks DA and NE reuptake), tricyclic antidepressants (block NE and 5-HT reuptake), benztropine (blocks DA reuptake)
6. Inhibition of transmitter metabolism	Interferes with inactivation by degradative enzymes and increases transmitter at the synapse	MAO inhibitors pargyline phenelzine iproniazid COMT inhibitors pyrogallol tropolones AChE inhibitor physostigmine
7. Receptor blocking	Interacts with the receptor but does not elicit the usual postsynaptic events With fewer receptors available for the usual transmitter, there is a net decrease in transmitter-receptor interaction and a feedback mechanism may increase transmitter turnover	phenothiazines (block DA receptor); butyrophenones (block DA receptor); d-Tubocurarine, atropine, benztropine (block ACh receptor)
8. Receptor stimulating	Stimulates the receptor like the usual transmitter, leading to an "increase" in transmitter-receptor interaction with decreased turnover of the transmitter	apomorphine (DA receptor agonist) clonidine (NE receptor agonist), morphine (opiate receptor agonist)

better understanding of the action of opiates but to new hypotheses about the mechanism of action of other compounds which affect mood and sensory processing. For example, it has been suggested that a mechanism of the therapeutic effect of lithium in the treatment of mania may be its effect on the conformation of the opiate receptor. Because of homeostatic processes, it is difficult to alter the bodily concentration of sodium; however, lithium, perhaps in conjunction with sodium, may alter the opiate receptor to the conformation favoring the dissociation of endogenous agonists, thus leading to a lowering of euphoric mood. This idea receives support from observations that lithium tends to block the action of exogenous euphoriants such as heroin and stimulants (Byck, 1976).

Pharmacological research strategies may be relevant to specific etiological and physiological hypotheses:

Administration of Methyl Donors. Some hallucinogens are methylated derivatives of either indoleamines or catecholamines. The transmethylation hypothesis for schizophrenia suggests that abnormal transmethylation of an endogenous amine may form a hallucinogen and lead to the cognitive and other disturbances found in schizophrenia. To test this hypothesis, methyl donors (e.g., methionine and betaine) have been administered to schizophrenic patients and alterations in symptomatology concurrently assessed. A problem in interpreting results is the difficulty in distinguishing toxicity from a more specific exacerbation of schizophrenic symptomatology (Rosengarten and Friedhoff, 1976).

An enzyme capable of forming the hallucinogen dimethyltryptamine (DMT) has been demonstrated in normal human plasma, red blood cells, and platelets. The enzyme activity in nondialyzed platelets of patients with schizophrenic and psychotic depressive illnesses is higher than the activity in normal volunteers, suggesting that a dialyzable inhibitor might be present in normal persons but reduced in the psychotic patients. When studied in monozygotic twins discordant for schizophrenia, it was found that the schizophrenic individuals had elevated enzyme levels as compared to their nonschizophrenic co-twins; interpretation must be tentative because of methodological difficulties, such as the possible effects of the illness and drugs and absence of more complete genetic studies (Wyatt et al., 1973b).

Administration of Methyl Acceptors. If transmethylation does, in fact, contribute methylated derivatives which are significant in producing schizophrenic symptoms, then methyl acceptor substances might be useful in treatment. Nicotinic acid and nicotinamide have been tried empirically, but have not been demonstrated to be useful therapeutically.

Administration of Amine Precursors. Precursors of amines have been given to normals in an attempt to induce psychotic symptoms, and to schizophrenic patients in order to exacerbate or elicit symptoms. For example, large doses of phenylalanine were administered daily to chronic schizophrenic patients for one-week periods with and without MAO inhibitors; no mental changes were evident (Pollin et al., 1961). Investigations using parallel methods (e.g., administration of tryptophan) to demonstrate an abnormality in central amine metabolism in psychotic children have not led to definitive behavioral correlations (Schain and Freedman, 1961). Administration of tryptophan has been useful in neurological diseases. For example, patients with myoclonic epilepsy, a debilitating, multicausal syndrome, have lower levels of serotonin metabolites in their CSF and respond positively to large doses of the serotonin precursor, tryptophan, when combined with a compound which blocks the utilization of tryptophan for peripheral serotonin synthesis (carbidopa) (van Woert et al., 1977a).

Isotope Methods. The advantages of isotopically labeled compounds are their marked sensitivity and specificity. The technical difficulty in the separation of a compound from all other substances in the tissue is simplified to a separation of the desired (isotopically labeled) compound from the few interfering radioactive substances (Beaven, 1975).

The use of labeled neurotransmitters for the estimation of turnover rates involves a variety of problems, especially the inability of the amine to penetrate the blood-brain barrier. In animals, labeled compounds can be administered by intracisternal or intraventricular injections. In man, isotopic precursors (e.g., labeled tyrosine or DOPA) cross the blood-brain barrier and are utilized in the synthesis of (labeled) dopamine or norepinephrine in the brain.

Chemical Lesions. In an organ with peripheral sympathetic innervation, the neuronal function may be studied by surgical denervation. However, a more widespread denervation involving multiple organs may be desired or the innervation of a single organ may not be adequately specific and separate for surgical denervation. Immunological and chemical techniques have been devised which selectively destroy monoamine nerve terminals and produce a general chemical ablation of sympathetic pathways. 6-hydroxydopamine is efficiently taken up by the sympathetic nerve endings in the periphery and causes degeneration of adrenergic nerve endings and a functional "chemical sympathectomy." When given by intraventricular injection, 6-hydroxydopamine selectively and permanently destroys dopaminergic and noradrenergic neurons in the brain. Similarly, 5, 6-dihydroxytryptamine preferentially destroys serotonergic nerve endings, although with somewhat less specificity (Breese, 1975; Thoenen and Tranzer, 1973). A major potential use of chemical ablation is the production of animal models of specific behavioral deficits (Shaywitz et al., 1976a).

IMPLICATIONS FOR CHILD PSYCHIATRY

Background

The possibility of a biological basis of early onset childhood psychosis—childhood autism, schizophrenia, and similar atypicalities of development—has been of interest to researchers and clinicians since the time that these syndromes were first described (Bryson and Hingtgen, 1971; Fish and Ritvo, 1977; Hingtgen and Bryson, 1972; Kanner, 1973; Rimland, 1964; Ritvo, 1976; Rutter, 1965). However, biochemical research efforts have tended to be unsystematic and lacking in rigor (Guthrie and Wyatt, 1975; Sankar, 1971; Sankar et al., 1963). Current advances in understanding CNS neurotransmission provide a framework for exploration of adult and childhood psychoses (Schildkraut, 1970; Schildkraut and Kety, 1967). The increasing use of psychoactive medication with children suffering from developmental difficulties offers another avenue for exploring the relation between CNS physiological and clinical phenomena. Widely prescribed medications, such as methylphenidate for attentional disturbances, chlorpromazine for psychotic disorganization, and impramine for enuresis, have a profound and definable impact on CNS biochemistry. What do their effects tell us about the underlying disorders?

Clinical researchers concerned with biogenic amines and behavior must remain aware of major methodological difficulties. Two overriding principles will be noted now and other issues discussed later. First, there are many levels of organization between the action of neurotransmitters at synapses and the integrated functioning of the nervous system revealed by the child's interactions in the world. Just as alterations in biogenic amine metabolism (e.g., depletion of amines by reserpine or their augmentation by MAO inhibition) may affect behavior and emotions organized at higher levels of CNS functioning, experience and cognitive processes may alter biogenic amine metabolism (Axelrod et al., 1970; Eleftheriou and Boehlke, 1967; Miller, 1971; Reis et al., 1971). For example, animals exposed to severe shock which they cannot avoid are later unable to learn to avoid shocks which they can control ("learned helplessness") (Overmier and Seligman, 1967). On the basis of pharmacological and behavioral studies, this disability has been explained as a deficit in motor activation associated with a depletion of central norepinephrine during the experience of inescapable shock. In contrast, animals initially allowed to escape from the shock do not develop central noradrenergic deficiency. Later they are better able to organize sufficient motor behavior and to perform adequately in avoidance-escape tests (Glazer et al., 1975; J. M. Weiss and Glazer, 1975; J. M. Weiss et al., 1975). Finding a deviation in catecholamine metabolism, thus, does not necessarily imply that this precedes or causes a child's difficulties; it may result from his experience (e.g., the stress of chronic perceptual problems, social isolation, or hospitalization).

The second principle is that there are many important, interacting biochemical and physiological processes in the human brain. The individual neurochemical systems operate in a functionally balanced manner, differing in various parts of the brain (for example, dopaminergic and cholinergic systems are both involved in diseases of the striate, as are other neuronal systems) (Antelman and Caggiula, 1977; Hornykiewicz, 1976; McGeer et al., 1976). And biogenic amine metabolism is only one fragment of a complex biological mosaic including structural and ultrastructural organization, endocrine regulation, genetic control mechanisms, and interactions between systems (e.g., D. J. Cohen, 1974, 1975; Landsberg and Axelrod, 1968; Plotnikoff et al., 1972; Prange et al., 1972; Sachar, 1975a, 1975b). Neurotransmitter physiology cannot provide a general theory of normal or deviant development.

Yet, there are many intriguing facets of developmental disturbances which may be illuminated by careful metabolic investigations, if seen in their context and interpreted with caution. In this section we will provide an overview of research strategies, types of hypotheses, and methodological considerations, with an emphasis on our laboratory studies of childhood psychosis.

CFS Metabolites: Technical Issues

The most direct, available method for studying biogenic amine metabolism in the human brain involves assay of cerebrospinal fluid (CSF) for major metabolites such as homovanillic acid (HVA) and 5-hydroxyindoleacetic acid (5HIAA). HVA and 5HIAA are actively excreted from the brain into the CSF, where their concentration is thought to reflect the state of the parent amines in the brain. Diseases and medications (such as the phenothiazines) which are associated with altered brain amines produce systematic changes in CSF metabolite concentrations (Goodwin and Post, 1975). However, the relation between central monoaminergic metabolism and CSF metabolite concentrations is not straightforward.

Interpretation of HVA and 5HIAA concentrations in the CSF is hazardous for several reasons. First, the CSF is a dynamic system in which components are constantly removed and replenished. The acid metabolites of dopamine and serotonin are among these components, and their concentration at any one moment reflects the resultant of brain turnover, secretion into the CSF, and active removal. A specific value may not reliably indicate brain function during a day. Second, the concentrations of HVA and 5HIAA in the CSF are so low that measurement error may obscure findings, especially using fluorometric methods. Third, the concentrations of the metabolites are not homogeneous throughout the course of the CSF; the metabolism of the spinal cord, for example, contributes to the 5HIAA concentration of the CSF obtained from the lumbar space. Fourth, concentration of the metabolites in the CSF does not reflect neurotransmitter function in all parts of the brain to an equal extent. Brain activity in areas adjacent to the ventricles (e.g., the basal ganglia) may be more accurately represented than activity in areas more distant from the CSF (e.g., medial forebrain bundle). Fifth, to obtain CSF one must perform a lumbar puncture, an uncomfortable procedure which introduces new parameters such as anxiety and physical manipulation. If CFS metabolites relate to an individual's state as well as an enduring behavioral or pathological trait, the procedures involved in obtaining CSF may influence biochemical findings. And, sixth, the CSF metabolite pool probably reflects global brain function; alterations in biogenic amine metabolism in small areas of the brain, even those near the ventricles, may have profound effects on CNS physiology yet lead to inconsequential change in the concentration of a metabolite in the lumbar CSF.

Two of these methodological problems—moment-to-moment variability and low metabolic concentration—may, in part, be overcome by the use of probenecid loading. Probenecid, a benzoic acid derivative, blocks membrane transport in various organs. In clinical medicine, it is used to block active transport in the kidney in order to achieve higher levels of penicillin in the blood (by blocking penicillin transport into the urine) or to reduce blood uric acid in patients with gout (by blocking reabsorption of uric acid from urine). In the brain, probenecid reduces the active reabsorbtion of the metabolites of biogenic amines, HVA, 5HIAA, and MHPG, from the CSF (Extein et al., 1973; van Praag et al., 1973). When their egress is blocked over a period of time (usually 8 to 18 hours), the concentrations of the metabolites increase and progressively become more reliable indicators of turnover of the parent amines in the brain substance during a representative period (Bowers, 1972; Bowers et al., 1969; Korf and van Praag, 1971; Post et al., 1975; Roos and Sjöström, 1969).

The use of probenecid, however, introduces its own methodological difficulties. First, it tends to produce stomach irritation and nausea, a stress which may have significant CNS impact and, further, which is mediated by biogenic amine systems in the brain. Second, the blockade produced by probenecid is not all-or-none but progressive; until a relatively high level of probenecid is reached, the concentrations of the metabolites are, in part, a function of the degree of blockade which has been achieved. This relationship must be considered in interpreting biogenic amine metabolite data. If not, the HVA and 5HIAA concentrations in the CSF may primarily relate to how much probenecid actually entered the brain (or CSF) rather than to the metabolic turnover of dopamine and serotonin in the brain. Differences between individuals (and populations) must also be considered. More cooperative patients may ingest, or retain, more of the prescribed probenecid than less compliant individuals, and there may be individual and group differences in gastrointestinal absorption and the effect of the medication in producing blockade. It is also possible that there are subtle interactional effects between CNS metabolic turnover and the degree of emesis elicited by probenecid. To assess these possibilities, and control for their effect, probenecid must be measured in the CSF and the metabolite concentration expressed in relation to the level of probenecid achieved (D. J. Cohen et al., 1974). This may be done by analysis of covariance or by use of a ratio of metabolite to probenecid concentration (e.g., ng of HVA/ μg probenecid). As the probenecid blockade appears to follow a logarithmic course, HVA and 5HIAA may be expressed as a ratio to the logarithm of CSF probenecid (D. J. Cohen et al., 1977a, 1977b).

CSF Metabolites: Clinical Studies

We have used the probenecid method to study the physiology of biogenic amine metabolism in children with the following diagnoses: childhood autism, aphasia, severe atypical development, multiple tic syndrome, epilepsy, minimal cerebral dysfunction, and a variety of neurological conditions. Normal control information is virtually impossible to obtain, for ethical and practical reasons. Instead, investigators interested in studying CSF metabolites must rely on contrast and comparison patient groups and the limited information on children with other neurological conditions (such as headache, disc disease, and peripheral neuropathies) from whom it is possible to obtain CSF with probenecid loading. Because of the need for approximately 10–12 hours of probenecid loading (125 mg/kg, given in four divided oral doses), control data cannot be obtained from diagnostic studies done in emergencies (such as to rule out the diagnosis of meningitis in a child with fever and a stiff neck).

There are very broad ranges of HVA and 5HIAA in the CSF of the childhood groups, as has been observed in studies of adults (D. J. Cohen et al., 1974, 1977b). This broad within-group variance may obscure between-group differences. It appears overly optimistic to hope that the major childhood psychoses (or adult psychoses) may be characterized by profound alterations in amine metabolism reflected in the CSF (of the magnitude of the alterations in amine metabolism found in neurological disorders such as Parkinson's or phenylketonuria). However, a number of intriguing observations and hypotheses about the physiology of brain functioning in children have emerged.

The two major amine metabolites, HVA and 5HIAA, correlate with each other, covarying for probenecid, suggesting that there may be functional interrelationships between these systems in the brain. The nature of the relationship, however, may differ between diagnostic groups, reflecting differences in the balance between serotonergic and dopaminergic systems. To evaluate the possibility that these systems are differently attuned in different conditions, one may compare regression curves or construct a simple ratio of HVA/5HIAA for individuals and groups. This ratio may also suggest the degree of relative biochemical heterogeneity within a diagnostic group. Similarly, there may be differences in the effectiveness of probenecid blockade in various diagnostic groups.

Early Childhood Psychosis. CSF metabolite concentrations span a considerable range within the autistic and nonautistic, early childhood psychosis groups. In the context of a large within-group variance, the detection of between-group differences is very unlikely. Instead, it appears more worthwhile to delineate subgroups and relate metabolites to specific behavioral disturbances within a diagnostic group. This approach has been valuable in adult psychiatry, e.g., in defining the relation between CSF metabolites and motor retardation in depression (van Praag et al., 1975). To explore this with psychotic children, we have assessed major areas of disability and behavior, e.g., language, activity, movement abnormalities, and social relatedness (Ritvo, 1976; Rutter, 1971a, 1971b) in children with autism and other types of severe developmental disturbances. For this, operationally defined rating scales (completed by researchers, teachers, and parents) and the Behavior Rating Instrument for Autistic Children have been used (Ruttenberg, 1974). Various ratings, and rank ordering of ratings, are related to CSF metabolite values, within and across diagnostic groups.

In comparison with children with nonautistic, early-onset psychosis, autistic children appear to have lower levels of CSF 5HIAA (D. J. Cohen et al., 1977b). Within the autistic group, there may be a subgroup with especially elevated levels of HVA, absolutely and in comparison with 5HIAA; these children appear to have the most deviant behavior, with increased stereotypy and hyperactivity. The opportunity to study a set of monozygotic twins concordant for childhood autism permitted evaluation of this relationship, controlling for genetic and familial sources of variance. Within this twinship, one twin consistently was more hyperactive and engaged in more stereotypic behavior (flapping and twirling). Both with and without the use of probenecid loading, his HVA levels were higher than his co-twin's. Both children were treated in a blind fashion with haloperidol: the child with the higher HVA tolerated a larger dose before displaying toxicity, manifested in part by walking about in circles. The relevance of this pharmacological observation will be discussed later.

These biochemical-behavioral correlations have suggested the hypothesis that, in autistic and other psychotic children, increased dopamine turnover may be associated with increased activity and abnormal movement patterns (stereotypic behavior). Interestingly, the concentration of 5HIAA appears to be inversely associated with these disabilities. In some areas, dopaminergic and serotonergic systems have opposing effects; thus, an inverse relationship with activity or stereotypy would suggest the modulating effect of serotonin (Kostrzewa et al., 1974; Samanin and Garattini, 1975). Also, there are suggestions from animal studies and psychopharmacological research with humans that sensory stimulation and responsiveness to environmental input are associated with increased serotonin turnover (Aghajanian et al., 1975; Sheerd and Aghajanian, 1968). Thus, relatively higher serotonin turnover in emotionally disturbed children may suggest that a child is more responsive to the environment. However, there are many points of question and conjecture. For example, it is possible that elevated HVA may be related to global dysfunction or severity, or that amine changes may be secondary to behavioral disturbance (Post and Goodwin, 1973).

The response of autistic children to medication may be of theoretical interest. By and large, autistic children respond to medications in the same manner as adults with schizophrenia or the multiple tic syndrome (to be described below): dopamine blocking or inhibiting compounds (such as the phenothiazines and haloperidol) reduce the severity of the syndrome while dopamine-releasing drugs (stimulants) exacerbate symptomatology. When phenothiazines (such as thioridazine) or haloperidol are effective for autistic children, the children show a decrease in stereotypic behavior, self-destructive repetitive acts (such as hand biting), bizarre behavior, and overall anxiety and disorganized activity. Of these, stereotypy and repetitive behaviors seem particularly sensitive. There may be improvement in social relatedness and greater availability for special education. When autistic children are treated with stimulants, their response may be as disastrous as the exacerbation of psychotic disturbances seen in adults with schizophrenia (Janowsky et al., 1973). Within 40–60 minutes after their second or third dose, autistic and severely atypical children become agitated, hold their hands over their ears, cry, moan, and walk about in circles; they often become remarkably distressed and disorganized.

These pharmacological observations are consistent with the important role of neurotransmitters in phenotypically dissimilar syndromes. To help clarify the nature of the different biochemical systems, it may be useful to study various neuropsychiatric disorders which share important features—e.g., attentional difficulties or abnormal movement patterns—with the childhood psychoses.

Epilepsy and Movement Disorders. In spite of methodological problems, certain diagnostic group differences are of special interest for child psychiatrists. For example, children with some forms of epilepsy appear to have marked reductions in biogenic amine metabolites (Shaywitz et al., 1975b). This reduction is consistent with the demonstration, in animals, that depletion of CNS amines reduces seizure threshold, and suggests new approaches to the diagnosis and treatment of complex seizure disorders in childhood. Similarly, the finding that HVA appears to be reduced in the CSF of children with Parkinson's disease may help delineate a subgroup responsive to L-dopa.

Children with the syndrome of chronic, multiple tics (generally designated with the poetic eponym of Gilles de la Tourette) have a characteristic history of many years of multiform, changing, ticlike motor behaviors of varying complexity (grimaces, head nods, shoulder jerks, hand tapping, gyrations, pacing, etc.) and unusual vocalizations (hissing, grunting, nonintelligible sounds, small words, and, occasionally, curse words) (Mahler, 1949; Moldofsky et al., 1974). Patients with this syndrome are almost always of normal intelligence and have good reality testing, and most manage to function in society in spite of their psychologically painful, compulsive handicap. Increased research and therapeutic interest has followed the discovery that haloperidol, a butyrophenone with wide use in psychiatry, may dramatically improve all aspects of the disorder (Ayd, 1974; Shapiro et al., 1973). Metabolically, haloperidol is a potent inhibitor of dopaminergic activity, possibly because of its effect on presynaptic dopaminergic neurons or its antagonist action at the dopamine receptor (L. L. Iverson, 1975). The clinical efficacy of haloperidol in Tourette's syndrome suggests that the ticlike or stereotypic behaviors may be related to dopaminergic overactivity.

A similar conclusion is supported by a variety of animal and pharmacological studies. For example, localized injection of dopamine-releasing agents, specific lesions involving dopaminergic pathways, and chemical blocks of dopaminergic pathways all suggest that dopamine metabolism is associated with stereotypy (e.g., see Garver et al., 1975; Randrup and Munkvad, 1970). Similarly, one clinically familiar effect of the chronic abuse of amphetamines (dopamine releasing drugs) is repetitive, meaningless activity.

Rather than having elevations of HVA in the CSF, following probenecid, children with the syndrome of chronic multiple tics appear to have either normal or slightly reduced levels of the dopamine metabolite and significantly reduced levels of the serotonin metabolite (D. J. Cohen et al., 1977c). There appears to be an inverse relation between the severity of the disorder and 5HIAA accumulation (especially the relation of 5HIAA to HVA turnover). The association between serotonergic and dopaminergic systems was demonstrated in an adult with chronic multiple tics treated with a short course of dextroamphetamine. With medication, the patient experienced a marked exacerbation of movement and phonic tics, accompanied by decreased CSF HVA and increased CSF 5HIAA. These findings suggested that the stimulant medication led to compensatory feedback inhibition of presynaptic dopaminergic neurons and mobilization of inhibitory serotonergic functioning. Possibly, the syndrome of Gilles de la Tourette involves both functional dopaminergic overactivity and serotonergic inhibitory underactivity, associated with supersensitivity of dopamine receptors or some other mechanism (D. J. Cohen et al., 1977c; Klawans and Margolin, 1975; Kostrzewa et al., 1974).

Occasional patients with chronic multiple tics who are unresponsive to haloperidol are helped by 5-hydroxytryptophan (which augments serontonergic systems) (van Woert et al., 1977b). As in studies of depression (Åsberg et al., 1976; Maas, 1975), future research may be able to delineate subgroups of patients with tics on the basis of metabolite concentrations (high or low HVA or 5HIAA), drug response (efficacy of haloperidol or tryptophan, or degree of exacerbation with stimulants), and clinical symptomatology (e.g., presence of self-destructive behavior or type of phonic tics). Similar observations on the relation between serotonin and dopamine mechanisms, and the effect of medication were raised in relation to childhood psychosis. In evaluating hypotheses, a number of research strategies will be required. One line of study will be described as an example of a research strategy in biological child psychiatry.

In the brain, dopamine-sensitive adenylate cyclase is located in postsynaptic neurons where it functions at the specific receptor site, leading to the synthesis of cyclic AMP when stimulated by dopamine (or dopaminelike chemicals). Cyclic AMP serves as the second messenger, translating the extracellular dopamine signal into intracellular physiological events (Daly, 1976; Greengard, 1976). Thus, the activity of the receptor may be reflected in the concentration of cyclic AMP in the CSF using probenecid blockade (Cramer et al., 1973). In theory, the presence of normal concentrations of HVA and elevated CSF cyclic AMP would be consistent with overactivity of the dopamine receptor. A ratio of HVA to cyclic AMP could be constructed to reflect presynaptic to postsynaptic signal modulation. However, the range of individual and group differences in amine and receptor settings may preclude valid assessment of the relation between these systems by simple, static determinations. The use of pharmacological intervention makes it possible to perform dynamic, physiological studies. Clinical observations of Tourette's syndrome have demonstrated that compounds which release and enhance dopamine (methylphenidate and dextroamphetamine) exacerbate the symptomatology while those which block dopaminergic activity (haloperidol) alleviate symptoms. CSF neurotransmitter metabolites (HVA, 5HIAA, and MHPG) and receptor functioning (cyclic AMP) may thus be simultaneously measured in three clinical states: when the patient is free of medication; when his disorder is exacerbated by dopamine releasers; and when he is clinically improved with haloperidol. Similar correlations between aspects of a disorder, CSF parameters, and drug intervention may assist in the evaluation of catecholaminergic involvement in various disorders (including the psychoses) where basal measurements have not provided definitive information.

Attentional Disorders. Dopaminergic disturbances have been hypothesized in another group of behavioral disturbances of childhood—minimal brain dysfunction (MBD), the hyperkinetic behavioral disturbance (HBD), or neuropsychiatric processing disorders. These children suffer from attentional difficulties, impulsivity, hyperactivity or unfocused motor behavior, and a variety of cognitive and perceptual problems (Cantwell, 1975; D. J. Cohen, 1976; Young, 1975). Some of these problems may be associated, on the basis of animal studies, with dopaminergic pathways, e.g., dysfunction involving the mesolimbic projection. The most compelling line of evidence linking MBD and the processing disorders with dopamine pathways, however, is the improvement in attention and behavioral regulation in many children treated with dopamine-releasing drugs, such as methylphenidate and dextroamphetamine (de la Cruz et al., 1973; Fish, 1971), although it is obvious that improvement with a particular medication does not necessarily indicate a preexisting deficiency state. The therapeutic efficacy of amphetamine in improving arousal, vigilance, and goal-directed performance, especially in children who are operating at a lower motivational state, is consistent with animal and adult pharmacology of the stimulants (Dews and Morse, 1961; B. Weiss and Laties, 1962).

Attempts to demonstrate a dopamine disturbance using urinary execretion of metabolites have so far been unrevealing. However, there has been a suggestion of reduced HVA following probenecid blockade in the CSF of some children with MBD (Shaywitz et al., 1975a, 1977). This finding is consistent with results using an animal model of the MBD phenotype produced by injecting newborn rat pups with 6-hydroxydopamine (Kostrzewa and Jacobowitz, 1974) which leads to preferential and permanent reduction of brain dopamine. Treated rats displayed a period of behavioral hyperactivity during the early phases of development and more lasting cognitive difficulties (Shaywitz et al., 1976a) with reduced activity when treated with stimulants (Shaywitz et al., 1976b). Another rat model has shown that amphetamine facilitates normal attachment behavior in immature animals but not in mature animals (B. Campbell and Randall, 1977).

Overview. There is a confluence of suggestions—from clinical observation, animal models, response to medication, and studies of CSF metabolites—that dopaminergic pathways are implicated in various types of behavioral disorders (Garver et al., 1975; Snyder et al., 1974). In childhood autism and severe atypical development, overactivity of dopaminergic pathways is indicated by response to medications and by metabolic-behavioral correlations. But this overactivity seems to be only one aspect of a complex disorder, and may follow upon some more basic CNS abnormality. For children with chronic multiple tics, pharmacological and comparative studies also suggest involvement of dopaminergic and serotonergic systems; however, the biochemical lesion appears more discrete, and the response to treatment may be more gratifying. For at least some children with attentional and processing disorders, a similar model seems appropriate; clinical experience with stimulants, animal models, and preliminary CSF findings suggest dopaminergic underactivity in some.

Yet, it is essential to remain cautious in the interpretation of this type of data. It is more accurate to suggest a role for dopaminergic overactivity in association with increased stereotypy in autistic children than to hypothesize that autism is the result of dopaminergic abnormalities. Similarly, the evidence for attentional disorders and multiple tic syndrome is suggestive: it is far from definitive. Much remains to be learned about functioning at other levels of neurological and behavioral organization in order to place the biogenic amine hypotheses in context.

Enzymes

Monoamine Oxidase (MAO). Studies of CSF metabolites focus on the end result of metabolic pathways. There are other points at which these systems may be studied (fig. 6). Several lines of evidence have implicated MAO in serious psychiatric disturbances of adulthood (Carpenter et al., 1975; Meltzer and Stahl, 1974; Murphy and Wyatt, 1972), and the availability of MAO in human platelets makes it particularly convenient for neuropsychiatric investigation. Reductions in platelet MAO activity have been found in about 50 percent of adults with prolonged schizophrenia and in both individuals in monozygotic twinships discordant for schizophrenia (Wyatt et al., 1973a). The central role of MAO in brain amine metabolism is also indicated by the usefulness of medications which inhibit MAO in the treatment of adult depression (MAO inhibitors and tricyclic antidepressants). However, there may be important differences in the control and function of MAO in peripheral platelets and in the CNS which must be considered in the interpretation of platelet data.

MAO has been studied in autistic and normal children and their families (M. Campbell et al., 1976; D. J. Cohen et al., 1977d; J. A. Roth et al., 1976). Test-retest studies indicate that the enzyme is a relatively stable biological marker, particularly in males, although there is a negative relation with age during the childhood years. In females, the effect of cyclic changes in hormone levels is apparent, but the sex difference in platelet MAO activity is present even in girls who have not entered puberty. The higher levels of MAO in females at all ages

(J. A. Roth et al., 1976) and the impact of estrogens (Holzbauer and Youdim, 1973) may have interesting implications for understanding the metabolic correlates of sex-related behavioral differences.

Platelet MAO activity is potentially a useful marker in studies of vulnerability for adult disorders, for investigation of the possible continuity between psychoses in childhood and adulthood, and for the delineation of subgroups among these disorders. The mean platelet MAO activity of a group of autistic children was not different from that of a group of normal children (D. J. Cohen et al., 1977d).

Twin and family studies demonstrate the strong genetic contributions to MAO activity in platelets (Nies et al., 1973). This genetic setting must be considered in evaluating the meaning of an individual's MAO level. For example, a child with a behavioral disturbance may have MAO activity within the normal range for children of his age; however, when seen in the context of his family's MAO, his level may be quite deviant. This fact—so obvious in relation to other biological indices, such as height—is easier to recognize than to study when invasive procedures (such as lumbar puncture) are required. Since platelet MAO activity may be determined by simple venipuncture, it has been possible to study it in parents and siblings of autistic children. The MAO levels of autistic children do not deviate from their family setting (D. J. Cohen et al., 1977d).

Similar genetic studies will be required for other biological markers.

Creatine Phosphokinase (CPK). While the search for metabolic correlates of psychiatric disorders has increasingly concentrated on CNS metabolism, it is possible that valuable clues may emerge from metabolic studies of other systems. One such observation has been the replicable finding of tenfold or higher elevations in serum CPK in acutely psychotic adults. There are various reasons why CPK, an enzyme involved in muscle energy metabolism, may be elevated in very disturbed patients, e.g., as the result of muscle trauma from injections or exercise. But these obvious artifacts probably have been excluded by careful clinical studies. The finding of elevated CPK has led to intensive investigation of neuromuscular changes in acute psychosis and to a puzzling finding of small changes in muscle and nerve structure (Meltzer, 1972, 1974; Meltzer and Crayton, 1974). How the behavioral and neuromuscular atypicalities are related remains a mystery.

While sudden bursts of exercise—such as running stairs or playing tennis—may elevate CPK in healthy young adults, the prolonged hyperactivity of autistic children does not. Their CPK levels are similar to normal siblings and age-mates.

Surprisingly, CPK in the blood of children with severe antisocial and aggressive personality disorders appears to be mildly elevated (D. J. Cohen et al., 1976b). The degree of elevation observed in these children is similar to the small, but significant, elevation which has been found in first-degree blood relatives of adults with acute psychosis. The elevations in both groups may suggest a vulnerability to the later development of psychosis, a fate to which severely disturbed children are prone (Garmezy, 1974). In the future, investigation of such biological markers, integrated with clinical and longitudinal studies, may lead to sophisticated multivariate models of vulnerability (D. J. Cohen, 1974; Garmezy, 1972).

Diagnostic Issues

The lack of clear criteria for differential diagnosis poses major dilemmas in biological studies of childhood disorders. On the one hand, biological measures may assist clinical investigators in separating phenotypically similar syndromes into subgroups, as is now becoming increasingly possible in the classification of adult depressions on the basis of urinary MHPG and CSF metabolites (Maas, 1974). On the other hand, subtle biological differences between syndromes may be blurred when different subgroups are initially intermixed. Discrepancies in the literature may also result from different diagnostic criteria and from such practical questions as how well an investigator studies his patients before classification. In the quest for large samples, detailed clinical study may be short-circuited. This diagnostic muddle is nowhere more clear than in relation to so-called minimal cerebral dysfunction. Are one investigator's MBD patients the same as another's hyperactive, attentionally disordered, or learning-disabled children? Are the upset children from disturbed families appropriately classified with the disruptive, inattentive children from stable families, even if both groups respond to similar kinds of intervention? (D. J. Cohen et al., 1975; D. J. Cohen, 1976; Satterfield et al., 1974; Wender, 1971; Young, 1975; Zahn et al., 1975).

The problems associated with diagnosis are well exemplified by a current controversy concerning the uptake and efflux of serotonin by the platelets of autistic children.

During the 1950s and 1960s, many investigators studied the possible role of abnormal serotonin metabolism in adult schizophrenia and other disorders. This interest led to studies of indoleamines in autistic and other psychotic children and the discovery of a group of retarded, autistic children with elevated blood serotonin (Coleman, 1973; Lucas et al., 1971; Ritvo et al., 1970; Sankar, 1970; Schain and Freedman, 1961; Yuwiler et al., 1971).

Because serotonin is concentrated in platelets, the platelet model has been used extensively in research with autism (Stahl, 1977). In Down's syndrome, there is a well-defined defect in active transport across the platelet membrane resulting in reduced levels of serotonin (Bayer and McCoy, 1974; McCoy et al., 1974). There have been attempts to define similar abnormalities in membrane function in platelets of autistic children. In 1970, Boullin, Coleman, and O'Brien reported that efflux of serotonin from platelets was markedly elevated in six autistic children compared to normal controls. The autistic children satisfied the usual diagnostic criteria and, critically, had scores of greater than +20 on the Rimland E-2 diagnostic checklist. This study was repeated in a blind fashion with psychotic children who had E-2 scores above +20 (Kanner's syndrome) and as controls, psychotic children with lower scores (autisticlike children) (Boullin et al., 1971). The results again indicated abnormal elevations of platelet efflux of serotonin in autistic children, a finding often cited as the only replicable biochemical abnormality of childhood autism. Further replications using larger samples were essential. Another group of investigators attempted a replication using careful biochemical methods. Unfortunately, their findings failed to confirm the original differences between autistic and normal children's platelet efflux (Yuwiler et al., 1975).

Were the autistic children studied by both groups similar? One of the original investigators, Rimland, believed they were not (Rimland, 1977). The Yuwiler et al. study did not define the autistic population by the Rimland E-2 checklist and included children whose psychological disturbance in perceptual constancy was, according to Rimland, inconsistent with the diagnosis of childhood autism by his criteria. If they were autisticlike, Yuwiler's sample was similar to the "control" psychotic children of the second Boullin et al. study (1971) for whom the original investigators would predict normal efflux of serotonin. Rimland (1977) thus denied the relevance of the Yuwiler et al. (1975) study to the original hypothesis.

Carefully described populations, truly collaborative studies, sharing of videotapes and other data, and the development of new procedures for diagnostic assessment may reduce the likelihood of such controversies. Without advances in diagnosis and in organization of research, it is possible that important findings may be discredited by inadequate replications, that spurious results may enter the scientific literature, or that valuable findings will stand in isolation without opportunity for further confirmation or development by various research groups. These difficulties characterize the history of research in childhood psychosis.

Diet and the Brain

Many well-defined physical and behavioral syndromes are related to gross disturbances in diet, to the inability appropriately to utilize food, to unusual physiological reactions to normal dietary constituents, or to dietary deficiencies at crucial periods of development. Familiar examples are pellagra and pernicious anemia, malabsorption syndromes, favism and other inborn errors of metabolism, protein-calorie malnutrition (Kwashiorkor), and true reactive hypoglycemia. Some conditions respond dramatically to dietary management or replacement—e.g., injections of Vitamin B_{12}, gluten-free diets, avoidance of the fava bean, control of carbohydrate intake. In addition, there are commonsense observations on the importance of reasonable diet for optimal performance in childhood, e.g., that hungry children are less likely to concentrate in school. There is increasing popular interest in the relation between diet and behavior. Research on the impact of subtle dietary variations on long-term behavioral change is, however methodologically difficult, and few, if any, studies have been done in childhood in which description of method, results, and controls have approached rigorous standards. Until such studies are reported, there are no grounds for authentic, scientific judgments concerning clinical care.

Investigations with animal models have demonstrated an "openness" of brain neurotransmitter metabolism to the influence of dietary precursor availability (Wurtman and Fernstrom, 1976). Brain concentration of serotonin is partially controlled by the availability of dietary tryptophan (Green and Grahame-Smith, 1976). This regulatory system is dependent on an active transport system for the precursor into the brain, for which tryptophan must compete with other neutral amino acids. Tryptophan uptake into the brain is affected by the amount of ingested protein, and its amino acid composition, as well as by alterations in concentrations of plasma amino acids which result from the release of insulin following ingestion of carbohydrates (Fernstrom and Wurtman, 1972). Tyrosine and phenylalanine compete with tryptophan for the carrier system, and the brain uptake of tyrosine appears to affect the synthesis of catecholamines (Wurtman et al., 1974). Acetylcholine is more sensitive to diet than indoleamines and catecholamines. Augmenting dietary choline increases ACh synthesis and release at the synapse, altering postsynaptic dopaminergic function (e.g., in the caudate, where the concentration of the catecholamine-synthesizing enzyme, tyrosine hydroxylase, increases in response to choline administration) (Ulus and Wurtman, 1976). The sensitivity of the cholinergic system to dietary manipulation is therapeutically useful in the treatment of tardive dyskinesia, a movement disorder associated with chronic use of neuroleptics. The amelioration of this syndrome with choline suggests an underlying imbalance between cholinergic and dopaminergic activity in the striatum (as in Parkinson's disease). In addition to precursors, the availability of dietary vitamins (which serve as cofactors in the synthesis of neurotransmitters) and inorganic ions has a clearly defined impact on CNS metabolism.

The role of neurotransmitters in the monitoring of fluctuations of metabolic state is evident in the hypothalamic control of satiety and hunger. Depletion or disruption of indoleamine and catecholamine pathways leads to profound disturbances in eating and in body weight (Breisch et al., 1976; Saller and Stricker, 1976). The availability of precursors and other compounds necessary for normal neuronal functioning may enter into complex feedback systems and affect organized behavior patterns (such as food-seeking). The anorectant effect of stimulants appears to depend on such mechanisms, and the significance of neurotransmitter metabolism for studies of disorders of eating and mood (such as anorexia nervosa and forms of obesity) is a promising new area of study.

Diet and Methodological Artifact. Issues concerning diet have important methodological implications in the study of psychopathology. Skeptics have often noted that the biological study of schizophrenia has frequently turned out to be the study of artifacts—drugs, environmental experiences of severely ill individuals, as well as what patients eat and don't eat. There are many differences between the lives of severely disturbed and normal children, too, and biological studies of childhood are no less likely to be misled by "accidents" which accompany developmental disturbances. Some of these artifacts may be avoided by scrupulous consideration of the effects of medication, which may persist for weeks or months after discontinuation and assessment of the impact of diet on amino acids, minerals, and vitamins associated with CNS metabolism (e.g., by measuring blood levels of substances such as phenylalanine, choline, iron, and folate). Other differences between "normals" and "index patients" are intrinsic to the problems being studied and may affect biological studies, e.g., differences in social stimulation, frequency of rejection, opportunities for successful coping with painful affects, or gross physical activity. Because of the multiplicity of differences and the difficulties of research, in practice it is often quite difficult to construct rigorous control and contrast groups. Investigators can only try to do their best, and interpret with caution. However, there are other differences which may remain unnoticed for too long, with both practical and scientific importance. What is eaten by a child is a good example.

Autistic children, it is well known, often have odd diets. During their early years, they may avoid solids or particular foods, such as meats; one food fad may follow another (e.g., craving for spiced or salty meats or avoidance of liquids). Diet may, of course, have a significant impact on CNS metabolism, especially if there are major abnormalities in the availability of vitamins (or their relative deficiency) or essential amino acids (Herbert and Tisman, 1973). Such alterations are likely to occur in childhood autism. As an example, we have studied one autistic child during a period of excitement and months later when acutely depressed; in the intervening period, he was hospitalized, became withdrawn and agitated, stopped eating, and lost weight. Assay of blood and CFS revealed a serious folic acid deficiency and a change of CSF amine metabolities. For this one child, it was not possible to determine the specific relationship between clinical state, diet, and altered amine metabolism. However, the general importance of folic acid in CNS metabolism is clear, and we have since found a number of severely disturbed children with reduced levels. While minor or even moderate reductions of folate (or other vitamins) may have little impact on behavior of children with preexisting developmental difficulties, it is possible that such deviations from normal may lead to significant artifacts in biological studies.

Just as they have odd food habits, autistic children may ingest inedible objects (such as dirt, leaves, paper, and twigs) and mouth objects of all sorts. In retarded and normal children, continuing pica leads to blood lead determination. Even "subclinical" levels of lead may have behavioral and neurological effects (de la Burdé and Choate, 1972; Feldman et al., 1973; Needleman, 1973). Yet, autistic children are rarely screened. Studies of blood lead in developmentally disabled and normal children have revealed that, as a group, autistic children have elevated blood lead which, in some cases, have been found to be well above the toxic range (D. J. Cohen et al., 1976a). Because of their global difficulties, autistic children may not show the usual behavioral signs of lead toxicity, and parents, teachers, and clinicians may overlook subtle changes in attention, irritability, or episodes of cramps.

The clinical value of screening autistic children with pica for lead, and perhaps other metals, is obvious. Scientifically, the presence of elevated lead in this population is an example of the type of unpredicted variable which may become a research artifact. It is an especially relevant example since lead is a potent inhibitor of many enzymes—including such brain enzymes as adenylate cyclase—and differences in lead between clinical groups may result in finding differences in their amine metabolism (Nathanson and Bloom, 1975; Sauerhoff and Michaelson, 1973; Snowdon and Sanderson, 1974).

Future studies will, no doubt, reveal other methodological pitfalls, as well as other ways in which diet may affect behavioral regulation.

Prospects

Advances in neurochemistry will become increasingly meaningful to clinicians as they integrate biochemical knowledge with information from other areas (e.g., Mason, 1968; Wyatt et al., 1971). Studies of psychosocial dwarfism, anorexia nervosa, depression, and normal adolescent development, for example, offer particularly clear areas for integration of neurochemical, endocrine, and clinical data (Cytryn et al., 1974; D. J. Cohen and Frank, 1975; Sachar, 1975a, 1975b). There are promising new developments in neuroendocrinology (e.g., in the dopaminergic regulation of prolactin secretion) and in pharmacodynamics (e.g., in the metabolic fate of stimulant medications) which appear especially relevant to studies of childhood psychopathology.

The discovery of a class of extremely potent, naturally occurring compounds, the endorphins and enkephalins, which affect sensory and emotional processing, has raised the possibility that they may be involved in modulating pain and pleasure. The turning away from sensory stimulation and the unusual sensitivities of some autistic children, the hypervigilance of individuals with organic and "functional" psychoses, the anhedonia which accompanies various depressive syndromes, the nature of drug dependency, and other clinical phenomena suggest themselves as subjects to be investigated in light of emerging knowledge of the peptide neurotransmitters. The potential of reversal of opioid peptide activity with antagonists of morphine, and for augmentation with agonist compounds, will, no doubt, stimulate a new epoch in clinical research.

In addition to the paths opened by basic research, child psychiatrists have available to them very sensitive research settings for studying brain-behavior relationships—their offices and clinics (D. J. Cohen, 1975). There are hundreds of thousands of children receiving psychoactive medication, and the observation and description of the effects of medication in ecologically relevant environments (such as the school and home) are of theoretical and practical interest. Clinicians who prescribe and care for children on medication are in the best position to learn about long-term effects and the acute impact of metabolism-altering compounds; their careful observations cannot be replaced by laboratory studies and are essential for the advancement of pediatric psychopharmacology.

REFERENCES

Abrams, W. B. & Solomon, H. M. (1969), The human platelet as a pharmacologic model for the adrenergic neuron. *Clin. Pharm. Ther.*, 10:702–709.

Aghajanian, G. K. (1972), LSD and CNS transmission. *Ann. Rev. Pharm.*, 12:157–168.

—— Haigler, H. J., & Bennett, J. L. (1975), Amine receptors in CNS: III. In: *Handbook of Psychopharmacology*, ed. L. L. Iverson, S. D. Iverson, & S. Snyder. New York: Plenum Press, 6:63–96.

Antelman, S. M. & Caggiula, A. R. (1977), Norepinephrine-dopamine interactions and behavior. *Science*, 195:646–653.

Åsberg, M., Thoren, P., Träskman, L. I., Bertilsson, L., & Ringberger, V. (1976), "Serotonin depression." *Science*, 191:478–480.

Axelrod, J. (1966), Methylation reactions in the formation and metabolism of catecholamines and other biogenic amines. *Pharm. Rev.*, 18:95–113.

—— (1971), Noradrenaline. *Science*, 173:598–606.

—— (1972), Dopamine-B-hydroxylase. *Pharm. Rev.*, 24:233–243.

—— (1974a), Neurotransmitters. *Sci. American*, 230:58–71.

—— (1974b), The pineal gland. *Science*, 184:1341–1348.

—— & Cohn, C. K. (1971), Methyltransferase enzymes in red blood cells. *J. Pharm. Exp. Ther.*, 176:650–654.

—— Mueller, R. A., Henry, J. P., & Stephens, P. M. (1970), Changes in enzymes involved in the biosynthesis and metabolism of noradrenaline and adrenaline after psychosocial stimulation. *Nature*, 225:1059–1060.

—— & Tomchick, R. (1958), Enzymatic O-methylation of epinephrine and other catechols. *J. Biol. Chem.* 233:702–705.

Ayd, F. J., Jr. (1974), Haloperidol. *Dis. Nerv. Syst.*, 33:459–469.

Balch, T. S., Chase, T. N. & Jacobowitz, D. M. (1973), Dopamine histofluorescence. *Brain Res.*, 52:419–423.

Barbeau, A. (1974), Drugs affecting movement disorders. *Ann. Rev. Pharm.*, 14.91–113.

Barchas, J. & Usdin, E. (1973), *Serotonin and Behavior*. New York: Academic Press.

Bayer, S. M. & McCoy, E. E. (1974), Serotonin uptake and adenine nucleotide metabolism in platelets of Down's syndrome patients. *Biochem. Med.*, 9:232–255.

Beaven, M. A. (1975), Radiochemical assay procedures for drugs and transmitters. In: *Handbook of Psychopharmacology*, ed. L. L. Iversen, S. D. Iversen, & S. H. Snyder. New York: Plenum Press, 1:253–290.

Björklund, A., Nobin, A., & Stenevi, U. (1973), The use of neurotoxic dihydroxytryptamines as tools for morphological studies and localized lesioning of central indolamine neurons. *Z. Zellforsch*, 145:479–501.

Black, I. B. & Geen, S. C. (1975), Postmortem changes in brain catecholamine enzymes. *Arch. Neurol.*, 32:47–49.

Bloom, F. E. (1972), Localization of neurotransmitters by electron microscopy. *Proc. Assoc. Res. Nerv. Ment. Dis.*, Research publication #50:25–57.

—— Segal, D., Ling, N., & Guillemin, R. (1976), Endorphins. *Science*, 194:630–632.

Born, G. V. R. & Gillson, R. E. (1959), Studies on the uptake of 5-hydroxytryptamine by blood platelets. *J. Physiol.*, 146:472–491.

Boullin, D. J., Coleman, M., & O'Brien, R. A. (1970), Abnormalities in platelet 5-hydroxytryptamine efflux in patients with infantile autism. *Nature*, 226:371–372.

——— ——— & Rimland, B. (1971), Laboratory predictions of infantile autism based on 5-hydroxytryptamine efflux from blood platelets and their correlation with the Rimland E-2 score. *J. Aut. Child. Schizo.*, 1:63–71.

Bowers, M. B., Jr. (1972), Clinical measurement of central dopamine and 5-hydroxytryptamine metabolism. *Neuropharmacology*, 11:101–111.

—— Heninger, G. P., & Gerbode, F. A. (1969), Cerebrospinal fluid 5-hydroxyindoleacetic acid and homovanillic acid in psychiatric patients. *Int. J. Neurpharm.*, 8:255–262.

Breese, G. R. (1975), Chemical and immunochemical lesions by specific neurotoxic substances and antisera. In: *Handbook of Psychopharmacology*, ed. L. L. Iversen, S. D. Iversen, & S. H. Snyder. New York: Plenum Press, 1:137–189.

Breisch, S. T., Zemlan, F., & Hoebel, B. (1976), Hyperphagia and obesity following serotonin depletion by intraventricular P-cholorophenylalanine. *Science*, 192:382–385.

Brodie, B. E., Costa, E., Dlabac, A., Neff, N. H., & Smookler, H. H. (1966), Application of steady state kinetics to the estimation of synthesis rate and turnover time of tissue catecholamines. *J. Pharm. Exp. Ther.*, 154:493–498.

Bryson, C. Q. & Hingtgen, J. N. (1971), *Early Childhood Psychosis*. Rockville, Md.:, National Institute of Mental Health.

Byck, R. (1976), Peptide transmitters. *Lancet*, 2:72–73.

Campbell, B. & Randall, P. J. (1977), Paradoxical effects of amphetamine on preweanling and postweanling rats. *Science*, 195:888–891.

Campbell, M., Friedman, E., Green, W. H., Small, A. M., & Burdock, E. I. (1976), Blood platelet monoamine oxidase activity in schizophrenic children and their families. *Neuropsychobiology*, 2:239–246.

Cantwell, D. P. (1975), *The Hyperactive Child*. New York: Halsted Press.

Carpenter, W. T., Jr., Murphy, D. L., & Wyatt, R. J. (1975), Platelet monoamine oxidase activity in acute schizophrenia. *Amer. J. Psychiat.*, 132:438–441.

Chalmers, J. P. & Wurtman, R. J. (1971), Participation of central noradrenergic neurons in arterial baroreceptor reflexes in the rabbit. *Circ. Res.*, 28:480–491.

Chase, T. N., Gordon, E. K., & Ng, L. K. Y. (1973), Norepinephrine metabolism in the central nervous system of man. *J. Neurochem.*, 21:581–587.

—— Murphy, D. L. (1973), Serotonin and central nervous system function. *Ann. Rev. Pharmac.*, 13:181–197.

Clement-Cormier, Y. C., Kebabian, J. W., Petzold, G. L., & Greengard, P. (1974), Dopamine-sensitive adenylate cyclase in mammalian brain. *Proc. Nat. Acad. Sci. USA*, 71:1113–1117.

Cohen, D. J. (1974), Competence and biology. In: *The Child in His Family*, ed. E. J. Anthony & C. Koupernik, New York: Wiley, 3:361–394.

—— (1975), Psychosomatic models of development. In: *Explorations in Child Psychiatry*, ed. E. J. Anthony, New York: Plenum Press, pp. 197–212.

—— (1976), The diagnostic process in child psychiatry. *Psychiat. Ann.*, 6:404–416.

—— Caparulo, B. K., Shaywitz, B. A., & Bowers, M. B., Jr. (1977a), Assessment of cerebrospinal monoamine metabolites in children using the probenecid method. *Israel Ann. Psychiat.* (in press).

—— —— —— —— (1977b), Dopamine and serotonin in neuropsychiatrically disturbed children. *Arch. Gen. Psychiat.*, 34:545–550.

—— & Frank, R. (1975), Preadolescence. In: *Mental Health in Children*, ed. D. V. S. Sankar. Westbury, N.Y.: PJD Publications, pp. 129–165.

—— Granger, R. H., Provence, S. A., & Solnit, A. J. (1975), Mental health services. In: *Issues in the Classification of Children*, ed. N. Hobbs, San Francisco: Jossey-Bass, pp. 88–122.

—— Johnson, W. T., & Caparulo, B. K. (1976a), Pica and elevated blood lead level in autistic and atypical children. *Amer. J. Dis. Child.*, 130:47–48.

—— —— —— & Young, J. G. (1976b), Creatine phosphokinase (CPA) levels in children with severe developmental disturbances. *Arch. Gen. Psychiat.*, 33:683–686.

—— Shaywitz, B. A., Caparulo, B. K., Young, J. G., & Bowers, M. B., Jr. (1977c), The syndrome of chronic multiple tics of Gilles de la Tourette (submitted for publication).

—— —— —— Johnson, W. T. & Bowers, M., Jr. (1974), Biogenic amines in autistic and atypical children. *Arch. Gen. Psychiat.*, 31:845–853.

—— Young, J. G., & Roth, J. A. (1977d), Platelet monoamine oxidase in early childhood autism. *Arch. Gen. Psychiat.* (in press).

Cohen, E. L. & Wurtman, R. J. (1976), Brain acetylcholine. *Science*, 191:561–562.

Coleman, M. (1973), Serotonin and central nervous systems syndromes of childhood. *J. Aut. Child. Schizo.*, 3:27–35.

—— & Mahanand, D. (1973), Baseline serotonin levels in Down's syndrome patients. In: *Serotonin in Down's Syndrome*, ed. M. Coleman. New York: American Elsevier, pp. 5–24.

Collins, G. G. S. & Sandler, M. (1971), Human blood platelet monoamine oxidase. *Biochem. Pharm.*, 20:289–296.

Cooper, J. R., Bloom, F. E., & Roth, R. H. (1974), *The Biochemical Basis of Neuropharmacology.* New York: Oxford University Press.

Costa, E. & Meek, J. L. (1974), Regulation of biosynthesis of catecholamines and serotonin in the CNS, *Ann. Rev. Pharm.*, 14:491–511.

Coyle, J. T. (1975), A practical introduction to radiometric enzymatic assays in psychopharmacology. In: *Handbook of Psychopharmacology*, ed. L. L. Iversen, S. D. Iversen, & S. H. Snyder, New York: Plenum Press, 1:71–99.

Cramer, H., Ng, L. K. Y. & Chase, T. N. (1973), Adenosine 3', 5'-monophosphate in cerebrospinal fluid. *Arch. Neurol.*, 29:197–199.

Cryer, P. E. & Weiss, S. (1976), Reduced plasma norepinephrine response to standing in autonomic dysfunction. *Arch. Neurol.*, 33:275–277.

Cytryn, L., McKnew, D. H., Logue, M., & Desai, J. B. (1974), Biochemical correlates of affective disorders in children. *Arch. Gen. Psychiat.*, 31:659–661.

Dahlström, A. & Fuxe, K. (1965), Evidence for the existence of monoamine neurons in the central nervous system. *Acta Physiol. Scand.* (Suppl. 247), 64:1–85.

Daly, J. W. (1976), The nature of receptors regulating the formation of cyclic AMP in brain tissue. *Life Sci.*, 18:1349–1358.

Davis, J. M. (1975), Critique of single amine theories. In: *Biology of the Major Psychoses*, ed. D. X Freedman. New York: Raven Press, pp. 333–342.

de la Burdé, B. & Choate, M. S., Jr. (1972), Does asymptomatic lead exposure in children have latent sequelae? *J. Pediat.*, 81:1088–1091.

de la Cruz, F. F., Fox, B. H., & Roberts, R. H., eds. (1973), *Minimal Brain Dysfunction.* *Ann. N.Y. Acad. Sci.*, Vol. 205.

Dews, P. B. & Morse, W. H. (1961), Behavioral pharmacology. *Ann. Rev. Pharm.*, 1:145–174.

Doba, N. & Reis, D. J. (1974), Role of central and peripheral adrenergic mechanisms in neurogenic hypertension produced by brainstem lesions in rat. *Circ. Res.,* 34:293–301.

Eleftheriou, B. E. & Boehlke, K. W. (1967), Brain monoamine oxidase in mice after exposure to aggression and defeat. *Science,* 155:1693–1694.

Euler, U. S. von (1972), Synthesis, uptake and storage of catecholamines in adrenergic nerves. In *Catecholamines,* ed. H. Blaschko & E. Muscholl. New York: Springer Verlag, pp. 186–230.

Extein, I., Korf, J., Roth, R. H., & Bowers, M. B., Jr. (1973), Accumulation of 3-methoxy-4-hydroxyphenylglycol-sulfate in rabbit cerebrospinal fluid following probenecid. *Brain Res.,* 54:403–407.

Falck, B., Hillarp, N.-A., Thieme, G., & Torp, A. (1962), Fluorescence of catecholamines and related compounds condensed with formaldehyde. *J. Histochem. Cytochem.,* 10:348–354.

Feldman, R. G., Haddow, J., Kopito, L., & Schwachman, H. (1973), Altered peripheral nerve conduction velocity. *Amer. J. Dis. Child.,* 125:39–41.

Fernstrom, J. D. (1974), Modification of brain serotonin by diet. *Ann. Rev. Med.,* 25:1–8.

——— & Wurtman, R. J. (1972), Brain serotonin content. *Science,* 178:414–416.

Fish, B. (1971), The "one child, one drug" myth of stimulants in hyperkinesis. *Arch. Gen. Psychiat.,* 25:193–203.

——— & Ritvo, E. R. (1977), Childhood psychosis. In: *Handbook of Child Psychiatry,* ed. J. Noshpitz (in press).

Freedman, D. X., Giarman, N. H., & Lovell, R. A. (1971). Psychotomimetic drugs and brain 5-hydroxyindole metabolism. *Biochem. Pharm.,* 19:1181–1188.

Fuxe, K. & Jonsson, G. (1974), Further mapping of central 5-hydroxytryptamine neurons. In: *Serotonin—New Vistas,* ed. E. Costa, G. L. Gessa, & M. Sandler. New York: Raven Press, 10:1–12.

Gál, E. M. (1974), Tryptophan 5-hydroxylase. In: *Serotonin—New Vistas,* ed. E. Costa, G. L. Gessa, & M. Sandler. New York: Raven Press, 11:1–11.

Garmezy, N. (1972), Models of etiology for the study of children at risk for schizophrenia. In: *Life History Research in Psychopathology,* ed. M. Roff, L. Robbins, & M. Pollack. Minneapolis: University of Minnesota Press, 2:9–23.

——— (1974), Children at risk: The search for the antecedents of schizophrenia. Parts I & II. *Schizo. Bull.,* 8:14–90; 9:55–125.

Garver, D. L., Schlemmer, R. F., Jr., Maas, J. W., & Davis, J. M. (1975), A schizophreniform behavioral psychosis mediated by dopamine. *Amer. J. Psychiat.,* 132:33–38.

Giarman, N. J. & Freedman, D. X. (1965), Biochemical aspects of the actions of psychotomimetric drugs. *Pharm. Rev.,* 17:1–25.

Gillis, C. N. & Roth, J. A. (1976), Pulmonary disposition of circulating vasoactive hormones. *Biochem. Pharm.,* 25:2547–2553.

Glazer, H. I., Weiss, J. M., Pohorecky, L. A. & Miller, N. E. (1975), Monoamines as mediators of avoidance-escape behavior. *Psychosom. Med.,* 37:535–543.

Goldstein, A. (1976), Opioid peptides (endorphins) in pituitary and brain. *Science,* 193:1081–1086.

Goldstein, M. Freedman, L. A., & Bonnay, M. (1971), An assay for dopamine-B-hydroxylase activity in tissues and serum. *Experientia,* 27:632–633.

Goodall, M. C. (1959), Metabolic products of adrenaline and noradrenaline in human urine. *Pharm. Rev.,* 11:416–425.

Goodwin, F. K. & Post, R. M. (1975), Studies of amine metabolism in affective illness and schizophrenia. In: *Biology of the Major Psychoses,* ed. D. X. Freedman. New

York: Raven Press, 54:299–332.

Green, A. R. & Grahame-Smith, D. G. (1976), Effects of drugs on the processes regulating the functional activity of brain 5-hydroxytryptamine. *Nature,* 260:487–491.

Greengard, P. (1976), Possible role for cyclic nucleotides and phosphorylated membrane proteins in postsynaptic actions of neurotransmitters. *Nature,* 260:101–108.

—— McAfee, D. A., & Kebabian, J. W. (1972), On the mechanism of action of cyclic AMP and its role in synaptic transmission. In: *Advances in Cyclic Nucelotide Research,* ed. P. Greengard & G. A. Robinson. New York: Raven Press, 1:337–355.

Groves, P. M., Wilson, C. J., Young, S. J., & Rebec, G. V. (1975), Self-inhibition by dopaminergic neurons, *Science,* 190:522–529.

Guillemin, R. (1977), Endorphins, brain, and peptides that act like opiates. *New Eng. J. Med.,* 296:226–228.

Guldberg, H. C. & Marsden, C. A. (1975), Catcchol-O-methyl transferase. *Pharm. Rev.,* 27:135–206.

Guthrie, R. D. & Wyatt, R. J. (1975), Biochemistry and schizophrenia: III. *Schizo. Bull.,* 12:18–32.

Harvey, J. A., Heller, A., & Moore, R. Y. (1963), The effect of unilateral and bilateral medial forebrain bundle lesions on brain serotonin. *J. Pharm. Exp. Ther.,* 140:103–110.

Henry, D. P., Starman, B. J., Johnson, D. G., & Williams, R. H. (1975), A sensitive radioenzymatic assay for norepinephrine in tissues and plasma. *Life Sci.,* 16:375–384.

Herbert, V. & Tisman, G. (1973), Effects of deficiencies of folic acid and Vitamin B_{12} on central nervous system function and development. In: *Biology of Brain Dysfunction,* ed. G. E. Gaull, New York: Plenum Press, 1:373–392.

Hillarp, N.-A., Fuxe, K., & Dahlström, A. (1966), Demonstration and mapping of central neurons containing dopamine, noradrenaline, and 5-hydroxytryptamine and their reaction to psychopharmaca. *Pharm. Rev.,* 18:727–741.

Hingtgen, J. N., & Bryson, C. Q. (1972), Recent developments in the study of early childhood psychoses, *Schizo. Bull.,* 5:8–54.

Hökfelt, T. (1973), Neuronal catecholamine storage vesicles. In: *Frontiers in Catecholamine Research,* ed. E. Usdin & S. Snyder. New York: Pergamon Press, pp. 439–446.

—— Fuxe, K., Goldstein, M., & Johansson, O. (1974a), Immunohistochemical evidence for the existence of adrenaline neurons in the rat brain. *Brain Res.,* 66:235–251.

—— Ljungdahl, A., Fuxe, K., & Johansson, O. (1974b), Dopamine nerve terminals in the rat limbic cortex. *Science,* 184:177–179.

Holzbauer, M. & Youdim, M. B. H. (1973), The oestrous cycle and monoamine oxidase activity. *Brit. J. Pharm.,* 48:600–608.

Hornykiewicz, O. (1966), Dopamine (3-hydroxytyramine) and brain function. *Pharm. Rev.,* 18:925–964.

—— (1973), Metabolism of dopamine and L-DOPA in human brain. In: *Frontiers in Catecholamine Research,* ed. E. Usdin & S. Snyder. New York: Pergamon Press, pp. 1101–1107.

—— (1974), Some remarks concerning the possible role of brain monoamines (dopamine, noradrenaline, serotonin) in mental disorders. *J. Psychiat. Res.,* 11:249–253.

—— (1976), Neurohumoral interactions and basal ganglia function and dysfunction. In: *The Basal Ganglia,* ed. M. D. Yahr. New York: Raven Press, pp. 269–278.

Hughes, J., Smith, T. W., Kosterlitz, H. W., Fothergill, L. A., Morgan, B. A., & Morris,

H. R. (1975), Identification of two related pentapeptides from the brain with potent opiate agonist activity. *Nature,* 258:577–579.

Iversen, L. L. (1967), The Uptake and Storage of Noradrenaline in Sympathetic Nerves. London: Cambridge University Press.

—— (1971), Role of transmitter uptake mechanisms in synaptic neurotransmission. *Brit. J. Pharm.,* 41:571–591.

—— (1975), Dopamine receptors in the brain. *Science,* 188:1084–1089.

—— Iversen, S. D., & Snyder, S. H., eds. (1975), *Handbook of Psychopharmacology,* Vol. 4. New York: Plenum Press.

—— —— —— (1976), *Handbook of Psychopharmacology, Section II: Behavioral Pharmacology in Animals.* New York: Plenum Press.

Iversen, S. D., & Iversen, L. L. (1975), *Behavioral Pharmacology.* New York: Oxford University Press.

Jacquet, Y. F., & Marks, N. (1976), The C-fragment of beta-lipotropin. *Science,* 194:632–635.

Janowsky, D. S., El-Yousef, M. K., Davis, J. M., & Sekerke, H. J. (1973), Provocation of schizophrenic symptoms by intravenous administration of methylphenidate. *Arch. Gen. Psychiat.,* 28:185–191.

Jouvet, M. (1969), Biogenic amines and the states of sleep. *Science,* 163:32–41.

Kanner, L. (1973), *Childhood Psychosis.* Washington, D. C.: Winston & Sons.

Kaufman, S. & Friedman, S. (1965), Dopamine-B-hydroxylase. *Pharm. Rev.,* 17:71–100.

Klawans, H. & Margolin, D. (1975), Amphetamine-induced dopaminergic hypersensitivity in guinea pigs. *Arch. Gen. Psychiat.,* 32:724–732.

Koelle, G. B. (1975), Neurohumoral transmission and the autonomic nervous system. In: *The Pharmacological Basis of Therapeutics,* ed. L. S. Goodman & A. Gilman. New York: Macmillan, pp. 404–444.

Kopin, I. J. (1964), Storage and metabolism of catecholamines. *Pharm. Rev.,* 16:179–191.

—— (1968), False adrenergic transmitters. *Ann. Rev. Pharm.,* 8:377–394.

—— (1972), Metabolic degradation of catecholamines. In: *Catecholamines,* ed. H. Blaschko & E. Muscholl, New York: Springer Verlag, pp. 270–282.

Korf, J. & van Praag, H. M. (1971), Amine metabolism in the human brain. *Brain, Res.,* 35:221-230.

Kostrzewa, R. M. & Jacobowitz, D. M. (1974), Pharmacological actions of 6-hydroxydopamine. *Pharm. Rev.,* 26:200–288.

—— Samanin, R., Bareggi, S. R., Marc, V., Garattini, S., & Valzelli, L. (1974), Biochemical aspects of the interaction between midbrain raphe and locus coeruleus in the rat. *Brain Res.,* 82:178–182.

Krnjevic, K. (1975), Acetylcholine receptors in vertebrate CNS. In: *Handbook of Psychopharmacology,* ed. L. L. Iversen, S. D. Iversen, & S. H. Snyder, New York: Plenum Press, 6:97–126.

Laduron, P. (1975), Scope and limitation in dopamine-B-hydroxylase measurement. *Biochem. Pharm.,* 24:557–562.

Lake, C. R., Ziegler, M. G., Coleman, M. D., & Kopin, I. J. (1977), Age-adjusted plasma norepinephrine levels are similar in normotensive and hypertensive subjects. *New Eng. J. Med.,* 296:208–209.

—— —— & Kopin, I. J. (1976), Use of plasma norepinephrine for evaluation of sympathetic neuronal function in man. *Life Sci.,* 18:1315–1326.

Landsberg, L. & Axelrod, J. (1968), Influence of pituitary, thyroid, and adrenal hormones on norepinephrine turnover and metabolism in the rat heart. *Circ. Res.,* 22:559–571.

Langer, S. Z. (1973), The regulation of transmitter release elicited by nerve stimulation through a presynaptic feedback mechanism. In: *Frontiers in Catecholamine Research.* ed. E. Usdin & S. Synder. New York: Pergamon Press, pp. 543–549.

Levine, R. J. & Landsberg, L. (1974), Catecholamines and the adrenal medulla. In: *Duncan's Diseases of Metabolism,* ed. P. K. Bondy & L. E. Rosenberg. Philadelphia: W. B. Saunders, pp. 1181–1224.

Lucas, A. R. Warner, K., & Gottlieb, J. S. (1971), Biological studies in childhood schizophrenia. *Bio. Psychiat.,* 3:123–128.

Maas, J. W. (1974), Clinical biochemistry and the choice of the appropriate medication for the psychiatric patient. In: *The Psychobiology of Depression,* ed. J. Mendels. New York: Spectrum Publications, pp. 1–5.

____ (1975), Biogenic amines and depression. *Arch. Gen. Psychiat.,* 32:1357–1361.

____ & Landis, D. H. (1968), *In vivo* studies of the metabolism of norcpinephrine in the central nervous system. *J. Pharm. Exp. Ther.,* 163:147–162.

____ ____ (1971), The metabolism of circulating norepinephrine by human subjects. *J. Pharm. Exp. Ther.,* 177:600–612.

Mahler, M. S. (1949), A psychoanalytic evaluation of tic in psychopathology of children. *The Psychoanalytic Study of the Child.* 3/4:279–310.

Mason, J. W. (1968), A review of psychoendocrine research on the pituitary-thyroid system. *Psychosom, Med.,* 30:666–681.

Matthysse, S. (1973), Antipsychotic drug actions. *Federation Proc.,* 32:200–205.

McCoy, E. E., Segal, D. J., Bayer, S. M., & Strynadka, K. D. (1974), Decreased ATPase and increased sodium content of platelets in Down's syndrome. *New Eng. J. Med.,* 291:950–953.

McGeer, P. L., Hattori, T., Singh, V. K., & McGeer, E. G. (1976), Cholinergic systems in extrapyramidal function. In: *The Basal Ganglia,* ed. M. D. Yahr. New York: Raven Press, pp. 213–222.

Meltzer, H. Y. (1972), Central core fibers in an acutely psychotic patient. *Arch. Gen. Psychiat.,* 27:125–132.

____ (1974), Serum creatine phosphokinase and serum aldolase levels in acutely psychotic patients. In: *Enzymology in the Practice of Clinical Medicine,* ed. P. Blume & E. Frier. New York: Academic Press, pp. 351–379.

____ & Crayton, J. W. (1974), Muscle abnormalities in psychotic patients. II. *Biol. Psychiat.,* 8:191–208.

____ & Stahl, S. M. (1974), Platelet monoamine oxidase activity and substrate preferences in schizophrenic patients. *Res. Commun. Chem. Path. Pharm.,* 7:419–431.

Miller, N. E. (1971), *Selected Papers.* Chicago: Aldine Atherton.

Moldofsky, H., Tullis, C., & Lamon, R. (1974), Multiple tic syndrome (Gilles de la Tourette's syndrome). *J. Nerv. Ment. Dis.,* 159:282–292.

Molinoff, P. B. & Axelrod, J. (1974), Biochemistry of catecholamines. *Ann. Rev. Biochem.,* 40:465–500.

Moskowitz, M. A. & Wurtman, R. J. (1975), Catecholamines and neurologic diseases. *New Eng. J. Med.,* 293:274–280, 332–338.

Mukherjee, C., Caron, M. C., & Lefkowitz, R. J. (1975), Catecholamine-induced subsensitivity of adenylate cyclase associated with loss of B-adrenergic receptor binding sites. *Proc. Nat. Acad. Sci., USA,* 72:1945–1949.

Murphy, D. L. & Donnelly, C. H. (1974), Monoamine oxidase in man. In: *Neuropsychopharmacology of Monoamines and Their Regulatory Enzymes,* ed. E. Usdin. New York: Raven Press, pp. 71–85.

—— & Wyatt, R. J. (1972), Reduced monoamine oxidase activity in blood platelets from schizophrenic patients. *Nature*, 238:225–226.

Nagatsu, T., Ikuta, K., Numata (Sudo), Y., Kato, T., Sano, M., Nagatsu, I., Umezawa, H., Matsuzaki, M., & Takeuchi, T. (1976), Vascular and brain dopamine B-hydroxylase activity in young spontaneously hypertensive rats. *Science*, 191:290–291.

Nathanson, J. A. & Bloom, F. E. (1975), Lead-induced inhibition of brain adenyl cyclase. *Nature*, 255:419–420.

Needleman, H. L. (1973), Lead poisoning in children. *Seminars in Psychiatry*, 5:47–54.

Neff, N. H. & Costa, E. (1966), The influence of monoamine oxidase inhibition on catecholamine synthesis. *Life Sci.*, 5:951–959.

Nies, A., Robinson, D. S., Lamborn, K. R., & Lampert, R. P. (1973), Genetic control of platelet and plasma monoamine oxidase activity. *Arch. Gen. Psychiat.*, 28:834–838.

Oldendorf, W. H. (1974), Blood-brain barrier permeability to drugs. *Ann. Rev. Pharm.*, 14:239–248.

Olson, L. (1974), Post-mortem fluorescence histochemistry of monoamine neuron systems in the human brain. *J. Psychiat. Res.*, 11:199–203.

Overmier, J. B. & Seligman, M. E. P. (1967), Effects of inescapable shock upon subsequent escape and avoidance learning. *J. Comp. Physiol. Psychol.*, 63:23–33.

Passon, P. & Peuler, J. D. (1973), A simplified radiometric assay for plasma norepinephrine and epinephrine. *Anal. Biochem.*, 51:618–631.

Pastan, I. (1972), Cyclic AMP. *Sci. American*, 227:97–105.

Pert, C. B., Pert, A., Chang, J.-K., & Fong, B. T. W. (1976), (D-Ala²)-Met-Enkephalinamide. *Science*, 194:330–332.

Pletscher, A. (1968), Metabolism, transfer, and storage of 5-hydroxytryptamine in blood platelets. *Brit. J. Pharm. Chemother.*, 32:1–16.

—— (1972), Regulation of catecholamine turnover by variations of enzyme levels. *Pharm. Rev.*, 24:225–232.

—— (1973), The impact of monoamine research on drug development. In: *Frontiers in Catecholamine Research*, ed. E. Usdin & S. Snyder. New York: Pergamon Press, pp. 27–37.

—— DaPrada, M., Berneis, K. H., & Tranzer, J. P. (1971), New aspects on the storage of 5-hydroxytryptamine in blood platelets. *Experientia*, 27:993–1002.

Plotnikoff, N. P., Prange, A. J., Jr., Breese, G. R., Anderson, M. S., & Wilson, I. C. (1972), Thyrotropin releasing hormone. Science, 178:417–418.

Pohorecky, L. A. & Wurtman, R. J. (1971), Adrenocortical control of epinephrine synthesis. *Pharm. Rev.*, 23:1–35.

Pollin, W., Cardon, P. V., Jr., & Kety, S. S. (1961), Effects of amino acid feedings in schizophrenic patients treated with iproniazid. *Science*, 133:104–105.

Post, R. M., Fink, E., Carpenter, W. T., & Goodwin, F. K. (1975), Cerebrospinal fluid amine metabolites in acute schizophrenia. *Arch. Gen. Psychiat.*, 32: 1063–1069.

—— & Goodwin, F. K. (1973), Simulated behavior states. *Biol. Psychiat.*, 7:237–254.

Prange, A., Wilson, I., Knox, A., McClane, T., Breese, G., Martin, B., Alltop, L., & Lipton, M. (1972), Thyroid-imipramine clinical and chemical interaction. *J. Psychiat. Res.*, 9:187–205.

Rall, T. W. (1972), Role of adenosine 3′, 5′-monophosphate (cyclic AMP) in actions of catecholamines. *Pharm. Rev.*, 24:399–409.

Randrup, A. & Munkvad, I. (1970), Biochemical, anatomical and psychological investigations of stereotyped behavior induced by amphetamines. In: *Amphetamines and*

Related Compounds, ed. E. Costa & S. Garratini. New York: Raven Press, pp. 695–713.

Reid, J. L. & Kopin, I. J. (1974), Significance of plasma dopamine-B-hydroxylase activity as an index of sympathetic neuronal function. *Proc. Nat. Acad. Sci., USA,* 71:4392–4394.

Reis, D. J., Moorhead, D. T., Rifkin, M., Joh, T. H., & Goldstein, M. (1971), Changes in adrenal enzymes synthesizing catecholamines in attack behavior evoked by hypothalamic stimulation in the cat. *Nature,* 299:562–563.

Rimland, B. (1964), *Infantile Autism.* New York: Meredith.

____ (1977), Platelet uptake and efflux of serotonin in subtypes of psychotic children. *J. Aut. Child. Schizo.* (in press).

Ritvo, E. R., ed. (1976), *Autism.* New York: Spectrum.

____ Yuwiler, A., Geller, E., Ornitz, E. M., Saeger, K., & Plotkin, S. (1970), Increased blood serotonin and platelets in early infantile autism. *Arch. Gen. Psychiat.,* 22:566–572.

Robinson, D., Sourkes, T., Nies, A., Harris, L. S., Spector, S., Bartlett, D. L., & Kaye, I. S. (1977), Monoamine metabolism in human brain. *Arch. Gen. Psychiat.,* 34:89–92.

Roos, B. E. & Sjöström, R. (1969), 5-Hydroxyindoleacetic acid (and homovanillic acid) levels in the cerebrospinal fluid after probenecid application in patients with manic-depressive psychosis. *Pharm. Clin.,* 1:153–155.

Rosengarten, H. & Friedhoff, A. J. (1976), A review of recent studies of the biosynthesis and excretion of hallucinogens formed by methylation of neurotransmitters or related substances. *Schizo. Bull.,* 2:90–105.

Roth, J. A. & Gillis, C. N. (1975), Some structural requirements for inhibition of type A and B forms of rabbit monoamine oxidase by tricyclic psychoactive drugs. *Mol. Pharm.,* 11:28–35.

____ Young, J. G., & Cohen, D. J. (1976), Platelet monoamine oxidase activity in children and adolescents. *Life Sci.,* 18:919–924.

Roth, R. H., Walters, J. R., & Aghajanian, G. K. (1973), Effect of impulse flow on the release and synthesis of dopamine in the rat striatum. In: *Frontiers in Catecholamine Research,* ed. E. Usdin & S. H. Snyder. New York: Pergamon Press, pp. 567–574.

Ruttenberg, B. A. (1974), *Behavior Rating Instrument for Autistic and Other Atypical Children.* Philadelphia: Developmental Center for Autistic Children.

Rutter, M. (1965), The influence of organic and emotional factors on the origins, nature and outcome of childhood psychosis. *Develppm. Med. Child Neurol.,* 7:518–527.

____ (1971a), *Infantile Autism.* Edinburgh: Churchill & Livingstone.

____ (1971b), The description and classification of infantile autism. In: *Infantile Autism,* ed. D. Churchill, G. Alpern, & M. DeMeyer, Springfield, Ill.: Charles C. Thomas, pp. 8–28.

Sachar, E. J. (1975a), Neuroendocrine abnormalities in depressive illness. In: *Topics in Psychoendocrinology,* ed. E. J. Sachar. New York: Grune & Stratton, pp. 135–156.

____ (1975b), *Topics in Psychoendocrinology.* New York: Grune & Stratton.

Saller, C. F. & Stricker, E. M. (1976), Hyperphagia and increased growth in rats after intraventricular injection of 5, 7-dihydroxytryptamine. *Science,* 192:385–387.

Samanin, R. & Garattini, S. (1975), The serotonergic system in the brain and its possible functional connection with other aminergic systems. *Life Sci.,* 17:1201–1210.

Sandler, M. & Youdim, M. B. H. (1974), Monoamine oxidases. *Int. Pharmocapsychiat.,* 9:27–34.

Sankar, D. V. S. (1970), Biogenic amine uptake by blood platelets and RBC in childhood schizophrenia. *Acta Paedopsychiat.* (Basel), 37:174–182.

—— (1971), Studies on blood platelets, blood enzymes, and leukocyte chromosome breakage in childhood schizophrenia. *Behav. Neuropsychiat.*, 2(11–12):2–10.

—— Cates, N., Broer, H. H., & Sankar, D. B. (1963), Biochemical parameters of childhood schizophrenia (autism) and growth. In: *Recent Advances in Biological Psychiatry*, ed. J. Wortis. New York: Plenum Press, pp. 76–83.

Satterfield, J., Cantwell, D., & Satterfield, B. (1974), Pathophysiology of the hyperactive child syndrome. *Arch. Gen. Psychiat.*, 31:839–844.

Sauerhoff, M. W. & Michaelson, I. A. (1973), Hyperactivity and brain catecholamines in lead-exposed developing rats. *Science*, 182:1022–1024.

Schain, R. J. & Freedman, D. X. (1961), Studies of 5-hydroxyindole metabolism in autistic and other mentally retarded children. *J. Pediat.*, 58:315–320.

Schanberg, S. M., Schildkraut, J. J., Breese, G. R., & Kopin, I. J. (1968), Metabolism of normetanephrine-H³ in rat brain. *Biochem. Pharm.*, 17:247–254.

—— Stone, R. A., Kirshner, N., Gunnells, J. C., & Robinson, R. R. (1974), Plasma dopamine-B-hydroxylase. *Science*, 183:523–525.

Schildkraut, J. J. (1970), *Neuropsychopharmacology and the Affective Disorders.* Boston: Little, Brown.

—— & Kety, S. S. (1967), Biogenic amines and emotion. *Science*, 156:21–30.

Seeman, P. (1972), The membrane actions of anesthetics and tranquilizers. *Pharm. Rev.*, 24:583–655.

—— & Lee, T. (1975), Antipsychotic drugs. *Science*, 188:1217–1219.

Shapiro, A. K., Shapiro, E., & Wayne, H. (1973), Treatment of Tourette's syndrome with haloperidol, review of 34 cases. *Arch. Gen. Psychiat.*, 28:92–97.

Sharman, D. F. (1973a), The catabolism of catecholamines. *Brit. Med. Bull.*, 29:110–115.

—— (1973b), Metabolites of catecholamines in the cerebrospinal fluid. In: *Frontiers in Catecholamine Research*, ed. E. Usdin & S. Snyder. New York: Pergamon Press, pp. 1055–1061.

Shaywitz, B. A., Cohen, D. J., & Bowers, M. B., Jr. (1975a), CSF amine metabolites in children with minimal brain dysfunction (MBD). (Abst.): *Pediat. Res.*, 9:385.

—— —— —— (1975b). Reduced cerebrospinal fluid 5-hydroxyindoleacetic acid and homovanillic acid in children with epilepsy. *Neurology*, 25:74–79.

—— —— —— (1977), CSF amine metabolites in children with minimal brain dysfunction (MBD). *J. Pediat.*, 90:67–71.

—— Yager, R. D., & Klopper, J. H. (1976a), Selective brain dopamine depletion in developing rats. *Science*, 191:305–307.

—— —— —— & Gordon, J. W. (1976b), A paradoxical response to amphetamine in developing rats treated with 6-hydroxydopamine. *Nature*, 261:153–155.

Sheerd, M. H. & Aghajanian, G. K. (1968), Stimulation of midbrain raphe neuron. *Life Sci.*, 7:19–29.

Sjoerdsma, A. (1959), Serotonin. *New Eng. J. Med.*, 261:181–188, 231–237.

Smith, A. D. & Winkler, H. (1972), Fundamental mechanisms in the release of catecholamines. In: *Catecholamines*, ed. H. Blaschko & E. Muscholl. New York: Springer Verlag, pp. 538–617.

Snowdon, C. T. & Sanderson, B. A. (1974), Lead pica produced in rats. *Science*, 183:92–94.

Snyder, S. H. (1977), Opiate receptors in the brain. *New Eng. J. Med.*, 296:266–271.

—— Banerjee, S. P., Yamamura, H. I., & Greenberg, D. (1974), Drugs, neurotransmitters, and schizophrenia. *Science*, 184:1243–1253.

_____ & Bennett, J. P., Jr. (1976), Neurotransmitter receptors in the brain. *Ann. Rev. Physiol.*, 38:153–175.

_____ Taylor, K. M., Coyle, J. T., & Meyerhoff, J. L. (1970), The role of brain dopamine in behavioral regulation and the actions of psychotropic drugs. *Amer. J. Psychiat.*, 127:199–207.

Stahl, S. (1977), The human platelet as a diagnostic and research tool for the study of biogenic amine metabolism and neurologic disorders. *Arch. Gen. Psychiat.* (in press).

Stjärne, L. (1972), The synthesis, uptake and storage of catecholamines in the adrenal medulla. *Catecholamines*, ed. H. Blaschko & E. Muscholl. New York: Springer Verlag, pp. 231–269.

Stone, R. & DeLeo, J. (1976), Psychotherapeutic control of hypertension. *New Eng. J. Med.*, 294:80–84.

Sutherland, E. W. (1972), Studies on the mechanism of hormone action. *Science*, 177:401–408.

Thierry, A. M., Blanc, G., Sobel, A., Stinus, L., & Glowinski, J. (1973), Dopaminergic terminals in the rat cortex. *Science*, 182:499–501.

Thoenen, H. & Tranzer, J. P. (1973), The pharmacology of 6-hydroxydopamine. *Ann. Rev. Pharm.*, 13:169–180.

Trendelenburg, U. (1972a), Factors influencing the concentration of catecholamines at the receptors. In: *Cathecholamines*, ed. H. Blaschko & E. Muscholl. New York: Springer Verlag, pp. 726–761.

_____ (1972b). Classification of sympathomimetic amines. In: *Catecholamines*, ed. H. Blaschko & E. Muscholl. New York: Springer Verlag, pp. 336–362.

Udenfriend, S. (1966), Tyrosine hydroxylase. *Pharm. Rev.*, 18:43–51.

Ulus, I. H. & Wurtman, R. J. (1976), Choline administration. *Science*, 194:1060–1061.

Ungerstedt, U. (1971), Stereotaxic mapping of the monoamine pathways in the rat brain. *Acta Physiol. Scand.*, Suppl. 367:1–29.

van Praag, H. M., Flentge, F., Korf, J., Dols, L. C. W., & Schut, T. (1973), The influence of probenecid on the metabolism of serotonin, dopamine and their precursors in man. *Psychopharmacologia* (Berl.), 33:141–151.

_____ Korf, J., Lakke, J. P. W. T., & Schut, T. (1975), Dopamine metabolism in depressions, psychoses, and Parkinson's disease. *Psychol. Med.*, 5:138–146.

van Woert, M. H., Rosenbaum, D., Howieson, J., & Bowers, M. B., Jr. (1977a), Long-term therapy of myoclonus and other neurologic disorders with L-5-hydroxytryptophan and carbidopa. *New Eng. J. Med.*, 296:70–75.

_____ Yip, L. C., & Balis, M. E. (1977b), Purine phosphoribosyl-transferase in Gilles de la Tourette syndrome. *New Eng. J. Med.*, 296:210–212.

Vane, J. R. (1969), The release and fate of vasoactive hormones in the circulation. *Brit. J. Pharm.*, 35:209–242.

Vogt, M. (1954), The concentration of sympathin in different parts of the central nervous system under normal conditions and after the administration of drugs. *J. Physiol.* (Lond.), 123:451–481.

Weiner, N. (1970), Regulation of norepinephrine biosynthesis. *Ann. Rev. Pharm.*, 10:273–290.

_____ (1974), A critical assessment of methods for the determination of monoamine synthesis and turnover rates *in vivo*. In: *Neuropsychopharmacology of Monoamines and Their Regulatory Enzymes*, ed. E. Usdin. New York: Raven Press, pp. 143–160.

_____ & Bjur, R. (1972), The role of intraneuronal monoamine oxidase in the regulation of norepinephrine synthesis. In: *Monamine Oxidases,* ed. E. Costa & M. Sandler. New York: Raven Press, pp. 409–419.

Weinshilboum, R. & Axelrod, J. (1971), Serum dopamine-B-hydroxylase activity. *Circ. Res.,* 28:307–315.

—— Thoa, N. B., Johnson, D. G., Kopin, I. J., & Axelrod, J. (1971), Proportional release of norepinephrine and dopamine-B-hydroxylase from sympathetic nerves. *Science,* 174: 1349–1351.

Weise, V. K. & Kopin, I. J. (1976), Assay of catecholamines in human plasma. *Life Sci.,* 19:1673–1686.

Weiss, B. & Laties, V. G. (1962), Enhancement of human performance by caffeine and the amphetamines. *Pharm. Rev.,* 14:1–36.

Weiss, J. M. & Glazer, H. I. (1975), Effects of acute exposure to stressors on subsequent avoidance-escape behavior. *Psychosom. Med.,* 37:499–521.

—— —— Pohorecky, L. A., Brick, J. , & Miller, N. E. (1975), Effects of chronic exposure to stressors on avoidance-escape behavior and on brain norepinephrine. *Psychosom. Med.,* 37:522–534.

Wender, P. H. (1971), *Minimal Brain Dysfunction in Children.* New York: Wiley.

Wilk, S. & Watson, E. (1973), VMA in spinal fluid. In: *Frontiers in Catecholamine Research,* ed. E. Usdin & S. Snyder. New York: Pergamon Press, pp. 1067–1069.

Wise, C. D., Baden, M. M., & Stein, L. (1974), Post-mortem measurement of enzymes in human brain. *J. Psychiat. Res.,* 11:185–198.

—— & Stein, L. (1973), Dopamine-B-hydroxylase deficits in the brains of schizophrenic patients. *Science,* 181:344–347.

Wurtman, R. J. & Fernstrom, J. D. (1976), Control of brain neurotransmitter synthesis by perecursor availability and nutritional state. *Biochem. Pharm.,* 25:1691–1696.

—— Larin, F., Mostafapour, S., & Fernstrom, J. D. (1974). , Brain catechol synthesis. *Science,* 185:183–184.

Wyatt, R. J., Murphy, D. L., Belmaker, R., Cohen, S., Donnelly, C. H., & Pollin, W. (1973a), Reduced monoamine oxidase activity in platelets. *Science,* 179(4076):916–918.

—— Saavedra, J. M., Belmaker, R., Cohen, S., & Pollin, W. (1973b), The dimethytryptamine-forming enzyme in blood platelets. *Amer. J. Psychiat.,* 130:1359–1361.

—— Schwartz, M. A., Erdelyi, E., & Barchas, J. D. (1975), Dopamine-B-hydroxylase activity in brains of chronic schizophrenic patients. *Science,* 187:368–370.

—— Termini, B. A., & David, J. (1971), Biochemical and sleep studies of schizophrenia. *Schizo. Bull.,* 4:10–66.

Young, J. G. (1975), Review of *Minimal Brain Dysfunction,* by M. B. Gross & W. C. Wilson, and *Speaking of Children,* by C. Ellingson. *Children Today,* 4:30–31.

Yuwiler, A., Ritvo, E. R., Bald, D., Kipper, D., & Koper, A. (1971), Examination of circadian rhythmicity of blood serotonin and platelets in autistic and nonautistic children. *J. Aut. Child. Schizo.,* 1:421–435.

—— —— Geller, E., Glousman, R., Schneiderman, G., & Matsuno, D. (1975), Uptake and efflux of serotonin from platelets of autistic and nonautistic children. *J. Aut. Child. Schizo.,* 5:83–98.

Zahn, T., Abate, F., Little, B. C., & Wender, P. H. (1975), Minimal brain dysfunction, stimulant drugs, and autonomic nervous system activity. *Arch. Gen. Psychiat.,* 32:381–387.

Zeller, E. A. (1959), The role of amine oxidases in the destruction of catecholamines.

Pharm. Rev., 11:387–393.

Ziegler, M. G., Lake, C. R., & Kopin, I. J. (1976), Plasma noradrenaline increases with age. *Nature,* 261:333–334.

_____ _____ _____ (1977), The sympathetic-nervous-system defect in primary orthostatic hypotension. *New Eng. J. Med.,* 296:293–297.

Zivkovic, B., Guidotti, A., & Costa, E. (1974), On the regulation of trytophan hydroxylase in brain. In: *Serotonin—New Vistas,* ed. E. Costa, G. L. Gessa, & M. Sandler. New York: Raven Press, 11:1–11.

Part III

LANGUAGE DEVELOPMENT

The use of language has always been recognized by child and adult psychiatrists as a decisive source of psychological data as well as a most important diagnostic and therapeutic instrument. In the past, clinicians tended to view the child's ability to communicate verbally in a global fashion. A child had language or didn't, and differences in language use were evaluated quantitatively as more or less. Deviations from the norm were identified, described and labeled phenomenologically (pronomial confusion, echoing, stuttering, dyslexia, receptive or expressive aphasia, etc.). This global approach was exemplified by René Spitz's view, a generation ago, that the psychoanalytic study of the young child was limited by the inability to use free association and verbal communication, and that adequate investigation had to wait until the individual's language use had matured (R. Spitz, Relevancy of Direct Infant Observation, *Psychoanalytic Study of the Child*, 5:66, 1950).

These earlier studies, it must be emphasized, did lay the groundwork for the research directions of recent years, which have expanded dramatically our concepts and knowledge of the child's language. The key to this recent work has been the increasing use of a developmental approach in analyzing the nature and meaning of both normal and deviant language phenomena at successive age-stage levels.

Nelson's review of language acquisition and use from infancy onward highlights our increasing understanding of the richness and complexity of this process, made possible by such a developmental approach. Both normal and deviant courses are detailed, the startling array of individual differences is emphasized, and the effectiveness of alternative modalities of expressive language development in children with physiological blocks to speaking is indicated.

Lewis' review offers a synthesis of the phenomena of language, cognitive and personality development. The prerequisites for language development are detailed, and deficits correlated with theoretical and clinical issues. The central role of language as the mediator between cognitive and emotional development is emphasized.

7

ASPECTS OF LANGUAGE ACQUISITION AND USE FROM AGE 2 to AGE 20

Keith E. Nelson

The Pennsylvania State University

General cognitive processes may underlie development of such diverse skills as producing well-structured sentences, forming basic concepts, conversing, understanding metaphor, and using language flexibility to describe and order events. Three aspects of the child's language development are central in accounting for both normal and deviant courses of acquisition: (1) how the young child uses some (but not most) language exchanges with others to construct sophisticated sentences—a theory of "cognitive comparisons" is offered; (2) relationships between early language strengths and the levels of language skills after age 4 years; and (3) the possibility that some children may be better able to master language in a mode other than speech.

Describing language development between 2 and 20 would have been less complex either 2 or 20 years ago than it is at present (1977). Twenty years ago the process of language acquisition was so widely assumed to be a simple learning process and the actual observations on what children say and do in learning language so limited that very little of excitement or depth could have been offered. In contrast, 2

Reprinted with permission from *Journal of the American Academy of Child Psychiatry*, Vol. 16, No. 4, Autumn, 1977, 584–607.

years ago many investigators felt that fresh and detailed evidence had carried us to the verge of understanding how the child masters speech. Moreover, similar acquisition patterns were emerging cross-culturally (Ferguson and Slobin, 1973). But now it is becoming increasingly clear that that first large wave of detailed observations of children's utterances, the wave which crested about 2 or 3 years ago, is rapidly being overtaken by a series of new waves which reveal aspects of language acquisition poorly represented or not represented at all in the first set of investigations. In this regard, I believe we can currently discern about four major shifts in discussion of language acquisition and use.

One shift is from a concern only with speech to a recognition that both first and later languages may be acquired in other modes—particularly in sign language and in printed or written forms. This recognition carries with it implications for theories of language development and for strategies and models of intervention with children who are faring poorly in language acquisition. On this latter point, there is growing evidence that when production or comprehension is blocked in one mode (e.g., speech), effective detours through other modes (e.g., sign language) may allow the child to use his or her considerable cognitive capacities in language learning. Typewriting (Fourcin, 1975) and sign language (English and Prutting, 1975) have been used as expressive language vehicles for individuals with well-defined physiological blocks to speaking. The sign language (not finger spelling) of the deaf has recently shown especially wide promise as a language mode to replace or supplement speech in the communication of children (Cohen et al., 1976; Caparulo and Cohen, 1977), and other children with severely limited speech skills (Bonvillian et al., 1976). In the case of one 9-year-old autistic boy whose prior failure to use or understand speech was well documented, the introduction of sign language has led not only to a sizable vocabulary and meaningful, varied sentences, but also to considerable improvement in social skills and to expanded teaching possibilities—including the beginnings of reading (Bonvillian and K. E. Nelson, 1977).

A second, related shift is a move away from a widespread bias favoring the view that innate, language-specific mechanisms are required to explain children's success in mastering language. This view actively tended to discourage inquiry into certain topics. With the recent shift toward the alternative view that general cognitive processes may be sufficient to explain most of language learning, interest has been kindled in such essential topics as these: the child's language "environment" (the language of parents, siblings, and others) and variations therein; the relations between progress in sentences and concurrent and prior cognitive progress; and perhaps of greatest import, analyses over time of children *as they are learning* new sentence forms and new concepts rather than analyses only *after* new acquisitions have emerged. It could well turn out that the primary aspects of language acquisition that set it apart from other early learning lie not in any specific abilities for dealing with language but rather in the large amount of time the child devotes to the task and the great quantity of highly structured exemplars (an abundance unmatched by any nonlinguistic stimuli) that serve as language input. However, we are not yet sure of the *specific* characteristics of input language which are *necessary* for the child's success in early, intermediate, or late stages of first or second language acquisition.

The selective search for and emphasis upon patterns in language development that are invariant across children are being replaced by more inclusive empirical research that has already yielded a startling array of individual differences. One challenge is to build new theories that encompass the child-to-child (and mother-to-mother) variations instead of treating them as irrelevant. The wide extent of the variations also increases the prospect that early language variations may underlie later childhood and adulthood diversity in language and thinking skills, including the generation of clear and appropriate sentences, sensitivity to poetry and other figurative expression, and the use of language to guide convergent and divergent thinking.

Another shift has been from an almost exclusive concern with how sentences are constructed to wide-ranging research on how language is used, including analyses of contrasting language forms and functions in different contexts and of the ways that conversations are constructed. As part of this change in outlook, there is a growing sophistication in dealing with (if not yet solving) two extremely tough problems that were largely ignored in most early efforts (Piaget [1951] excepted) at describing language development—the problem of the child's *intentions* in language and in early symbolic play (which may be a fundamental step toward language), and the role of *nonverbal context* in early communication.

These recent redirections of effort and attitudes will reappear intermittently as topics in the following review of what happens in language growth between age 2 and age 20. The account will touch on what is known (with an emphasis on recent work) and indicate how further observations and theorizing are likely to develop.

SYNTAX AND SEMANTICS BETWEEN 2 AND 5 YEARS

The child's first sentences at around 2 years of age are short and often are understandable only in relation to unnamed but salient elements of the context. The sentences are simple in terms of syntactic structure and semantic complexity. Then the language system gradually expands to include longer and more complex sentences based upon increasingly complex and adultlike sets of rules. A discussion of these kinds of general characteristics of the child's syntax and semantics between 2 and 5 will be followed by a look at specific changes in certain areas of syntax and semantics and in the strategies the child uses in dealing with language.

Among the most striking characteristics of early utterances are the widespread and flagrant errors children make in using "our" language. As a sampling, I offer the following series of error types: (1) Using the right dimension, but confusing the ends or values. "Mommy, I'm warming off my soup." Or, an adult: "Do you have a leopard?" Child: "Yes, I don't have." (2) Using the wrong dimension. Child to man's voice on telephone: "Daddy, Daddy." Mother: "That's not your Daddy." Child: "Well, it *looks* like him." (3) Treating common nouns as proper and vice versa. Child, speaking of a dog named Dylan: "You want to look at the Dylan's teeth?" (4) Inflections that are duplicated ("But that's mines"), misplaced ("They doing come out"), missing ("Where Mommy shoe?"), or overgeneralized ("They goed away"). (5) Conglomerating rather than differentiating terms. Child: "It's 1:15 thirty." (6) Employing the wrong verb. "I happened elephants." (7) Employing the wrong tense. "We swim tomorrow." (8) Overdoing the "do" or "did" (or other verbs), as in "I did do it blow it" or in "Did Judy did?"

This mixed collection offers a hint of the extraordinary range and novelty that young children show in their errors. Behind these errors there is without doubt a process of construction of language by the child, a process of using rules or patterns to generate sentences that are novel in relation to particular prior sentences either heard by the child or produced by the child. Note, however, that in this assortment of novel children's sentences there is only one—"I happened elephants"—that might be ambiguous, let alone incomprehensible in context. The errors made will change as the child's language system changes between 2 and 5, and the changes predominantly will be stepwise, orderly advances toward the adult syntactic and semantic system and toward precision in communication. But throughout this period the child will succeed in producing sentences that generally are comprehensible, in context, to adults. At about age 5 the child will have achieved control of a remarkably high proportion of the adults' system for sentence production and comprehension. The same words, the same dimensions, and the same kinds of sentence structures that adults use, generally can be used by the 5-year-old. Moreover, the child at 5 is capable of using this system with high success even when contextual support is minimal. In using the system to communicate, the 5-year-old, like the adult, retains the meanings of prior sentences in a conversation, while generally forgetting the sentence structures which carried the meanings (Heras and K. E. Nelson, 1972).

While these general descriptions are in agreement with most observations on child language, several qualifications seem to be required. One is that we are now learning that not all children experience the same difficulties and errors or use the same strategies. This means that in theory building, care must be taken to see that the necessary search for common properties and common sequences of language mastery across children does not lead us to a model of systematic change in language which posits more regularity than most individual children demonstrate. This caution that holds for normal language acquisition holds even more strongly when the role of parents and educators in dealing with language-limited or language-delayed children is considered, where an ability to diagnose and respond appropriately to the child's level and pattern of language is crucial. A second qualification is that investigations of language have been less intensive in many ways at age 5 years than at earlier stages in language acquisition. As a closer look is taken, we may well discover that earlier observations overestimate how "complete" and how "context-free" a system 5-year-olds possess and underestimate the range of individual differences in regard to the final stages of language acquisition. Another qualification concerning language at 5 is that the use of sentences in discourse, in conversation, involves language skills beyond those usually considered in semantic and syntactic descriptions. From the few recent explorations on this topic it appears that children's acquisition of skill in discourse is completed much later than 5. Whatever the timetables, eventually the language system and its acquisition should be described in coordinated fashion for conceptual, syntactic, and discourse components.

Semantic development and syntactic development for the most part are very tightly interrelated, but for a moment I shall consider semantic concepts and information that can be studied in partial isolation from syntax. Especially for concepts like "lions" and "daisies" and "lobsters" and "big," concepts labeled by nouns or adjectives, there is now a fair amount of data from controlled observations as well as from naturalistic accounts. And once the 18- to 24-month-old child is regularly using words to mark such concepts, and no doubt in many instances to aid the formation of the concepts, a process of verbal semantic retrieval can also be studied. For example, the child who knows the meaning of "apple" can retrieve the information from memory to give correct answers to such questions as: "Does an apple have seeds?" "Is an apple a fruit?" "Are apples red?" Observations on semantic concepts and semantic retrieval support four central conclusions: (1) The child develops the ability to form well-structured concepts with associated labels (words or signs) at an earlier age (evident at 18 months) than he or she can systematically organize the rapid storage and retrieval of such conceptual information. Semantic retrieval is much slower at 7 years than in adulthood, although the organization at the two ages appear similar (K. E. Nelson and Kosslyn, 1975). Between 2 and 7 there are sharp decreases in retrieval time and movement away from idiosyncratic bases for organization of information storage and retrieval. (2) As children develop between ages 2 and 5, they become increasingly proficient at rapidly forming new concepts (given equal exposure to exemplars at each age). (3) At age 2 (K. E. Nelson and Bonvillian, 1974) as well as at age 5 very limited exposure to exemplars of a concept and their concept name is a sufficient base for concept acquisition. (4) Individual differences in the rate and pattern of semantic development are prevalent, even when differences between children in available evidence (which also have clear effects) are eliminated by design.

A recent study (K. E. Nelson and Bonvillian, 1977), which we have dubbed the "Fiffin Project," illustrates the last two conclusions. Early semantic development in 19 children was studied in a series of 11 sessions spaced between age 2 years and age 2½ years for each child. The children were systematically exposed to objects serving as learning-set exemplars for 18 unfamiliar concepts. The mothers of the children verbally labeled learning-set exemplars, whereas another set of exemplars (never named by adults) served as generalization tests. The mothers' presentation and naming of the objects largely mirrored the kinds of interaction observable under "naturalistic" conditions in children's homes. However, this natural style of interaction was supplemented by careful data recording and controls over which concept exemplars were employed and how often they were seen. Concept names included made-up names such as "fiffin" and English nouns like "hedgehog" and "sifter." All the children learned on the basis of few exemplars appropriately to produce, generalize, and comprehend concept names, and such learning proved possible when only a single exemplar was the basis of learning, but measures of the pattern and extent of concept learning showed marked individual differences for these 2- to 2½-year-olds. The courses of mastery for individual concepts by individual children were highly varied. In terms of overall comprehension, scores ranged from 29 percent for 1 child to a maximum of 75 percent. A similarly wide range held for the production of concept names: from 7 to 70 percent success. Furthermore, the relation between comprehension and production differed among children, with 1 child showing parity, 6 children leading in their comprehension, and 11 children showing production scores that led comprehension. Finally, the breadth of the concepts formed also showed remarkable diversity across children; some children overgeneralized nearly all of the concept names (e.g., "fiffin," "lobster") to inappropriate objects (e.g., hedgehogs), whereas other children showed *no* such overgeneralization. The long-term implications of these sorts of early differences between children will be addressed later in this paper.

The fuzzy boundaries between "syntactic" and "semantic" aspects of language development are perhaps never fuzzier than when strategies for sentence interpretation are considered. Between age 2 and 5 it is clear that children first form, and then abandon, many strategies for "reading" sentence interpretation from recurrent, but often misleading clues in the sentences or in the world. A case that illustrates both types of clues is the children's use of the actor-action-object strategy (Bever, 1970); Strohner and K. E. Nelson, 1974) to deal with sentences like "Bill chased John" or "John was chased by Bill" as if the first noun is always the actor. As a probabilistic inference from the predominantly active sentences (e.g., "Mary pushed Joan") that most children hear, this is not unreasonable. But it does, of course, lead to misinterpretation of "John was chased by Bill," "The red bird is being fed by the yellow bird," and other reversible passive sentences. The clues considered so far in this example are all clues within the sentences. Clues in the world also apply to this strategy, however, because children who rely on this strategy (usually 3- to 4-year-olds) modulate their tendency to do so depending upon context—for example, context manipulations of, say, pictures that draw the child's initial attention to the *object* in the sentence lead to less reliance on this strategy. Surprisingly, although we can document many such strategies that children may use, at least briefly, in interpreting sentences during the 2 to 5 period, the extent of individual differences is unclear. It further remains to be determined which strategies are necessary steps in language acquisition, and which are optional, transient, specialized shortcuts to assigning meanings to selected kinds of sentences.

If we now turn to syntactic rules and their changes across the period bordered approximately by the child's second and fifth birthdays, a central problem for theory (and also for intervention to aid language acquisition) is explaining how new syntactic terms are introduced into the child's language system. We can address this problem in highly specific terms because extensive work on syntax acquisition describes highly (but not perfectly) predictable sequences of acquisition for many forms. That is, we can ask how a child who produces and understands certain kinds of syntactic forms at one stage of acquisition succeeds in taking a new step toward what prior research has shown to be the next likely stage. Questions will serve as an illustrative case. Children begin in the simplest way, by using intonation alone to mark a question, "Allgone cookie?" At intermediate stages children begin to use "who" and "what" and other *Wh* words, but without the necessary coordination with other sentence elements such as negatives and auxiliaries. The resulting sentences include the following sorts: "What he can sit on?" "Why you do that?" "Why not me can't drive?" In addition, auxiliaries are used correctly at this time as the first words in questions answerable by "yes" or "no" ("Did the man fall?" or "Can you open it?") In the final stages of question acquisition, the child manages to use *Wh* question words, auxiliaries at sentence beginnings and in other sentence positions, and negatives, in complex, appropriately coordinated fashion (Brown et al., 1967). The pinnacle of question acquisition is thus represented by such queries as "The girl left, didn't she?" "When will the rain stop?" "The dog couldn't catch the cat, could he?"

Similar sequences in syntactic development have been indicated for concurrent languages, used by children who were acquiring the two languages in the period between 1 and 5 years of age. In addition, some limited progress has been made in describing successive steps in second-language acquisition after age 5. Especially when the child's learning is based upon communication in context (as in cases where American families live in Spain and the children learn Spanish [Hatch, 1976]) parallels to early syntactic development in a first language emerge. When one considers the children's needs, it is clear that use of more than one language is often essential to their success in communication with parents, peers, and teachers. Beyond that, a full analysis of the acquisition and use of more than one language could prove extremely valuable to the construction of theories of syntactic acquisition and discourse mastery in first languages. As one example, a great deal might be learned about the child's understanding of discourse routines by examining conversations in the early stages of second-language acquisition. Perhaps sophisticated discourse will be evident, but with very unsophisticated sentences. More generally, the usual lockstep of advancing discourse skill together with advancing sentence structures might be partially broken to provide new looks at the processes in both areas.

In the next section a model of syntax acquisition is proposed for first-language acquisition, a model which could be extended to provide an account of second-language acquisition. As a lead-in to that model, it is essential to emphasize again the great novelty of children's sentences. Most sentences in a first or second language are not direct imitations of prior sentences of adults, but new sentences. A good illustration of this observation is that when young children are learning two languages simultaneously, with different monolingual adults as the sources of input, children may produce well-structured sentences that begin in one language (say, English) and end in another (e.g., Spanish, Chinese), even though no models of such sentences are provided by adults. An even more essential observation is that when direct, immediate imitations of adult sentences do occur, they almost certainly do not serve as the means for introducing new syntactic forms into the child's first language system (and may serve that function only rarely in second-language acquisition). If this conclusion is correct, a child who had never produced complex "tag" questions such as "The bunny is soft, isn't it?" is not going to introduce such sentence structures (or their new syntactic components) into his or her first language system in the process of imitating an immediately preceding adult sentence of this form. So far, the evidence overwhelmingly supports the notion that the heart of syntactic development, the acquisition of new syntactic forms, consists of processes other than direct imitation.

TOWARD A THEORY OF SYNTAX ACQUISITION

The model to be proposed rests in significant part on the outcomes of two experiments (K. E. Nelson et al., 1973; K. E. Nelson, 1977) with children of about 3 years of age. In both experiments adults verbally interacted with the children in ways designed to facilitate the children's syntax acquisition, and the outcomes showed this goal to be achieved. Much of the conversation was intended to be like that of mothers with their young children. The basic experimental technique adults used in their intervention was frequent "recasting." Recasting consists of replying to the child's sentence with a new sentence highly similar in meaning, but with a recast or restructured wording. As one example, the child's sentence "The tulip is yellow" could be recast as "That tulip is yellow, isn't it?" The reasoning behind this kind of manipulation was that the child could compare directly the pair of sentence structures produced (original and recast) and on the basis of such comparison could make revisions in his or her system of sentence generation that would include new syntactic forms. Particularly in the second experiment (K. E. Nelson, 1977) the evidence shows that intervention did lead the children to begin using new forms they did not use before intervention. In that study, for instance, recasts into tag-question forms (e.g., "The cow isn't talking, is it?") were employed by adults with some children, who then introduced tag questions into their language.

The "cognitive comparison" model of syntax acquisition described next is not a complete model, but it does make explicit seven assumptions that all have direct or indirect empirical support for first-language learning. Stated in these explicit terms, further research should make revision or rejection or acceptance possible for both first- and second-language acquisition.

Assumption 1. In order fully to acquire syntactically governed language the child must engage in active communication in meaningful contexts with partners who are fluent in the language and who display (separately or in combination) a full range of grammatical structures. Counterexamples include observations of one hearing child (of deaf parents) who failed to learn English from television shows (see Bonvillian et al., 1976). Additional counterevidence comes from families in which the bilingual parents speak one language only when talking to each other, with the result that the children overhear their parents' conversations but do not learn the language involved.

Assumption 2. Adults and older children do not directly teach young children to use syntactically appropriate sentences, do not know how to do such teaching, and produce sentences that for the most part play no essential role in the child's syntax acquisition. (However, the same sentences may be vitally important for acquisition of discourse skills, conceptual skills, and social skills.) In addition, it may be that certain characteristics of the specialized speech that most children hear could slow or even prevent progress in syntax development. For example, very slow parental speech could burden memory and extremely simple sentences grammatically could handicap acquisition of complex forms (DePaulo and Bonvillian, 1977; Brown, 1977). Determination of whether or how the general characteristics of mothers' speech aid or hinder language acquisition will necessarily require some reliance on longitudinal and experimental research designs, because at any one point in development naturalistic observations cannot distinguish between the mother's language influence on the child's language and the reverse direction of effect.

Assumption 3. The child as active agent derives information about syntactic structures from the available evidence, the sentences used by adults and older children, in a process of cognitive comparison between structures already present in the child's system and certain partially contrasting structures used by others. A "current sentence structure" already in the child's system can be employed as a basis of comparison to a new sentence structure when comprehension alone is involved on the child's part (Lenneberg, 1962; Fourcin, 1975). However, comparisons are more likely to lead to revisions in the child's system when the child also produces the current sentence structure.

Assumption 4. When a cognitive comparison between a new sentence structure and a current sentence structure occurs, three outcomes are possible: (a) there is no discrepancy between the structures, and the child codes this as a confirmation of the usefulness of the current structure; (b) a discrepancy occurs, but the child cannot code adequately the nature of the discrepancy; and (c) a "codable discrepancy" is noted, in which the child's language system gains information on some explicit differences between current structures and those sentence structures being used by others. Codable discrepancies are rarely noted by the child, in part for attentional and motivational reasons, but chiefly because the child's memory is limited and because most of the highly specific kinds of new sentences children require for comparison at each stage simply do not occur very frequently in input. The complete absence of such required forms for a period will lead to a plateau in syntax acquisition, and, conversely, relatively high frequencies of such forms will tend to accelerate the child's progress. The particular new sentence examples required for syntactic changes in the child's system, it should now be clear, are not constant from one area of syntax to another or from one stage to the next.

Assumption 5. A certain minimum number of codable discrepancy comparisons involving a new form are required before the child will *revise* the system to incorporate the new form, but this minimum is fairly small and it declines as the child's system develops. The changes almost always are *advances* toward a more complete system of appropriate, adultlike language, but changes can be away from conventional language structures if the language models for the child are severely deviant. There are three kinds of support for the assumption that for syntactic change relatively few instances of comparison by the child may suffice: (a) the child acquires forms that are only rarely used by adults (Brown and Hanlon, 1970); (b) intervention studies that have involved adult use of "recasts" of the child's sentences over a period of less than 8 hours, and therefore a small number of opportunities for new comparisons by the child, have nevertheless accelerated syntactic progress (K. E. Nelson et al., 1973; K. E. Nelson, 1977); (c) the frequently observed rapid pace of the child's acquisition of new forms in naturalistic observations. Of course, all linguistic change is not rapid or based on limited evidence. Certainly we should not discount the possibility that in very early language development highly overlearned routines or "scripts" (Schank and Abelson, 1975) concerning bedtime, eating, and dressing could be a fundamental steppingstone to the child's explorations of *pretended* enactments of routines and thus to the child's first symbolic representation of sentencelike relationships (Piaget, 1951). Nevertheless, for syntactic development, as in the cases of acquisition of semantic concepts like "dog" or "fiffin" or basic concepts such as object permanence (K. E. Nelson, 1974), a small amount of the right kind of evidence typically is sufficient to induce cognitive change.

Assumption 6. The process of system revision is primarily a short-term process for 2-year-olds and remains so for 3- to 5-year-olds, but with increasing development the child brings to bear increasing levels of information (on discrepancies) retrieved from long-term memory. This factor combines in effect with the assumption on the changing number of useful, codable discrepancies required as the child develops. An illustrative pair of speculations that can be tested is the following: in first-language learning, 3 to 10 codable discrepancies within 12 hours are needed for any system change at age 2½, but at age 4 years 1 to 3 codable discrepancies within 2 weeks may be sufficient for change to be induced. Once a first language is nearly mastered, the time-span involved for further syntactic system changes may be even more open—with the child sometimes drawing on codable discrepancies heard across many months, when additional revisions are made in the first language and when syntax revisions in second-language learning occur. In both cases, paradoxically, the number of instances of codable discrepancy required before new structures are incorporated into the child's system often may be higher than it is for 2½-year-olds. In a sense the conqueror or near-conqueror of a complex first language may adopt quite conservative strategies regarding the evidence that demands further changes in or extensions of the established language system.

Assumption 7. Among the most useful elements for stimulating syntactic change are "recast comparisons" in which the following sequence of sentences occurs: the child produces a sentence (e.g., "The glass broke") that is immediately given a reply which retains the basic meaning of the child's sentence but displays it in a new sentence structure (e.g., "The glass fell and broke"). Other kinds of comparisons besides recast comparisons are no doubt useful and perhaps necessary to the child's advances in syntax. Prime possibilities to be explored are any comparisons (like recasts) in which the same topic is redisplayed, but with analyses over many statement-reply-statement exchanges "chained" together. There is growing evidence that different mother-child pairs have varying success at constructing such conversational "chains" which maintain a topic, as well as varying frequencies of using recasts and other specific types of reply. However, it is assumed that the comparison process remains fundamentally the same regardless of the particular sentence structures that enter the comparison.

A strategy for discovering what kinds of comparisons do make a difference in the child's syntactic progress would be to use experimental intervention procedures similar to those described for studies on recasts, with a search for *convergence* between the experimental results and correlational, naturalistic observations concerning the relation between sentence types in input speech and the children's progress in acquiring particular syntactic structures. One cross-study example of such convergence is already apparent in the case of recasts: relatively rapid syntactic growth for children has been shown to be related to adults' use of recasts in the intervention investigations cited above, in line with recent cross-sectional work by Newport (1976). Her correlations (Table IX) revealed that the maternal variable most strongly and consistently related to advanced levels of language in her sample of children was the mother's frequent use of recasts that did not include an exact repetition of the child's utterance (labeled "partial plus" imitation by Newport). Another kind of convergence that should be sought is between data from infrequent "sampling" (e.g., an hour a week or month) of a small part of the child's speech (the standard procedure currently) and *intensive* accounts of most of the child's speech. Our theories and our remedial treatment strategies are likely to lack closure and power until enough children are observed on highly intensive schedules—say, 6 to 9 hours a day—to show how and when genuine advances in language are accomplished. I have termed such intensive scrutiny of a child's language the "shadow technique," as the child is indeed never far from some familiar observer (e.g., the mother). So far I know of only two children observed under any sort of intensive sampling procedure, but the data we have provide at least two forms of convergent support for the ideas and evidence offered above: (1) 2-year-olds lacking tag-question forms (e.g., "He ran, didn't he?") can be induced to introduce them into their system, by providing adult tag–questions in recasts and other replies to the child's sentences; (2) the process of adding to or revising language primarily rests upon short-term memory (minutes or hours, not days) in the 2-year-old.

One of the implications of this model in relation to disturbances or delay in syntactic acquisition is that most such instances probably do not rest in syntactic peculiarities in the input provided by mothers, fathers, other adults, or older children. As argued above, a few appropriate examples of every form may be all that is required, a point also supported by the usual success of children in acquiring speech despite almost incredible variations within and between cultures in who spends time with the language learner—talkative adults, relatively nontalkative adults, adults as well as older children of various ages, or older children almost exclusively—and in the provision of one or many language models.

A great many of the difficulties which autistic or aphasic children experience in language may lie in various kinds of failure to establish the early communication system and the early conceptual system (Caparulo and Cohen, 1977; Lewis, 1977; Shapiro, 1977). These are the systems that the child then links, as Katherine Nelson (1974, 1977) describes, to a syntactically governed combinatorial system. However, I believe that the transitions from early words to the child's first word combinations and then to more complex sentences may involve more continuity in process than I perceive in Katherine Nelson's account. Cognitive comparison processes as described above may be applied well before age two, at the time of the child's very first productions of two related words—either in a successive pattern with two briefly separated words (Bloom, 1975; Dore et al., 1976) or together in one utterance (as marked by pauses and intonation). In any event, it is clear that the above model assumes a complex, but efficient process of comparing sentence structures, which is handled well by most children. The onset of this complex process or its continued operation could easily be prevented by relatively specific deficits in attention to what others say, in memory, in articulation, or in speech perception. This line of thinking leads once again to the suggestion that a child fully capable of mastering language can be blocked from realization of that potential if means for overcoming or detouring around the child's serious but specific cognitive deficits are not discovered.

ON CONSEQUENCES FOR LATER LANGUAGE AND THINKING
OF EARLY INDIVIDUAL DIFFERENCES
IN LANGUAGE ACQUISITION

We have seen that children vary sharply in their pace and pattern of early semantic and syntactic acquisition. Yet at about age 5 years most children show in their syntactic skills relatively few contrasts with the syntactic skills of adults. In many instances then, it is clear that some of the early individual differences do not persist into later years; for example, a 3-year-old who is relatively slow in acquiring appropriate future-tense usage is nevertheless not likely to have continued difficulties with future-tense forms at age 5.

The certainty that many early individual differences are replaced by a common level of skill at around age 5, however, does not preclude the possibility that some early individual differences may lead to later individual differences of importance. Detailed data on this topic are just beginning to appear, so the general observation for now must be that we have not discovered what characteristics of language in the 2- or 3-year-old are related to continued individual differences in 5- or 6-year-olds or older children or adults. However, returning to the children in the "Fiffin Project" (K. E. Nelson and Bonvillian, 1977) described earlier, I shall take a brief look at certain relationships that have emerged in the study of these 19 children.

We wanted to determine if the strong individual differences in semantic development evident at age 2½ years would predict skills at age 4½ years, and to compare the levels of prediction obtained with predictions from a general cognitive measure at 2½ (the Bayley Mental Developmental Index). At age 4½ the children were observed in two sessions. Six measures were obtained: (1) sentence meaning and structure score, from a sentence imitation test employing diverse inflections and sentence structures; (2) syntactic complexity as indicated in the maximum length of the child's own sentences; (3) concept learning score, defined (as were the data on concept acquisition at 2½) in terms of the children's success in mastering a set of unfamiliar concepts labeled by nouns; (4) concept breadth for those concepts acquired; (5) Stanford-Binet IQ; and, (6) descriptive communication—skill in flexible language use, in generating a verbal description incorporating many features useful for recognition of a particular picture by a listener. Correlations were obtained between each of these variables and scores at 2½ years on the Bayley test, on sentence length, on production of all concept names, on comprehension of all concept names, and on two measures of "concept breadth"—concept acquisi-

tion based on single exemplars named by adults, and overgeneralization of the concept names. The Bayley scores on mental development
gave no significant predictions. Each of the other variables were useful in predicting skills at age 4½ and they were useful in contrasting
ways. High production scores for typical concept names at 2½ were
most strongly related to concept-learning success ($r = +.52, p < .03$)
and to IQ ($r = +.58, p < .01$) at 4½ years of age. On the other hand,
concept-comprehension scores were predictive only of high performance on the measure of sentence meaning and structure at age 4½,
the sentence-imitation test ($r = +.60, p x .01$). Yet another pattern held
for the measure of concept acquisition based on single named exemplars, a measure reflecting the child's tendency to build a general concept using very narrow evidence. This measure gave strongest predictions to the 4½-year-olds' high scores on concept breadth
($r = +.57, p < .02$) and descriptive communication ($r = +.52, p < .03$).
Similarly, the child's tendency to *over*generalize (another indicator of
breadth) concepts at 2½ years was also related ($r = .58, p < .01$) to
breadth of concepts at 4½ years of age.

If one looks for reasons behind these contrasting prediction patterns of early production and early comprehension, a good prospect is
the contrast in communication requirements when production and
comprehension are demonstrated. Production can be demonstrated
simply by using the name for a concept, for example, "lobster," upon
encounter with an exemplar for the concept—regardless of what an
adult may say or do in the situation. Early production measures of
concept learning predict later production measures of concet learning,
a very straightforward outcome. But why should early comprehension
scores predict later sentence-imitation skills, skill in capturing sentence
meaning and structure? After all, in one way the child has an even
simpler task in comprehension than in production since the child
need not say anything to show comprehension, as the child can point
to a lobster when an adult says "lobster." However, for the child, the
typical comprehension context may be more likely than the typical
prediction context to involve understanding of a sentence just produced by an adult. The child's ability to understand and respond to
sentences like "Show me the hedgehog" or "Where is the hedgehog?"
or "Bring me the hedgehog" will be reflected in the child's overall
comprehension performance, even though success in responding to
such statements sometimes can be achieved by keying solely or primarily on the noun which names the concept. Thus, since early comprehension scores partially reflect sentence-processing skills, the association of high concept comprehension at 2½ with skills in imitating
sentences at 4½ is less surprising than it appears at first inspection.

And, in regard to skills in dealing with sentences, the results show that 2½-year-olds' sentence lengths predict both sentence imitation ($r = .55, p < .02$) and sentence lengths ($r = .65, p < .01$) in the same children as 4½-year-olds.

The Fiffin Project, in comparison with prior longitudinal studies, provides some of the first strong evidence that detailed aspects of language development at age 2 to 2½ years are predictive (although standardized mental scores are not) of later syntactic, semantic, and communication skills. One set of factors which could have made a difference in the particular early-language to later-language stabilities observed is that in this study the children's scores in both production and comprehension were based upon the same set of concepts for all the children, with concept learning over a period of months in which all the children had controlled "input" exposure to exemplars and to the names ("lobster," "fiffin," etc.) for the concepts. Perhaps in contrast to Katherine Nelson's suggestion (1977) that early information on production tells little about later language skills, we will discover that different kinds of production as well as different kinds of comprehension hold different clues to future language skills. Any broad survey of the literature on the relations between comprehension and production measures of particular skills would show that production levels can either lead or trail comprehension levels, and it could prove to be the case that the most reliable predictors are the early measures that best represent the *leading surface* of change in the child's language—regardless of whether production or comprehension is the label on the measure.

So far next to nothing is known about early precursors of children's skills at 5–10 years in using figurative language or in using language to guide thinking. Also unknown is whether functional aspects of early communication are tied to any stable individual differences over periods of years. It should be interesting to determine, for example, if children relatively strong at 3 years in using language to control, or instruct, or query other children are also skilled in these same areas when 7 or 8 years of age. Finally, it may be worth distinguishing in our longitudinal studies between the later consequences of early individual differences in the rate of learning conceptual and syntactic regularities and the later consequences of early individual differences in the strategies children rely on in their efforts at learning.

FURTHER OBSERVATIONS ON CHANGES BETWEEN 2 AND 20

This section offers a brief survey of findings in three areas in which research to date has been sparse: children's discourse skills; syntactic developments after age 5 years; and figurative language. A common focus of discussion for these areas will be the child's developing consciousness or awareness of language and its uses.

Syntax beyond 5. Between 5 years and adolescence it appears that most children acquire the small minority of syntactic structures that were lacking at age 5. Increased skill in using embedded clauses and other complex clause structures usually is part of this growth. Chomsky (1969) and Maratsos (1974) have documented one interesting example in this field, the child's ability correctly to interpret sentences such as "The monkey promises (or tells) the dog to jump off." In this sentence and in other sentences at issue in the research, a complement verb (e.g., "to jump") occurs and the tricky part is to assign the correct subject—is it the monkey who will jump or the dog? Children at 5 generally "know" (but certainly cannot state) that with typical main verbs the noun phrase closest to the complement verb serves as its subject; thus if the sentence is "The monkey *tells* the dog to jump off," then "the dog" as the closest noun phrase is correctly treated by the children as the subject of "to jump." But mastery of exceptions to the rule for certain main verbs, notably "promises," does not occur until close to age 10. During this same period the child's ability explicitly to judge or explain the structure of sentences also improves, although few adults ever reach a high level of skill in this regard. The development of writing and reading skills, of course, also is usually concentrated in this period between age 5 and late adolescence, and these skills may be a large influence on the child's increasing ability to "turn back" on language in a conscious way to judge and shape sentences on the basis of their structure.

Constructing Conversations. Sophisticated discourse skills, like sophisticated reflections on the structures of sentences, continue developing through adolescence and into adulthood. At any period in development central questions about discourse routines and skills concern how the speaker and listener accomplish desired functional or pragmatic goals in their talk, how they signal intentions and recognition of intentions in their speech and nonverbal behavior, how they keep a conversation going on one shared theme, how they shift topics, and how they initiate and terminate conversations. The few investigations in this area (e.g., Garvey and Hogan, 1973; Bates, 1974; Gleason and Weintraub, 1975) suggest that around 2½ or 3 years children have a very clear notion of turn taking—I talk then it's your turn, and then mine again, and so forth—even though they miss many cues that adults rely on to guide decisions on turn behavior. At this same time some simple, fixed routines are applied over and over. One example is the summons-answer-explain routine Garvey and Hogan describe. This can be seen in the sequence, "You know what?" (child 1), "What?" (child 2), "You can come over to my house to play" (child 1). Beyond this early level, individual routines become more elaborated and less fixed, combinations of routines begin to be employed, and additional new routines are acquired.

The "trick-or-treat" routine for Halloween illustrates gradual elaboration of a routine as well as several other aspects of discourse. Gleason and Weintraub (1975) find that between 3 and 10 years children rely less and less on adult coaching, prompting, and encouraging. In addition, the routine begins as an implicit nonverbal request (standing at the door), moves next to a simple "trick-or-treat," and then gradually elaborates into a full routine with "trick-or-treat," "thank you," replies to the comments or questions of the treat-giver, and "good-bye" all incorporated.

These observations and a few related findings suggest to me intriguing changes across development in a number of senses. At first, in keeping discourse going, the young child seems *necessarily* to rely heavily on support from context, from others more skilled in discourse, and from the nonverbal behavior of both communication partners. Between 2 and 12 the child develops discourse skills sufficient to insure smooth, successful conversations of diverse sorts without necessary reliance on more skilled partners or on nonverbal or contextual support. But during the same time period the child is becoming increasingly skilled at using, in discourse, aspects of nonverbal behavior and verbal and nonverbal context to express or comprehend a whole range of information that escaped the attention or understanding of the young child. Included in this improving proficiency are tendencies to remember and use verbal context which is more and more removed from the immediately preceding sentences in a conversation, and to anticipate what may happen in the remainder of the conversation. Not all of these changes in the use of context and nonverbal behavior are subject to awareness. However, there is also a concomitant advance in the ability consciously to analyze and manipulate contextual and nonverbal clues as well as verbal tools of discourse. As a result of such skill shifts, the conversations of 10-year-olds or 16-year-olds are leagues above the conversations of 5-year-olds in complexity of verbal sequences as well as in complexity of information conveyed about emotional warmth, social class, interest, fatigue, and a wealth of other factors.

The processes by which discourse skills develop are undoubtedly tied in many ways to the processes involved in syntactic and semantic development. One possible connection is that particular kinds of discourse situations or routines may be crucial to certain steps in syntax acquisition. For example, it could be the case that some kinds of comparison sequences, in which the child's sentences (e.g., simple questions) and the adult's sentences (e.g., recast questions) in reply are compared by the child, occur almost exclusively in a few well-defined discourse routines. If this speculation is upheld, I anticipate the routines most heavily involved in the child's syntactic growth will be ones in which variations in auxiliary verbs and questions play a central role.

Figurative Language. Consider the following expressions: "A seed is like a pregnant lady"; "Clouds are like pillows"; "A friendship where the snow has fallen"; "The prison guard was a hard rock"; "The rose is out of town." Skills in understanding and producing figurative expressions, such as these similes and metaphors, are even slower to develop to a sophisticated level than skills in discourse. An open pair of questions for both kinds of skills is how "input" variations influence the pattern and rate of development. A common link between figurative language, discourse, and the child's knowledge of grammaticality is that high ability in each case involves a tendency to go beyond sentence production and comprehension to a conscious analysis of the sentence itself and how it can be compared (in form, in conotation, in imagery, as a tool for achieving discourse goals) with other sentences.

From recent research (Billow, 1975; Gardner, 1973; Gardner et al., 1977; Kogan, 1975; Milchman and K. E. Nelson, 1976; Pollio and Pollio, 1974) on children's abilities to understand and produce figurative expressions, a tentative sequence of development emerges. At a first level, 3- to 4-year-olds can understand some similes and metaphors, but very few. However, they can easily understand premetaphor expressions such as pantomime, in which actions and objects are used in a nonliteral way to represent other objects and actions. Moreover, the children who are most advanced in understanding pantomime also tend to be the most skilled in understanding verbal metaphor and simile. Symbolic play and pantomime may serve as a direct foundation for the development of the understanding of figurative verbal expressions. On a second level, children between 5 and 12 years become more and more aware that figurative expressions are not meant literally, but the children still rely often on incidental and concrete similarities between the terms of the expression as a basis for interpretation, rather than relying on the particular comparisons crucial to the meaning of the simile or metaphor. At a final stage the late adolescent or adult who reaches that stage (not all, and perhaps not even a majority do) knows and can explain what is meant by abstract figurative expressions and can produce original examples.

CONCLUSION

In terms of individual differences, more and more observations are accumulating that demonstrate that there are many ways (involving physical, personality, and cognitive dysfunction) to "go wrong" in language development, to fail to develop a full mastery of language. Increasingly there is evidence that successful paths of language acquisition also are highly varied. Children who use language fluently when they are 6-year-olds differ in the preceding developmental course, showing different rates, contrasting beginning steps, diverse strategies, and even different modes (speech, sign language, print). One implication of these findings is that there may be few fixed, language-specific abilities involved in language acquisition. Rather, general cognitive skills may underlie language acquisition and each child may use these skills to construct an initial, tentative language system that is idiosyncratic. The child at first must be flexible, capable of assessing cognitively some of the differences between his or her tentative system and the structures of adult language. Revision follows assessment, leading to new comparisons and a continuing cycle toward full mastery of the language employed by adults with the child. This is a remarkably open process with the burden squarely on the child to seek out and effectively utilize the necessary comparisons at each step in language acquisition, rather than upon the adult to teach and guide the child. This very characteristic makes it possible for nearly all children to acquire language regardless of the particular spoken language or sign language of their families, and despite considerable neglect or communicative reticence on the part of some parents and older siblings. But this same characteristic, an open process with the child's cognitive efforts as the primary base for mastering language, contributes to the enormous difficulty adults experience in trying to guide or stimulate language growth when the child (as in autism) is seriously delayed or deviant in language. To paraphrase an observation made above, just as there are many ways for children gradually to achieve the "match" between their own communication attempts and the communication system used by adults, there are many ways of failing to progress toward such a "match." Therefore in treatment and educational programs for language-limited children, an open search for the particular modes or styles of communication with a child that are helpful to the child's own efforts is likely to prove more productive than set reliance on any one program.

Interrelations between different areas of language and cognitive growth are being explored much more intensively now than in the past 15 years, but firm information on this topic is still limited. With this qualification, several generalizations can be drawn from the literature. Understanding the child's intentions appears to be one factor that is essential to understanding the child's progress in most areas of language, from first sentences to figurative and playful language to broad strategies of communication—and also to understanding individual differences in language development. Across areas as superficially different as structuring questions and naming concepts (e.g., "lobster," "flower"), there is much commonality in the child's processes of forming and revising working hypotheses or rules on the basis of a small amount of evidence or observation. A related process that also is important in semantic and syntactic, as well as conversational (discourse) and written, aspects of communication is the developing child's growing ability to monitor accurately ongoing communication and to relate current performance to past behavior and to future plans. Development of such self-monitoring is a central part not only of language mastery but also of the child's developing skills in problem-solving and memory. Finally, for normal language acquisition and for disorders of language acquisition there is an expanding recognition that the processes of representation in language are closely related to the processes of flexible symbolic representation generally. Indeed, the child may have to master nonlinguistic, playful symbolic representation before the child can learn to use words in any symbolic sense. Subsequent mastery of precise, literal expression through language may go hand in hand with futher refinement of nonlinguistic representational skills. The developmentally late skills of using language figuratively, but still with considerable precision, may require a return to the qualities of playfulness and flexibility that characterized the child's first attempts at representation.

REFERENCES

Bates, E. (1974), Acquisition of pragmatic competence. *J. Child Language,* 1:277–281.
Bever, T. G. (1970), The cognitive basis for linguistic structures. In: *Cognition and the Development of Language,* ed. J. R. Hayes, New York: Wiley, pp. 279–362.
Billow, R. M. (1975), A cognitive developmental study of metaphor comprehension. *Develpm. Psychol.,* 11:415–423.

Bloom, L. (1975), *One Word at a Time.* The Hague: Mouton.

Bonvillian, J. D. & Nelson, K. E. (1976), Sign language acquisition in a mute autistic boy. *J. Speech & Hear. Dis.,* 41:339–347.

—— —— (1977), Development of sign language skills in autistic, retarded, and aphasic children. In: *Understanding Language Through Sign Language Research,* ed. P. Siple. New York: Academic Press (in press).

—— —— & Charrow, V. R. (1976), Languages and language-related skills in deaf and hearing children. *Sign Language Studies,* 12:211–250.

Brown, R. (1977), Word from the language acquisition front. Read at the annual meeting of Eastern Psychological Association, Boston.

—— Cazden, C., & Bellugi, U. (1967), The child's grammar from I to III. In: *Minnesota Symposia on Child Psychology,* ed. J. P. Hill, Minneapolis: University of Minnesota Press, 2:28–73.

—— & Hanlon, C. (1970), Derivational complexity and order of acquisition in child speech. In: *Cognition and the Development of Language,* ed. J. R. Hayes, New York: Wiley, pp. 11–53.

Caparulo, B. K. & Cohen, D. J. (1977), Cognitive structures, language, and emerging social competence in autistic and aphasic children. *This Journal,* 16:620–645.

Chomsky, C. S. (1969), *The Acquisition of Syntax in Children from 5 to 10.* Cambridge, Mass.: M.I.T. Press.

Cohen, D. J., Caparulo, B. K., & Shaywitz, B. (1976), Primary childhood aphasia and childhood autism. *This Journal,* 15:604–615.

DePaulo, B. M. & Bonvillian, J. D. (1977), The effect on language development of the special characteristics of speech addressed to children. *J. Psycholing. Res.* (in press).

Dore, J., Franklin, M. B., Miller, R. T., & Ramer, A. L. H. (1976), Transitional phenomena in early language acquisition. *J. Child Language,* 3:13–28.

English, S. T. & Prutting, C. A. (1975), Teaching American sign language to a normally hearing infant with tracheostenosis. *Clin. Pediat.,* December: 1141–1145.

Ferguson, C. A. & Slobin, D. I., eds. (1973), *Studies of Child Language Development.* New York: Holt.

Fourgin, A. M. (1975), Language development in the absence of expressive speech. In: *Foundations of Language Development,* ed. E. H. & E. Lenneberg. New York: Academic Press, 2:263–268.

Gardner, H. (1973), *The Arts and Human Development.* New York: Wiley.

—— Winner, E., Bechhofer, R., & Wolf, D. (1977), The development of figurative language. In: *Children's Language,* ed. K. E. Nelson. New York: Gardner Press (Halsted/Wiley) (vol. 1, in press).

Garvey, C. & Hogan, R. (1973), Social speech and social interaction. *Child Develpm.,* 44:562–568.

Gleason, J. B. & Weintraub, S. (1975), The acquisition of routines in language. *Language in Society,* 5:129–136.

Hatch, E. (1976), Language teaching and language learning. In: *Handbook of Perception,* ed. E. C. Carterette & M. P. Friedman. New York: Academic Press, 8:363–386.

Heras, I. & Nelson, K. E. (1972), Retention of semantic, syntactic, and language information by young bilingual children. *Psychonomic Sci.,* 29:391–393.

Kogan, N. (1975), Sensitivity to metaphor in children and adults. Read at the annual meeting of the American Psychological Association.

Lenneberg, E. (1962), Understanding language without the ability to speak. *J. Abnorm. Soc. Psychol.,* 65:419–425.

Lewis, M. (1977), Language, cognitive development, and personality. *This Journal*, 16:646–661.

Maratsos, M. (1974), How preschool children understand missing complement sentences. *Child Developm.*, 45:700–706.

Milchman, M. S. & Nelson, K. E. (1976), The development of pantomime comprehension and comprehension of verbal simile and metaphor (unpublished manuscript).

Nelson, K. (1974), Concept, word, and sentence. *Psychol. Rev.*, 81:267–285.

_____ (1977), First steps in language acquisition. *This Journal*, 16:563–583.

Nelson, K. E. (1974), Infants' short-term progress toward one component of object permanence. *Merrill-Palmer Quart.*, 20:3–8.

_____ (1977), Facilitating children's syntax acquisitions. *Develpm. Psychol.*, 13:101–107.

_____ & Bonvillian, J. D. (1974), Concepts and words in the two-year-old. *Congition*, 2:435–450.

_____ _____ (1977), Early language development. In: *Children's Language*, ed. K. E. Nelson, New York: Gardner Press (Halsted/Wiley) (vol. 1, in press).

_____ Carskaddon, G., & Bonvillian, J. D. (1973), Syntax acquisition. *Child Develpm.*, 44:497–504.

_____ & Kosslyn, S. M. (1975), Semantic retrieval in children and adults. *Develpm. Psychol.*, 11:807–813.

Newport, E. (1976), Motherese. In: *Cognitive Theory*, ed. N. J. Castellan, D. B. Pisoni, & G. R. Potts. Hillsdale, N.J.: Erlbaum (vol. 2, in press).

Piaget, J. (1951), *Play, Dreams, and Imitation*. New York: Norton.

Pollio, M. & Pollio, H. (1974), The development of figurative language in children. *J. Psycholing. Res.*, 3:185–206.

Schank, R. C. & Abelson, R. P. (1975), Scripts, plans and knowledge. Read at the 4th International Joint Conference on Artificial Intelligence, Tbilisi.

Shapiro, T. (1977), The quest for a linguistic model to study the speech of autistic children. *This Journal*, 16:608–619.

Strohner, H. & Nelson, K. E. (1974), The young child's development of sentence comprehension. *Child Develpm.*, 45:567–576.

PART III: LANGUAGE DEVELOPMENT

8

LANGUAGE, COGNITIVE DEVELOPMENT, AND PERSONALITY

Melvin Lewis

Yale Child Study Center, Yale University

Prerequisites for language development include genetic factors, an intact central nervous system, adequate psychological care, specific linguistic stimulation, and cognitive-developmental structures. Deficits in any of these areas may lead to impairments in language development, which sometimes are etiologically specific. A dismaturation between nonlinguistic representation and symbolic language development may also occur. "Affective conservation" in particular may be delayed, leading to anxiety. Misunderstanding may result from a failure to recognize the differential rates of development of specific cognitive functions, including affective conservation and language. Certain peculiarities in language usage and specific speech patterns reflect neurotic conflicts. Maturation of language development, associated with maturation of cognitive development, enables the child to deal with anxiety more effectively

Reprinted with permission from *Journal of the American Academy of Child Psychiatry,* Vol. 16, No. 4, Autumn, 1977, 646–661.

Appreciation is expressed to Dr. Dorothy Otnow Lewis, for her original contribution on the work of Valéry, and to Drs. Robert S. Adams and Seymour Handler, who were co-leaders with Dr. Lewis in a study group on Language, Structuralism, and Child Psychoanalysis from which some of the material in this paper was drawn.

*than previously when the child's ability to comprehend and concep-
tualize experiences was still limited. Attention to cognitive functions, particularly symbolic language development, may enhance
treatment.*

Language development, biological development, cognitive development, personality development and its variations, and social experiences are interrelated. My purpose here is to explore some theoretical
and clinical relationships between each of these lines of development.

Definitions. The generic term *language* is used to include its symbolic,
semantic, and verbal speech components. Clearly, the most distinguishing human function is symbolic language: the ability to use sig-
nifiers to refer to significates. As Lieberman and Crelin (1971) put it,
"Man is human because he can say so" (p. 222). A *symbol* is truly representational in that it enables a discourse about things independent
of the things themselves. This linguistic use of the term symbol must
be distinguished from the psychoanalytic use of the term, which con-
notes an affect-laden, primordial image that is more or less universally
understood and virtually transcends the ordinary understanding of
language; and from the psychoanalytic term protosymbol (Peller,
1965), meaning a prestage of a psychoanalytic symbol found in young
children who are close to their bodies and their functions. The transitional object (Winnicott, 1953) is an example of a psychoanalytic prestage that occurs before a true symbolic representation is established.

LANGUAGE AND SYMBOLIC DEVELOPMENT

The acquisition of language begins with the child's genetic predisposition for dealing with complex patterns and the potential anatomical development for human speech (Lieberman, 1968). At 1 or 2
months of age, even before babbling, infants can discriminate between
speech stimuli that mark differences in speech-sound categorization;
e.g., "pa" vs. "ma" (Morse, 1974). A normal child with an intact central nervous system appears to have the capacity to learn any known
language, provided the child receives the appropriate linguistic stimulation.

Exactly how language develops is yet to be determined; our understanding of the phenomenon of language is incomplete, notwithstand-
ing the contributions of Chomsky (1972), Lenneberg (1967), K. Nelson (1977), K. E. Nelson (1977), and many others (see the review of
Vetter and Howell, 1971). All children appear to follow the same
sequence in the development of phonology, syntax, and semantics, all

of which, while interrelated and interdependent, can be more or less separately traced (Boltaxe, 1976).[1] Chomsky's 1957 theory of generative transformational grammar suggests that in some way, perhaps through "innate intellectual structures," the child develops a basic grammar that can generate an infinite number of sentences, and an optional transformational grammar that transforms the underlying basis of a sentence into its various forms, e.g., passive, interrogative, and so on.

Alternatively, the inner structures may derive from the sensorimotor schemas; indeed, the formation of such schemas during the long sensorimotor period may be essential for the subsequent emergence of language and linguistic competence. Language in this view is one expression of what Piaget terms the "semiotic" function, which includes symbolis games, imagery, and imitation (Inhelder, 1971).

The child begins to use language as a symbolic instrument, initially, and necessarily, through the help of the mothering person, whom we can call "the mother." The mother, for example, will use a word, "Dada" or "Mama," then "Daddy" and "Mommy," as a symbol, and in so doing she helps in the organization of the symbolizing process that is taking place within the infant. She does not create that process within the infant, but she facilitates its development. Initially, of course, considerable overextension occurs; a child may call all men "Daddy," or all four-legged animals "doggie," until further accommodation of the concepts, or schemas, of "Daddy," or "doggie" occurs.

This description of the role of the mother's spoken language is highly condensed and oversimplified. It is very likely, for example, that the mother's spoken words initially are experienced by the infant as tones and rhythms, rather than as words with meanings, and as such are part of the unprecedented kinesthetic, tactile, visual, auditory, olfactory, and gustatory bombardment that the infant tries to assimilate and organize into schema. Eventually, the percept of, say, "mother" and word "Mother," already linked, become better defined. There is ample evidence that mothers are sensitive language teachers of their children (Moerk, 1974). The sensitive timing, repetition, and associated pleasurable affects with which the mother uses words for labeling, shaping, etc., all serve specifically to stimulate the development of language.

---

[1]phonology: the sound structure of morphemes, phonemes, and words
syntax: categories such as noun, verb, sentence
semantics: the meaning of words and utterances and the relations between them.

At the same time, prior to the development of language as well as subsequently, it seems possible to "know" (insofar as we know what it means to know) about what one sees or hears or feels, even though one is not yet able to label, describe, and communicate to others one's experience of "knowing" in this self-evident, experiential sense. For example, an infant "knows" (or at least responds and remembers) when he or she experiences what we as adults choose to call, say, love, or knows (in this same sense) when he or she is being held, say, by an anxious mother—and knows this long before he or she has developed symbolic language to the point where he or she can use the words mother, love, or anxiety. In Piaget's terms, early schemata of experience precede symbolic language. Interestingly, in language acquisition, comprehension too precedes production: children understand words and sentences long before they can say them.

While the symbolizing function appears to begin before language is fully developed, it requires the full development of language to further its own development toward precision and increased communication. Even this is probably not a correct way of putting the matter; it is highly unlikely that symbolic function in general, and language in particular, are two completely separate and independent processes, at least not once the mechanisms of assimilation and accommodation have proceeded to the point where a significant coalescence of functions has occurred.

Yet, nonlinguistic representational thinking continues even while symbolic verbal language develops. Representational activity may take place, for example, in action and through images, as well as by symbolic language (Bruner, 1964). Indeed, a child may use gesture, music, or painting as expressive instruments for abstract concepts, yet may not have language. Language, in this context, is only part of the symbolic function. Furth (1966), for example, has clearly shown that deaf children who have virtually no language can solve cognitive problems and apparently have representation without the help of language. In any case, as Sinclair (1975) has pointed out, "Knowledge in the deeper sense, those operations and concepts that make it possible to absorb information and fit it into a meaningful framework, do[es] not stem from language" (p. 224). In Piaget's (1937) account of the sensorimotor state of development, the first roots of knowledge and its logical organization are in activity.

Even from a psychoanalytic perspective the motor-spatial aspects of communication are important. Ritvo (1976), for example, has described how the modes for expressing wishes, defenses, and transference in child analysis are frequently corporal rather than linguistic, in the sense that the "child uses his own bodily actions, the space in which the analysis takes place, the physical properties and representational potentialities of the objects he and the analyst are using (p. 9).

Further support for a nonverbal way of conceptualizing is found in the work of Bogen (1969) who suggests the idea of two distinct minds, each related to a particular hemisphere (the left for language and verbal activity; the right for nonlanguage and nonverbal functions such as the capacity for apposing or comparing perceptions, schemas, and engrams). Musical capacity in particular, for example, has been associated with the right hemisphere (Alajouanine, 1948; Critchley, 1953; Schlesinger, 1962; Luria, 1966).

SYMBOLIC DISMATURATION

Given this postulated duality—nonlinguistic representative thinking and symbolic language—it is possible to conceptualize a disharmony, or dismaturation, between the two. A child may have a capacity for nonlinguistic representational thinking, but, for one reason or another, may not have adequate symbolic language through which to express himself or herself. On the other hand, some children may appear to have a well-developed symbolic language, or at least a grammar and a vocabulary, yet at the same time have a poorly developed cognitive capacity for independent abstract thought. During the phallic-oedipal period (about age 3 years), children begin to use certain aspects of language, particularly syntax, which appear to be more mature than their cognitive level (Bloom, 1970), and early postoedipal children will try out long words at a time when they have not yet fully consolidated operational thinking.[2] This sometimes misleads adult into thinking that the child comprehends more than he or she actually does.

A somewhat different kind of disharmony, or intrinsic dismaturation, may occur in which language fails to achieve autonomy. For example, Hanfmann et al. (1944) described Goldstein's patient, Lanuti, whose verbal behavior was adequate, but only in the context of concrete, everyday situations; without that situational support, "words and objects were merely shifting patterns of sounds or colors" (p. 46). The dismaturation here is intrinsic within the line of cognitive function and has to do with the degree of autonomy and stability of the comprehension and use of symbolic language, i.e., the degree to which symbolic language per se is independent of the actual presence

---

[2]An "operation" is a symbolic or representational act which is part of an established conceptual organization.

of the things and stimuli being depicted. In this respect the brain-damaged adult's utterances are quite similar to a young child's utterances in that they appear to depend upon the support of the nonlinguistic context. For example, if one asks a young child a question "out of the blue," one often draws a blank (Bloom, 1975). Such children characteristically tend to respond more readily when they are asked to talk about events that are in a more immediately perceived context (Brown and Bellugi, 1964).

This kind of intrinsic dismaturation—symbolic language development that appears to be advanced but is not yet autonomous and completely free from immediate perception—is seen most clearly prior to the time when the capacity for concrete operational thinking begins to appear, when the child is still tied to immediate perceptions and has not yet achieved conservation. Conservation is a keystone phenomenon here, in the following way. We know that the appearance of conservation itself is a slowly evolving process, having different rates for different qualities, such as weight and length. For example, the conservation of visual objects occurs quite early, usually by the end of the sensorimotor period (by age 2 years). Quantity is conserved at 6–8 years, and weight, around 9–12 years. The variation in age at which different conservations are achieved is probably related to how easily the particular property can be dissociated from the child's own action. Length, for example, can be objectified more readily than weight.

Affects may undergo a similar operation. Harter (1976) has developed the concept of "affective conservation," which appears to be a late phenomenon in the differential lag just mentioned. The fact that feelings are least related to body configurations, and are so powerfully associated with immediate subjective experiences, may account for the delay in the child's capacity to conceptualize them, conserve them, and take distance from them. In this view, affects are conceptualized as properties that the child masters, in much the same way that the child masters length, height, weight, and so on. In psychoanalytic practice, too, the observation has been made that verbalization of perceptions precedes verbalization of feelings (Katan, 1961).

This kind of unevenness, or dismaturation, in the ontogenetic emergence of certain logical operations, including autonomous symbolic language and conservation of affects—an unevenness that Piaget terms *décalage*—is of great interest, since it is also accompanied by a particular phenomenon of thought and language seen early in the concrete operational stage. At this stage the child cannot yet think about his or her own thinking. Clinically, this manifests itself as a difficulty the child has in observing his or her own thoughts. For example, a 6- or 7-year-old child may have an impressive vocabulary and appear to have this observing function, but in fact the child may not yet have reached this level of conceptual functioning.

Specifically, some internal distancing appears to be necessary for a child to talk about a need more or less independent of that need and of the child's immediate wish to have that need gratified. Werner and Kaplan (1963) have used the terms *distancing* and *distance* to mean the "material dissimilarity between the uttered patterns and the depicted event" (p. 102) that occurs, for example, when a child "translates" onomatopoetic expressions into a given linguistic form. Distance in their sense is the young child's shift from language which is initially bound to the immediate perception, to the use of spoken words at a distance from the depicted event, which enables the child to communicate concepts through words independent of the actual presence of the concrete thing or event.

I am here extending their meaning of the terms distance and distancing to include the special case in which distance can be taken from the perception of feelings. This particular capacity is a later phenomenon, appearing characteristically when the stage of concrete operational thought is established.

Psychoanalytic ego development, Piaget's cognitive development, and language development possibly describe different aspects of this phenomenon in which distance from feelings can be achieved. Thus, at the same time that a child makes a shift from the pleasure principle to the reality principle as he or she consolidates the resolution of the oedipal conflict, the child also makes a shift from preoperational to operational thinking, and furthermore experiences important shifts in language development. These linguistic shifts include a modification in language usage; extremes, e.g., "I hate you," occur less frequently, and more precise labeling and classifying appear. Other categorical shifts in the child's language development that also occur at this time include a shift from syntagmatic responses to paradigmatic responses (Francis, 1972).[3] Psycholinguists have shown that certain other linguistic patterns begin to be understood in their generality by children when they are 6 or 7, or older (Sinclair and Ferreiro, 1970). Prior to this age young children link temporal succession to succession of

---

[3]Syntagmatic associations are response items that are in a different grammatical class than the stimulus (i.e., the words just "go together"), e.g., hot-bath, or apple-eat; whereas paradigmatic associations are response items that belong to the same grammatical class as the stimulus; e.g., hot-cold, or apple-pear.

enunciation; e.g., a young child will interpret the sentence, "The girl goes upstairs when the boy has parked the car," as if it meant that the girl goes upstairs first and the boy parks the car afterward (Ferreiro, 1971). After this age, the child is no longer tied to this concrete perception of sequence. Further, as K. E. Nelson (1977) has noted, between 5 and 10 years of age children become more conscious of the structure of the language they use.

Put another way, at the point that the child is no longer dominated by oedipal strivings and can take distance from them, he or she can also conceptualize intellectually the relationship between two different, and perhaps opposite, perceived feelings (loving and hating), without being perplexed by or tied to either one; furthermore, at the same time the child has acquired the important linguistic capacities just mentioned.

While all these shifts—ego developmental, cognitive, and linguistic—occur at about the same time, it is not yet clear whether one follows from the other, or whether they are each different manifestations of a common developmental shift. Interestingly, from a psychoanalytic viewpoint, the child at this stage also shifts from a "phobic" to an "obsessional" organization characteristic of latency.

Symbolic language now increases the possibility of distinguishing between wishes and fantasies on the one hand, and reality on the other, and thus helps to establish secondary process (Katan, 1961). In psychoanalytic theory, language not only serves to organize external experiences; it is also the first and most fundamental step toward conscious drive mastery (A. Freud, 1936).

As Peller (1966) said, "Language gives us both a distance from and a new intimacy with our own selves" (p. 462). Children who have difficulty in impulse control also have associated language difficulties, while improvement in the facility of language tends to foster between impulse control, and vice versa (Katan, 1961).

When there is a differential delay (décalage) or incomplete development in the capacity to take distance from the perception of feelings, whether for ego developmental, cognitive, or linguistic reasons, the child experiences a perplexing and anxiety-arousing state, since the dilemma cannot be understood, much less resolved. When maturation occurs, the dilemma evaporates, and the child is suddenly less anxious. Indeed, we may now conceptualize latency in cognitive and linguistic terms as well as affective terms.

During the early oedipal struggle the child is also at the stage of preoperational thinking. The child at this stage is dominated by his or her immediate experience of a feeling, and the feeling itself has an "all-or-none" quality. The child cannot take distance from the feeling, and each feeling in turn seems at times all-encompassing. Clinically, the child's love-hate language at this stage is an expression of this experience.

When the child enters the postoedipal period, a parallel shift occurs in cognitive development; the child moves to the stage of operational thinking: through conservation of affects, the child can now take distance from his or her feelings. For example, the child can now talk about past feelings as opposed to talking only about presently experienced, or perceived, feelings (the child also has a better sense of time at this stage). The child can now also recall that such feelings in the past went away and were replaced by opposite feelings. Further, the child can now observe that peers have similar episodes of positive and negative feelings. That is to say, the child not only can talk about a feeling when he is not necessarily experiencing it, but he can also comprehend intellectually that his total emotional state is made up of a number of different, changing, and sometimes conflicting feelings. Lastly, at this same time the child has a better command of language, due in part to all the linguistic shifts just mentioned. This total accomplishment enables the child to have more control (and therefore less fear) of feelings.

If these cognitive and language shifts do not occur, or if there is a dismaturation between them, one can imagine a state of cognitive and/or language fixation in which the child continues to have difficulty in taking distance from feelings (which are often polarized), and continues to treat them and talk about them as real and almost overpowering.

ENVIRONMENTAL DEFICITS, LANGUAGE, AND SYMBOLIC DEVELOPMENT

Several external factors may influence this early development, particularly early symbolic language development. Infants who have been "maternally" deprived, and perhaps particularly deprived of verbal stimulation (Langmeir and Matejcek, 1975), suffer an incomplete development of the capacity to symbolize, especially the capacity for language and abstract thinking (Provence and Lipton, 1962).

More recently, attention has been paid to the long-range effects of patterns of care in the neonatal period. For example, Ringler et al. (1975) have demonstrated that the amount of mother-child contact in the neonatal period influences the amount and kind of speech patterns used by mothers interacting with their children as late as 2 years of age. Specifically, they found that mothers who had experienced an additional 16 hours of contact with their infants, besides the usual minimum contact in the first 3 days after birth, used significantly more questions, adjectives, words per proposition, and fewer command words and content words when talking with their children than did the mothers in the control group. Ringler and his colleagues suggested that this difference in maternal language stimulation, brought about by hospital care practices, might be an important factor in shaping linguistic behavior in the young child.

Certain other environmental and child-rearing practices also influence language development and, consequently, social development. Twins, for example, who are reared in close proximity and without much adult stimulation, will develop idioglossia. Luria and Yudovich (1959) gave a dramatic example of gross speech retardation in their study of two 5-year-old identical twin boys: "As a rule our twins' speech acquired meaning only in a concrete-active situation. Outside this situation a word either did not possess any kind of permanent meaning, or only indicated what they were talking about without disclosing sufficiently clearly in what sense it was being used" (p. 40). When the twins were separated and placed in a special social situation in which they were compelled to speak with others in order to communicate with them, a rapid development of speech occurred.

The role of physical deprivation in the development of language is less clear. The lack of clarity has principally to do with the difficult methodological problems in the research in this area. All that can be said with certainty is that factors such as severe malnutrition, associated as they often are with multiple insults, produce a language deficiency which is not easily reversed by nutritional rehabilitation (Lefèvre, 1975).

LANGUAGE, INSTINCTUAL DEVELOPMENT, AND PLAY

Returning now to later language and personality development, particularly instinctual development, it is clear, although it has hardly been studied, that expressive language can be exercised in the service of discharging aggression and sexuality, or as a defense against anxiety. A child may say to a parent "I hate you" when he needs some psychological distance from his parents and from his own impulses. Similarly, the spoken word of a parent, or analyst, may be received as a pleasurable experience, or as a painful experience, and thus is a powerful socializing instrument. Spoken language, in the form of talking alone to oneself during play may also be the precursor of that inner, soundless speech, or private language, which probably plays an important role in the capacity for abstract thought, a development which occurs at later stages. Indeed, language performance in the form of speech can be considered a special form of play, and as such it is a mode of mastery. For example, playing with words is particularly pleasurable for the latency child, who enjoys puns and riddles. Words are then used in the same way as a joke or a dream, in that through ambiguity and innuendo a forbidden impulse or wish is expressed. The special use of words in this manner serves a function similar to that served by play in general, and thinking in particular; namely, a trial of action and controlled discharge, with consequent mastery.

Play symbols, including words as play symbols, are usually egocentric and idiosyncratic for the individual child, at least until the child is capable of operational thinking. That is, the meanings the child attaches to his or her play symbols are, for the most part, the child's own meanings, and are different from the more universal and conventionally assigned meanings that are generally attached by adults to words used in language. Further, such play symbols, together with symbol representation in psychoanalysis (and again unlike words in adult language), usually share some particular attribute of the thing which they signify (Jones, 1916). In this sense, play symbols in the young child represent earlier modes of thinking. It is usually not until 7 or 8 years of age that the child's private play and private language give way to the public (adult) signs. Again, the shifts in language development noted earlier occur concomitantly, and perhaps necessarily, with this change in play.

At the same time the use of words during childhood has certain limitations by virtue of their concreteness, the child's tie to the perceptual aspects of words as opposed to their symbolic meaning, the child's limited capacity to comprehend metaphor, and the young child's conceptual limitations in the use of words involving such concepts as time, life, death—all of which may place a constraint on the use of words. Children frequently attach their own idiosyncratic meanings to certain words,[4] particularly words that refer to body parts, body functions, and anxiety-arousing functions (usually of an aggressive, but sometimes sexual content). Children also avoid using certain words because such usage may represent an irretrievable discharge of a forbidden instinctual wish or impulse (the word cannot be taken back).

---

[4]"When I use a word," Humpty Dumpty said, in a rather scornful tone, "it means just what I choose it to mean—neither more nor less." "The question is," said Alice, "whether you *can* make words mean so many different things." "The question is," said Humpty Dumpty, "which is to be master—that's all" (Lewis Carroll, 1866).

SPOKEN LANGUAGE, NEUROTIC CONFLICT, AND PERSONALITY DEVELOPMENT

Language, then, seems to be both an integral part of personality development and a reflection of that development. Moving to the clinical situation, we have an opportunity to observe spoken language, particularly in relation to neurotic conflict and personality development. Spoken language is of course the single most important source of data as well as the most useful therapeutic instrument in child therapy.

Young children appear to regard words as an integral part of a wish or act; to think or say a word may be tantamount to gratifying the wish or committing the act. (Perhaps this is so because initially the word *is* part of the concept and a sensorimotoric part at that.)

It is interesting to note that Freud (1905) said, "children, who, as we know, are in the habit of still treating words as things, tend to expect words that are the same or similar to have the same meaning behind them" (p. 120). Again, in 1909, Freud stated, "It must never be forgotten how more concretely children treat words than grown-up people do, and consequently how much more significant for them are similarities of sound in words" (p. 59). Sirota (1969) gives a more recent example in which a 2-year-old child developed an acute phobic reaction on hearing the word "urine," which the child misunderstood as "you're in" while on the toilet.

Attempts have been made to define the specific relationship between personality and certain aspects of language behavior (Mahl and Schulze, 1964). Glauber (1944) once suggested that speech style, and possibly language content, parallel certain basic character types he proposed. For example, voluminous and indistinct speech was said to occur in the narcissistic-oral character, and rapid and distinct speech in the compulsive character. McCarthy (1954), too, has suggested that children with certain types of personality may have associated language disorders, although the personality types described did not fit into any well-defined category, but included instead the shy, timid, immature, tense, hostile, and aggressive child. None of these suggestions has been specifically validated. In children who have hysterical mechanisms, constricted use of certain affect-laden words occurs and the style of speech may betray an overidentification with the ambivalently loved parent (identification with the aggressor). The personality, so to speak, has made an imprint on the use of words. There is also some evidence to suggest that a particular style of language and speech development occurs along with the development of obsessional neuroses in children (Adams, 1973). However, more systematic studies are required to confirm these observations.

Children who have specific primary disorders of language, speech, or reading development may, of course, develop secondary reactions, including autistic behavior, hyperactivity, temper tantrums, enuresis, antisocial behavior, or withdrawal (Chess and Rosenberg, 1974; Butler et al., 1973; Rutter and Yule, 1973).

LANGUAGE AND INTERPRETATION IN CHILD ANALYSIS

The role of verbal language as a therapeutic instrument in psychotherapy must be considered. In psychoanalysis, the analyst uses words to interpret the past, current reality, or the transference—or all three (Lewis, 1974). Indeed, perhaps the most effective verbal interpretations are those that not only contain all three elements, but also have what Hartmann (1951) called "multiple appeal." This concept may be extended to include the special appeal that words have for children. Words when spoken have a concretizing effect as they provide labels, shape, and control over affects and previously ill-defined fantasies. More important, when words and experiences are linked, or rather reestablished, through the alleviation of repression by analytic interpretation, a reorganization of experiences occurs. Spoken language in interpretation, however briefly it is used, also appears to have a special effect—it serves as an instrument for a rapprochement with elemental feelings, and may thereby be the means by which a reorganization of inner feelings occurs. According to the French structuralists, the unconscious of one person and an "other" is bridged by language, and the unconscious itself "is structured like a language" (Lacan, 1957, p. 103). Unfortunately, the mechanism by which this rapprochement occurs has not been explored scientifically. However, we have some insight into this process from poetry and some poets. Valéry, for example, believed that the very understanding by another person of words by one person means that the words themselves vanish from the mind of the other person and are "replaced by their counterpart, by images, relationships, impulses. . . . Understanding consists in the more or less rapid replacement of a system of sounds, intervals, and signs by something quite different, which is, in short, a modification of interior reorganization of the person to whom one is speaking" (p. 64f.).

Humboldt, in 1836, alluded to this same process: "Men do not understand one another by causing one another to produce exactly the same concept but by touching the same link in each other's sense perceptions and concepts, by striking the same key in each other's individual instrument whereupon corresponding, but not identical, concepts arise in each of them. When the link in the chain, the key of the instrument, is touched in this way the whole organism vibrates and the concept that springs from the self stands in harmony with everything surrounding—even at a great distance—the individual link" (p. 169).

Yet, even for this aesthetic response to occur, certain levels of language, cognitive, and personality developments are necessary. In linguistic terms, the required specific level of language (semantic) development is that which occurs between 6 and 8 years of age, when the shifts mentioned earlier take place. In cognitive terms, the required general level of cognitive development, which may be pivotal, is probably the stage of operational thinking. In psychoanalytic terms, there is a marked shift from primary process to secondary process, from the pleasure principle to the reality principle, from the oedipal struggle to the postoedipal state.

In any event, when this response occurs, it is experienced subjectively as a sense of discovery, enlightenment, insight, and pleasure— surely desirable experiences! The sense of discovery, of course, also occurs spontaneously in the child, particularly when the child moves from a preoperational to an operational level of thinking, and makes a parallel shift in language development, with or without treatment. In psychoanalytic terms, one can say metaphorically that through language there is almost a direct leap from primary process to conscious awareness (Loewald, 1976).

It would appear from a pragmatic viewpoint that anything that facilitates cognitive growth will enhance emotional development, and vice versa. While in psychoanalysis there is the expectation that the more the child understands about his or her feelings, the more easily intellectual development will proceed, the converse also appears to be true; namely, the more the child's cognitive development, as reflected in the child's language, proceeds, the easier it will be for the child to understand his or her feelings and make connections. One obvious implication here is the need to give concomitant attention, through language, to the cognitive and emotional development in the child who is in psychotherapy.

Language, in the sense of symbolization, is the great mediator between cognitive and emotional development. In providing the child with a means to put his or her feelings into words, language enhances the child's mastery over feelings and allows greater energy for cognitive growth. Conversely, the cognitive leaps reflected in language development promote the mastery of emotions necessary for healthy growth and adaptation.

REFERENCES

Adams, P. L. (1973), *Obsessive Children*. New York: Brunner/Mazel.
Alajouanine, T. (1948), Aphasia and artistic realization. *Brain*, 71:229–241.
Bloom, L. (1970), *Language Development*. Cambridge, Massachusetts: M.I.T. Press.
———— (1975), Language development review. In: *Review of Child Development Research*, ed. F. R. Horowitz. Chicago: University of Chicago Press, 4:245–303.
Bogen, J. E. (1969), The other side of the brain. *Bull. Los Angeles Neurolo. Soc.*, 34(3):135–162.
Boltaxe, C. (1976), Personal communication.
Brown, R. & Bellugi, U. (1964), Three processes in the child's acquisition of syntax. *Harvard Educ. Rev.*, 34:133–151.
Bruner, J. S. (1964), The course of cognitive growth. *Amer. Psychologist*, 19:1–15.
Butler, N. R., Peckham, C., & Sheridan, M. (1973), Speech defects in children age 7 years. *Brit. Med. J.*, 1:235–257.
Carroll, L. (1866), *Alice's Adventures in Wonderland*. New York: Macmillan.
Chess, S. & Rosenberg, M. (1974), Clinical differentiation among children with initial language complaints. *J. Aut. Childh. Schizo.*, 4:99–109.
Chomsky, N. (1957), *Syntactic Structures*. The Hague: Mouton.
———— (1972), *Language and Mind*. New York: Harcourt, Brace Jovanovich.
Critchley, M. (1953), *The Parietal Lobes*. London: E. Arnold.
Ferreiro, E. (1971), *Les relations temporelles dans le langue de l'enfant*. Geneva: Droz.
Francis, H. (1972), Toward an explanation of paradigmatic-syntagmatic shift. *Child Developm.*, 43:949–959.
Freud, A. (1936), *The Ego and the Mechanisms of Defence*. London: Hogarth Press.
Freud, S. (1905), Jokes and their relation to the unconscious. *Standard Edition*, 8. London: Hogarth Press, 1960.
———— (1909), Analysis of a phobia in a 5-year-old boy. *Standard Edition*, 10:3–149. London: Hogarth Press, 1955.
Furth, H. G. (1966), *Thinking Without Language*. New York: Free Press.
Glauber, I. (1944), Speech characteristics of psychoneurotic patients. *J. Speech Dis.*, 9:18–30.
Hanfmann, E., Rickers-Ovsiankina, M., & Goldstein, K. (1944), Case Lanuti: extreme concretization of behavior due to damage to the brain cortex. *Psychol. Monogr.*, 57:1–72.
Harter, S. (1976), A cognitive-developmental approach to children's expression of conflicting feelings and a technique to facilitate such expression in play therapy. *J. Consult. Clin. Psychol.* (in press).
Hartmann, H. (1951), Technical implications of ego psychology. *Psychoanal. Quart.*, 20:31–43.
Humboldt, W. (1836), *Über die Verschiedenheit des menschlichen Sprachbaus*. Berlin-Boner: Drummer.
Inhelder, B. (1971), The sensory-motor origins of knowledge. In: *Early Childhood*, ed. D. N. Walcher & D. N. Peters. New York: Academic Press, pp. 141–155.
Jones, E. (1916), The theory of symbolism. In: *Papers on Psychoanalysis*. Baltimore:

Williams & Wilkins, 1958, pp. 103–124.

Katan, A. (1961), Some thoughts about the role of verbalization in early childhood. *The Psychoanalytic Study of the Child*, 16:184–188.

Lacan, J. (1957), The insistence of the letter in the unconscious. In: *Structuralism*, ed. J. Ehrmann. Garden City, N.Y.: Anchor Books, 1970, pp. 101–136.

Langmeir, J. & Matejcek, Z. (1975), *Psychological Deprivation in Children*. New York: Halsted Press, 3rd ed.

Lefévre, A. B. (1975), Language development in Malnourished children. In: *Foundations of Language Development*, ed. E. H. Lennenberg & E. Lennenberg. New York: Academic Press, 2:279–296.

Lennenberg, E. H. (1967), *Biological Foundations of Language*. New York: Wiley.

Lewis, M. (1974), Interpretation in child analysis. *This Journal*, 13:32–53.

Lieberman, P. (1968), Primate vocalization and human linguistic ability. *J. Acoust. Soc. Amer.*, 44:1574–1584.

—— & Crelin, E. S. (1971), On the speech of Neanderthal man. *Linguistic Inquiry*, 2:204–222.

Loewald, H. W. (1976), Primary and secondary process and language. Freud Anniversary Lecture, Psychoanalytic Association of New York.

Luria, A. R. (1966), *Higher Cortical Functions in Man*. New York: Basic Books.

—— & Yudovich, F. I. (1959), *Speech and the Developmental Process in the Child*. London: Staples Press.

McCarthy, D. (1954), Language disorders and parent-child relationships. *J. Speech Hear. Dis.*, 19:512–523.

Mahl, G. F. & Schulze, G. (1964), Psychological research in the extra-linguistic area. In: *Approaches to Semiotics*, ed. Thomas A. Sebeok. The Hague: Mouton, pp. 51–124.

Moerk, E. (1974), Changes in verbal child-mother interactions with increasing language skills of the child. *J. Psycholing. Res.*, 3:101–116.

Morse, P. (1974), Infant speech. In: *Language Perspectives*, ed. R. Schiefelbusch & L. Lloyd. Baltimore: University Press, pp. 19–53.

Nelson, K. (1977), First steps in language acquisition. *This Journal*, 16:563–583.

Nelson, K. E. (1977), Aspects of language acquisition and use from age 2 to age 20. *This Journal*, 16:584–607.

Peller, L. E. (1965), Language and development. In: *Concepts of Development in Early Childhood Education*, ed. P. B. Neubauer. Springfield: Thomas, pp. 59–83.

—— (1966), Freud's contribution to language theory. *The Psychoanalytic Study of the Child*, 21:448–467.

Piaget, J. (1937), *The Construction of Reality in the Child*. New York: Basic Books, 1954.

Provence, S. & Lipton, R. C. (1962), *Infants in Institutions*. New York: International Universities Press.

Ringler, N. M., Kennell, J. H., Jarvella, R., Navojosky, B. A., & Klaus, M. H. (1975), Mother-to-child speech at 2 years. *J. Pediat.*, 86:141–144.

Ritvo, S. (1976), Position paper for Panel on the Essential Components of the Child Analytic Situation. Read at the Association for Child Psychoanalysis, Kansas City, Missouri.

Rutter, M. & Yule, W. (1973), Specific reading retardation. In: *The First Review of Special Education*, ed. L. Mann & D. Sabatino. Philadelphia: Buttonwood Farms, 2:1–50.

Schlesinger, B. (1962), *Higher Cerebral Functions and Their Clinical Disorders*. New York: Grune & Stratton.

Sinclair, H. J. (1975), The role of cognitive structures in language acquisition. In: *Foundations of Language Development*, ed. E. H. Lennenberg & E. Lennenberg. New

York: Academic Press, 1:223–238.

—— & Ferreiro, E. (1970), Compréhension, production et répétition de phrases au mode passif. *Arch. Psychol.*, 40(160):1–42.

Sirota, M. (1969), Urine or you're in. *The Psychoanalytic Study of the Child*, 24:232–270.

Valéry, P. (1939), Poetry and abstract thought. In: *Paul Valéry*, tr. D. Folliot. New York: Vintage Books, 1961, pp. 52–81.

Vetter, H. J. & Howell, R. W. (1971), Theories of language acquisition. *J. Psycholing. Res.*, 1:31–64.

Werner, H. & Kaplan, B. (1963), *Symbol Formation*. New York: Wiley.

Winnicott, D. W. (1953), Transitional objects and transitional phenomena. In: *Collected Papers*. London: Tavistock Publications, 1958, pp. 229–242.

Part IV

TEMPERAMENT STUDIES

This section is of special interest to us, the editors, inasmuch as temperament has been a major focus of our own research studies. When, in the mid 1950s, we began to explore the possible significance of the infant's own intrinsic behavioral style for later development, the exclusively environmentalist view was firmly in the ascendency. It is true that a number of observations had been reported in the preceding two decades of individual differences in infants and young children in specific discrete areas of functioning. However, no long-term investigations had explored in any systematic fashion the influence such characteristics might have on developmental course. When we undertook a more comprehensive and systematic study of temperament and launched the New York Longitudinal Study in 1956, our psychiatric colleagues, with few exceptions, assumed we were returning to some outdated and discredited constitutionalist view.

In the past few years the climate of opinion has changed radically, and each year has seen an increasing number of studies of temperament, its relationship to other organismic and environmental factors, and its significance for healthy and deviant psychological functioning. We would attribute this change in the main to four developments: 1) the gradual realization that an exclusively environmentalist view was inadequate to explain individual differences in psychological development; 2) the weight of careful research studies documenting the active role in the parent-child interaction played by the infant's own perceptual and behavioral characteristics from the moment of birth on; 3) the resolution of the age-old argument over heredity and constitution versus environment in biology and psychology in favor of the view that an individual's characteristics are always the product of a constantly evolving nature-nurture interactional process; and 4) the influence of the findings of our own longitudinal studies of temperament.

In the current year, we have selected four articles from the large number of publications on temperament. Rapoport and her coworkers examine the correlation between newborn dopamine-β-hydroxylase blood level and infant temperament. This opens up the important area of investigation into the relationship between temperament and other organismic characteristics of the young infant. Plomin and Rowe report a comparison of identical and fraternal twins which indicates a significant genetic component in temperament. Our own data on continuities and discontinuities in the expression of temperamental characteristics from early infancy to adolescence in the New York Longitudinal Study are summarized. The findings are interpreted in terms of a model in which organism-environment interaction is considered to produce new behavioral patterns at succeeding age periods, which then interact with recurrent and new features of environment. Finally, Cameron reports an analysis of the preschool data of the New York Longitudinal Study in which the relationships between parental characteristics and changes in children's temperament over time were examined. As in our own report, Cameron emphasizes that temperament is neither an inborn, immutable characteristic nor just a function of past experience, but a reflection of both.

PART IV: TEMPERAMENT STUDIES

9

NEWBORN DOPAMINE-β-HYDROXYLASE, MINOR PHYSICAL ANOMALIES, AND INFANT TEMPERAMENT

Judith L. Rapoport, Cheryl Pandoni, Marilyn Renfield,
Georgetown University School of Medicine
C. Raymond Lake, and Michael G. Ziegler
National Institute of Mental Health

The authors examined newborn anomaly scores for 193 normal infants in relation to obstetrical history, newborn dopamine-β-hydroxylase (DBH), and 5-month (N=185) and 1-year (N=123) infant behavior, determined by a questionnaire completed by their mothers. There was no significant relationship between anomaly score and obstetrical history or 5-month infant temperament; low

Reprinted with permission from *American Journal of Psychiatry*, Vol. 134, **676–679**, 1977. Copyright 1977, the American Psychiatric Association.

Work done at Georgetown University School of Medicine was supported by Alcohol, Drug Abuse, and Mental Health Administration grant MH-20802 from the National Institute of Mental Health Psychopharmacology Branch and grant RR-60-14 from the National Institutes of Health Clinical Research Center.

The authors would like to thank Dr. M. Waldrop, Child Research Branch, National Institute of Mental Health, and Dr. David Abramson, Chief, Neonatology Division, Georgetown University Hospital, for their help with the screening study; Dr. John Bartko, Biometry Branch, National Institute of Mental Health, for statistical advice; and Mr. S. Potter and Mr. G. Palmer for technical assistance with the biochemistry.

significant correlations were found between newborn DBH and 1) infant irritability and unsociable response and 2) 1-year anomaly scores and reported activity levels. The authors discuss the possible importance of these findings.

In previous reports (1, 2) plasma dopmaine-β-hydroxylase (DBH) was found to correlate with the total score of minor physical anomalies of head, face, hands, and feet in a population of 81 hyperactive 6- to 12-year-old boys, but no correlation with any behavioral or cognitive measure was found. Minor anomalites werc also significantly associated with either maternal prenatal difficulties or paternal hyperactivity and with early onset of hyperactive behavior. Because these anomalies have been related to hyperactivity and aggressivity in preschool-aged children (3), a newborn screening for minor physical anomalies and follow-up of infant behavior was instituted at the Department of Pediatrics of Georgetown University Hospital during 1974–1975.·The present report is the first of a series on this newborn screening and follow-up.

Dopamine-β-hydroxylase catalyzes the conversion of dopamine to norepinephrine. The enzyme is localized in the norepinephrine-containing granules of the adrenal medulla and in storage vesicles of sympathetic nerve terminals. DBH is released from sympathetic nerves along with norepinephrine upon stimulation of the nerve (4). Prolonged stress can lead to sharp elevations in plasma DBH (5) and eventually in tissue DBH (6). During the first year of life, DBH activity is very low; there is about a 10-fold increase in enzyme activity from birth to the second decade (7, 8).

The purpose of this study was to examine newborn anomaly scores in relation to obstetrical history, newborn DBH, and subsequent infant behavior at 5 months and 1 year of age.

METHOD

During a 14-month period 933 normal newborn infants from white intact families were screened in the nursery of Georgetown University Hospital. Details of the selection process have been reported elsewhere (9). In addition to all "high" and "low" anomaly newborns, a subgroup having "middle" anomaly scores was selected for the study.

When infants were selected for the study, the mothers gave the researchers permission to examine their obstetrical charts and to obtain 0.5 ml of blood from the infants by heel-stick at the time of the PKU screening; the mothers also agreed to participate in a longitudinal study of infant temperament. The initial study sample included 196 infants—69 high, 64 middle, and 63 low anomaly newborns.

Obstetrical records of the 196 patients were scored by one of the authors (C.P.) for such background factors as maternal age and education, drug ingestion during pregnancy, previous miscarriages or abortions, bleeding or toxemia during the index pregnancy, length of labor, analgesia and anesthesia during labor, and infant Apgar scores at 1 and 5 minutes.

Approximately 0.5 ml of blood was obtained from each infant by heel puncture and was centrifuged for 5 minutes. Plasma samples were coded, stored at $-4\,^\circ$ C, a temperature at which DBH is stable, and assayed within 6 months. DBH was assayed by the radioenzymatic method of Molinoff and associates (6); tyramine was used as substrate at pH 5.5 in 1.7×10^{5}M $CuSO_4$, and 10 μl of plasma were incubated in a total volume of 300 μl. One unit of DBH activity represents 1 nmol/ml per hour of octopamine generated from tyramine. A mean of 23.6 ($\pm$16.1) units was obtained for the sample (range $=$ 2.5–80.1).

When the infants were 5 months old, 185 mothers completed the Carey Infant Temperament Scale (10), a 70-item questionnaire about an infant's behavior in a variety of specific situations (bathing, eating, dressing, play, etc.). The questions were devised to describe infant mood, activity, regularity, intensity, and adaptability because these dimensions of temperament have shown some value in predicting the development of behavior disorders in early childhood (11). Each item has three possible answers, generally dealing with two extremes and an intermediate position. For example, one question (item 9) asks about adjustment to change in feeding schedule and three choices are presented: easy adjustment, slow adjustment after several tries, or no adjustment after several tries. Responses were scored 1, 2, or 3 for the purpose of this study. The questionnaire has shown some relation to common pediatric problems during the first year of life (12) and is being widely used in current research.

As part of a continuing follow-up study 123 of the infants were seen at 1 year of age, at which time developmental testing and parent interviews were conducted and minor physical anomalies were reassessed; mothers again completed the infant temperament questionnaire. Details of sample selection have been presented elsewhere (9). The examining pediatrician for the 1-year-old group was blind to the newborn anomaly score and newborn DBH values.

RESULTS

Weighted anomaly score showed a low but significant positive correlation with maternal age (Pearson r=.17, p<.05). Mean maternal age for the present sample (28.7±4.7 years) was higher than that for the previous clinical sample of Quinn and Rapoport (2) (25.3±6.0 years), in which no relationship between anomaly score and maternal age was found. There was no significant relationship found between anomaly score and any of the prenatal or obstetrical variables.

Mean infant age at the time of blood sampling was 2.05 days (SD= 1.13) with a range of 1–4 days. DBH activity did not correlate significantly with any prenatal or obstetrical variables, including length of labor or use of drugs for anesthesia or analgesia during labor or delivery. There was no significant relationship with infant age at time of blood sampling (4=.08).

The 5-month infant temperament questionnaire was completed by 185 mothers. Each of the 70 items was examined in relation to sex, anomaly score, and DBH. No significant relationships were found between the anomaly score and any 5-month temperament item.

Six items from the questionnaire received different responses for males than for females (χ^2 from 6.19 to 11.11, df=2, p<.05). The items (and numbers) were as follows: females were reported to be more regular in sleep pattern (item 17), more protesting of minor procedures (item 44), more responsive to sounds (item 51), more adaptive on repeated exposure to sounds (item 53), more reactive to people (item 55), and calmer in play (item 70). These items did not seem to reflect a uniform dimension either when scored using Carey's a priori categories or in their factorial loading (described later).

Ten items on the 5-month temperament scale showed a low but significant relationship with DBH (r=.16 to .21). All of these items dealt with negative mood or fussing and crying in infancy. Specifically, there was a low but significant tendency for infants with higher newborn DBH not to adjust to change in schedule (item 25), to fuss persistently if a diaper is soiled (item 33), to fuss when in the doctor's office (item 47), to cry persistently when getting a "shot" (item 48), to cry loudly and persistently when sick (item 50), to react negatively to sounds and lights (item 53), to react negatively to strangers (item 56), to have an intensely negative response to strangers (item 57), and to have glum and unfriendly responses to familiar persons (item 58).

All of these responses were characteristic of more difficult infants in the original New York longitudinal study (11) and in Carey's a priori scoring scheme.

Factor analysis of the temperament scale was attempted for the sample, using a principal components analysis. The scale did not factor well—25 factors had an eigen value of 1 or more. When fewer factors were generated for the questionnaire data, an analysis yielded 5 factors accounting for 27% of the variance. Fewer than 5 factors did not account for the clinically meaninful variables, and 6 subdivided these variables finer than was felt necessary.

Factor I (9 items) dealt with items of contented, adaptable behavior. Factor II (12 items) contained items of activity and vigor. Factor III (9 items) contained responses dealing with negative responses to people and crying behavior. Factors IV and V (8 and 7 items, respectively) dealt with mildness and regularity.

Six of the 10 items that correlated significantly with DBH loaded significantly on Factor III (crying-negative). The other 4 items did not load on any factor. The correlation between DBH and the Factor II score for the sample was .25 (p<.01). No significant correlations were found between sex or anomaly score and any factor scores.

Newborn DBH was also examined in relation to 1-year temperament, behavior, and physical examination. Four items from the 1-year temperament scale showed significant correlation with DBH (Pearson r=.17 to .27). Specifically, 1-year-olds with higher newborn DBH values tended to have an intense, dramatic dislike of new foods (item 21) and were again rated as more fussy on items 33, 48, and 58, listed before for 5-month-old infants.

Newborn DBH also showed a low correlation with 1-year anomaly score (r=.17) and pediatric interview ratings of 1-year activity (r=.21). Detailed discussion of the 1-year behavioral data has been presented elsewhere (9).

DISCUSSION

The present study of infants selected at birth on the basis of newborn anomaly score, within a normal infant population, did not reveal any relationship between anomaly score and obstetrical history. However, our previous observation of a significant relationship between obstetrical risk and anomalies was made for a significantly younger sample of mothers, all of them parents of hyperactive children. Follow-up data for our sample at 1 year indicate that within the high anomaly group a history of prenatal difficulties predicts reported irritability and hyperactivity at 1 year of age (9), while this is not true for low anomaly 1-year-olds. Thus the lack of association between risk factors and anomaly score obtained in this study may be a result of sampling differences between the two studies.

The significant correlation between newborn DBH and the 1-year anomaly score suggests the possibility that minor insults early in fetal development that produce the anomalies might have a permanent influence on catecholamine metabolism.

The low but significant relationship between newborn DBH acitivity and items of fussy, negativistic infant behavior at 5 months and 1 year is of some interest. We considered the possibility that increased amounts of crying in the newborn period per sc might account for both for slightly elevated levels of DBH and greater crying behavior at 5 months. This did not seem a likely explanation, however, as all of the 196 infants were crying during the heel-stick procedure. Furthermore, amount of crying during the newborn period has no significant relationship to crying at 5 months of age (13). Crying was clinically assessed for our sample during the newborn screening: only 2 infants were thought to have a "weak cry." Both of these had unremarkable DBH values with respect to the rest of the sample (25.0 and 39.7 units, respectively).

The relationship between newborn DBH and 5-month irritability and crying is made more meaningful by the association of 6 of the 10 behavioral items with a factor of "fussiness," which emerged on the factor analysis. Because DBH may reflect peripheral autonomic activity, it is tempting to speculate about a physiologic basis for "hypersensitive" behavior described for some infants (14). However, even if DBH were found to reflect peripheral sympathetic nervous system activity during the first year of life, there is considerable instability of autonomic nervous system functioning in infancy, and autonomic measures in infancy may have little predictive value for later functioning (15).

It should be stressed that predictions from behavior during the first year of life to later social and emotional development are neglibgible (16) and that the present low correlations between DBH and temperament should be replicated in an independent study. In a continuing study we are examining the relationship of both DBH activity and 5-month and 1-year temperament to follow-up behavioral status.

REFERENCES

1. Rapoport, J.L., Quinn, P.O. & Lamprecht, F.: Minor physical anomalies and plasma dopamine-beta-hydroxylase activity in hyperactive boys. Am. J. Psychiatry 131:386–390, 1974.

2. Quinn, P.O., & Rapoport, J.L.: Minor physical anomalies and neurologic status in hyperactive boys. Pediatrics 53:742–747, 1974

3. Waldrop, M., Pederson, F., & Bell, R.O.: Minor physical anomalies and behavior in pre-school children. Child Dev. 39:391–400, 1968

4. Gewirtz, G.P., & Kopin, I.J.: Release of dopamine-β-hydroxylase activity with forced immobilization. Nature (New Biol) 230:278–288, 1971

6. Molinoff, P.B., Brimijoin, W.S., Weinshilboum, R.M., et al.: Neurally mediated increase in dopamine-β-hydroxylase activity. Proc. Natl. Acad. Sci. USA 66:453–458, 1970

7. Freedman, L.S., Ohuchi, T., Goldstein, M., et al.: Changes in serum dopamine-β-hydroxylase activity with age. Nature (New Biol) 236:310–311, 1972

8. Weinshilboum, R.M., & Axelrod, J.: Reduced plasma dopamine-β-hydroxylase activity in familial dysautonomia. N. Engl. J. Med. 285:928–942, 1971

9. Quinn, P.: Minor physical anomalies: a newborn screening and one year follow-up. J. Am. Acad. Child. Psychiatry (in press)

10. Carey, W.B.: Measuring infant temperament. J. Pediatr. 81:414–418, 1970

11. Thomas, A., Chess, S., & Birch, H.L.: Temperament and Behavior Disorders in Children. New York, New York University Press, 1968

12. Carey, W.B.: Clinical applications of infant temperament measurements. J. Pediatr. 81:824–828, 1972

13. Fisichelli, V.R., Karelitz, S., Fisichelli, R.M., et al.: The course of induced crying activity in the first year of life. Pediatr. Res. 8:921–928, 1974

14. Bergman, P., & Escalona, S.K.: Unusual sensitivities in very young children. Psychoanal. Study Child 4:333–353, 1949

15. Lipton, E.L., Steinschneider, A., & Richmond, J.B.: Autonomic functioning in the neonate. VII: Maturational changes in cardiac control. Child. Dev. 37:1–16, 1966

16. Rutter, M.: Psychological development—predictions from infancy. J. Psychol. Psychiatry 11:49–62, 1970

10

A TWIN STUDY OF TEMPERAMENT IN YOUNG CHILDREN

Robert Plomin and David C. Rowe

University of Colorado

Temperament was assessed in 182 young children (91 pairs of twins, average age of 3.6 years) with use of the Colorado Childhood Temperament Inventory (CCTI). The CCTI represents a merger of dimensions suggested by two approaches to the study of the development of temperament: the New York Longitudinal Study and Buss and Plomin's temperament theory. Of the six traits measured by the CCTI, genetic factors were implicated in the etiology of five (sociability, emotionality, activity, attention span-persistence, and soothability). One trait, reaction to food, showed no genetic influence and indicated strong between-family environmental effects. A negative correlation between emotionality and soothability may also have a genetic basis. These results suggest that the development of certain personality traits—those that we include as temperament—are substantially influenced by heredity.

A. INTRODUCTION

Behavioral genetics adds a genetic perspective to the psychobiological approach to the study of behavior. With respect to human behavior, the spotlight is now on the genetics of psychopathology and

Reprinted with permission from *The Journal of Psychology,* vol. 97, 107–113, 1977.

This research was supported in part by an award from the William T. Grant Foundation and NIMH 28076 to the senior author.

cognitive abilities, but many other behaviors (often thought to be environmentally determined) are likely to be better understood when analyzed from a viewpoint that considers both genetic and environmental hypotheses. This paper focuses on early development of human behaviors that are usually referred to as personality traits (e.g., activity level, emotionality, and social responsiveness).

The possible influence of genes in the development of such behaviors is suggested by evolutionary (6), phylogenetic (5), and developmental considerations. The possibility of hereditary effects is also suggested by preliminary results of behavioral genetic studies (2). There are, however, very few behavioral genetic investigations of personality development in early childhood, a time when important interactions between genes and environment are likely. One reason for this is the absence of a theory to guide the search through the myriad of childhood behaviors. Another reason has been the unavailability of measuring instruments appropriate for young children.

An important source of data about human behavioral development is the New York Longitudinal Study [NYLS (14, 15, 16)] in which the personality development of 141 children from birth to adolescence was studied by means of intensive parental interviews. Although the interview protocols captured a detailed picture of behavioral development, this rich source of information has lain fallow—perhaps because the interview format is not amenable to objective replication or quantitative analysis.

Another source of information about human behavioral development is Buss and Plomin's (2) temperament theory of personality development. They define "temperament" as a behavioral trait with an inherited component. The temperaments hypothesized by Buss and Plomin were assessed in preschool children by means of a parental rating measure. Results of a twin study using this measure suggested that the temperaments are genetically influenced (10).

An instrument for parents to use in rating the behavior of their young children has recently been constructed from a merger of the empirically based dimensions of the New York Longitudinal Study and the temperaments of the Buss and Plomin theory of personality development. This questionnaire, called the Colorado Childhood Temperament Inventory (CCTI), measures six dimensions of behavior in early childhood: sociability, emotionality, activity, attention span-persistence, reaction to food, and soothability. The instrument is psychometrically and factorially adequate, and the six dimensions are quite independent. The CCTI is described in greater detail in the Method section and in Rowe and Plomin (13).

The purpose of this report is to present the results of a twin study of the temperament of young children whose behavior was assessed with use of the CCTI. One goal of behavioral genetic analyses such as the twin study method is to understand the relative roles of environmental and genetic factors in behavioral development. Eventually, we hope to determine the *specific* environmental effects (prenatal, parental, familial, extrafamilial) and genetic factors (number, mode of transmission, linkage) that are involved, the pathways from genes to behavior, and genotype-environment correlations and interactions (11). In the meanwhile, a twin study is a proper first step toward untangling genetic and environmental influences associated with individual differences in human behavioral development.

B. METHOD

The authors (13) developed a measure of early childhood temperament that merges the NYLS and the Buss and Plomin theory of personality development. An objective set of items representative of the nine temperaments proposed by the NYLS group was constructed from the NYLS interview protocols. The NYLS items were factor analyzed together with items from the Buss and Plomin temperament theory of personality development. Six factors emerged. The first three factors were primarily from the Buss and Plomin system: sociability (highest loading item: "Child is very sociable"), emotionality ("Child tends to be somewhat emotional"), and activity ("Child is always on the go"). The next three factors were primarily from the NYLS: attention span-persistence ("Child persists at a task until successful"), reaction to food ("Child consistently dislikes many kinds of food"), and soothability ("If talked to, child stops crying"). The CCTI is a parental rating instrument composed of the five highest-loading items on each of these factors. The average alpha reliability of the six scales was .80, and the average one-week test-retest reliability (for which we randomly selected one of the twins for the mother to rate again) was .68. It should be mentioned that in means analyses and factor analyses, the results were essentially the same for boys and girls and for younger (1-3 years) and older (4-7 years) children.[1]

A total of 182 children (91 pairs of twins) were rated by their mothers on the CCTI. The children were in the age range of 1 to 7 years (average age, 3.6 years). The mothers were recruited with the help of mothers of twins clubs and returned our material by mail.

---

[1] The CCTI and a detailed description of the factor analyses and other item and scale analyses are available from the authors.

They were, for the most part, white and middle class (average family income, $17,056; average years of schooling, 14.4).

In the past, it was necessary to diagnose zygosity of twins by blood analysis. However, it has been demonstrated (e.g., 3, 9) that physical markers such as hair color and texture are as useful as, and considerably less expensive than, analyses of genetic markers in the blood. The accuracy of prediction when physical characteristics are used to predict blood-diagnosed zygosity is greater than 90%. With use of a method similar to that of Nichols and Bilbro, 36 pairs of twins were diagnosed as identical, and 31 as same-sex fraternal; of these, 28 identical pairs and 25 fraternal pairs were classified as "certain" in their zygosity diagnoses. Although this method has been shown to be quite accurate, it should be pointed out that any errors in diagnosis are conservative in terms of a genetic hypothesis: misclassifying fraternal twins as identical would only decrease the identical twin correlation and *vice versa*, thus decreasing the difference between identical and fraternal twin correlations which is the essence of the estimate of genetic influence in a twin study. There were 24 pairs of opposite-sex fraternal twins.

The twin study method compares the similarity between identical twins to the similarity between fraternal twins. Although the quantitative genetic theory behind the twin method would permit a precise identification of the phenotypic variance explained by genetic factors [see McClearn and DeFries (8)], the purpose of the present study was a preliminary screening of human temperaments early in life. With this goal in mind, the twin method may be considered as a natural experiment in which genetically identical pairs of individuals are compared to pairs who share only half of their segregating genes on the average. No matter whether a pair is identical or fraternal, of course, the twins are of the same age, and they are raised prenatally in the same womb and postnatally in the same family. Thus, if identical twins arc more similar than fraternal twins, this can be ascribed to their greater genetic similarity. It has sometimes been suggested that more similar treatment of identical twins may, in some cases, make their personalities more alike than those of fraternal twins; however, direct tests of this possibility provide no support for it (4, 7, 12).

C. RESULTS AND DISCUSSION

Of major interest are intraclass correlations of F ratios for identical and same-sex fraternal twins rated on the six temperaments measured by the CCTI (table 1). For five of the six temperaments, it can be seen

TABLE 1

INTRACLASS CORRELATIONS[a] AND F RATIOS[b] FOR IDENTICAL AND SAME-SEX FRATERNAL
TWINS RATED ON THE COLORADO CHILDHOOD TEMPERAMENT INVENTORY

Trait	Intraclass correlations		F ratio
	Identical	Fraternal	
Sociability	.56	.05	2.50**
Emotionality	.60	.27	2.25*
Activity	.73	.05	2.62**
Attention span-persistence	.59	−.27	3.61**
Reaction to food	.43	.49	<1.00
Soothability	.76	.06	3.93**

[a] Intraclass correlations were determined by computing product-moment correlations with use of a double-entry method which establishes equal means and variances for the classes by entering the twins twice with their order reversed.
[b] F ratios are the ratio of the variance of fraternal twin intrapair absolute differences to the variance of identical twin intrapair absolute differences.
* $p < .05$.
** $p < .01$.

that the identical twins were considerably (and significantly) more similar than the fraternal twins. It is noteworthy that the correlations for identical and fraternal twins were also significantly different when only those identical and same-sex fraternal twins which had been classified as "certain" in their zygosity diagnoses were considered. In addition, the opposite-sex fraternal twin correlations were not significantly different from those for same-sex fraternal twins (with the exception of soothability, for which the opposite-sex twin correlation was significantly higher), suggesting that sex differences do not generally interact with twin similarity for these temperaments.

Thus, there appears to be substantial genetic influence during early development for the temperaments of sociability, emotionality, activity, attention span-persistence, and soothability. It is important to note that one of the CCTI behavioral dimensions (the least general one), reaction to food, showed no difference in similarity between identical and fraternal twins. Twin studies often seem to indicate that nearly every behavior is heritable to some extent, but this is a clear example of a behavior for which individual differences show *no* genetic influence. Moreover, because both identical and fraternal twin correlations are significant, between-family environmental influences (i.e., effects of common familial environment) are implicated in the reaction of youngsters to food. This finding may seem obvious, but it, too, is important. Although cognitive abilities usually indicate environmental influence of this type, most personality traits surprisingly *do not* (7).

In addition to the influence of genetic factors suggested by significant differences between identical and fraternal twin correlations, quantitative estimates of this influence can also be obtained. However, it is imperative to study the pattern of the correlations (rather than to blindly apply heritability estimates), and one must also be wary of the large standard errors which are involved. In the present case, the fraternal twin correlations are lower than would be predicted from the identical twin correlations. This fact makes the estimation of heritability more hazardous than usual, especially since the sample sizes did not number in the hundreds for each type of twin. Because the purpose of the present study was to screen genetic and environmental influences upon early personality development, the significant differences between identical and fraternal twin correlations will suffice to indicate the possibility that genetic factors play a large role in the early development of these personality traits.

An untapped resource in behavioral genetic investigations is the analysis of genetic and environmental contributions to the *covariance among behaviors,* in contrast to the usual analysis of the variance of the behaviors considered individually. Although the six behavioral dimensions of the CCTI are relatively independent, there is a correlation of −.42 between emotionality and soothability. This means that the more emotionally labile child is less easily soothed. It would be interesting to determine the extent to which the correlation is attributable to genetic or environmental factors. The correlation can be genetically determined if pleiotropism occurs (that is, if the same gene or gene system that leads to emotionality also leads to soothability). It can be environmentally determined if the same environmental factors contribute to both behaviors (for example, if parents reinforce the emotionality of their children by soothing them with affection and attention).

The same techniques that are used to differentiate genetic and environmentally determined if the same environmental factors contribute to both behaviors (for example, if parents reinforce the emotion- The methods are described elsewhere (7) and will be considered here only to aid in the understanding of the etiology of the correlation between emotionality and soothability. The variance in both traits has a genetic component, as indicated by the significant difference between the identical and fraternal twin correlations in Table 1. These correlations represent the correlation between behavior X in one twin and that same behavior X in the co-twin. The analysis of covariance among behaviors uses the same procedures except that the "cross-correlation" of behavior X in one twin and behavior Y in the co-twin is obtained. Rather than analyzing the phenotypic variance of a single behavior, the phenotypic *covariance* between the two traits is analyzed. In the case of emotionality and soothability, the correlation is −.42, the cross-correlation for identical twins is −.33, and the cross-correlation for fraternal twins is .11. Thus, the identical twin cross-correlation is nearly as great as the phenotypic correlation, while that for fraternal twins is low and nonsignificant. Results of this analysis indicate that genetic factors may play a substantial role in determining the correlation between emotionality and soothability.

These data have far-reaching implications for the study of personality development. Developmental research has come to view the child as actively interacting with his environment, but it does not consider the source of this self-directed activity. For example, research on the direction of effects issue in socialization (e.g., 1) suggests that the child may affect his environment as much as the environment affects the child, but it does not specify why a certain child interacts in a certain way with his environment and another child acts differently. It is likely that a major source of consistent, directional push in personality development is temperament.

REFERENCES

1. Bell, R. Q. A reinterpretation of the direction of effects in studies of socialization. *Psychol. Rev.*, 1968, **75**, 81–95.
2. Buss, A. H., & Plomin, R. A Temperament Theory of Personality Development. New York: Wiley Interscience, 1975.
3. Cohen, D., Dibble, E., Grawe, J., & Pollin, W. Separating identical from fraternal twins. *Arch. Gen. Psychiat.*, 1973, **29**, 465–469.
4. DeFries, J. C., & Plomin, R. Behavioral genetics. *Ann. Rev. Psychol.*, 1977, in press.
5. Diamond, S. Personality and Temperament. New York: Harper, 1957.
6. Freedman, D. S. Human Infancy: An Evolutionary Perspective. Hillsdale, N.J.: Erlbaum, 1974.
7. Loehlin, J. C., & Nichols, R. C. Heredity, Environment, and Personality: A Study of 850 Twins. Austin: Univ. Texas Press, 1976.
8. McClearn, G. E., & DeFries, J. C. Introduction to Behavior Genetics. San Francisco: Freeman, 1973.
9. Nichols, R. C., & Bilbro, W. C. The diagnosis of twin zygosity. *Acta Genet.*, 1966, **16**, 265–275.
10. Plomin, R. A twin and family study of personality in young children. *J. of Psychol.*, 1976, **94**, 233–235.
11. Plomin, R., DeFries, J. C., & Loehlin, J. C. Genotype-environment interaction and correlation in the analysis of human behavior. *Psychol. Bull.*, 1977, **84**, 309–322.
12. Plomin, R., Willerman, L., & Loehlin, J. C. Resemblances in appearance and the equal environments assumption in twin studies of personality traits. *Behav. Genet.*, 1976, **6**, 43–52.
13. Rowe, D. C., & Plomin, R. Temperament in early childhood. *J. Personal. Assess.*, 1977, **41**, 150–156.
14. Thomas, A., Chess, S., & Birch, H. Temperament and Behavior Disorders in Children. New York: New York Univ. Press, 1968.
15. ——. The origin of personality, *Sci. Amer.*, 1970, **223**, 102–109.
16. Thomas, A., Chess, S., Birch, H., Hertzig, M., & Korn, S. Behavioral Individuality in Early Childhood. New York Univ. Press, 1963.

11

TEMPERAMENTAL INDIVIDUALITY FROM CHILDHOOD TO ADOLESCENCE

Stella Chess and Alexander Thomas
New York University Medical Center

Continuities and discontinuities in the expression of temperamental characteristics from early infancy to adolescence of the subjects in the New York Longitudinal Study are reported. The findings are interpreted in terms of a model in which organism-environment interaction is considered to produce new behavioral patterns of succeeding age periods. As these new patterns interact with recurrent and new features of environment, in some instances the same temperamental factors continue influential as in the past, in other instances different aspects of temperament become ascendent, or the influential temperamental attributes may be distorted, or temperamental issues may dwindle in significance.

The New York Longitudinal Study has followed the behavior development of 136 children from early infancy into adolescence. A major focus of this study has been on individuality in behavioral styles, or temperament, and its influence on normal and deviant psychological functioning at different age periods. A number of pre-

Reprinted with permission from *Journal of the American Academy of Child Psychiatry*, Vol. 16, 1977, 218–226.

This paper was presented at the annual meeting of the American Academy of Child Psychiatry, St. Louis, Missouri, October 25, 1975.

vious publications have reported our methods of data collection, the definition of, and scoring criteria for, nine categories of temperament, and the identification of several constellations of temperamental characteristics with special functional significance (Thomas et al., 1963, 1968). We have also reported on the significance of these temperamental characteristics for the ontogenesis and evolution of behavior disorders in children (Chess et al., 1967; Gordon and Thomas, 1967; Thomas et al., 1968; Chess, 1968) and academic achievement (Chess et al., 1976). In addition, studies have been conducted on the role of temperament in special populations, such as children with paranatal brain damage (Thomas and Chess, 1975), mildly retarded children (Chess and Hassibi, 1970), special environmental stresses (Thomas et al., 1974), and children with multiple handicaps as a result of congenital rubella (Chess et al., 1971).

In these reports we have at all times emphasized that a given pattern of temperament does not, as such, result ipso facto in any fixed psychological outcome. Normal and deviant development is at all times the result of a continuously evolving interaction between a child with his individual characteristics and significant features of his intrafamilial and extrafamilial environment. Temperament is only one attribute of the growing child—albeit a highly significant attribute—and must at all times be considered in its internal relations with abilities and motives and in its external relations with environmental opportunities and stresses.

In the past few years a number of workers both in this country and abroad have utilized our conceptualization and characterization of temperament to identify temperamental individuality in a variety of populations (Cooper and Tapia, 1971; Torgersen, 1972; Gregg, 1973; Graham et al., 1973; Carey, 1973; Seegars, 1974; Colvin and Brown, 1974; Sameroff, 1975; and Scholom, 1975). The significance of temperament in the reactions of children to a mentally ill parent (Graham et al., 1973), in the production of infant colic (Carey, 1973) and night-awakening (Carey, 1974) and in school adjustment (Scholom, 1975) has been reported, and twin studies have indicated a genetic component to temperament (Rutter et al., 1963; Torgersen, 1972).

As we have followed the development of our study sample from infancy into adolescence, we have been struck by the consistency of one or another temperamental characteristic in some of the youngsters. In others, such continuity has not been evident. The issue of continuity or discontinuity of a significant psychological trait—whether it be intelligence, temperament, psychodynamic patterning, etc.—is of theoretical and practical interest. One position is expressed by Bronson (1974), "Along with some others, I see our apparent inability to make empirical predictions about later personality from the early years as so much against good sense, common observation, and the thrust of all developmental theories that I can take it only as an indictment of established paradigms and methods rather than as evidence of a developmental reality" (p. 276). Another position is stated by Sameroff (1975) in a review of the literature on early influences on development,

> Despite the reasonableness of the notion that one should be able to make long-range predictions based on the initial characteristics of a child or his environment, the above review has found little evidence for the validity of such predictions. One view of the inadequacy of developmental predictions sees their source in the scientist's inability to locate the critical links in the causal chain leading from antecedents to consequence. A second view, propounded above, is that such linear sequences are non-existent and that development proceeds through a sequence of regular restructuring of the relations within and between the organism and his environment [p. 285].

Some of the issues involved in determining continuity or discontinuity of temperament and their relevance to the questions posed by Bronson and Sameroff above can be illustrated through the longitudinal behavioral data of four of our study subjects.

1. Carl requested a discussion with one of us (S.C.) after his first term in college because of feelings of depression and inability to cope with the academic and social situation at college. He had made virtually no friends and found studying difficult, experiences he could not recall ever having had before. He had done well academically in high school, had many friends, found school enjoyable, and had a wide range of interests, including the piano. In the interview he was alert, articulate, and in very good contact. He did not appear depressed, but rather bewildered at what was happening, exclaiming, "This just isn't me!"

The anterospective longitudinal data showed that in earlier life Carl had been one of our most extreme "difficult child" temperamental types, with intense, negative reactions to new situations and slow adaptability only after many exposures. This was true whether it was the first bath or first solid foods in infancy, the beginning of nursery school and elementary school, first birthday parties, or the first shopping trip. Each experience evoked stormy responses, with loud crying and struggling to get away. However, his parents learned to anticipate Carl's reactions, knew that if they were patient, presented only one or a few new situations at a time, and gave Carl the opportunity for repeated exposure to the new, he would finally adapt positively. Furthermore, once he adapted, his intensity of responses gave him a zestful enthusiastic involvement, just as it gave his initial negative reactions a loud and stormy character. His parents recognized that the difficulties in raising Carl were due to his temperament and not to their being "bad parents." The father even looked on his son's shrieking and turmoil as a sign of "lustiness." As a result of this positive parent-child interaction Carl never became a behavior problem even though the "difficult child" as a group is significantly at higher risk for disturbed development (Thomas et al., 1968).

In this later childhood and high-school years Carl met very few new situations and developed an appropriately positive and self-confident self-image. However, the entry to college away from home suddenly confronted him simultaneously with a number of new situations—strange surroundings, an entirely new peer group, new types of faculty approaches and learning demands, and a complex relationship with a girl student with whom he was living. This resulted in a recrudescence of his "difficult child" pattern of response to the new and brought him for help.

Only one discussion was necessary with Carl, consisting primarily in clarifying for him his temperamental pattern and the techniques he could use for adapting to the new. Actually, Carl had already begun to take these steps on his own—cutting down the number of new subjects, insisting with himself that he study each subject daily for specific times, attenuating his involvement with the girl, and making a point of attending peer social group activities, no matter how uncomfortable he felt. By the end of the academic year his difficulties had disappeared and his subsequent functioning has been on the previous positive level. He was told that similar negative reactions to the new might occur in the future. His response was, "That's all right. I know how to handle them now."

2. David, in contrast to Carl, appears to have developed a marked change in an initially striking temperamental characteristic. When seen at age 17 for the direct interview done in adolescence with all our study youngsters, David was obese and conspicuously apathetic and lethargic. He reported little interest or involvement in any kind of outside activities. The time-related interview with his parents confirmed this observation of David as a very "low-active" adolescent.

In his early years David had been consistently one of the most motorically active children in our study sample. He was always in motion, with a cheerful and friendly manner. However, David's home environment was marked by constant discord and destructive competition between his parents. They repeatedly preached to David and others what a superior child he was (David did indeed have a superior IQ), and that any difficulties he had in school were due to poor teaching. As time went on David's school performance deteriorated, as did his overall interests and other activities. The parents held the school and teachers entirely responsible for their son's growing school underachievement, and over time David internalized his parents' almost paranoid projection of blame. Motivation dwindled, any critical self-evaluation was entirely absent, and disinterest and apathy became a progressively dominant feature of his functioning. These attitudes of the parents and the boy led to complete resistance to psychotherapy.

3. Nancy presented almost the opposite kind of change. When seen in the routinely scheduled interview at age 17, she was bright, alert, and lively. She was involved in a number of activities that interested her, and reported an active social life, good school functioning, and a pleasant relationship with her parents. Although her parents described her as "hot-headed," they did not consider this a problem.

Yet it would have been very difficult to predict this favorable development into adolescence in Nancy's early years. Like Carl, she was a difficult child temperamentally from early infancy onward. But unlike Carl's parents, Nancy's parents responded to her intensity, irregularity in biological functions, negative reactions, and slow adaptability in a way that produced extreme stress and difficulty in development in the youngster. The father was highly critical of her behavior, rigid in his expectations for quick positive adaptation, and punitive when Nancy did not respond to his demands. The mother was intimidated by both husband and daughter, and vacillating and anxious in her handling of her child. By age 6 years Nancy developed explosive anger outbursts, fear of the dark, thumb-sucking and hair-pulling, and poor peer group relationships. Her symptoms and clinical findings were severe enough to warrant the diagnosis of Neurotic Behavior Disorder, moderately severe. Psychotherapy was instituted with some improvement. But the dramatic change occurred when in the 4th and 5th grades Nancy showed evidence of musical and dramatic talent. This brought increasingly favorable attention and praise from teachers and other parents. This talent also ranked high in her parents' own hierarchy of desirable attributes. Nancy's father now began to see his daughter's intense and explosive personality not as signs of a "rotten kid" as heretofore, but as evidence of a budding artist. She was now a child he could be proud of, and he could afford to make allowances for her "artistic" temperament. With this view of Nancy and her temperament, the mother was also able to relax and relate positively to her daughter. Nancy was permitted to adapt at her own pace, the positive aspects of her temperament came into evidence, and her self-image improved progressively. By adolescence all evidence of her neurotic symptomatology and functioning had disappeared and she was considered as recovered from her neurotic disorder.

4. Norman was seen at age 17 by one of us (S.C.) who had followed him since age 4½ because of persistent behavior disturbance. At age 17 he had already dropped out of two colleges in one year, and was planning to go abroad for a work-study program. He was in good contact, but dejected and depressed. He was extraordinarily self-derogatory, said he couldn't finish anything he started, was lazy, and didn't know what he wanted to do. "My father doesn't respect me, and let's face it, why should he." He talked of "hoping to find myself" in a vague, unplanned way.

Norman had always been a highly distractible child with a short attention span. Intelligent and pleasant, the youngest in his class throughout his school years due to birth date, he started his academic career with good mastery. However, at home his parents were impatient and critical of him even in the preschool years because of his quick shifts of attention, dawdling at bedtime, and apparent "forgetfulness." By his 5th year he showed various reactive symptoms such as a sleep problem, nocturnal enuresis, poor eating habits, and nail tearing. Year by year his academic standing slipped. His father, a hard-driving, very persistent professional man, became increasingly hypercritical and derogatory of Norman. The father equated the boy's short attention span and distractibility, which were the opposite of his own characteristics, with irresponsibility, lack of character and will-power. He used these terms openly to the boy and stated that he "disliked" his son. The mother grew to understand the issue, but no discussion with the father as to the normalcy of his son's temperament and the impossibility of the boy's living up to the father's standards of concentrated hard work succeeded in altering the father's attitude. He remained convinced that Norman had an irresponsible character and was headed for future failure—indeed a self-fulfilling prophecy. There were several times when the boy tried to comply with his father's standards and made himself sit still with his homework for long periods of time. This only resulted in generalized tension and multiple tics and Norman could not sustain this effort so dissonant with his temperament—another proof to himself and his father of his failure. Direct psychotherapy was arranged in early adolescence, but Norman entered this with a passive, defeated attitude and the effort was unsuccessful. His subsequent development was all too predictable.

DISCUSSION

These four vignettes do not by any means exhaust the different developmental paths taken by our study youngsters. They are also not unique, and do suggest certain implications for theory and practice.

1. There are different aspects to any individual's temperamental characteristics. One type of expression of a temperamental trait may be evident in new, unfamiliar situations. Once a positive adaptation has been made and the activity has become routinized, another and even conspicuously different aspect of the same trait may become manifest (Carl).

2. The significance of established temperamental characteristics as a factor to be considered in the development of deviant behavior or symptomatology can easily be missed unless careful history-taking includes specific questions which can elicit information on temperament. This was dramatically evident in Carl's case.

3. No single aspect of the child or environment—whether it be intellectual level, temperament, parental characteristics, relationships to sibs or peers, etc.—no matter how important in general, is necessarily a significant etiological factor in every instance of behavior problem development. In the case of David, temperament did not appear to play an influential role in the ontogenesis of his behavior disorder. Furthermore, a conspicuous temperamental characteristic of his early years was later altered by psychodynamic factors which led to an opposite behavioral course.

4. At the opposite extreme are the individuals in whom environmental factors intensify a specific temperamental characteristic. Thus, in Norman's case, his father's deogatory and hypercritical value judgments on himself led to increasing drifting, shifting quickly from one vague plan to another, grasping at straws—all in all, a caricature of his temperamental characteristics of distractibility and short attention span.

5. In many cases the developmental course of a youngster can be decisively influenced by new factors emerging—either in the child or in the environment, and in the interaction between the two, which could not have been predicted ahead of time. Thus, in the case of Nancy, in her preschool years there would have been no way of pre-

dicting the emergence of her artistic talents, the profound influence this would have on her father's attitude and behavior toward her, and the qualitative change this would make in her development. In the case of Norman, it would also have been very hard to predict in the boy's infancy that his father would be so unresponsive to his son's many positive qualities and so rigidly unyielding in his condemnation of the boy's temperamental characteristics. This is in line with the conclusions of Rutter (1970) and Sameroff (1975) regarding the limits of predictability from early childhood to later life. Prediction has an "iffy" quality. If a child with such and such characteristics interacts with an environment of such and such features, and if no unexpected new factors arise in the child or the environment, then we can predict such and such a developmental course. But new factors do arise, making prediction hazardous.

6. The discontinuities in behavior evident in so many of our study sample as we have followed their development from infancy into adolescence (Thomas and Chess, 1972; 1976) can be understood in terms of an interactionist model or what Sameroff (1975) has called a transactional model. This concept has been well stated by Schneirla and Rosenblatt (1961):

> Behavior is typified by reciprocal stimulative relationships. ... Mammalian behavioral development is best conceived as a unitary system of processes changing progressively under the influence of an intimate interrelationship of factors of maturation and of experience—with maturation defined as the developmental contributions of tissue growth and differentiation and their secondary processes, experience as the effects of stimulation and its organic traces on behavior [p. 231].

Using such an interactionist model, we can view temperament as interacting with environment together with other organismic characteristics to produce certain consequences in behavior. As these new behavioral patterns interact with recurrent and new features of environment, in some instances the same temperamental features will continue influential as in the past, in other instances different aspects of temperament may become ascendant, or the influential temperamental attributes may be distorted, or temperamental issues may dwindle in significance. The same variability in significance and manifestation over time can occur for intellectual level or other organismic characteristics and for any specific aspect of the intra- or extrafamilial environment. To put it simply, if the past is no longer evident in the present, it may mean that it is gone because it has entered into a new form as a consequence of dynamics of discontinuity in development.

REFERENCES

Bronson, W. C. (1974), Mother-toddler interaction. *Merrill-Palmer Quart.*, 20:275–301.
Carey, W. (1973), Measurement of infant temperament in pediatric practice. In: *Individual Differences in Children*, ed. J. C. Westman. New York: Wiley, pp. 293–306.
—— (1974), Night waking and temperament in infancy. *J. Pediat.*, 84:756–758.
Chess, S. (1968), Temperament and learning ability of school children. Read at 95th annual meeting of the American Public Health Association.
—— & Hassibi, M. (1970), Behavior deviations in mentally retarded children. *This Journal*, 9:282–297.
—— Korn, S., & Fernandez, P. (1971), *Psychiatric Disorders of Children with Congenital Rubella*. New York: Brunner/Mazel.
—— Thomas, A., & Birch, H. G. (1967), Behavior problems revisited. *This Journal*, 6:321–331.
—— —— & Cameron, M. (1976), Temperament: its significance for school adjustment and academic achievement. *N.Y. Univ. Educa. Rev.*, 3:24–29.
Colvin, R. W. & Brown, T. J. (1974), High-risk indices in early recognition and prevention of handicap. Read at annual meeting of the American Psychological Association, New Orleans.
Cooper, B. J. & Tapia, F. (1971), Nine measurable qualities of temperament: a learning program. Dept. of Psychiatry, University of Missouri.
Gordon, E. & Thomas, A. (1967), Children's behavioral style and the teacher's appraisal of their intelligence. *J. School Psychol.*, 5:292–300.
Graham, P., Rutter, M., & George, S. (1973), Temperamental characteristics as predictors of behavior disorders in children. *Amer. J. Orthopsychiat.*, 43:328–339.
Gregg, G. S. (1973), Clinical experience with efforts to define individual differences. In: *Individual Differences in Children*, ed. J. C. Westman. New York: Wiley.
Rutter, M. (1970), Psychological development: predictors from infancy. *J. Child Psychol. & Psychiat.*, 11:49–62.
—— Korn, S., & Birch, H. G. (1963), Genetic and environmental factors in the development of primary reaction patterns. *Brit. J. Clin. Psychol.*, 2:161–173.
Sameroff, A. J. (1975), Early influences on development: fact or fancy? *Merrill-Palmer Quart.*, 21:267–294.
Schneirla, T. C. & Rosenblatt, J. S. (1961), Behavioral organization and genesis of the social bond in insects and mammals. *Amer. J. Orthopsychiat.*, 31:223–253.
Scholom, A. M. (1975), The relationship of infant and parent temperament to the prediction of child adjustment. Dissertation, Michigan State University.
Seegars, J. E. (1974), High-risk indices in early recognition, intervention and prevention of handicap. Read at annual meeting of American Psychological Association, New Orleans.
Thomas, A. & Chess, S. (1972), Development in middle childhood. *Sem. in Psychiat.*, 4:331–341.
—— —— (1975), A longitudinal study of three brain-damaged children. *Arch. Gen. Psychiat.*, 32:457–465.
—— —— (1976), Evolution of behavior disorders into adolescence. *Amer. J. Psychiat.*, 133:539–542.

_____ _____ & Birch, H. G. (1968), *Temperament and Behavior Disorders in Children*. New York: New York University Press.

_____ _____ _____ Hertzig, M. E., & Korn, S. (1963), *Behavioral Individuality in Early Childhood*. New York: New York University Press.

_____ _____ Sillen, J., & Mendez, O. A. (1974), Cross-cultural studies of behavior in children with special vulnerabilities to stress. In: *Life History Research in Psychopathology*, ed. D. Ricks, A. Thomas, & M. Roff. Minnesota: University of Minnesota Press, 3:53–67.

Torgersen, A. (1972), Temperamental differences in twins. Dissertation, Psykologisk Institutt, Oslo.

12

PARENTAL TREATMENT, CHILDREN'S TEMPERAMENT, AND THE RISK OF CHILDHOOD BEHAVIORAL PROBLEMS:

1. Relationships Between Parental Characteristics and Changes in Children's Temperament Over Time

James R. Cameron

Children's Division, Napa State Hospital, Imola, Calif.

Preschool children's temperament scores, correlated with eight parental domains, revealed that parental intolerance, inconsistency, and conflict were associated with negative temperament changes; strictness and maternal concern/protectiveness with both positive and negative changes, depending on age and sex. Implications with respect to the etiology of children's behavioral problems are explored.

Reprinted with permission from *American Journal of Orthopsychiatry*, Vol. 47, 568–576, 1977. Copyright 1977, the American Orthopsychiatric Association, Inc.

The research is based on data, supplied by Drs. Stella Chess and Alexander Thomas, from the New York Longitudinal Study.

Research projects aimed at the early detection of emotional or behavioral problems in children, or projects aimed at identifying "at risk" populations in terms of such variables as prematurity, low birth weight, low socioeconomic background, or schizophrenic parents, have met with some theoretical, but limited practical success. While a number of studies [1,2,3,4,5] have demonstrated statistically significant relationships between such early predictive factors and a variety of subsequent emotional and behavioral problems, the results of these studies have *not* produced many successful prevention programs. Certainly we can hold economic and political roadblocks accountable to some degree, but the murkiness of our understanding as to how specific risk factors metamorphize into childhood psychopathology must be held largely accountable for our poor prevention record. We have hesitated, undoubtedly appropriately, from embarking upon large-scale prevention programs out of fear of wasting time and effort, and because of the possibility of inflicting harm through needless meddling in the lives of children and their parents.

This and a subsequent paper aim to help clarify this murkiness by reporting the interrelationships between a pair of risk domains (children's temperament and parental behaviors) and the incidence and form of childhood behavioral problems. Chess, Thomas and their co-workers in the New York Longitudinal Study[7] have already described the significant relationships between certain temperament constellations in children and increased incidence of behavioral problems. This initial paper, also based on the NYLS data, extends that work to report on the relationships between certain parental-familial factors and children's temperament during their initial five years, and in particular *changes* in their temperament during that period.*

THE IMPORTANCE
OF TEMPERAMENT CHANGE

The Chess and Thomas results indicated an infant's temperament is linked significantly to the risk of developing certain forms of childhood behavioral problems. Given that linkage, the potential influence of parental behavior in determining the strength of the link becomes a crucial area for investigation. Stated metaphorically, the Chess and Thomas results indicate that a child's temperament reflects geologi-

---

*The following paper will describe links between parental characteristics and the incidence of behavioral problems, as well as how the manifest *form* of the behavioral problems relates to early infant temperament.

cally the "fault lines" in his emerging personality, with a child with a particular fault line more prone to subsequent "behavioral earthquakes." To continue the metaphor, parental and other environmental influences may represent the "strain" on those fault lines. Presumably, children who do eventuall exhibit behavioral "earthquakes" are likely to have a history of *both* vulnerable fault lines *and* collected strain.

If this geological compromise to the nature-nurture issue is valid, we should expect changes to occur in the child's temperament presaging the emergence of behavioral problems, just as strain and minor tremors along a fault line predate sudden, major earth shifts. Translating these assumptions into a testable hypothesis, we should expect to find significant correlations between familial-parental factors and early *shifts* in those temperament variables that Chess and Thomas previously reported to be linked to higher risk for the eventual emergence of behavioral problems.

DATA GATHERING PROCEDURES

The raw data for the parent-child correlations reported here were collected through procedures reported in detail in a prior publication.[7] Briefly summarized, these procedures involved 136 children, 69 boys and 67 girls, whose parents were interviewed periodically and intensively during the first five years of the child's life, and at less frequent intervals subsequently. The parents were recruited from the friends and acquaintances of the project's principal investigators, from patients from a pediatrician's practice, and from friends of both groups, and thus formed a relatively stable and socioculturally homogeneous sample for the study. Information on each child's temperament was gathered regularly through structured interviews with both parents, where the parents were asked to provide concrete descriptions of how their child responded to specific daily situations likely to reveal temperamental characteristics. Information on the parents themselves was obtained through another structured interview procedure, administered to both parents separately but simultaneously (when available) as close as possible in time to the child's third birthday.

The nine temperament variables employed by the NYLS have been described in detail;[6,7] these traits, as paraphrased from the NYLS reports, run as follows:

1. *Activity level:* The level, tempo, and frequency with which a motor component is present in the child's functioning.

2. *Rhythmicity:* The degree of regularity among the repetitive biological functions, including rest and activity, sleeping and waking, eating and appetite, and bowel and bladder.

3. *Approach-withdrawal:* How the child typically reacts to any new stimulus, such as food, people, toys, or procedures.

4. *Adaptability:* The ease with which the child's initial response pattern can be modified in the direction desired by the parents (or others).

5. *Intensity:* The energy content of the child's response, regardless of whether that response is negative or positive.

6. *Sensory threshold:* The level of extrinsic stimulation necessary to evoke a discernible response.

7. *Quality of mood:* The amount of pleasant, joyful, friendly behavior, as contrasted with unpleasant, crying, unfriendly behavior.

8. *Distractibility:* The effectiveness of extraneous environmental stimuli in interfering with, or in altering the direction of, the child's ongoing behavior.

9. *Persistence:* The child's maintenance of an activity in the face of obstacles to its continuation.

Yearly through the first five years, each child was scored on a three-point scale for each temperament variable, based on parents' reports of the child's behavior in specific, age-relevant situations. Care was taken to insure **adequate** validity and reliability in the employment of these scales.

PARENTAL DATA

The focused interview administered around the child's third birthday covered a wide variety of parenting-related issues. Included were such topics as the degree of parental conflict and tension; the degree of warmth, protectiveness, and permissiveness directed toward the study child; and the degree and forms of discipline employed. A rater, reviewing transcripts of these interviews, coded each set of parents on a wide variety of such parenting variables. These interviews also provided data on typical demographic and background variables, such as the number of children in the home, the degree of crowding, and parents' estimated income and intelligence.

DATA ANALYSIS

Of the 99 items of information initially available from the third-year parental interview, 70 were selected as meeting basic statistical criteria for use in correlational analyses. Only the mother's responses to the interview questions were used, since in the overwhelming majority of cases both parents provided identical responses; where they differed, the mother's influence was assumed to be stronger in shaping the child's temperament.

These 70 parental information items were then subjected to cluster analysis by means of the Tryon system.[8] Cluster analysis was chosen over more traditional methods of factor analysis because there were no *a priori* expectations that any statistically independent dimensions of parenting existed within these data. On the contrary, the intention was simply to "map out" the territory of parental behavior, locate items within that territory that seemed to coexist, and then rate each set of parents on those groupings of items. The parental cluster scores thus derived through the Tryon system could then be correlated with scores on the children's temperament scales, and with changes in those scores across time.

For this purpose, the data on children's temperament were transformed to provide the needed temperament *change* scores across the first five years. To generate these change scores, data for each temperament scale for all children across all five years were pooled and then transformed into deviation scores, which were then comparable across both children and time. For each child in each area of temperament, a set of ten change scores was computed, reflecting temperament change across intervals of time ranging from one through four years.

ANALYSIS OF PARENTAL DATA

Eight oblique parental clusters were extracted from the 70-item correlational matrix. The clusters are described below in their order of importance, based on the amount of matrix variance assumed by each cluster. These variance data, plus the intercorrelations among these oblique dimensions, appear in Table 1.

Dimension 1: *Parental disapproval, intolerance, and rejection.* Parents with high scores on this cluster of items are biased against and show relatively little tolerance or feeling for the study child. They also tend to express anxiety regarding child rearing generally and are more frequently described by the interviewer as "cold and detached." In addition, they prefer other children in the family to the study child, whom they perceive as manifesting severe behavioral deviations.

Dimension 2: *Parental conflict regarding child rearing.* This cluster focuses on the degree of between-parent disagreement, conflict, or con-

Table I

INTERCORRELATIONS BETWEEN EIGHT PARENTAL DIMENSIONS EXTRACTED FROM
NYLS THIRD-YEAR PARENTAL INTERVIEWS

PARENTAL DIMENSION	DIMENSION						
	2	3	4	5	6	7	8
1. Disapproval (.21) a	.21	−.08	−.03	.02	.04	.34	.02
2. Conflict (.17)		−.11	−.06	−.18.	−.12	.18	.05
3. Strictness/permissiveness (.15)			−.02	.06	−.19	−.16	−.02
4. Maternal concern, protectiveness (.13)				.10	.08	−.02	.23
5. Depressed living standards (.12)					.37	.13	.16
6. Limitations on material support (.12)						.08	.10
7. Inconsistent discipline (.12)							−.09
8. Large family orientation (.10)							

a Dimensions are ranked according to the amount of matrix variance assumed, as indicated in parentheses.

fusion regarding how to handle the study child. The parental conflict in approach and handling of the child spreads over to the parents' mutual perceptions, which tend to be negative toward each other. High-conflict parents also express relatively little self-confidence in their child rearing abilities.

Dimension 3: *Parental strictness vs. permissiveness.* Parents scoring high on items in this cluster tend to give in to their child *less* often, and also, judging from this cluster's correlations with Dimensions 1 and 4, are likely to be more approving and accepting of their child. In contrast, low scoring parents may give in to their child's request, but do not necessarily approve of their child's behavior.

Dimension 4: *Maternal concern and protectiveness.* Mothers scoring high on these items are highly concerned for their child's safety and spend considerable time within the home in supporting, protecting, and working for their children. These mothers tend to have few interests outside the home and find it relatively hard to use deprivation as a form of punishment.

Dimension 5: *Depressed living standards.* This cluster of items reflects the amount of financial stress and crowding experienced by the family, as well as its general standard of living. Presumably, it also measures the family's capacity to provide for the study child in a material way. (Since the bulk of the parents in this study were well-paid business executives or professionals, low scores on this cluster cannot be equated with poverty or the lower socioeconomic levels).

Dimension 6: *Limitations on the child's material supports.* A more direct measure of the material supports for the study child appears through this small cluster of items. High-scoring families on this mini-cluster tend to find it necessary to protect their home from their child, rather than integrating household and children's needs. As might be expected, this dimension correlates significantly with Dimension 5.

Dimension 7: *Inconsistent parental discipline.* A doublet of items managed to emerge as a relatively independent cluster, despite its similarity with the content of Dimension 2. Its existence seems to reflect a relationship between the sheer frequency of disciplinary issues in a home and the number of conflicts that can arise around discipline.

Dimension 8: *Large family orientation.* The reasons for the cohesion among these items are somewhat vague, but perhaps suggest the mother's desire for a large family and a strong maternal role. Oddly, mothers with such an orientation seem to have relatively less information on their study child. The modest but positive correlations between this cluster and those of Dimensions 4–6 (*Maternal concern and protectiveness, depressed living standards,* and *limited material supports*) suggest that this dimension may reflect middle to upper-middle-class attitudes.

INITIAL LEVELS AND CHANGES
IN CHILDREN'S TEMPERAMENT

Parental Traits and Negative Changes

Parental Dimension 1 (*Parental Disapproval, Intolerance, and Rejection*) shows the strongest association with both yearly temperament scores and change scores across the first five years. By the second year, the more rejecting mothers are associated with daughters who are significantly (.05) less persistent and less active in their reactions and have reportedly higher thresholds. By their fourth year, they are associated with daughters who are described as less adaptable, less positive in mood, but now more intense in their responses. In their fifth year, the associations with greater intensity continue, but there are associations now also with greater sensitivity (lower thresholds) and more withdrawal. The picture suggested by these correlations is one of an initial passive response on the part of the daughters to the parents' negative feelings, but subsequently a more intense protestation.

The cold and detached, anxious, and generally "negative" mothers depicted by this cluster were less associated with any temperament characteristics of their sons. However, by age three there was a significant *negative* correlation between son's adaptability and maternal rejection scores.

Inconsistent parental discipline (Dim. 7), which, as mentioned, was strongly associated with the *parental disapproval* dimension, paralleled that dimension in its associations with the children's temperament. By the children's fourth year, less adaptable sons and daughters were associated with the more inconsistent parents, while daughters were also more negative in mood, more intense in reaction, and, by the fifty year, lower in thresholds. Unlike the *parental rejection* dimension, however, *parental inconsistency* was associated with reduced rhythmicity in both the first and second year, particularly among the daughters. Presumably, parental inconsistency and daughters' disrhythmicity intermeshed during the first two years of the daughters' life, with each party perhaps adding to the disorganization of the other.

Parental Dimension 2, measuring conflict regarding child rearing practices, provided a slight echo of the temperament associations of Dimensions 1 and 7. By the children's third birthday and on past their fourth, the less adaptable sons and daughters belonged to such conflicting parents.

The final cluster of parental traits associated with what might be seen as deteriorating temperament scores was Dimension 5, *depressed living standards.* Only scattered significant associations emerged, but in the directions that might be expected: financially more depressed families possessed children who, in their second year, were comparatively less rhythmic in patterned functions, at three were less positive in mood, and by their fifth year were both more intense and more withdrawing.

In summarizing what appears to be a set of negative influences, it is clear that the child's capacity to adapt is the chief victim. Parental Dimensions 1, 2, and 7 share negative correlations with the adaptability of both sons and daughters, while, in the three-to-five years period, two of these three dimensions seemed to share an additional negative influence over daughters' mood and sensitivity.

Parental Traits and Complex Changes

Parental strictness (Dim. 3) provided some interesting associations with children's temperament at different ages. By the second year, there is a modest, positive correlation between this dimension and boys' (but not girls') *adaptability*. By the fourth and fifth years, there is a negative relationship with *persistence* (the greater the strictness, the less the persistence), particularly among daughters.

Presumably, sons of strict parents appear more adaptable at the "terrible two" stage, while daughters' behavior is more malleable in the four-to-five years period. However, the effect of *parental strictness* on the sons' behavior is shortlived: by the fifth year, the correlation with boys' adaptability has turned slightly negative, and a significant and negative change-score correlation (−.31) emerges over the second-to-fourth year period. Moreover, the association with sons' mood, a positive .22 at the second year, has shifted steadily to a negative −.23 by the fifth year. One explanation would be that parental strictness reaps "positive" rewards with sons' behavior at the two-year level, but subsequently mobilizes the sons' resistance.

Maternal concern and protectiveness (Dim. 4) proved to be another two-edged sword. At age two, these more solicitous parents were associated with children (and particularly sons) who reacted with greater degrees of intensity, perhaps in response to the perceived latitude granted by their parents. Over the next three years, however, this maternal protectiveness-child intensity relationship dwindled, to be replaced by a significant association between maternal protection and an increase in outgoingness (*approach-withdrawal*), particularly among sons, and with a corresponding shift toward more positive mood.

A point ably demonstrated by these two parental dimensions is that a parental trait or approach cannot be evaluated in absolute terms, but is relative at least to the age and sex of the child. To berate as a "poor mother" the oversolicitious caretaker of the boisterous two-year-old (whose intense reactions jangle one's ears) is to fail to recognize the possible advantages such mothering may generate at a later date in childhood. By the same token, the well-behaved two-year-old under the strict rein of his parents may be smoldering under that rein three years later.

Unrelated Parental Traits

Both Dimensions 6 and 8 (*material support limitations* and *large family orientation*) revealed fewer "significant" correlations than expectable by chance. The safest conclusion might be that these two dimensions possessed insufficient reliability or validity to determine whether any relationship did exist.

VARIATIONS IN CHANGEABILITY
OF TEMPERAMENT TRAITS

The correlational results indicated that not all temperament traits were associated significantly with parental behaviors with the same frequency. As Table 2 shows, *adaptability* and *intensity* were the temperament traits with the highest number of significant ($p<.05$) associations. Moreover, most of these significant associations were in the fourth-to-fifth year period, as was true generally for all associations between children's temperament and parental clusters. Only *rhythmicity* showed a preponderance of associations in the first two-year period, when presumably such factors as parental inconsistency could disturb a child's homeostatic functioning. Interestingly, *activity level,* a temperament scale that one might expect would affect parental dispositions or be affected by them, showed no significant correlations with any of the eight parental dimensions at any age. It was also interesting that the bulk of the significant associations reported in Table 2 were with the daughters' temperament scores.

DISCUSSION

Granted the truth of the "correlation does not indicate causation" maxim, one is tempted to conclude from these findings that parental treatment can modify a child's temperament. A child prone at birth to irregular sleep and eating schedules could easily become more irregular with inconsistent parenting. Similarly, an infant not blessed with easy adaptability might, in the face of cold, detached, and anxious parenting, drop off still further in adaptability. The fact that the parental interview was conducted around the children's third birthday, together with the fact that the number of significant parental trait correlations with the first three years of temperament data was relatively low, suggests that initial temperament levels had less effect on parental attitudes by the third year than these parental attitudes had on later temperament characteristics.

Finally, given our "geological hypothesis" that evidence of "strain" should develop in those temperament variables that Chess and Thomas found linked with higher risk for behavioral problems, it is important to note the correspondence between the temperament variables Chess and Thomas found in the fourth and fifth years to be "risk predictive" and the temperament variables associated in the same years with parental dimensions. (The chi-square comparing the years with significant associations between temperament scales and risk, as

Table 2

NUMBER OF SIGNIFICANT CORRELATIONS BETWEEN TEMPERAMENT VARIABLES
AND PARENTAL DIMENSIONS IN EACH OF THE FIRST FIVE YEARS

VARIABLE	YEARS					TOTAL
	1	2	3	4	5	
1. Adaptability		1	2	4a	a	7
2. Intensity		2	a	2a	2a	6
3. Threshold		1		a	2a	3
4. Distractibility				2a	1	3
5. Persistence		1		1a	1b	3
6. Approval-Withdrawal				1	2b	3
7. Mood				2b	b	2
8. Rhythmicity			2	a		2
9. Activity	a				b	0
Total	0	7	2	12	8	29

To highlight the mediating role that specific temperament traits may play between parental influence
and childhood behavioral disturbance, the years when each variable significantly discriminated between active or passive clinical cases and nonclinical cases has been noted, as follows:
a active clinical cases;
b passive clinical cases.

against the years with significant associations between temperament
scales and parental dimensions, measured 3.60, with $p<.10>.05$.)

CONCLUSIONS

Three points emerge from this study that seem to restate in different ways our "geological" metaphor. First, it seems clear that children's temperament is neither an inborn, immutable characteristic nor
just a function of past experience, but a reflection of both. Secondly,
we have additional evidence to support the position that most experienced clinicians seem to hold: that parental behavior *plus* children's
temperament forms the matrix from which children's behavioral problems may emerge. And, finally, as we generate our statistical or
intuitive-clinical equations to predict which children may develop behavioral problems, we should consider (among other factors) the potential *interaction* between the child's *specific* temperament and the *particular* parental response or attitude that we see developing on the
horizon.

REFERENCES

1. Fish, B. 1957. The detection of schizophrenia in infancy. J. Nerv. Ment. Dis. 125(1): 1–24.
2. Fish, B. and Hagin, R. 1973. Visual-motor disorders in infants at risk for schizophrenia. Arch. Gen. Psychiat. 28(6):900–904.
3. Graham, P., Rutter, M. and George, S. 1973. Temperamental characteristics as predictors of behavioral disorders in children. Amer. J. Orthopsychiat. 43(3):328–339.
4. Mellsop, G. 1972. Psychiatric patients seen as children and adults: childhood predictors of adult illness. J. Child Psychol. Psychiat. 13(2):91–101.
5. Smith, A. et al. 1972. Prediction of developmental outcome at seven years from prenatal and postnatal events. Child Developm. 42(2):495–507.
6. Thomas, A., Chess, S. and Birch, H. 1968. Temperament and Behavior Disorders in Children. New York University Press, New York.
7. Thomas, A. et al. 1963. Behavioral Individuality in Early Childhood. New York University Press, New York.
8. Tryon, R. and Bailey, D. 1966. The BC TRY computer system of cluster and factor analysis. Multivariate Behav. Res. 1(1):95–111.

Part V

PARENT-CHILD INTERACTION

It was not so long ago—even as recently as 15 to 20 years ago—that the dominant professional ideology laid the causation of all child psychopathology, from simple behavior problems to juvenile delinquency to schizophrenia, at the doorstep of the mother. This ideology did spring from substantial clinical studies, in which such phenomena as maternal rejection, maternal overprotection, and maternal deprivation were shown to have significant undesirable consequences for a child's psychological development. However, these findings, as well as certain influential theoretical concepts, led unfortunately to one-sided simplistic views in which the mother, and secondarily other family members, were considered the exclusive causative agents in a child's deviant development. Such views were bolstered by concepts of the newborn infant as a *tabula rasa,* a passive responder to environmental influences.

Research studies of the past 15 to 20 years, as indicated in Part I on *Developmental Issues* and Part IV on *Temperament Studies,* above, have completely altered these simplistic views. It is clear that even the newborn infant has a sophisticated repertoire of active responses to the environment, and that these have a marked influence on the process of parent-child interaction. It is no longer possible to seriously consider any aspect of a child's psychological development exclusively in terms of parental characteristics and behavior. But old ideas die hard! Thus, in recent years some professionals ascribed the rebellion and anti-establishment attitudes of many college students to an excessively permissive upbringing by their parents. And in January of this year a new book on child care was advertised in the *New York Times* with the prominent headline, "If a mother goes to work, does her baby pay for it?"

The articles in the present section represent significant additional inquiries into the complexities of the parent-child interactional process. Goldberg reviews the literature which explicates the ways in which the competent infant is instrumental in establishing those social conditions which are considered supportive of infant development. Kellam et al. report a study of the relationship between types of family organization and the mental health of children in a poor, black urban community. Beit-Hallahmi and Rabin review the history of the kibbutz movement and kibbutz child-rearing practices in Israel and the results of research in kibbutz socialization. The great interest in the kibbutz has sprung from its special characteristics in which the child is reared in varying degrees apart from his parents. The most striking general finding is that the majority of studies, and especially those complying with the more rigorous methodological standards, found few differences between kibbutz and non-kibbutz groups with regard to child personality. Farran and Ramey report that infant-day-care-reared children overwhelmingly preferred to be near and to interact with their mothers rather than their teachers, indicating that the attachment bond to the mother had indeed been formed. Gauthier and co-workers studied the mother-child relationship in younger asthmatic children. They found no substantiation for the frequently formulated thesis of a psychogenic etiology originating in pathological attitudes and behavior of the mother. Instead they were struck by the fact that a majority of the mothers in their series were very adequate indeed and did not conform to the cliché of the "asthmatogenic mother."

13

SOCIAL COMPETENCE IN INFANCY: A MODEL OF PARENT-INFANT INTERACTION

Susan Goldberg

Brandeis University

The recent years of research on infant development have brought us out of the "dark ages" during which we believed that the infant began life as a passive blob confronted with the task of making sense out of sensory chaos. Our current view considers the newborn infant to be active, capable of organizing complex information, selectively attentive, and capable of rapid learning. Upon careful examination, it appears that our acceptance of the young infant as a competent though immature organism has been largely confined to the domain of perceptual and cognitive skills. When we consider research on early social relations, we find that while we were documenting the "remarkable" perceptual and cognitive abilities of young infants, early social development continued to be studied under the "passive blob model" of the infant. Recognition of the infant as an active and competent contributor to the developing social relationships with caretakers has

Reprinted with permission from *Merrill-Palmer Quarterly*, 1977, Vol. 23, No. 3, 163–177.

The ideas presented in this paper are based upon longitudinal research with parents and infants supported by OCD grant no. 90-C-388 to the author. Newborn work for this project is based at Boston Hospital for Women. The first draft of this manuscript was read by Barbara Quinn and David Schneider, and their comments and suggestions are appreciated.

been late in coming, and in spite of several recent contributions (e.g., Lewis & Rosenblum, 1974) is not yet widespread.

The purpose of this paper is to make explicit the ways in which the competent infant is instrumental in establishing those social conditions which are considered supportive of infant development. I will argue that the infant is preadapted to be selectively attentive to the kinds of stimulation provided by people and that the infant is equipped with a repertoire of behaviors which effectively capture adult attention and facilitate effective adult-infant interactions. This, in turn, facilitates development. Moreover, I wish to argue that the central reciprocity in early social relationships between infants and caretakers is mediated by mutual enhancement of "feelings of efficacy" as defined by White (1959). The model which I propose focuses upon conditions that contribute to feelings of efficacy generated in caretakers and infants by their interactions, namely the extent to which each member of the dyad provides the other with contingency experience. Although I mean to include caretakers other than parents, I shall refer primarily to parents since parents are usually the primary caretakers. Consequently, most of the relevant research has been done with parents, usually mothers.

THE ROLE OF COMPETENCE MOTIVATION IN INFANT DEVELOPMENT

The notion that feelings of efficacy play an important role in infant development is not a new one. In his original exposition, White (1959) argued that many behaviors (e.g., exploration, curiosity) which could not be understood within the traditional drive-reduction model of motivation could be subsumed under a general need to interact effectively with the environment. White argued that this motive was an intrinsic one, though it was influenced by experience. Effective behavior would give rise to feelings of efficacy which would, in turn, strengthen the motive. He further suggested that the behavior of the human infant is particularly illustrative of competence motivation. Much of the behavior of infants is selective, directed, and persistent in the absence of appropriate rewards, indeed, often in the face of repeated punishments—such as the many falls experienced in learning to walk. White relied heavily upon Piaget's observations of infants. Piaget (1952, 1954) considered the infant to be an active organism interacting with the environment. Though he did not concern himself extensively with motivation, Piaget credited the infant with selective, directed, persistent behavior.

Later, Hunt (1960) used the term "intrinsic motivation" to describe the motivational significance of environmental feedback from information-seeking activities. He too argued that this motivation is particularly evident in infant behavior.

Subsequently, a number of researchers emphasized the importance of contingency experience in facilitating infant development and began to provide supporting data. The term contingency experience is generally used to mean experiences which are controlled by or dependent upon the infant's behavior. The amount of control the infant actually has is less important than the infant's perception of a relationship between behavior and its consequences. Thus, if an infant's memory span is less than 10 seconds contingency experiences will not be perceived unless responses to infant behavior follow that behavior within 10 seconds.

Watson (1967) suggested that infants are programmed to search for contingencies from birth and reported that social behaviors indicative of pleasure (such as smiling and cooing) first occur to objects (human or inanimate) which provide a high level of contingency experience. He later argued that adult behavior toward infants is adapted to the contingency-seeking characteristics of the baby. Adults naturally play "games" with babies, and Watson argued that such games are important to infants not because they are played by people, but because they provide contingency experience. In fact, "people are important to infants because they play the game" (Watson, 1972). Parenthetically, we might consider that what keeps adults playing such games is probably the contingency experience provided by infant attention, smiles, and vocalizations.

In fact, many researchers assume that competence motivation must be learned or maintained by contingency experience. Lewis and Goldberg (1969) and later Ainsworth and Bell (1974) argued that an important aspect of maternal responsiveness to infants is that it provides contingencies which allow the baby to learn that he or she is effective (i.e., can control or influence the environment). A high level of contingency experience, as provided by a caretaker who responds to infant behaviors with short latencies and appropriate behaviors, should lead to or support the expectation that behavior will be effective. This expectation then enhances exploration and practice of new skills, and facilitates infant development. Both Lewis and Goldberg (1969) and Ainsworth and Bell (1974) provide data from their laboratories showing that infants whose mothers were more attentive and responded promptly to cries were developmentally advanced relative to infants of unresponsive mothers. In addition, at least one early intervention program has found that the provision of contingency experience for retarded failure-to-thrive babies resulted in significant developmental advance in comparison with a control group (Ramey, Starr, Pallas, Whitten, & Reed, 1975).

Although authors disagree as to whether competence motivation is present from birth or not, the specific form it takes, and the role played by learning, there is general agreement that contingency experience is important for enhancing or maintaining competence motivation in infants.

COMPETENCE MOTIVATION AND DEVELOPMENT OF PARENTAL BEHAVIOR

Parents, when they become parents, have a lengthy history of experience which determines their general expectation of being effective. Their expectations of effectiveness as parents are initially derived from general levels of competence motivation, but will be enhanced, maintained, or depressed by their experience with the infant. Furthermore, parents, in spite of being parents, continue to interact with the environment in roles which may be irrelevant to their behavior as parents. However, interactions with the infant represent one domain which can potentially provide contingency experiences that function in two ways. First they become the primary experiences which determine feelings of efficacy in the parental role. In one study (Seashore, Leifer, Barnett, & Leiderman, 1973) maternal self-confidence was assessed by a paired comparison questionnaire administered to mother of premature infants. For primiparous mothers self-confidence was higher among mothers allowed to care for their babies in the nursery than for those denied early contact. Again, the extent to which the parent controls the infant in some absolute sense is less important than the parent's perception of being able to control infant behavior. Secondarily, contingency experience provided by the infant influences general levels of competence motivation. Just as the infant derives feelings of efficacy from parent-provided contingency experience, we shall assume that parents derive feelings of efficacy from infant-provided contingency experiences. In this context, the role played by parenthood may be extremely important for individuals who have few other domains in which they can have effective control (e.g., lower class single mothers). No one who has observed parents playing games with infants can doubt that the infant-provided contingencies are motivating for parents. Fraiberg (1974) relates that in observing parents of blind infants she was struck by what appeared to be a characteristically excess amount of gross body stimulation of the infant. However, it soon became evident that tactile and kinesthetic stimulation reliably elicited smiles from the infant where vocalizations failed and eye contact was impossible. Hence parents had adopted the mode of interaction which guaranteed reliable payoff.

Unlike infants whose intentions and goals are initially not clearly defined, I shall assume that parents have specific goals that serve as criteria for judgment of effectiveness. Some of these are long range goals, while others are more immediate. This discussion is concerned with immediate goals in specific interactions. I shall assume that parents wish to terminate or avoid infant behaviors which they find noxious and wish to maintain or elicit those infant behaviors which they find pleasant. Although there is probably general agreement about the desirability of some behaviors (e.g., crying is not likely to be judged pleasant by any parent), there will be individual differences in evaluating other behaviors which depend on parental attitudes and temperament (e.g., a high level of motoric activity may delight some parents and distress others) as well as contextual variables (e.g., motor activity may be desirable when the dyad is engaged in social play but undesirable during diaper changes). I assume that parents monitor infant behavior, make decisions about whether or not to intervene and about what form such intervention should take. Furthermore, they evaluate their effectiveness on the basis of the subsequent infant behaviors. If, after a parent intervention, aversive behavior is terminated or reduced and/or pleasant behavior is enhanced or elicited, this is a desirable outcome. If, on the other hand, aversive behavior continues or pleasant behavior fails to occur or terminates, this is an undesirable outcome. Feelings of effectiveness (hence enhancement of competence motivation) should occur when parents are able to make decisions about intervention easily and when interventions are followed by desirable outcomes. When parents have difficulty making decisions and when interventions are followed by undesirable outcomes, feelings of failure are generated. In the subsequent discussion, I shall argue that the normally competent infant is capable of providing contingency experiences which give rise to feelings of effectiveness on the part of parents.

THE COMPETENT NEWBORN

Thus far, competence has been discussed as a motive rather than in terms of skills and abilities. In this section I will consider the competencies of the normal newborn infant. Ainsworth and Bell (1974) have differentiated several ways of defining competence in infancy which are particularly appropriate for our purposes. The first, which defines competence in terms of an absolute scale of abilities, considers newborns helpless and incompetent relative to older children and adults. This is the definition which has been overemphasized in the past when we stressed the passivity, dependency, and limited perceptual abilities of the newborn. A second definition considers adequacy of functioning within the repertoire of age-appropriate behaviors. Thus, a competent newborn is one who sucks and roots efficiently, alerts to stimulation selectively, modulates states of arousal, and cries loudly when uncomfortable. These behaviors ordinarily enable the infant to function effectively within the environments normally encountered by newborns. However, the third definition considers the effectiveness of infant behaviors in the specific environment relevant to a given infant. An infant, then, is competent to the extent that s/he is effective in eliciting attention and appropriate care from the environment. Thus, a newborn's repertoire, though efficient in the age-appropriate sense, can be totally ineffective when paired with an unresponsive caretaker. Similarly, a newborn with distinct limitations or handicaps may be extremely effective when complemented by an unusually sensitive and responsive caretaker. It is this third definition which is most relevant to our purposes for it is when a parent-infant dyad is competent in this sense that mutual feelings of efficacy are enhanced. Under normal conditions there is a unique fit of infant skills to the adult behaviors directed toward infants which guarantees a high level of mutually produced contingency experience.

Reviews of the abilities of young infants consistently note that the perceptual systems of infants are preadapted to characteristic features of human behavior (Appleton, Clifton, & Goldberg, 1975; Richards, 1974; Stern, 1974; Trevarthen, 1973). In the visual modality, young infants are particularly attentive to movement (Carpenter, 1974; Haith, 1966), borders of high contrast (Salapatek, 1968; Salapatek & Kessen, 1966), and facelike stimuli in preference to other forms (Haaf & Bell, 1967). When face to face with infants, adults systematically exaggerate those facial features to which infants are attentive. Adults will normally present their faces at the distance where newborns are believed to focus best (7-9 inches), move their heads, and exaggerate facial expressions and movements (Stern, 1974). The result is a display in which there is constant movement of high contrast borders, and which the infant's behavior can control.

In the auditory mode, infants are selectively attentive to the bandwidth of frequencies which include human voices (Eisenberg, 1965). Furthermore, young infants are able to discriminate different voices (Boyd, 1975), come to prefer voices over other sounds, prefer female over male voices (Kagan & Lewis, 1965), and are able to make some of the discriminations which are unique to speech perception (Trehub & Rabinovitch, 1972; Eimas, Siqueland, Jusczk, & Vigorito, 1971). When adults vocalize to infants, there is systematic enhancement of these attention-getting features. The voice is pitched higher than normal and tonal changes and articulation are exaggerated, slowed, and repeated (Stern, 1974).

There is less information about infant capacities in other modalities. In studying tactile and kinesthetic responses, it is consistently reported that swaddling and rocking soothe and quiet infants (Ambrose, 1969; Birns, Blank, & Escalona, 1960; De Lucia, 1969; Pederson & Ter Vrugt, 1973; Ter Vrugt & Pederson, 1973). Being placed in the upright position typically elicits states of alertness with visual scanning (Korner & Grobstein, 1966; Korner & Thoman, 1972). Both the shoulder position and rocking are maneuvers that parents routinely use in attempting to console crying infants.

Thus, the complement of infants' selective attention to human features is the normal behavior of adults toward infants, which appears to be preadapted to capitalize upon the skills and preferences of the infant. Hence, there is a high probability that normal adult behaviors will lead to desirable outcomes in infant behavior, namely maintenance of infant attention, elicitation of smiling and vocalizing, and effective manipulation of states of arousal.

It is also the case that many infant behaviors are effective in eliciting adult attention and appropriate intervention. Any infant behavior can potentially evoke adult behaviors which produce contingencies for the infant. I will confine the discussion to a few of the more salient behaviors which have been studied systematically: feeding behavior, crying, smiling, and vocalization. These are introduced as illustrative examples rather than as an exhaustive catalog.

Feeding Behavior (Sucking, Rooting)

A common observation in feeding situations is that when the infant stops sucking (regardless of who the feeding adult is) the most frequent adult response is to "jiggle" the baby. Kaye and Brazelton (1971) observed adult-infant pairs in the feeding situation and studied sucking response over time as well as adult "jiggles". They found that the adult's "jiggle" had no particular effect in stimulating the infant to resume sucking. Instead, they suggest, cessation of sucking is a behavior which infants use to provoke stimulation from the adult. Dunn and Richards (1974) also report that during feeding, mothers' looking, talking, and touching are patterned by the infants' sucking behavior. Talking, looking at and touching were least likely to occur when the baby was sucking.

The rooting reflex is often assumed to function in helping the infant to locate the nipple. Blauvelt and McKenna (1959, 1962) filmed sequences of mothers feeding neonates and observed that infant movements appeared to control adult interaction. The specific effect of rooting was to elicit change in maternal orientation giving the infant better access to the nipple. It is not rooting alone that enables the infant to locate the nipple. It is rather the combination of rooting and change in maternal orientation in response to it. Thus, feeding is a cooperative effort in which adults use infant behavior as a guide for their own.

Crying

The infant cry is probably one of the most powerful stimuli for eliciting adult attention that is available to the infant. Much parental behavior in the early months is directed toward finding the appropriate terminator of infant cries. Wolff (1969) has differentiated spectrographically four different types of cries which are recognized by mothers and nurses. Wolff further reported that each type of cry evokes different adult behaviors. Hence, the infant is provided with a set of contingencies which provide the opportunity to learn that different vocal communications bring different results.

The effectiveness of cries in bringing adult attention is well documented in our culture. Dennis and Dennis (1951) in attempting to raise two infants with minimal interaction with adults reported that they always responded to cries. David and Appell (1961) found that in an institution, the amount of attention given to infants when crying was greater than that given to infants when quiet. A nurse very rarely went to a quiet awake baby between feeds. It was crying that brought attention.

Robson and Moss (1970) studied mother-infant interactions in homes for 54 primiparous mothers and their infants at 1 and 3 months. Of over 2000 episodes in which infant crying or fussing occurred, 77% were followed by maternal response. It appears that adults respond to infant cries with great regularity.

Smiling, Fixation, Vocalization

Although these behaviors are not frequent in newborns, they become increasingly important as social signals as the infant matures. Even the infrequent occurrences in newborns are probably salient for parents and the emergence of social play seems to depend upon the emergence of these behaviors.

Ambrose (1963) has suggested that since the human infant is initially unable to maintain proximity with his mother by following (as is the case in most sub-human species), either the mother must take the initiative or the infant repertoire must include some behaviors which increase proximity. He suggests that initially crying serves this function, and the data presented above support this contention. Eventually, Ambrose suggests, this role is "taken over" by smiling. If this is correct, it suggests that early parent-infant interactions are controlled by parents seeking to terminate crying while in later interactions they increasingly seek to elicit and maintain smiling. Robson and Moss (1970) interviewed 54 primiparous mothers and found that strong affection for the infant was first reported after the infant had begun to make eye contact and smile. Moss (1967) earlier reported an increase in affectionate maternal behavior around the third month when infant smiling, vocalization, and visual regard were becoming frequent infant behaviors. A similar finding is reported by Wolff (1963) who noted the beginning of visual regard at 4-6 weeks of age. Up to this time, interaction between infant and mother was predominantly in routine caretaking situations. After the appearance of visual regard, social play occurred with increasing frequency. Since infant smiling seems to be a necessary ingredient in parent-infant social interaction, Ambrose (1963) suggested that eye contact is a precondition for social learning. Both Robson (1967) and Hutt and Ounsted (1966) describe situations in which gaze aversion by children is indicative of abnormality and is disturbing to adults. Hutt and Ounsted suggest that eye contact between two individuals signals readiness to interact and thus functions as a releaser mechanism for social interaction.

Fraiberg and her co-workers (Fraiberg, 1968, 1971, 1974; Fraiberg & Freedman, 1964) noted that without intervention, parents of blind infants experience great difficulty interacting with their infants and often avoid social interactions. These parents (and the research staff) seem to miss the feedback from eye contact and eye contacts followed by smiles.

Sequential analysis of adult-infant interaction shows that smiling and vocalizing by infants elicits smiling and vocalizing by adults. The event most frequently following infant smile is adult smile (Gewirtz & Gewritz, 1969) and the event most likely to follow infant vocalization is adult vocalization (Gewirtz & Gewrirtz, 1969; Lewis & Ban, 1973; Lewis & Wilson, 1972).

Thus, although the young infant's behavioral repertoire is limited, some of its elements have a high probability of eliciting specific adult responses. The fact that adults react predictably in systematic fashion to infant behavior demonstrates that ordinarily, infant behaviors are effective in bringing adult attention and caretaking. Normally adult behavior toward infants is highly contingent upon infant behavior. Thus, the normally competent infant can be instrumental in bringing about his or her own contingency experience. It appears that there are preadapted patterns of behavior for both adults and infants which normally guarantee that their interactions are characterized by mutually produced contingency experience. Hence feelings of efficacy should be maintained or enhanced for both members of the dyad.

INFANT INDIVIDUALITY AND PARENTAL COMPETENCE MOTIVATION

Clearly there will be individual differences in both parents and infants within the range of normal competence. Hence, differences are expected in the developing social relationships. Previous authors have discussed the ways in which individual differences in parental behavior produce (or fail to produce) characteristic differences in their offspring (e.g., Ainsworth & Bell, 1974; Lewis & Goldberg, 1969). In this section I will consider some infant characteristics which have important effects on parental feelings of efficacy. Parents' feelings of efficacy are derived from parental evaluation of interactions. Hence, parent perception of infant characteristics and behavior is probably a more powerful determinant of interactions than any other assessment of the infant. Since there has been little research on parents' perception of their infants, I will assume that under normal circumstances, parent perceptions are systematically related to independent assessments of infant characteristics. However, this assumption needs to be validated by research.

Readability

Readability is defined as the extent to which an infant's behaviors are clearly defined and provide distinctive signals and cues for adults. Distinctiveness of states of arousal, promptness and appropriateness of responses to stimulation, and energy invested in persistent sustained behaviors contribute to an infant's readability. In practical terms, readability refers to the ease with which adults can say "s/he's hungry, tired, looking at me," etc. An infant who is easily "read" enhances adult feelings of efficacy: (a) because they can easily recognize states and signals; (b) because decisions about interventions are facilitated; and (c) because there is a high probability that adults will decide upon appropriate interventions and produce desirable outcomes. We have observed newborns for whom we find it difficult to rate behavior on the Brazelton Scales (1972) and for whom our reliability is poor. We suspect that these are babies who are difficult for parents to "read" as well. Korner (1974) speaks of using the category "indeterminate" in state ratings when state cannot be rated as clearly in one of the other categories (e.g., the infant is crying and asleep; or awake but marginally alert). An infant with a high proportion of "indeterminate" state ratings is one who should be difficult to "read". Fraiberg (1974) reports that parents of blind infants who do not produce normal facial expressions must be taught to "read" expressions in the infants' hands.

Predictability

When a parent tries to read infant cues, it is often for the purpose of predicting future behavior (e.g., how soon will the baby awaken, express hunger, be sleepy). Predictability is defined as the extent to which an adult can reliably anticipate behavior from contextual events and/or immediately preceding behaviors. Regularity of sleep/wake and feeding cycles (which Thomas, Chess, & Birch, 1968, call rhythmicity), modulation of states of arousal, and reliability of responses to specific stimuli or interventions will determine how accurately adults can predict behavior for a given infant. When an infant is highly predictable, adults' feelings of efficacy are enhanced: a) because they make successful predictions; b) because decisions about interventions are easily made; and c) because they have a high probability of choosing interventions which will produce the desired outcomes. When a highly predictable infant whimpers for a few minutes after the evening feeding, a parent can decide that, because these whimpers have regularly subsided in a few minutes every evening and been followed by sleep, the infant can be ignored. Furthermore, there is a high probability that ignoring the infant's whimpers will be followed by the infant falling asleep. On the other hand, the same behavior in the same context for an unpredictable baby presents the adult with a difficult decision.

The adult is likely to feel ineffective and helpless, unable to anticipate the infant's subsequent behavior. Furthermore, whatever decision the adult may make about intervention has a high probability of leading to undesirable outcomes. One of the characteristics of "difficult" babies in the study of temperament by Thomas, Chess, and Birch (1962) was little regularity in hunger, excretion and sleep/wake cycles. What I have been suggesting here is that even unpleasant behavior such as crying, withdrawal, or failure to respond to adult intervention is more understandable (and less likely to generate feelings of failure) when it occurs in predictable fashion.

Responsiveness

By responsiveness, I mean the quality and extent of infant reactions to stimulation. It includes attentiveness to faces and voices, to inanimate objects, the ease with which attention can be elicited and sustained, and how readily adult intervention can console cries. In any specific interaction with an infant, adults judge their effectiveness most directly by infant reactions to their behavior. A baby who alerts to visual and auditory stimulation, sucks immediately and energetically when objects are placed in his or her mouth, and is easily quieted or roused, is likely to provide immediate direct response to adult caretaking interventions. The responsive baby is the one who reacts to stimulation with short latencies and appropriate behavior—i.e., is a good contingency producer for parents.

Figure 1 illustrates in graphic fashion the influences of these infant characteristics on adult feelings of effectiveness or failure. As the adult monitors infant behavior, the ability to make decisions about interventions is a joint function of parent feelings of effectiveness and infant predictability and readability. When infants are highly predictable and readable, parents are able to arrive at decisions quickly, make decisions easily, and have a high probability of making appropriate decisions. Note that this condition enables the parent to act in precisely the fashion that provides a high level of contingency experience for the infant. This is the pattern of adult behavior which we usually describe as sensitive and responsive. When the infant is unpredictable and difficult to read, decisions require a longer time, are difficult to make, and are less likely to be appropriate. Hence, the adult is likely to behave in a fashion that results in a low level of contingency experience for the infant. This is the pattern of behavior we are likely to label unresponsive or ineffective on the part of the parent.

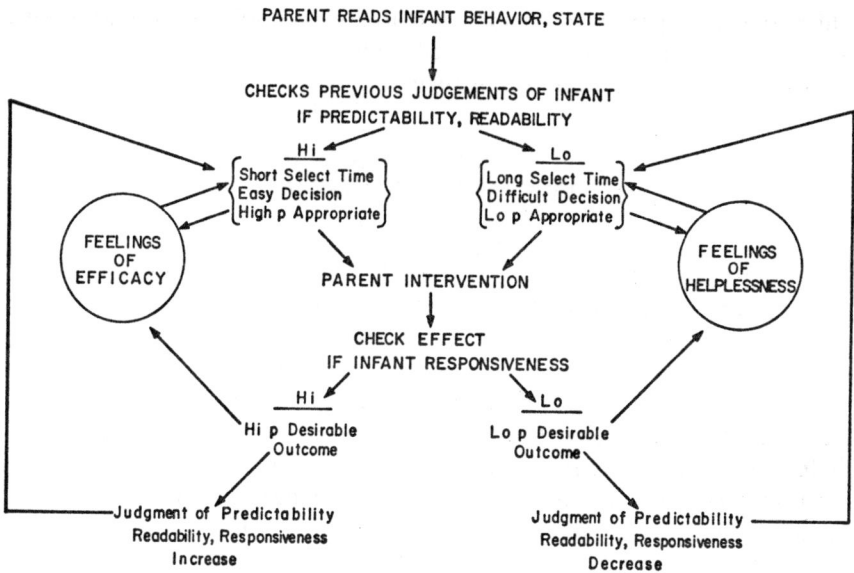

PARENT READS INFANT BEHAVIOR, STATE

CHECKS PREVIOUS JUDGEMENTS OF INFANT
IF PREDICTABILITY, READABILITY

Hi

Short Select Time
Easy Decision
High p Appropriate

Lo

Long Select Time
Difficult Decision
Lo p Appropriate

FEELINGS
OF
EFFICACY

PARENT INTERVENTION

FEELINGS
OF
HELPLESSNESS

CHECK EFFECT
IF INFANT RESPONSIVENESS

Hi

Hi p Desirable
Outcome

Lo

Lo p Desirable
Outcome

Judgment of Predictability
Readability, Responsiveness
Increase

Judgment of Predictability
Readability, Responsiveness
Decrease

Figure 1

A model of parent-infant interaction.

Having made a decision and responded in some way to infant behavior, adults judge the effectiveness of their behavior on the basis of infant responsiveness. The highly responsive infant is likely to respond in ways that adults characterize as desirable outcomes, enhancing the adults' feelings of effectiveness. Once a parent has elicited a desired infant behavior through intervention upward corrections in estimates of the infant's predictability and readability will be induced. The unresponsive infant will more often fail to respond to interventions as the adult wished, leaving the adult feeling ineffective and helpless. Furthermore, the adult in this case will subsequently correct previous estimates of infant predictability and readability downward.

Normally, as a baby matures, s/he becomes more readable, predictable, and responsive in the eyes of adults. As the infant develops more precise voluntary control of behavior, gestural, and vocal facility in communication, and an understanding of the environment, behavior changes in the direction of increasing similarity to adult behavior. Adults are, therefore, better able to understand and manipulate infant behavior. At the same time, continuous experience with a particular child enables a parent to develop sensitivity and skill in caretaking and social interaction. Thus, the adults' ability to read, predict, and manipulate behavior should also improve.

IMPLICATIONS OF THE MODEL:
FOSTERING EFFECTIVE INTERACTIONS

It is important to note that the predictable, readable, responsive infant has the potential for "capturing" the initially unresponsive parent into cycles of effective interactions by generating parental feelings of efficacy. Similarly, the unpredictable, unreadable, unresponsive infant has the potential for "trapping" an initially responsive parent in cycles of ineffective interaction by generating parental feelings of failure and helplessness. This suggests that whenever parents are confronted with an infant of limited competence the potential risks of interactive failures are high. The model further suggests that the incompetent dyad can be helped toward effective interactions under conditions which (a) faciliate infant development (i.e., develop predictability, readability, and responsiveness), and (b) develop parental skills in predicting and reading infant behavior and foster sensitivity to the contingency experiences provided by the infant. These two types of intervention, both aimed at increasing mutual contingency experiences, should be broadly applicable to infants of limited competence regardless of the specific nature of the handicap.

The foregoing discussion suggests that the ideal parent-infant relationship is one in which each member of the dyad produces perfect contingencies for the other. Such a relationship is clearly impossible and undesirable. The repeated occurrence of the same sequence of predictable interactions can be expected to lead to boredom. Parents seem to know this and often use variations in timing and quality of behavior to maintain infant behavior in social games. The literature on infant learning and cognitive development suggests that the optimal level of contingency experience for the infant will change with increasing maturity. For the parents, the course of ordinary development guarantees the emergence of novel infant behaviors. Furthermore, both parent and infant behaviors serve multiple functions and will be influenced by many factors other than the dyadic relationship. Thus, while a high level of contingency is expected and desirable in parent-infant relationships, it is inevitable and fortunate that the contingencies cannot be perfect.

REFERENCES

Ainsworth, M. D. S., & Bell, S. M. Mother-infant interaction and the development of competence. In K. J. Connolly & J. S. Bruner (Eds.), *The growth of competence.* New York: Academic Press, 1974. Pp. 97–118.

Ambrose, A. The concept of a critical period for the development of social responsiveness in early human infancy. In B. Foss (Ed.), *Determinants of infant behavior* II. London: Methuen, 1963. Pp. 201–225.

Ambrose, A. (Ed.) *Stimulation in early infancy.* New York: Academic, 1969, p. 98 and following.

Appleton, C., Clifton, R. K., & Goldberg, S. The development of behavioral competence in infancy. In F. D. Horowitz, M. Hetherington, S. Scarr-Salapatek, & G. Siegel (Eds.), *Review of child development research,* Vol 4. Chicago: University of Chicago Press, 1975. Pp. 101–186.

Bell, S. M., & Ainsworth, M. D. S. Infant crying and maternal responsiveness. *Child Development,* 1972, Vol. 43, 1171–1190.

Birns, B., Blank, M., & Escalona, S. K. The effectiveness of various soothing techniques on human neonates. *Psychosomatic Medicine,* 1960, Vol. 28, No. 4, Part I, 313–322.

Blauvelt, H. Capacity of a human neonate reflex to signal further response by present action. *Child Development,* 1962, Vol. 33, 21–28.

Blauvelt, H., & McKenna, J. Mother neonate interaction: Capacity of the neonate for orientation. In B. M. Foss (Ed.), *Determinants of infant behavior* I. London: Methuen, 1959. Pp. 3–28.

Boyd, E. F. Visual fixation and voice discrimination in 2-month-old-infants. In F. D. Horowitz (Ed.). Visual attention, auditory stimulation and language discrimination in young infants. *Monographs of the Society for Research in Child Development,* 1975, Vol. 39 (Serial No. 158), 63–77.

Brazelton, T. B. *Neonatal behavior assessment scale.* London: National Spastics Society Monographs, 1972.

Carpenter, G. C. Visual regard of moving and stationary faces in early infancy. *Merrill-Palmer Quarterly,* 1974, Vol. 20, 181–194.

David, M., & Appell, G. A study of nursing care and nurse-infant interaction. In B. M. Foss (Ed.), *Determinants of infant behavior* I. London: Methuen, 1961. Pp. 121–135.

DeLucia, L. D. To rock or not to rock that is the question. *Bulletin of Brown University Child Study Center,* 1969, 3.

Dennis, W., & Dennis, M. G. Development under controlled environmental conditions. In W. Dennis (Ed.), *Readings in child psychology.* New York: Prentice Hall, 1951. Pp. 104–131.

Dunn, J. B., & Richards, M. P. M. Observations on the developing relationships between mother and baby in the neonatal period. Unpublished paper, University of Cambridge, 1974.

Eimas, P. D., Siqueland, E. R., Jusczk, P., & Vigorito, J. Speech perception in early infancy. *Science,* 1971, Vol. 171, 303–306.

Eisenberg, R. B. Auditory behavior in the neonate. I Methodological problems and the logical design of research procedures. *Journal of Auditory Research,* 1965, Vol. 5, 159–177.

Fraiberg, S. Parallel and divergent patterns in blind and sighted infants. In *Psychoanalytic Study of the Child,* Vol. 23. New York: International Universities Press, 1968. Pp. 264–300.

Fraiberg, S. Intervention in infancy: A program for blind infants. *Journal of American Academy of Child Psychiatry,* 1971, Vol. 10, 381–405.

Fraiberg, S. Blind infants and their mothers: An examination of the sign system. In M. Lewis & L. A. Rosenblum (Eds.). *The effect of the infant on its caregiver.* New York: John Wiley & Sons, 1974. Pp. 215–232.

Fraiberg, S., & Freedman, D. Studies in the ego development of the congenitally blind child. In *Psychoanalytic Study of the Child,* Vol. 21. New York: International Universities Press, 1964. Pp. 113–169.

Gewirtz, H. B., & Gewirtz, J. L. Caretaking settings, background events and behavior differences in four Israeli childrearing environments: Some preliminary trends. In B. Foss (Ed.), *Determinants of infant behavior* IV. London: Methuen, 1969. Pp. 229–252.

Haaf, R. A., & Bell, R. Q. A facial dimension in visual discrimination by human infants. *Child Development,* 1967, Vol. 38, 895–899.

Haith, M. M. The response of the human newborn to visual movement. *Journal of Experimental Child Psychology,* 1966, Vol. 3, 235–243.

Hunt, J. McV. *Intelligence and experience.* New York: Ronald Press, 1961.

Hutt, C., & Ounsted, C. The biological significance of gaze aversion with particular reference to the syndrome of infantile autism. *Behavioral Science,* 1966, Vol. 11. 346–353.

Kagan, J., & Lewis, M. Studies of attention in the human infant. *Merrill-Palmer Quarterly,* 1965, Vol. 11, 95–127.

Kaye, K., & Brazelton, T. B. Mother-infant interaction in the organization of sucking. Paper presented at meeting of the Society for Research in Child Development. Minneapolis, April, 1971.

Korner, A. F. The effect of the infant's state, level of arousal, sex, and ontogenetic stage on the caregiver. In M. Lewis & L. A. Rosenblum (Eds.), *The effect of the infant on its caregiver.* New York: John Wiley & Sons, 1974. Pp. 105–122.

Korner, A. F., & Grobstein, R. Visual alertness as related to soothing in neonates: Implications for maternal stimulation and early deprivation. *Child Development,* 1966, Vol. 37, 867–876.

Korner, A. F., & Thoman, E. B. The relative efficacy of contact and vestibular proprioceptive stimulation in soothing neonates. *Child Development,* 1972, Vol. 43, 443–454.

Leifer, A. D., Leiderman, P. H., Barnett, C. R., & Williams, J. A. Effects of mother-infant separation on maternal attachment behavior. *Child Development,* 1972, Vol. 43, 1203–1218.

Lewis, M., & Ball, P. Variance and Invariance—mother-infant Interaction: A cross cultural study. Paper prepared for Burg Wartenstein Symposium No. 57. Cultural and Social influences in Infancy and Early Childhood. Gloggnitz, Austria, June 18–26, 1973.

Lewis, M. & Goldberg, S. Perceptual-cognitive development in infancy: A generalized expectancy model as a function of the mother-infant interaction. *Merrill-Palmer Quarterly;* 1969, Vol. 15, 81–100.

Lewis, M., & Rosenblum, L. *The effect of the infant on its caregiver.* New York: John Wiley & Sons, 1974.

Lewis, M., & Wilson, C. D. Infant development in lower class American families. *Human Development,* 1972, Vol. 15, 112–127.

Moss, H. A. Sex, age, and state as determinants of mother-infant interaction. *Merrill-Palmer Quarterly,* 1967, Vol. 13, 19–36.

Pederson, D. R., & Ter Vrught, D. The influence of amplitude and frequency of vestibular stimulation on the activity of two-month-old infants. *Child Development.* 1973, Vol. 44, 122–127.

Piaget, J. *The origins of intelligence in children.* New York: International Universities Press, 1952.

Piaget, J. *The construction of reality in the child.* New York: Basic Books, 1954.

Ramey, C. T., Starr, R. H., Pallas, J., Whitten, C. I., & Reed, V. Nutrition, response-contingent stimulation, and the maternal deprivation syndrome: Results of an early intervention program. *Merrill-Palmer Quarterly,* 1975. Vol. 21, 45–54.

Richards, M. P. M. The development of psychological communication in the first year of life. In K. J. Connolly & J. S. Bruner (Eds.), *The growth of competence.* New York: Academic Press, 1974. Pp. 119–132.

Robson, K. S. The role of eye contact in maternal-infant attachment. *Journal of Child Psychology and Psychiatry,* 1967, Vol. 8, 13–25.

Robson, K. S., & Moss, H. A. Patterns and determinants of maternal attachment. *Journal of Pediatrics,* 1970, Vol. 77, 976–985.

Salapatek, P. The visual investigation of geometric pattern by the one and two-month old infants. In C. S. Lavatelli & F. Stendler (Eds.), *Readings in child behavior and development.* New York: Harcourt Brace, 1972. Pp. 147–152.

Salapatek, P., & Kessen, W. Visual scanning of triangles by the human newborn. *Journal of Experimental Child Psychology,* 1966, Vol. 3, 155–167.

Seashore, M., Leifer, A. D., Barnett, C. R., & Leiderman, P. H. The effects of denial of early mother-infant interaction on maternal self-confidence. *Journal of Personality and Social Psychology,* 1973, Vol. 26, 369–378.

Stern, D. N. Mother and infant at play: The dyadic interaction involving facial, vocal, and gaze behaviors. In M. Lewis & L. A. Rosenblum (Eds.), *The effect of the infant on its caregiver.* New York: John Wiley & Sons, 1974. Pp. 187–213.

Ter Vrught, D., & Pederson, D. R. The effects of vertical rocking on the arousal level in two-month-old infants. *Child Development,* 1973, Vol. 44, 205–209.

Thomas, A., Chess, S., & Birch, H. *Temperament and behavior disorders in children.* New York: New York University Press, 1968.

Trehub, S. E., & Rabinovitch, M. S. Auditory-linguistic sensitivity in early infancy. *Developmental Psychology,* 1972, Vol. 6, 74–77.

Trevarthen, C. B. Behavioral embryology. In E. C. Carthette & M. P. Freidman (Eds.), *The handbook of perception* Vol. III. New York: Academic Press, 1973. Pp. 89–118.

Watson, J. S. Memory and contingency analysis in infant learning. *Merrill-Palmer Quarterly,* 1967, Vol. 13, 55–76.

Watson, J. S. Smiling, cooing and "the game." *Merill-Palmer Quarterly,* 1972, Vol. 15, 323–340.

White, R. W. Motivation reconsidered: The concept of competence. *Psychological Review,* 1959, Vol. 66, 297–333.

Wolff, P. H. Observations on the early development of smiling. In B. M. Foss (Ed.), *Determinants of Infant Behavior* II. London: Methuen, 1963. Pp. 113–138.

Wolff, P. H. The causes, controls and organization of behavior in the newborn. *Psychological Issues,* 1966, No. 1.

Wolff, P. H. The natural history of crying and other vocalizations in early infancy. In B. M. Foss (Ed.), *Determinants of Infant Behavior* IV. London: Methuen, 1969. Pp. 81–110.

14

FAMILY STRUCTURE AND THE MENTAL HEALTH OF CHILDREN

Sheppard G. Kellam, Margaret E. Ensminger

University of Chicago

and R. Jay Turner

University of Western Ontario, London

This study provides a map of variations of families and some of the core relationships between types of family and the mental health of children. Family types in a poor, black urban community were defined in terms of the adults present at home. The resulting taxonomy is based on two populations: half of the community's 1964 first-grade children and families and the entire 1966 first-grade children and families. Eighty-six family types were found, falling into ten major classes. Family type was found to be strongly related over time to the child's social adaptational status (SAS) and his or her psychological well-being. The results suggest that (1) mother alone families entail the highest risk in terms of social maladaptation and psychological well-being of the child; (2) the presence of certain second adults has important ameliorative functions—mother/grandmother families being nearly as effective as mother/father families, with mother/stepfather families similar to mother alone in regard to risk; and (3) the absence of the father was less important than the aloneness of the mother in relation to risk.

Reprinted with permission from *Archives of General Psychiatry*, Vol. 34, 1012-1022, 1977. Copyright 1977, American Medical Association.

The child-rearing family, a basic social unit in all societies, functions in the central roles of genetic transmitter, provider of nurturance, and, in most societies, as the primary socializer of the young. Across cultures the family appears in diverse forms. The presence or absence in the household of all types of blood relatives varies both from one society to another and within societies, as do the prescribed child-rearing roles of mother, father, and other kin.

This report is concerned with a central aspect of family structure—the different combinations of adults present in child-rearing families—and its relationship to the mental health of young school-children. In the homes of first graders in the Woodlawn area of Chicago, the site of these studies, there were no less than 86 different combinations of adults in one school year. We here present a taxonomy of these families according to adult membership in the household and relate the major family types to the mental health of the children.

Social structure refers not only to the membership of a social system but to the roles elaborated in that institution or organization. The addition or deletion of certain adults within a family system may influence the roles of the adults and so the quality of child rearing. Most researchers interested in relating the family to mental health have studied the nuclear family, ie, mother, father, and children. Those investigators interested in comparing types of families have most often used dichotomies, such as intact vs nonintact families, or father present vs father absent families. Herzog and Sudia[1] in an extensive summary of the father absence literature concluded that the results are ambiguous and that the importance of father absence to child rearing may be mediated and/or influenced by other factors of greater importance.

A disproportionate number of studies have focused on the nuclear family. Many researchers have been interested only in the development of mental health and illness in families where both mother and father are present. We attribute this concentration (1) to the historical importance of the nuclear family in psychiatric theory and (2) to a strong consensus among Americans of all social classes and ethnic groups that the mother/father family is inherently superior.[2] However, Adams[3] argues that although the nuclear family generally fulfills certain specified functions it is theoretically and empirically invalid to conclude that other family types cannot also fulfill these same functions. In a recent review of the psychiatric family literature, Bloch[4] observes that the concept of the nuclear family ". . . does not take into account the wide variation in family and household composition, even in Western industrial society, nor does it indicate the extent of the family that is psychologically meaningful to the individual."

Other taxonomies have been used. Gibson and Ludwig,[5] studying households having a disabled adult, established 19 categories of family, using as criteria marriage status, "childrenness," and the relationships of household members other than husband and wife. Five categories, based on the presence of mother, father, stepmother or stepfather, children, and other relatives, were found useful by Fischer and co-workers[6] studying a sample of New Orleans families. Minturn and Lambert,[7] anthropologists studying child rearing in six cultures, concluded that family structure variables such as household composition, family size, and parental work load were more important for the growing child than were specific child-rearing techniques. They suggest that these variables determine the time and energy that mothers have available to care for their children. In a study of Taiwan society, Olsen[8] also demonstrated the importance of household composition. She showed that the extent to which a mother is herself conforming and, in turn, emphasizes conformity in her children was related to the presence of the paternal grandmother in the home.

This article comes from a longitudinal psychiatric study of the children in first-grade classrooms between 1964 and 1969 in a Chicago community. The families of these children were categorized on the basis of adult household membership. We shall relate this taxonomy of family types to the children's mental health defined in terms of psychological well-being on the one hand and adequacy of social role performance, which we term "social adaptational status," on the other.

Figure (opposite page).—Taxonomy of various combinations of adults present in households of 1966 first graders' families. Fourteen possible categories of adults are listed on right and left sides in order of frequency of occurrence. Each occurring adult combination is indicated by a circle. Within each circle are initials of particular adults present; to left of each circle is number indicating frequency with which combination actually occurred in 1966.

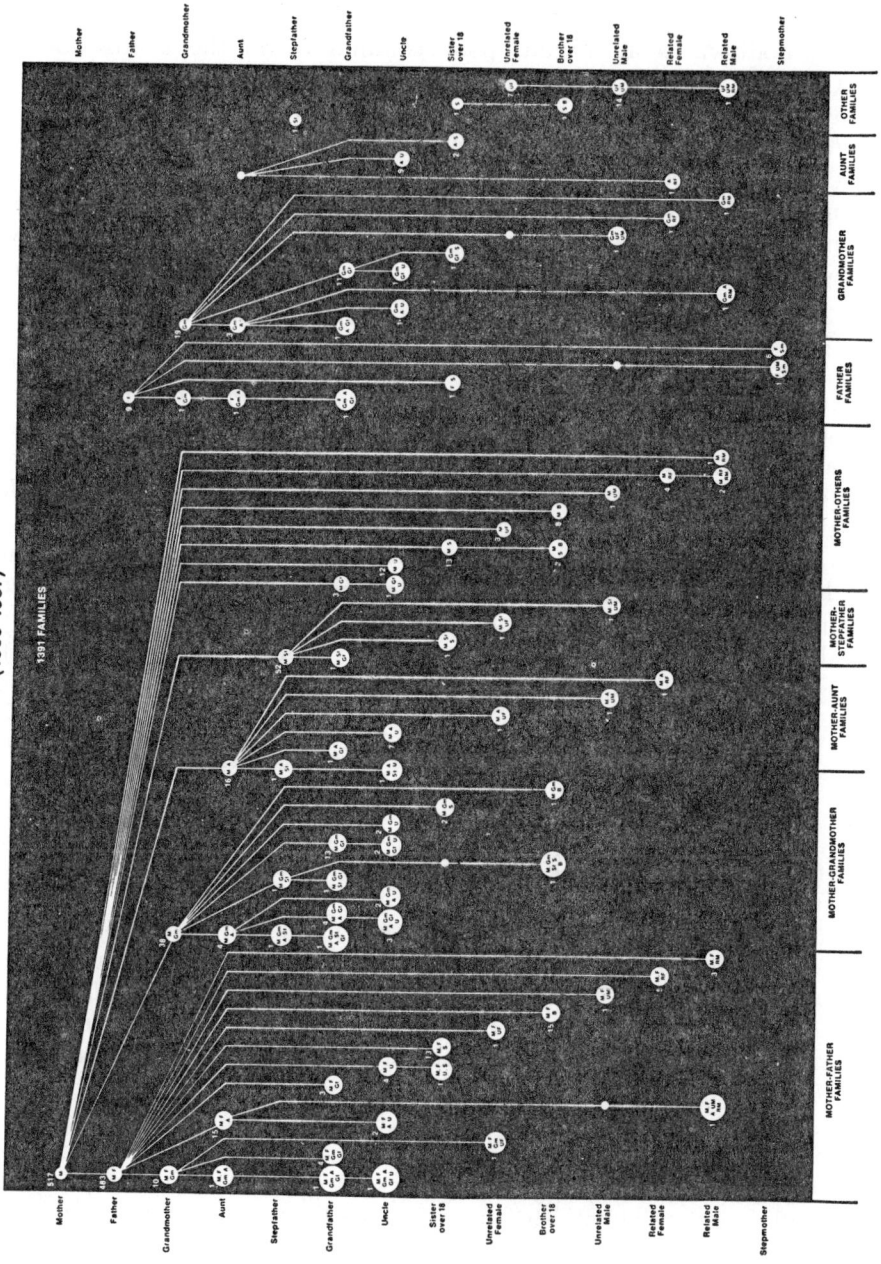

VARIATION IN FAMILIES OF WOODLAWN FIRST GRADE CHILDREN
(1966-1967)

STUDY POPULATION

Woodlawn is an urban, poor community on the south side of Chicago. It has undergone dramatic changes over the past 25 years. By 1964, the year of our first study of first-grade children, Woodlawn had become predominantly black and substantially overcrowded. According to 1967 data, Woodlawn had become a community of low median income and high unemployment, with three times as many residents on public assistance per 1,000 population as there were city-wide.[9] Despite this overall picture, there was and is heterogeneity within Woodlawn, some areas having higher median incomes and more home ownership than others.

Supported by a community board composed of leaders from the community's larger citizen organizations, the Woodlawn mental health studies have periodically assessed the mental health of first graders and reassessed at the end of third grade.[10] Each first-grade population from 1964 through 1969 was assessed; the number of first-grade children each year was about 1,700.

We collected extensive family data for a 50% random sample of the 1964 first graders and the entire class of 1969 first graders; trained interviewers from the National Opinion Research Center interviewed their mothers or mother surrogates. (An extensive nine-year follow-up reassessment of the 1966 population, now 16 years old, is in progress.)

DEFINING AND MEASURING MENTAL HEALTH

In the Woodlawn studies, we conceptualize mental health as being in two dimensions: (1) psychological well-being—how the individual feels inside about himself or herself—including affects, self-esteem, and psychopathology; and (2) social adaptational status (SAS)—a societal dimension measuring the adequacy of the individual's role performance as viewed by a significant other in a particular social field. We assert that SAS is more than the social reflection of the individual's internal mental status; SAS is the interface between the individual and society. This distinction permits us to study the concomitants of each dimension and their concurrent and longitudinal relationship. In a recent publication we have more fully discussed this conception, the measurement of these two dimensions, and their reliability and validity.[11] Because of space limitation we can only summarize our strategy here.

PSYCHOLOGICAL WELL-BEING

Psychological well-being was measured by ratings from clinicians, the children's mothers, and by the 1966 first graders themselves when they reached third grade. Clinicians made ratings at the beginning and end of first grade for both the 1964 and 1966 children and at the end of third grade for the 1964 children. The clinicians worked in pairs in a standardized group play context, making independent ratings and then consensus ratings of each child's symptom status, without access to SAS data or the mother's ratings. Symptoms were rated on scales of anxiety, depression, bizarre behavior, flatness, hyperkinesis, and on a global symptom scale. Half of the mothers in 1964 (randomly selected) and all the mothers in 1966 reported on the symptom status of their children during the mother interviews. The mother's rating scale was a 38-item inventory adapted from previous investigations of the epidemiology of symptoms among young children.[12-15] Because of a lack of resources, no clinicians examined the 1966 first graders at the end of third grade; instead, these children filled out a self-report instrument called the "How I Feel." Relevant here are the two global questions in the How I Feel referring to feelings of tension and nervousness and to feelings of sadness.

SOCIAL ADAPTATIONAL STATUS

In each stage of the life of an individual and in each social field, a *natural rater* sets the social tasks and assesses the adequacy of role performance. The teacher in the classroom, the parent in the home, the foreman on the job, significant others in the peer group, and one's spouse or mate in the heterosexual social field are all examples of natural raters within specific social fields.

Because of its central importance at this time of life transition, we have chosen the classroom as the social field, with the teacher as natural rater for measurement of children's SAS. We first determined what social tasks teachers expected children to accomplish. They were socializing with other children, dealing with rules and authority, learning up to ability, being relatively mature, and paying attention. We derived rating scales from this list and included a global scale, adapting/maladapting. Each Woodlawn child was rated by his or her teachers three separate times in first grade and once in third grade. We also collected grades, IQ scores, and achievement test scores as quasi-SAS measures.

In the course of our analysis of the teacher's ratings, we have found the single scale adapting/maladapting most informative. At times, however, it has been instructive to use five categories of SAS, one adapting plus four maladapting, called the *maladaptive modes*, which were derived by examination of the combinations of teacher ratings. The maladaptive modes consist of shyness or aggressiveness, alone or together usually associated with the characteristics that we identify as learning problems—not learning up to ability, acting immaturely, and not paying attention; there is also a mode consisting of learning problems without shyness or aggressiveness. Hence, the modes are (1) shyness with learning problems, (2) aggressiveness with learning problems, (3) both shyness and aggressiveness with learning problems, and (4) learning problems only.

In *Mental Health and Going to School*[11] we discuss at length the concept of social adaptation and SAS and report reliability and validity studies. Data were also presented showing that early social maladaptation was related to continued maladaptation at least as far as the third grade. We have now found, in the preliminary stages of the nine-year follow-up, a substantial relationship between the measures of early social adaptation and grade placement at age 15 to 16 years.

The teenagers should have been in ninth grade if their school careers had proceeded normally. While 73% of the children who were rated adapting early in first grade in 1965 (a pilot year) were found in ninth grade at the end of 1973, only 47.2% of those judged to be maladapting had achieved that grade level. Only 0.5% of first-grade adapting children were found in remedial programs, compared with 8.2% of early maladapting children. Turning to the social maladaptive modes, we found at follow-up only 37.8% of the first-grade shy-aggressive children at proper grade level, 43.3% of aggressive children, and 48.3% of shy children, about 10% of these maladapting children were found in remedial classrooms. Of those children viewed by their first-grade teachers as having learning problems, but not shyness or aggressiveness, 58.2% were found at proper grade level and 3.5% in remedial classrooms. Regression analyses show that the global measure, adapting/maladapting, of SAS is the best single predictor of grade placement and that the global SAS measure makes a contribution to grade placement independently of IQ and achievement tests.

We conclude, from these and other data, that SAS represents a potent dimension of mental health, and we believe it important to examine factors that may affect either early social adaptation or psychological well-being or both.

VARIATION IN FAMILY STRUCTURE

Family types were classified in terms of the adults present at home on the basis of information obtained in the family interview with the mothers (or mother surrogates) of the first-grade children. A taxonomy of the various combinations of adults present in the households of the 1966 population of first graders' families is shown in the Figure. We found ten different adult relatives present in the families, plus four residual categories of relatives and nonrelatives, male and female. There were 86 different combinations of these adults in 1966, while in 1964 there were 79 combinations.

The Figure is cumulative from top to bottom. If one begins, for instance, at the upper left hand corner with mother alone and descends directly downward to mother/father and then to mother/father/grandmother, it may be seen that mother alone families occur 517 times; mother/father 483 times; mother/father/grandmother ten times; mother/father/grandmother/aunt only once. When a combination does not contain the next relative listed in the left and right margins, it is shown by a line moving laterally and downward to the next included relative. Thus, there are 38 mother/grandmother families; four mother/grandmother/aunt families; and so on. While the number of families in many of the combinations are too small to analyze, the taxonomy illustrates the diversity that exists in the households of first-grade children in this community.

Eight major classes of families, plus a residual "other" category, may be seen in the cone-like clustering of family types. These are named across the bottom of the Figure. These nine, plus mother alone families, yield the ten major classes of families raising first-grade children in 1966 in Woodlawn.

RESULTS

The results of studies of family type and mental health will be presented in the following order.:

1. Concurrent studies of family type and SAS;
2. Concurrent studies of family type, other structural variables, and SAS;
3. Concurrent studies of family type, gender of child, and SAS;
4. Longitudinal studies of family type and SAS;
5. Concurrent studies of family type and psychological well-being;
6. Longitudinal studies of family type and psychological well-being;

7. Longitudinal studies of family type, SAS, and psychological well-being.

This series of analyses should demonstrate the existing associations between (a) family type and SAS, (b) family type and psychological well-being, and (c) family type, SAS, and psychological well-being.

Although our taxonomy yielded ten major categories of families, small numbers required combining some categories for analytic purposes. Our basic results will be described in terms of six major family types: mother alone, mother/father, mother/grandmother, mother/stepfather, mother/other, and mother absent families. For the same reason, multivariate analyses will involve only the three broader categories that our analyses suggested were most important: mother alone, mother/father, and mother/second adult.

The 1964 data will generally be presented first, followed by the 1966 data. Studies on the 1966 data can be considered independent replications of the 1964 studies. Concurrent relationships will be presented on the populations of first-grade families that were interviewed in 1964 (a 50% random sample) and in 1966 (the total population). Longitudinal relationships will be examined by studying family data and mental health measures in first grade along with mental health measures in third grade. These analyses include those children whose mothers were interviewed in first grade and who were still in Woodlawn for the third grade follow-up, 59% of the 1964 sample and 53% of the 1966 sample.

CONCURRENT STUDIES OF FAMILY TYPE AND SAS

Initially, we examined the distribution of social adaptation and maladaption across the six major family types found in Woodlawn. (In addition to the relationships between family type and SAS, two aspects of the data in Table 1 are notable. The first is the apparent high rate of maladapting children. Woodlawn is a high-risk community, and large numbers of children do show continuing maladaptation in school. One reason for the seemingly high rates, however, is that the children were rated by their teachers on five different tasks, and were included as maladapting in these analyses if rated maladapting on any of the tasks. The second aspect is the difference in maladaptation rates between 1964 and 1966. Rates of adaptation apparently changed considerably, partly as a function of the rapidly changing neighborhood and partly because of the effect of repeated measures on the teachers' ratings over the years. See *Mental Health and Going to School*[11] for fuller discussion of these issues.) Table 1 presents these distribu-

Table 1.—Family Type and First-Grade Social Adaptational Status

	Mother Alone	Mother/ Father	Mother/ Grandmother	Mother/ Stepfather	Mother/ Other	Mother Absent	Total Population
1964 first graders*							
Adapting, %	15.9	26.6	30.0	16.7	24.6	19.0	22.1
Maladapting, %	84.1	73.4	70.0	83.3	75.4	81.0	77.9
Total N	295	369	50	42	57	42	855
1966 first graders†							
Adapting, %	28.9	42.5	39.5	33.9	34.2	40.2	36.3
Maladapting, %	71.1	57.5	60.5	66.1	65.8	59.8	63.7
Total N	516	563	76	56	79	97	1,387

*$\chi^2 = 13.74; P < .02.$
†$\chi^2 = 22.77; P < .001.$

tions separately for the 1964 and 1966 cohorts. Our interpretation of these data will emphasize points of consistency across these two independent studies.

Mother alone families had fewer adapting children than any other family type. Mother/father and mother-grandmother families had higher rates of adapting children than any other family type. The relative ratios by family type showed substantial consistency, although the proportion of children rated as adapting increased notably from 1964 to 1966.

Not father absence, but mother aloneness predisposes children in mother alone families to social maladaptation. Both mother/father and mother/grandmother families appear to offer prevention against social maladaptation; but other types of second adult appear less effective, particularly stepfather.

If we look only at the maladapting children, some variation in mode of maladaptation by family type can be observed. The following trends appear more or less in both the 1964 and 1966 studies; although they are more evident in 1964, they are in the same direction but not significant in 1966. Maladapting children from mother alone families are more likely to be rated as shy-aggressive than are maladapting children from other family types. Mother/stepfather families and families in which the mother is absent have higher rates of aggressive children than other family types. There does not seem to be any relationship between family type and being rated as having learning problems only.

Having confirmed an association between family type and SAS, we now consider a series of additional questions. Primary among these are the following: (1) To what extent do other structural variables such as number of siblings present, number of adults present and income influence or account for the observed associations? (2) How do these associations differ for boys and girls? (3) Are family type and psychological well-being also related; and, if so, how does this relationship evolve over time? (4) Do family type, SAS, and psychological well-being interact over time; and, if so, how?

The answers require multivariate techniques that allow consideration of several categorical variables simultaneously. The recently elaborated technique of log-linear analysis of hierarchical models appears to meet this need.[16][24] This method is designed specifically for analysis of multivariate contingency tables of categorical or ordinal data that do not meet the assumptions required in conventional regression analysis. Since the technique is relatively new and may be unfamiliar to some readers, a brief description follows.

Hierarchical model analyses are based on fitting a series of models that take into account different orders of interactions among the variables under consideration. Estimated cell frequencies, based on the log-linear model, are compared with the observed cell frequencies by the likelihood ratio χ^2 statistic. If the value of χ^2 relative to the degrees of freedom is small enough, then the observed and expected cell frequencies are closer together and the model fits the data. When a fitting model is found, each interaction in the model is tested to assure its necessity within the most parsimonious model. The interaction among the variables not accounted for in the best fitting model are unimportant in the actual data and may be disregarded. However, if the value of χ^2 is large, a lack of fit of the model to the data is indicated and the model is rejected. The model would need to be revised to include additional interactions.

For example, one would first attempt fitting a model that uses the marginal distribution of each variable to determine expected cell frequency. If the model fits, we would conclude that, while there might be unequal distributions of cases across the categories of the variable, it is unnecessary to assume any relationships among the variables. If this model did not fit, (ie, the χ^2 is significant) at least one interaction is needed to describe the data. One would then add the two-variable interactions to the model, one at a time, to determine which interactions describe the data. Interactions would continue to be added in this way, remembering the increasing complexity of interpretation with higher order ones. If none of the models fit, it means that all interactions, including the highest order interaction, are needed to account for the data. Generally, due to the cell sizes and complexity of interpretation, we have limited each analysis to three variables. The model informs us of the relationships that exist and those that can be ignored.

When the most appropriate model is found, the effect parameters may be examined to see specifically how the variables are related. Effect parameters are partial coefficients that describe the direction and strength of a relationship for a single main effect or interaction while controlling for all other terms in the model. The effect parameters are standardized statistics indicating degree of difference between expected and observed values and may be interpreted as follows: a zero coefficient represents no difference between the expected and observed cell, a negative coefficient indicates fewer cases than expected in the cell; a positive coefficient indicates more cases in the cell than would be expected.

The analyses in this article will describe the model that best fits the data and the significant effect parameters for the model. We will also present contingency tables where they help in assessing the results.

Concurrent Studies of Family Type, Other Structural Variables, and SAS

Although adult membership in the homes of the children has a compelling logic as a basic way of defining family type, there are other structural family characteristics that may represent either alternatives or elaborations of our understanding of the relations between SAS and family type as defined by adult membership. In the following analyses the number of adults at home, the number of siblings, and family income are examined to determine their relations with family type and the SAS ratings of the children. Again, three basic family types, mother/father, mother alone, and mother/second adult, were used in these analyses.

Number of Adults and Number of Children.–Mother/second adult families in both populations had three or more adults present in the household significantly more often than did mother/father families ($p<.001$). On the other hand, mother and second/adult families had fewer children than the mother/father families in both populations; they also had fewer than mother alone families in the 1966 population, but not in 1964.

However, log-linear analyses showed that neither the number of adults nor the number of children present in the family affected the SAS/family type relationship and neither was related to the child's SAS when family type was held constant.

Family Income.—To assess its effects, we classified family income into three categories: "low" (less than $3,000/yr), "medium" ($3,000 to $6,000/yr), and "high" (more than $6,000/yr). These three categories are based on the distribution of income among Woodlawn families and reflect the general poverty of the community. Examination of our log-linear hierarchical model analyses made clear that, in Woodlawn, family type and amount of income are very closely identified. All fitting models for both cohorts indicate a relationship between income and family type, as shown in Tables 2 and 3. In both cohorts, mother/father families are underrepresented in the lowerest income category and overrepresented in the highest, while mother alone families are substantially overrepresented in the low and middle income categories.

On the central question of the effects of income level on the family type/SAS relationship, the results for 1964 are equivocal. Although one fitting model (Table 3) shows all possible two-way relationships to

Table 2.—Distribution of Family Type, Social Adaptational Status, and Family Income

	Mother/Father			Mother/Second Adult			Mother Alone			Total
	$3,000 or Less	$3,000-$6,000	$6,000+	$3,000 or Less	$3,000-$6,000	$6,000+	$3,000 or Less	$3,000-$6,000	$6,000+	
1964										
No. (%) adapting	10 (22.2)	34 (21.9)	52 (31.7)	15 (25.0)	15 (24.6)	4 (16.7)	27 (13.6)	15 (21.4)	4 (25.0)	...
No. (%) maladapting	35 (77.8)	121 (78.0)	112 (68.3)	45 (75.0)	46 (75.4)	20 (83.3)	172 (86.4)	55 (78.6)	12 (75.0)	...
Total N	45	155	164	60	61	24	199	70	16	794
1966										
No. (%) adapting	18 (42.9)	67 (37.4)	144 (44.7)	11 (21.6)	33 (40.7)	24 (35.8)	68 (29.4)	66 (27.9)	11 (39.3)	...
No. (%) maladapting	24 (57.1)	112 (62.6)	178 (55.3)	40 (78.4)	48 (59.3)	43 (64.2)	163 (70.6)	171 (72.2)	17 (60.7)	...
Total N	42	179	322	51	81	67	231	237	28	1,238

Table 3.—χ^2 Values for Some Models Pertaining to Data in Three-Way Table of Family Type (F), First-Grade Social Adaptational Status (1), and Family Income ($)*

Hypothesized Model	Likelihood Ratio (χ^2)	df	P
1964†			
(F) (1) ($)	296.89	12	< .000
(F,1) (1,$)	276.12	8	< .000
(F,1) (F,$)	8.32	6	< .215
(F,$) (1,$)	7.90	6	< .245
(F,$) (1)	18.50	8	< .018
1966			
(F) (1) ($)	468.88	12	< .000
(F,1) (F,$)‡	9.53	6	< .146
(F,1) (1,$)	434.46	8	< .000
(F,$) (1,$)	13.52	6	< .035

*The symbols in parentheses indicate the model being tested. For example, (F,1) (F,$) (1,$) specifies a model in which there is a two-way partial relationship between all possible pairs of variables; (F,1) (F,$) specifies a model in which there is a partial relationship between family type and current social adaptional status and a partial relationship between family type and family income. The best fitting model is one in which the actual data (1) does not differ significantly from the model being tested and (2) is the most parsimonious that fits the data. For example, for the 1966 population, both (F,1) (F,$) (1,$) and (F,1) (F,$) fit the data ($\chi^2$ is NS). However, (F,1) (F,$) is more parsimonious and is therefore the best fitting model.
†See text for explanation of analysis of best fitting model for 1964.
‡Best fitting model for 1966.

be maintained when the effects of the third variable are partialled out, there are two more parsimonious models that also fit. One of these shows the family type/SAS relationship to be unnecessary in explaining the data, while the other indicates that the income/SAS relationship is unnecessary. Income and family type are so closely related that, when one of these is controlled, the relationship among the other variables practically disappears.

While it is difficult to interpret the 1964 data with confidence, the results for 1966 provide a clearer picture. The best fitting model confirms the association between family type and SAS as well as that between family type and income. There is no relation between income and SAS when family type is held constant. The effect parameters show that mother/father families have more adapting children. In our view, these findings are consistent with the argument that, independent of the effects of income, family type is importantly related to the social adaptation of children. However, in this relatively poor neighborhood the range of income is skewed, making generalization to other communities with different income ranges hazardous.

Concurrent Studies of Family Type, Gender of the Child, and SAS

A wide array of personality theories assume that the growth and development and social role performance of boys is influenced by the presence of a father or father figure. The prediction follows from this that the SAS rating of boys will be more strongly affected by the father's absence than would the SAS rating of girls.

If the boys in mother alone families were the reason such families tended to have poorer ratings, then we would expect a three-way interaction indicating that boys in mother alone families were affected differentially. However, in both years the data are accounted for by a relationship between family type and SAS, as previously noted, and a relationship between sex and SAS. No relationship between family type, sex, and SAS was found in either 1964 or 1966 (Tables 4 and 5).

The effect parameters indicate that for both years, controlling on sex of the child, mother alone families are underrepresented in the adapting cell and mother/father families are overrepresented; and mother/second adult families did not differ significantly from the expected distribution of adaptation. The effect parameters indicate that in both cohorts, girls are more likely to be adapting regardless of family type.

We find no evidence in either study population to support the assumption that boys reared in families without a father or male adult are differentially affected. By adolescence, we may find such a result; hence, the teenage follow-up will be important.

Longitudinal Studies of Family Type and SAS

In both the 1964 and 1966 data, the SAS teacher ratings from the third grade show that adapting children were still more likely to come from families that were mother/father families in first grade and least likely to come from families that were mother alone families in first grade. In addition, we know from earlier analyses that the first-grade SAS ratings are related to third-grade SAS ratings.[11] Therefore, we examined the longitudinal relationship between early family type and third-grade SAS ratings, while controlling for the first-grade rating.

We obtained family type data only at the end of first grade. Family types may have changed by third grade, when follow-up mental health assessments were done, but we think that any influence due to such changes will have worked against the finding of relationships; therefore, the reported relationships are probably conservative. The term "family type" will refer, in the reports here of longitudinal studies, to family type at the end of first grade.

The ratings of children who remained in Woodlawn from first to

Table 4.—Distribution of Family Type by Social Adaptational Status by Sex

	Mother/Father		Mother/Second Adult		Mother Alone		Total
	Boys	Girls	Boys	Girls	Boys	Girls	
1964							
No. (%) adapting	37 (20.1)	61 (32.6)	15 (17.7)	21 (32.8)	19 (12.8)	28 (19.1)	...
No. (%) maladapting	147 (79.9)	126 (67.4)	70 (82.4)	43 (67.2)	129 (87.2)	119 (81.0)	...
Total N	184	187	85	64	148	147	815
1966							
No. (%) adapting	99 (37.3)	140 (46.5)	30 (29.7)	46 (41.8)	57 (21.7)	92 (36.4)	...
No. (%) maladapting	163 (62.2)	161 (53.5)	71 (70.3)	64 (58.2)	206 (78.3)	161 (63.6)	...
Total N	262	301	101	110	263	253	1,290

Table 5.—χ^2 Values for Some Models Pertaining to Data in Three-Way Table of Family Type (F), First-Grade Social Adaptational Status (1) and Sex of the Child (S)*			
Hypothesized Model	**Likelihood Ratio (χ^2)**	**df**	**P**
1964			
(F) (1) (S)	28.03	7	< .000
(F,1) (F,S)	13.89	3	< .003
(F,1) (1,S)†	3.49	4	< .479
(F,S) (1,S)	12.26	4	< .015
1966			
(F) (1) (S)	45.25	7	< .000
(F,1) (F,S)	21.39	3	< .000
(F,1) (1,S)†	2.77	4	< .500
(F,S) (1,S)	22.31	4	< .000

*See footnote to Table 3 for explanation of symbols.
†Best fitting model.

third grade were used in the longitudinal analyses. It is important to note that even though about half of the children were no longer in Woodlawn schools by third grade, there was not a differential mobility rate by family type. The proportion of mother/father families, mother alone families, and mother/second adult families remained about the same. However, in both populations, children rated as adapting in first grade remained in Woodlawn schools by third grade more often than if mobility had been random.

Because of the smaller number of children available for longitudinal analyses, we again used the three family types—mother alone, mother/father, and mother/second adult. While theoretically interesting to study, mother absent families were not included in the anlyses because of small numbers and great variability in terms of which adults were present. A very small number of these families were father alone families, a few were grandmother-led families and about half were foster families (see Figure for exact details).

When the hierarchical model analyses were done with the variables family type, first-grade social adaptational modes, and third-grade social adaptational modes, no different relationships with the different maladaptive modes were observed. Accordingly, only the adapting/maladapting distinction was employed in the hierarchical log-linear analyses that we will present.

The best fitting models substantiate the relation of family type to SAS (Table 6). The analyses on the 1964 population data indicate relationships between family type and first-grade SAS. A trend relates

Table 6.—χ^2 Values for Some Models Pertaining to the Data in the Three-Way Table of Family Type (F), First-Grade Social Adaptational Status (1), and Third-Grade Social Adaptational Status (3)*

Hypothesized Model	Likelihood Ratio (χ^2)	df	P
1964 (N = 504)			
(F) (1) (3)	37.93	7	< .000
(F,1) (F,3)	21.25	3	< .000
(F,3) (1,3)	9.74	4	< .045
(F,1) (1,3)†	7.41	4	< .115
1966 (N = 729)			
(Γ) (1) (3)	66.64	7	< .000
(F,1) (F,3)	33.65	3	< .000
(F,3) (1,3)†	6.40	4	< .171
(F,1) (1,3)	17.15	4	< .002

*See footnote to Table 3 for explanation of symbols.
†Best fitting model.

family type and third-grade SAS, but is less than significant, ($P<.115$).

Family type relates directly to third-grade SAS for the 1966 population when we control for first-grade SAS; (again first- and third-grade SAS are related.) Thus, the trend in the 1964 data is confirmed.

Maladapting children from mother alone families not only occur in greater numbers in first grade, but their ratings deteriorate and they remain maladapting in greater numbers from first to third grade (Table 7). Mother/father families, in contrast, appear to protect their adapting children more adequately and to provide a better chance that early maladapting in school will be corrected over time. These are only trends in the 1964 population, more easily discernible in first-grade maladapting than in adapting children, but are quite evident in the 1966 population.

The results suggest intensification over time of the adaptational advantage associated with certain family types. Generative processes may be operating.

Concurrent Studies of Family Type and Psychological Well-Being

The psychological well-being measures described earlier include clinical ratings, mother ratings on a symptom inventory, and self ratings by the children in the 1966 population when these children were in third grade. In the 1964 population, there was some evidence that first-grade clinical symptoms were associated with mother aloneness, but this result was not replicated in the 1966 population. On ratings

Table 7.—Distribution of Family Type by First-Grade Social Adaptational Status by Third-Grade Social Adaptational Status

	Mother/Father		Mother/Second Adult		Mother Alone		Total
	First-Grade Adapting	First-Grade Maladapting	First-Grade Adapting	First-Grade Maladapting	First-Grade Adapting	First-Grade Maladapting	
1964							
No. (%) third-grade adapting	30 (42.9)	44 (26.5)	11 (44.0)	9 (12.9)	11 (37.9)	25 (17.4)	...
No. (%) third-grade maladapting	40 (57.1)	122 (73.5)	14 (56.0)	61 (87.1)	18 (62.1)	119 (82.6)	...
Total N	70	166	25	70	29	144	504
1966							
No. (%) third-grade adapting	69 (46.0)	47 (25.8)	21 (39.6)	11 (15.9)	26 (29.2)	24 (12.9)	...
No. (%) third-grade maladapting	81 (54.0)	135 (74.2)	32 (60.4)	58 (84.1)	63 (70.8)	162 (87.1)	...
Total N	150	182	53	69	89	186	729

made by the mothers, there was a tendency in both populations for mothers in mother alone families to ascribe more symptoms to their children than did other members, but this was significant only at the .10 level of probability. Our analyses, then, failed to provide convicing evidence for a relationship between family type and psychological well-being in the first grade.

Longitudinal Studies of Family Type and Psychological Well-Being

Third-grade data, however, show a different picture. Clinician ratings on the 1964 population in third grade revealed a prevalence of psychiatric symptoms of 7.3% in mother alone families and 3.9% in mother/father families. Although such small prevalences preclude meaningful probability tests, it does appear that children from mother alone families are almost twice as likely to be judged symptomatic by clinical raters.

The 1966 first-grade population was not rated by clinicians in third grade due to lack of resources, but the children rated themselves on how sad and nervous they felt. Children from mother alone families rated themselves as being more sad than did children from mother/father families, and the latter rated themselves less nervous than did children from either mother/second adult families or mother alone families (Table 8 and 9). These distributions show that children from mother/second adult families are in the middle on the sadness ratings and more like mother alone children on the nervousness ratings. We conclude that, while there may not be a concurrent relationship, there does appear to be a longitudinal relationship between family type and psychological well-being, at least as we have measured it.

Longitudinal Studies of Family Type, SAS, and Psychological Well-Being

A fundamental question in psychiatric theory concerns the relative importance of social role function and psychological well-being in the life course of the individual. In what ways do SAS and psychological well-being interact to produce later SAS and psychological well-being?

In many epidemiologic studies, rather low frequencies of symptoms have been observed in young children, at least when assessed by clinicians.[20][34] Those symptoms that do occur may express either the excessive burden of the social task demands or the degree to which the child is struggling to incorporate the social tasks into his or her own personal values. Another possibility is that symptoms in young children are relatively trivial, short-lived, and play no great role in the longitudinal mental health of the child.

Table 8.—Distribution of Family Type by 1966 First-Grade Social Adaptational Status and Third-Grade Self-Assessed Sadness

	Mother/Father Sadness			Mother/Second Adult Sadness			Mother Alone Sadness			Total
	1*	2	3	1	2	3	1	2	3	
No. (%) adapting	37 (52.1)	43 (48.9)	12 (30.8)	12 (63.2)	7 (36.9)	4 (26.7)	20 (35.1)	18 (39.1)	19 (34.5)	...
No. (%) maladapting	34 (47.9)	45 (51.1)	27 (69.2)	7 (36.9)	12 (63.2)	11 (73.3)	37 (64.9)	28 (60.9)	36 (65.5)	...
Total N	71	88	39	19	19	15	57	46	55	409

*1 indicates not at all sad; 2, a little sad; and 3, pretty much or a lot sad.

Table 9.—Distribution of Family Types by 1966 First-Grade Social Adaptational Status and Third-Grade Self-Assessed Nervousness

	Mother/Father Nervousness			Mother/Second Adult Nervousness			Mother Alone Nervousness			Total
	1*	2	3	1	2	3	1	2	3	
No. (%) adapting	43 (53.1)	27 (45.0)	22 (38.6)	5 (38.5)	14 (60.9)	4 (23.5)	11 (23.9)	28 (45.2)	18 (36.0)	...
No. (%) maladapting	38 (46.9)	33 (55.0)	35 (61.4)	8 (61.5)	9 (39.1)	13 (76.5)	35 (76.1)	34 (54.8)	32 (64.0)	...
Total N	81	60	57	13	23	17	46	62	50	409

*1 indicates not at all nervous; 2, a little nervous; and 3, pretty much or a lot nervous.

It is of central importance to determine the role of the family in the interrelations between social adaptation and psychological well-being. We examined the relationships among family type, SAS in first grade, and psychological well-being in third grade. The measure of psychological well-being was the self-assessment of sadness and nervousness made by the 1966 first-grade children when they reached the end of third grade. This measure was the only longitudinal measure of psychological well-being available with numbers large enough to analyze.

The results of the hierarchical log-linear analysis showed a relationship between third-grade sadness and family type, controlling on first-grade SAS (Tables 8 and 10). As the effect parameters indicate, children from mother/father families were least likely to rate themselves as "pretty much" or "a lot" sad, while children from mother alone families were most likely to rate themselves this way, regardless of first-grade SAS.

The analysis of family type and third-grade nervousness, controlling on first-grade SAS, was more complicated. The model as shown in Table 11 indicates that there is a three-way interaction among these variables. The contingency table and the effect parameters indicate that first-grade adapting children from mother alone families have a higher risk of later nervousness than do those from mother/father families, a finding similar to that regarding sadness (Table 9). However, later nervousness in children who had been maladapting in first grade is not influenced by family type. It may be that nervousness in third grade represents a response to prior school maladaptation, irrespective of family type.

In general, our data show that self-assessed sadness and nervousness occur with more intensity in children reared in mother alone families than in children from mother/father families and that early SAS influences later nervousness. Mother/second adult families show a somewhat inconsistent pattern, and the numbers involved place the reliability of observed differences in some doubt.

We have looked at how family type and early SAS affect later psychological well-being. We now turn to the mirror image of this issue—how family type and early symptoms affect later SAS. In order to do this, we examined the relationship between family type and third-grade social adaptational ratings, controlling for first-grade symptoms, as measured by the mother symptom inventory. Results indicate that early symptoms do not affect the relationship of family type with later SAS. In other words, family type continues to influence later SAS, and the presence of symptoms in first grade, as ob-

Table 10.—χ^2 Values for Some Models Pertaining to Data in Three-Way Table of Family Type (F), First-Grade Social Adaptational Status (1), and Third-Grade Self-Assessed Sadness (S), 1966*

Hypothesized Model	Likelihood Ratio (χ^2)	df	P
(F) (S) (1)	27.72	12	< .006
(F,1) (F,S)	10.50	6	< .105
(F,1) (1,S)	17.42	8	< .026
(F,S) (1,S)	8.12	6	< .229
(F,S) (1)†	14.46	8	< .070

*See footnote to Table 3 for explanation of symbols.
†Best fitting model.

Table 11.—χ^2 Values for Some Models Pertaining to Data in Three-Way Table of Family Type (F), First-Grade Social Adaptational Status (1), and Third-Grade Self-Assessed Nervousness (N), 1966*

Hypothesized Model†	Likelihood Ratio (χ^2)	df	P
(F) (1) N)	26.73	12	< .009
(F,1) (F,N)	14.09	6	< .028
(F,1) (N,1)	18.73	8	< .016
(F,N) (N,1)	14.02	6	< .029
(F,1) (F,N) (N,1)	9.75	4	< .044

*See footnote to Table 3 for explanation of symbols.
†None of the models fit the data. Since the saturated model (F,1) (F,N) (N,1) does not fit ($P < .05$), there is a three-way interaction among the variables, indicating that (F,1,N) is significant.

served by the mother, does not influence that longitudinal relationship.

In summary, these results suggest that early success and failure, as measured by the teachers' SAS ratings, do play some role in the relationship of family type and later psychological well-being; but early symptoms do not influence the relationship between family type and later SAS.

COMMENT

We began this article by suggesting that research into the relationships between mental health and the family would be enhanced by a more systematic and complete classification of types of families that occur in defined populations. The taxonomy of Woodlawn families—based on the combinations of adults at home—resulted in 86 different kinds of families raising the Woodlawn first-grade children in 1966. The studies of the types of families in relation to the children's social adaptation and psychological well-being just reported give us an opportunity to reassess our initial assumption that a classification of family variation would be useful.

In prior family research, father absence has been considered a category of family. The results of research into the impact of the father's absence have been ambiguous. One should not discard the concept of father absence, but rather one must be aware of the wide variation in the families in which the father is absent. This awareness allows for better specification of the alternatives to father's presence. Children from mother/grandmother families, for example, do as well on first-grade SAS as mother/father children. Mother alone children do the worst of all family types, with mother/stepfather children not much better. With such different outcomes within the father absence category, it is not surprising that the scientific literature on the effect of father absence is ambiguous.

Similarly, knowledge of the actual variation of types of families will benefit the study of variables such as sex, age, and number of adults at home, number of generations at home, and so on and their effects on the mental health of children.

In the Woodlawn studies presented in this article, the 86 kinds of families were grouped first into ten categories, then into six, and finally into three. One could question whether this collapsing of categories vitiates the advantage of the elaborate taxonomy. However, developing a taxonomy to classify the variety of families that exist in a community or population does not mean that family types cannot be combined for purposes of analysis; small numbers and theoretical requirements may necessitate such combinations. The difference is that our combining of types is based on knowledge of the existing kinds of families, as well as on theoretical and empirical grounds. In the Woodlawn studies, for example, the father absent category did not evolve from our combining types, due to the empirical results in both study populations that mother alone was the highest risk, mother/father the lowest, while the risk entailed by mother/second adult varied depending on who was the second adult.

We, therefore, conclude that the clarification and classification of types of families raising Woodlawn children enlightened our studies of family and mental health. The resulting family typology provides a substantial base for further studies seeking out the explanations of the relationships found between family type and the mental health of the children. However, the specific criteria we used for defining family types are by no means the only possible ones. Further study of other methods of classification is necessary.

A review of the major inferences drawn from the studies reported in this article will help to focus further discussion:

1. *Variation in types of child-rearing families in Woodlawn is very extensive.* The 79 kinds of families in 1964 and the 86 in 1966 provide compelling evidence. Yet most families were mother/father families with or without various other adults, and next in frequency were mother alone families. A great amount of attention, both by scientists and others, has been paid to "the black family." The family taxonomy of Woodlawn families provides very powerful evidence that no such homogeneous entity exists.

2. *Mother alone families entail a higher risk of child social maladaptation to first grade, a risk that grows even stronger by third grade.* While adapting children in mother alone families had some increased risk of becoming maladapting by third grade in 1964, the 1966 children showed a clearly increased risk. In both studies, first-grade maladapting children reared in mother alone families showed a clear tendency to remain maladapting in third grade.

3. *Mother/father families provide a lower risk of maladaptation of their first-grade children and lower likelihood of the children remaining maladapting by third grade even if they have been maladapting in first grade.* However, children from mother and certain second adult families, particularly mother/grandmother, did as well as mother/father. Mother/stepfather families, in contrast, did not do much better than mother alone.

4. *By third grade, there is a relationship between family type and psychological well-being. Again, mother alone families entail a higher risk.* In the first study population, although clinical symptoms were relatively infrequent, they were most often observed in third graders from mother alone families. In the second study population, self-ratings of sadness and (for the children adapting in first grade) tension were higher for third graders from mother alone families.

5. *Social adaptional status in first grade was important in the relationship of third-grade psychological well-being and family type.* Psychological well-being in first grade, however, did not play a role in the relationship of family type to third-grade SAS. In other words, early SAS, along with family type, was important in how the child felt inside later on, but early psychological well-being was not important to later SAS.

On the basis of the reported data and inferences drawn from the data, we can say that family type does contribute to the mental health of children—at least in urban communities such as Woodlawn. These studies do not, however, explain how to provide evidence as to the relative contribution of biological, social, or psychological mechanisms, any or all of which may be involved.

Woodlawn provides these results; perhaps they may be generalized to similar communities that are poor, urban, and black. In neighborhoods of different ethnic backgrounds or higher socioeconomic levels, mother alone families might occur with very different characteristics and different levels of risk. Income or other aspects of social class may alleviate the higher risk of mother alone families in other kinds of communities. In the studies reported in this article, the incomes of virtually all mother alone families were particularly low.

These studies, while preliminary, provide a basis for social policy and mental health care considerations. The aloneness of the mother, particularly in the urban ghetto, is undoubtedly worthy of more systematic study as an avenue for intervention. In planning mental health programs for children and families, perhaps treating the aloneness itself by programs of group discussion or even shared mothering may be potent strategies in need of further systematic design and evaluation.

The Woodlawn community, its families and children, and the board members have provided support and guidance for this research and service enterprise. Jeannette Branch, Director of the Southside Youth Program, has been involved in all aspects of the research and was responsible for the collection of the teacher ratings of social adaptational status.

Khazan Agrawal, Cecilia Bethe, Zanvel Klein, Gary Lebreche, and Anne Petersen of the Social Psychiatry Study Center provided assistance in many aspects of the study. Professor Peter Rossi, Richard Jaffe, and Paul Sheatsley of the National Opinion Research Center conducted the family interviews. Dr Anne Seiden helped in the development of the third-grade "How I Feel" instrument. Professors George Bohrnstedt, Bruce Dohrenwend, James A. Davis, and Richard J. Hill acted as consultants. Many of the computations were performed by Parin Verjee. Barbara Hill and Joseph Brinley provided editorial help.

These studies have been supported by State of Illinois Department of Mental Health grants 17-224 and 17-332; U.S. Public Health Service grant MH-15760 and Research Scientist Development Award 1 KO1-MN-47596; a grant from the Maurice Falk Medical Fund; and National Institute on Drug Abuse grant DA 00787.

REFERENCES

1. Herzog, E., & Sudia, E.E.: Children in fatherless families, in Caldwell, B.M., Ricciuti, H.N. (eds): *Review of Child Development Research.* Chicago, University of Chicago Press, Vol. 3, Pp. 141-232, 1973.
2. Schneider, D.M.: *American Kinship: A Cultural Account.* Englewood Cliffs, N.J.: Prentice-Hall Inc., 1968.

3. Adams, R.N.: An inquiry into the nature of the family, in Winch, R.F., Goodman, L.W. (Eds): *Selected Studies in Marriage and the Family*, Ed 3. New York: Holt, Rinehart & Winston Inc., 1968, Pp. 44-57.

4. Bloch, D.A.: The family of the psychiatric patient, in Arieti, S. (Ed): *American Handbook of Psychiatry*, Ed 2. New York: Basic Books, 1974, Pp. 179-201.

5. Gibson, G., & Ludwig, E.G.: Family structure in a disabled population. *J. Marriage Family* 30:54-63, 1968.

6. Fischer, A., Beasley, J. O., & Harter, C.L.: The occurrence of the extended family at the origin of the family of procreation: A developmental approach to Negro family structure. *J. Marriage Family* 30:290-300, 1968.

7. Minturn, L., & Lambert, W.W.: *Mothers of Six Cultures.* New York: John Wiley & Sons Inc., 1964.

8. Olsen, N.J.: Family structure and socialization patterns in Taiwan. *Am. J. Sociol.* 79:1395-1417, 1974.

9. DeVise, P.: *Chicago's Widening Color Gap.* Interuniversity Social Research Committee report No. 2, Chicago Regional Hospital Study, 1967.

10. Kellam, S.G., & Branch, J.D.: An approach to community mental health: An analysis of basic problems. *Semin. Psychiatry* 3:207-225, 1971.

11. Kellam, S.G., Branch, J.D., Agrawal, K.C., et al: *Mental Health and Going to School.* Chicago, University of Chicago Press, 1975.

12. Connors, C.: Symptom patterns in hyperkinetic, neurotic and normal children. *Child Dev.* 41:667-682, 1970.

13. Glidewell, J.C., Gildea, M.L., Domke, H.R., et al: Behavior symptoms in children and adjustment in public school. *Hum. Organization* 18:123-130, 1959.

14. Macfarlane, J.W., Allen, L., & Honzik, M.: *A Developmental Study of the Behavior Problems of Normal Children Between 21 Months and 14 years.* Berkeley, Calif.: University of California Press, 1934.

15. Lapouse, R., & Monk, M.: An epidemiologic study of behavior characteristics in children, *Am. J. Public Health* 48:1134-1144, 1958.

16. Burke, P.J., & Turk, A.T.: Factors affecting postarrest dispositions: A model for analysis. *Soc. Probl.* 22:313-332, 1975.

17. Davis, J.A.: Hierarchical models for significance tests in multivariate contingency tables: An exegesis of Goodman's recent papers, in Costner, L. (Ed): *Sociological Methodology 1972-1974.* San Francisco: Joseey-Bass Inc. Publishers, 1974.

18. Goodman, L.A.: The multivariate analysis of qualitative data: Interactions among multiple classifications. *J. Am. Stat. Assoc.* 65:226-256, 1970.

19. Goodman, L.A.: The analysis of multidimensional contingency tables: Stepwise procedures and direct estimation methods for building models for multiple classifications. *Technometrics* 13:33-61, 1971.

20. Goodman, L.A.: Partitioning of chi-square, analysis of marginal contingency tables, and estimations of expected frequencies in multidimensional contingency tables. *J. Am. Stat. Assoc.* 66:339-344, 1971.

21. Goodman, L.A.: A general model for the analysis of surveys. *Am. J. Sociol.* 77:1035-1086, 1972.

22. Goodman, L.A.: A modified multiple regression approach to the analysis of dichotomous variables. *Am. Sociol. Rev.* 37:28-46, 1972.

23. Goodman, L.A.: Causal analysis of data from panel studies and other kinds of surveys. *Am. J. Sociol.* 78:1135-1191, 1973.

24. Mosteller, F.: Association and estimation in contingency tables. *J. Am. Stat. Assoc.* 63:1-28, 1968.

15

THE KIBBUTZ AS A SOCIAL EXPERIMENT AND AS A CHILD-REARING LABORATORY

Benjamin Beit-Hallahmi

University of Haifa

and

Albert I. Rabin

Michigan State University

The Israeli kibbutz has attracted the attention of social scientists, especially psychologists, as a unique social experiment that offers a laboratory for studying the effects of variations in child rearing on personality development. This article reviews (a) the history of the kibbutz movement and kibbutz child-rearing practices and (b) the results of research in kibbutz socialization. The research indicates that the "kibbutz personality" is essentially nonpathological and effective. Recent changes in child-rearing patterns in the kibbutz, in the form of a return to traditional family child rearing, are viewed as part of an overall social change pattern that is likely to continue in the future. Implications for further work are discussed.

Reprinted with permission from *American Psychologist* Vol. 32, 532–541, 1977. Copyright 1977 by the American Psychological Association.

This article is a revised version of a paper presented to the 34th Annual Convention of the International Council of Psychologists, Paris, July 1976.

Comments on an earlier version by Daniel A. Wagner and Roberta J. Goldberg are gratefully acknowledged.

Martin Buber (1958) called the kibbutz "an experiment that did not fail." He did so after going over the history of Western utopian movements, all of which had as their central idea the commune, a relatively small social unit that would serve as the building block for the ideal society of the future. Since the beginning of the 19th century, various attempts have been made to found communes, but most of these, being little more than isolated groups of fervent believers even during their usually brief periods of existence, have failed. So far, the most successful attempt at building a utopian commune has been the Isaraeli kibbutz. In addition to being a social experiment—an experiment in utopia—the kibbutz has been regarded as a psychological experiment, that is, as a laboratory for testing hypotheses reagarding child-rearing practices and their consequences (Rabin, 1957). The interest shown by social scientists in the kibbutz has been similar to that shown in other social experiments that combined changes in social institutions with new patterns of child rearing, such as those in contemoporary China and Cuba. We present here a brief history of the kibbutz and the changes it has undergone, together with a survey of psychological studies of child rearing in the kibbutz , in order to make psychologists more conscious of the complexity of the current kibbutz situation and its implications for psychological research.

HISTORICAL BACKGROUND

There were particular circumstances that made the kibbutz such a success. Actually, it was an ideal solution to the problem of colonizing Palestine in the years before the founding of the State of Israel. Settling the land with groups of young, vigorous, and idealistic individuals having attachments only to the collective was more practical and logical than settling through the traditional way of family homesteading. This form of settlement was also more defensible, a fact worth considering given the hostile environment into which Zionist settlements entered. The kibbutz differed from its predecessors in utopianism in being a part of a national revival movement and in growing out of larger social groups that supplied its members. The idea of a voluntary membership commune grew out of a combination of nationalist and socialist ideologies, the same combination that led the Zionist-socialist movement to the founding of the State of Israel. Agricultural work was seen as the way to changing the abnormal social structure of Jews in the Diaspora, and thus agricultural settlements became the instruments of both national and social change. Marxist egalitarianism was added to nationalist aspirations, so that the kibbutz would become not just a national solution, but also a human one.

Beyond the particularistic ideals of national revival and reconstruction, the kibbutz movement shared in the universalistic ideals of returning to nature and creating a new human being. The movement, like others inspired by the teachings of Karl Marx, believed in the perfectibility of human nature, or at least in its possible amelioration. There was a strong belief in the changes that a revolutionary way of life would bring about in what seemed like persistent and undesirable human qualities. In a truly egalitarian commune, people would be less selfish, more secure, and more generous. The change in social structure was expected to lead to a psychological change in every individual. And if there were doubts about far-reaching changes in the first generation of kibbutz founders, who had been brought up in bourgeois society, then the aim of education for the kibbutz-born was defined as the creation of the new human being. Here, in forming a new child-rearing system, the kibbutz founders had a chance to make their children in the desired image of the collectivist, egalitarian, work-oriented person (Leon, 1969).

But what went into the creation of a new child-rearing system was more than just the positive vision of a better future generation. There was also the more negative element of rejecting what had been regarded as the traditional way of family life. One must remember that the founders of the kibbutz were in open rebellion against their own parents, a rebellion sometimes taking the form of a total rejection of the institution of the family. In the first years of the kibbutz, this attitude culminated in the absence of any formal marriages. The rebellion against traditional family patterns included a move toward equality between the sexes and the abolition of traditional sex roles, especially in the area of work. The ideal of the equality between the sexes and the breakdown of traditional sex roles has been one expression of the struggle against the traditions of an unjust and declining world. Thus, the emphasis was put on the dismantling of the traditional bourgeois family, with its close mother–child ties, which was perceived as promoting selfishness and individualism. Communal child rearing was seen, since the earliest days of the kibbutz movement, as a major task for the whole commune. Children were regarded as the source of future success and strength, and the best facilities were given to the children's houses. Since the kibbutzim in their earlier days were struggling and often barely surviving, children had to share in the hardships, but they still received the best of what the kibbutz could offer.

What should be kept in mind is that the kibbutz movement, very much like other communal movements, has always been a small minority within its own society. It has been very conscious of its minority status, despite other attributes that made it more influential than could be expected on a purely numerical basis. In its early years, the kibbutz movement regarded itself as an avant-garde destined to lead the rest of the Jewish people, or at least the rest of the Zionist movement, in its wake. When the masses did not follow, the consciousness of being a minority persisted. Today, the kibbutzim population makes up less than 3% of Israel's total population. In 1975 there were 241 kibbutzim in Israel, with a total population of over 92,000. The kibbutzim hold 33% of all cultivated land in Israel and produce about 33⅓% of the agricultural production and about 6% of the industrial production. Most kibbutzim are part of one of three distinct federations: the "rightist" (Ihud Hakibbutzim), the "moderate" (Hakibbutz Hameuhad), and the "leftist" (Hashomer Hatzair). The ideological distinctions that gave rise to the three federations, and that concerned their commitment to Marxist socialism, are much less pronounced today.

THE IDEOLOGY OF KIBBUTZ CHILD REARING

Child rearing has been a subject of intense discussion since the first days of the kibbutz. Hand in hand with the new practices, a new ideology emerged that sought to create a theoretical base for the roles of both parents and teachers. In hindsight, it may be claimed that the new child-rearing patterns were a practical necessity, on which an ideology was later imposed, in keeping with the overall ideology of the kibbutz movement. Whether the practice or the ideology came first will be determined by historians, but the fact is that kibbutz child rearing has been accompanied by an ideology that sought to rationalize its practices and served as a significant force in affecting parents and educators. There were two significant principles, having considerable psychological consequences, in the kibbutz child-rearing ideology.

The first stated that communal child rearing would work against individualism and identification with the family unit. The second stated that experts in child rearing could inculcate the ideology of the kibbutz with greater ability and objectivity than the parents. Almost every person can become a parent, but not every person can became an effective socializer. The socializer had to educate the child according to an ideal that should go against contemporary social realities. This explicit ideology led to relegating the parents to second place as socializing agents. The major socializing agents became the nurses, the teachers, and the peer group. Since the parents were no longer the sole representatives of authority, children's attitudes toward them, and especially toward the father, were expected to become more positive.

We cannot go here into all the details of the classical pattern of child rearing in the kibbutz, which can be found elsewhere (Rabin, 1965; Spiro, 1958). The main characteristics of the kibbutz tradition are that (a) child rearing is a communal, not a family, task; (b) kibbutz parents spend little time with their children compared to parents in a traditional family; and (c) education emphasizes communal and not individual goals. What is most important from a psychological point of view is the presence of multiple caretakers at an early stage in the children's development. This characteristic, and especially the limited contact with the mother, has raised several questions regarding its possible effects. Should the multiple caretaking be conceived as a form of maternal deprivation, maternal substitution, or multiple mothering? On the basis of available research, which will be covered later, we may conclude that the latter formulation is correct. The psychological characteristics of child rearing in the kibbutz can be summarized as follows: The number of significant others interacting with the child is higher than in the traditional family, but the relationships with some of these figures are nonexclusive and discontinuous. The *metapelet* (caretaker) takes care of a group of children and is likely to be changed several times during childhood. In the infants' and children's group, the child is exposed to a uniform, less personal treatment, and his needs are satisfied less readily than in the traditional family. We might say that the child in the kibbutz lives in two worlds: One is the family unit, where he spends some of his time in continuous, exclusive, and personalized interaction, and the other is the children's house, where interaction with adults is discontinuous, nonexclusive, and less personal. Since the child has to divide his attachments between these two worlds and among a large number of human objects (parents, teachers, and peers), one may ask whether this spread of feelings weakens the dependency on one significant figure, reduces the intensity of feelings toward parents, reduces the ambivalence toward parents, or diffuses identification over many objects. Rabin (1957, 1965) hypothesized that these conditions of reduced attachment and dependence would lead to a diffusion in identification, a reduction in ambivalence toward parents, and a reduction in sibling rivalry. Regev (Note 1) summarized these hypotheses into two: the moderation hypothesis and the diffusion hypothesis. The moderation hypothesis states that the kibbutz child has more moderate feelings toward objects in his environment, and the diffusion hypothesis states that the kibbutz child divides his attachment among a greater number of objects. The moderation and diffusion hypotheses have been cited by kibbutz educators as an indication of the success of kibbutz child rearing in creating a personality that is better suited for kibbutz life (Golan, 1961).

PSYCHOLOGICAL STUDIES OF CHILD REARING IN THE KIBBUTZ

The kibbutz as a natural laboratory has aroused the interest of two groups of researchers: psychodynamically oriented psychologists (Rabin, 1957; Rapaport, 1958) and anthropologists of the "culture and personality" school (Spiro, 1958). The anthropological approach to the kibbutz regards it as a different culture that leads to a different personality type. In the kibbutz, several social institutions, especially economics and the family, were different enough from those of other societies to designate it as a separate culture. At the same time, the kibbutz offered the advantage of being a part of Western culture, in the normal sense of the term, and its members could be easily communicated with. The first systematic observations of child rearing in the kibbutz appeared in the literature of the early 1950s (Irvine, 1952; Spiro, 1953). Since then, the number of social science publications on the topic has grown immensely (Rabin, 1971; Sharabany, 1975), and their conclusions can not be easily summarized in one article.

Some comments on methodology in kibbutz studies are in order. Research on child rearing in the kibbutz has been of several kinds: clinical-observational (Bettelheim, 1969; Caplan, 1954), anthropological (Spiro, 1958), and psychological-systematic (Kohen-Raz, 1968; Rabin, 1965). The number of systematic studies is surprisingly low, compared to the attention given to kibbutz child rearing in the literature. Some of the most quoted publications on the kibbutz (e.g., Bettelheim, 1969) are based on extremely limited observations, and when it comes to studies of the kibbutz system, there seems to be an almost inverse relationship between the frequency of citation and methodological rigor. Since the body of reliable findings is limited, one should proceed with caution toward inferences and conclusions. Speculations and inferences from observations and clinical data have their value, but they should be recognized as such. It should also be noted that the better-controlled studies (e.g., Nevo, in press) have found few differences between kibbutz and nonkibbutz groups.

The questions that psychologists have asked about the kibbutz child-rearing system were both in a theoretical nature (e.g., Will changes in mother-child relationships support psychoanalytic predictions?) and of an "applied" nature (e.g., What can be learned from the kibbutz experience to improve other child-rearing systems?). It is interesting to note that most psychological research on the kibbutz has focused on individual personality development and has not looked at some significant aspects of kibbutz life such as orientation toward work, alienation, and self-actualization. The clearly individualistic bias of academic psychology has to be regarded as the main cause for the concentration on individual personality dynamics.

Answers to several questions regarding kibbutz-born children are briefly summarized below. These questions include the extent of psychopathology, immaturity, identification with parents, and peer relations.

Psychopathology

Since the kibbutz caretaking situation was perceived as lying somewhere between maternal deprivation on one side and normal maternal contacts in the traditional family on the other, it was assumed that the relative deprivation would have its effect in the form of a greater prevalence of psychopathology. Some of the first observations on the kibbutz attempted to estimate the prevalence of pathological symptoms. Caplan (1954) found more symptoms only for younger ages (up to the age of 7), but Kaffman (1965) found no particular prevalence of psychopathology in kibbutz children. Nevo (in press) found no differences between kibbutz-born and city-born adults on the California Psychological Inventory.

Immaturity and Retarded Development Among Children

The evidence on this point is not clear. Some studies show retarded development in infancy (Caplan, 1954; Rabin, 1961, 1965), but the majority of studies dealing with kibbutz infants have shown no developmental retardation (Fried, 1960; Gewirtz, 1965; Kohen-Raz, 1968). Handel (1961) found less maturity among kibbutz adolescents, but Rabin (1965) found more maturity among 10-year-old children and among adolescents in the kibbutz. Some of the disagreement in findings may be due to different sampling, during different periods, while the kibbutz child-rearing system was undergoing significant changes. The more recent studies show no developmental deficits, a fact that can be explained as the result of more individualized and relaxed caretaking in infancy.

Identification with and Attitudes Toward Parents

The evidence shows quite clearly that identification of kibbutz children with their parents is more diffuse (Luria, Goldwasser, &

Goldwasser, 1963; Rabin, 1957, 1965; Rabin & Goldman, 1966; Spiro, 1953) but nevertheless positive. Since childhood experiences in the kibbutz are expected to reduce ambivalence toward parents, attitudes toward them are expected to be more positive. This is indeed the finding (Devereux et al., 1974; Rabin, 1965; Spiro, 1958). There is support for the claim that the father in the kibbutz has become more nurturant and less authoritarian compared to the father in the traditional family.

Peer Relations

Compared with the less intense parental identifications in the kibbutz, the peer group becomes very significant psychologically, and strong feelings of solidarity and group identity are formed (Etzioni, 1957; Golan, 1961; Rettig, 1966). Devereux et al. (1974) reported that peers in the kibbutz were perceived as secondary to the parents, and there was no difference from city children in this respect, but the kibbutz peers were seen as exerting more control.

Effectiveness as Adults

Only a few studies have looked at kibbutz-born adults, and follow-up studies of kibbutz children are now being carried out (Rabin & Beit-Hallahmi, Note 2); however, the available findings show the kibbutz-born young adult to be remarkably effective, productive, and well-adjusted in his overall functioning (Amir, 1969; Nevo, in press; Rabin, 1965).

Capacity for Intimacy

The diffusion of identification and the reduced attachment to a few objects at an early age would lead to a reduced capacity for (or the need for) intimacy (Bettelheim, 1969; Sprio, 1958). Support for this hypothesis was found by Handel (1961), who used only self-reports, and by Sharabany (1974), who compared friendships among 11- and 12-year-olds in the kibbutz and in the city.

The "Kibbutz Personality"

On the basis of the findings presented so far, we may conclude that the personality of the kibbutz-born is nonpathological, effective, shows only moderate but positive attachment to others, and shows a reduction in intimate rivalry and ambivalence. As noted above, the most striking general finding is that the majority of studies, and especially those complying with more rigorous methodological standards, found few differences between kibbutz and nonkibbutz groups. It is important to remember that in all cases, the control groups to whom the kibbutz groups were compared were made up of Israeli-born individuals. This means that the comparisons were made within the same basic culture, and it seems plausible that comparisons across cultures (e.g., a kibbutz group to an American group) would have produced clear differences. It has been suggested, with some supporting data, that Israeli culture as a whole is more collectivistic than most Western cultures today (Crandall & Gozali, 1969), and thus it becomes more difficult to separate the effects of kibbutz child rearing from the general effects of the culture. From a theoretical viewpoint, one may want to conclude that the case for the kibbutz as a separate culture producing a separate "personality" still has to be proven. From an "applied" viewpoint, one can point to the absence of pathology and to the presence of effectiveness and productiveness produced by multiple mothering. In any case, the limitations of our data base should be kept in mind. How newer developments in the kibbutz system may lead us to ask new questions and find better answers is discussed in the next section.

RECENT CHANGES IN KIBBUTZ CHILD-REARING PRACTICES

Over the past 15 years there has been a major trend toward closer parent–child contacts and toward more individual caretaking patterns in the communal child-rearing system. The changes have taken two major forms: (a) family sleeping arrangements for infants until a certain age (in some cases until adolescence) and (b) provision of more *metapelot* (caretakers) for the infants' house. Until 1950, family-based sleeping arrangements were in effect in only four kibbutzim. Since then, the new arrangement has spread over many more kibbutzim in the rightist federation and to some kibbutzim in the moderate federation, but the debate over sleeping arrangements has spread to all three kibbutz federations (Shepher, 1971). Changes from the communal sleeping arrangement to the family sleeping arrangement have been noted for some years now (Shepher, 1969).

In the family-based sleeping arrangement, the children return to their parents in the afternoon and then stay there until the next morning, when they go back to the children's house. This arrangement may begin at different ages. At some kibbutzim it starts at age 6; at others it starts at birth and extends until age 12. In this latter group, most of the crucial elements in traditional, kibbutz child rearing disappear. Under the family-based sleeping arrangement, the mother becomes the most significant figure, the parents become the main socializers, and the *metapelet* and the peer group recede in importance. The children's house may be compared to a day care center, the influence of which may be significant in some respects but cannot be compared to the influence of the "classical" children's house.

Family-based sleeping arrangements abolish the most unique aspect of kibbutz child rearing—multiple mothering at an early age. The children are transferred to communal children's houses later on, but the bond with the mother is formed at an early age. The parents not only spend more time together with their children but also become the main socializers. They no longer see the children only during recreation periods when parents and children play together, but they now have to discipline their children and train them in all areas of social behavior. Peer-group influence is reduced but not altogether abolished. The collectivist orientation in child rearing remains very much in existence, and the peer group remains very stable. Unlike city children, kibbutz children spend most of their time, until the age of 18, with a limited number of peers. They are exposed to fewer social stimuli, and their environment is more uniform. They are led to identify strongly with their peer group, and such an identification is likely to emerge. It is rare for city children to spend their time with the same peer group from kindergarten through high school, but this is exactly what happens in the kibbutz.

The return to traditional, nonkibbutz child-rearing patterns also involves a change in relation to siblings, who assume a more significant role in early childhood. In those kibbutzim where the infants are still in the infants' house, better caretaking in infancy can prevent whatever initial deprivation kibbutz infants may have suffered from in the past. It may also create greater attachment to the *metapelet* (nurse) in this initial stage. Something else that is changing and will continue to change is child-rearing attitudes. Studies of first-generation and second-generation kibbutz mothers indicate a change in terms of putting more emphasis on individual attention to children, encouraging more affectional ties with parents, and considering motherhood as an important role for every kibbutz woman (Rabin, 1964, 1970).

EXPLAINING THE CHANGE

The explanations for recent changes in child-rearing practices in the kibbutz may be sought in several areas. There might have been changes in the ideology of child rearing, based on the experiences over the years. There might have been wider structural changes within the kibbutz, and there might have been wider changes in the surrounding Israeli society that have influenced the kibbutz movement. We will try to examine all relevant factors, starting with possible changes in educational philosophy. Was it self-criticism by kibbutz educators and parents that led them to "mend their ways" in the more conservative direction? Has it been the development of greater psychological-mindedness and sensitivity to the shortcomings of "orthodox" methods? Has feedback from psychological studies affected the kibbutz community?

The relationship between the kibbutz movements and social science research has not always been an easy one. Initially, social scientists were critical, and kibbutz members were defensive. Psychoanalysts' preliminary interest in the kibbutz as a deviant or potentially pathological pattern of life, especially in the area of child rearing, has not endeared the researcher to the kibbutz community. Moreover, a utopian, struggling movement tends to view outside observers not sharing its ideology as potential critics and enemies. One should bear in mind that the kibbutz has always been a minority subculture, fighting against the destructive influences of the wider society that would reduce it to a smaller minority or abolish it altogether. We should remember that because of tensions with the wider society, very few utopian communes have survived as long as the kibbutz. In this context, it is easy to see why studies by outside researchers were regarded as hostile incursions, aimed at tarnishing the image of an idealistic enterprise. At the same time, there were other factors that led kibbutz movements to assume a different and more positive attitude toward social science research. The first factor was the special psychological-mindedness of the kibbutz leaders, especially in the area of education. Communal education in the kibbutz was based on theoretical foundations that included psychodynamic theory (Golan, 1961; Rabin & Hazan, 1973). Kibbutz educators have regarded themselves as an educational avant-garde, conscious of the psychological consequences of what they were planning. Psychoanalytic concepts have been in usage in the kibbutz movement since its beginning, and this prepared the ground for acceptance of psychological research as an ally (Katz & Lewin, 1973). The second factor was the feeling within the kibbutz that the results of psychological studies vindicated kibbutz child-rearing methods. Indeed, the "kibbutz personality" as it emerges from psychological studies is quite positive, and so there was little need to modify the child-rearing system that brought it about.

We chose to look at the changes in child-rearing practices in a wider context. We decided to ask whether these changes had been unique and isolated or whether there had been changes in other aspects of the kibbutz system that may have been related to the changes in patterns of child rearing. Changes in all kibbutz institutions have been observed, and they are all in the same direction of increased privatism and "familism." The changes have been economic, political, ideological, and psychological. A growing conservatism is being manifested in all of these areas, and the changes in child rearing are just one part of the general trend. In terms of the relationship between the original kibbutz ideology and later historical developments, we might say that the trend is from ideological purity to ideological compromise. Many of these changes are too recent to have been studied systematically, but they are easy to observe (Rabin, Note 3) and have been noted by all students of kibbutz life in recent years. Considerable evidence regarding the changes and the often heated discussions that accompanied them is available in the periodical literature of the kibbutz movement. There is general agreement on two points: the comprehensive nature of the changes, covering almost every aspect of kibbutz life, and the unified direction characterizing all of these changes.

One of the main aims of the kibbutzim has been settling the land, and the kibbutzim started as agricultural collectives. The past 25 years have seen a growing industrialization so successful as to turn many kibbutzim into holding companies for a variety of enterprises. The ideological change away from socialism has been correlated with the actual change in patterns of production and consumption. What was started as a deliberate attempt to create a working class is now a comfortable bourgeoisie. The second generation of the kibbutz, which is the first to be born and raised there, is now the dominant group in many kibbutzim. This generation has satisfied some, but not all, of the expectations of its parents. For this generation, and succeeding ones, the kibbutz is not a new venture into utopia but the reality into which they were born. They were not selected, much less self-selected like their parents. They are more pragmatic and less idealistic. Recent trends in the kibbutz include a "consumerist" lifestyle that consists of (a) aiming for higher living standards to match the life-style of the Israeli middle class, (b) greater freedom in making career choices, and (c) an emphasis on specialized higher education and individual success. All of these represent departures from the early kibbutz ideology. The importance of outside pressures on the kibbutz can not be minimized. The kibbutz, as a minority avant-garde movement, has treated the wider society with ambivalence. One of the aims of kibbutz education was to immunize and isolate youngsters from the influences of the nonkibbutz world, but the growing economic and political involvement of the kibbutz in the larger society has made isolationism impossible.

Historical changes in the wider context—the State of Israel—have brought about a different atmosphere in the kibbutz movement, which has entailed many changes in social realtionships and patterns of family life. Some of the important general changes in Israeli society that the kibbutz community could not escape were the rise in living standards, the general political and ideological trends in Israel—in the direction of greater conservatism, and the decline of socialist ideals. The general ideological climate in Israel in the last 25 years has changed in the direction of a growing alliance with capitalism and the United States and a decline in adherence to socialist ideas and movements. The kibbutzim were important tools of the Zionist movement before the founding of the state. Ever since then, the kibbutzim and Zionism as a whole have been suffering the pains of success. As patterns of idealistic and militant behavior became institutionalized, the tradition of kibbutz life was seen as dysfunctional.

The success of the Zionist movement in establishing the State of Israel and the later economic success of the kibbutz movement have given the initial utopian venture the character of a successful revolution that has lost its zeal and thus failed. The feeling of mission and struggle, the stand of opposition to traditional culture, and the support of social renewal can no longer be maintained. The kibbutz may be compared to other successful revolutionary movements whose success has brought about their decline and a return to pre-revolutionary behaviors. It is hard to be a successful revolution, and it may be even harder to survive as a successful utopia.

Ideology and Child-Rearing Practices

The connection between overall ideology and child-rearing patterns becomes clear once we look at changes within the three kibbutz federations (leftist, moderate, and rightist) in regard to child rearing and in regard to other aspects of kibbutz ideology. We would predict that the more orthodox (i.e., leftist) kibbutzim would keep the communal pattern of child rearing, while reforms in the direction of the traditional (nonkibbutz) family should appear in the less orthodox (i.e., rightist) kibbutzim. This is indeed the case, with clear connections between ideological orthodoxy in child rearing and in other areas. The rightist kibbutzim are also more involved in using hired work, which is contrary to the socialist kibbutz philosophy. Today, even the leftist kibbutzim employ hired workers, but their use is still self-conscious and limited. Changes in child-rearing patterns first appeared in the rightist kibbutzim and are now becoming more prevalent in the moderate kibbutz movement. The change in each individual kibbutz is decided upon by majority vote, following a decision in principle by the particular kibbutz federation.

Our suggestion here is that changes in child-rearing patterns in the more traditional direction are positively related to changes in the economic structure of the kibbutz in a more conservative direction. That is, there will be a positive correlation between changes to family-based sleeping arrangements and the prevalence of hired work in a kibbutz. Those kibbutzim that are more "orthodox" on child-rearing issues are likely to be more "orthodox" in other areas. Today, family-based sleeping arrangements are most common in the rightist kibbutz federation and are almost unknown in the leftist federation. Shepher (1967) reported a correlation between family sleeping arrangements and a greater degree of ideological indifference on the part of kibbutz members. Within the same kibbutz federation it was found that members of kibbutzim where communal sleeping arrangements were in effect showed a greater degree of ideological involvement and readiness for public-service roles compared to members from kibbutzim where the family-based sleeping arrangement was in effect.

Given recent changes in the kibbutz, it is possible to predict that the trend from kibbutz child rearing back to the traditional family will continue in the near future. Since, as we have shown, changes in economic, social, and ideological factors have brought about changes in child rearing, the continuation of those background trends in the "bourgeoisation" of the kibbutz will lead inevitably to a reduction in the differences between kibbutz and city child-rearing patterns. One can conceivably picture a point at which communal child rearing will be limited to only a few orthodox kibbutzim. The picture today is that "classical" communal child rearing exists only in the leftist kibbutz movement (Hashomer Hatzair), with the other two kibbutz movements undergoing changes in the direction away from communal child rearing.

Sex Roles and Child-Rearing Patterns

A case may be made for the connection between the recent changes in child-care patterns and the development of sex-role specialization in the kibbutz. Complete sexual equality and sharing of work responsibility has been one of the ideals of the kibbutz movement. The needs of the kibbutz in its earlier years were for more manpower for physical, mainly agricultural work, and women were regarded as equal partners in sharing the burden. Communal child rearing contributed to the freeing of women from the traditional tasks of mothering so that they were available as workers. The idea of sexual equality has been far from reality even in the earlier days of the kibbutz (Rabin, 1970; Tiger & Shepher, 1975), but the present situation is similar to those found in other areas of kibbutz life. Recent developments in the kibbutz show a pattern of consistent movement toward more traditional patterns of sex roles, marriage, and family life and a clear revival of the traditional division of labor between the sexes. As Tiger and Shepher (1975) show, there is a clear polarization of work between men and women, with men predominantly in production and women predominantly in communal services. Women are involved in the same types of jobs that fit the traditional female role, except that most of these jobs serve the whole community and not just the family. Thus, women are concentrating in communal service jobs, including the kitchen, the laundry, the infants' and the children's houses, etc. Women are almost exluded from agricultural field work or industrial jobs (Tiger & Shepher, 1965).

Talmon (1974) indicates that women in the kibbutz have been in favor of greater family autonomy and a greater role for the family in child rearing. Her explanation for the apparently greater familism of women is based on the change in women's roles in the kibbutz over time. In the early days of the kibbutz movement, women were equal partners in the labor system, since the birth rate was low and the members were all young. Gradually, women's reproductive role became predominant, limiting their involvement in hard physical labor. Men dominated the productive work roles in the kibbutz, since work was becoming more specialized and demanded permanent work assignments.

The economic success of the kibbutz and the rise in living standards made the participation of women in heavy physical labor unnecessary. Manpower in the kibbutz became less of a problem, and one of the practical reasons for communal child care was thus removed. The service jobs in which women have specialized are for the most part routine, thankless jobs. Investing more in the family is one major way in which kibbutz women can find more personal satisfaction, as opposed to the frustrations and impersonality of the communal service jobs. Rabin (1970) presents data on the discontent of kibbutz women with their service jobs and on their support for familism. The growing return to family-based sleeping arrangements has been correlated with the return to the traditional division of labor among the sexes (Shepher, 1967). It is possible to conceive of the kibbutz now as a collective of families and no longer a collective of individuals. Within this collective, women are returning to their traditional roles as family caretakers and are withdrawing from the roles of collective caretakers. Since these new roles are more satisfying to women, it is understandable why women have become the main supporters of familism (Talmon, 1974). Men in the kibbutz continue to derive their satisfactions and status from their productive work jobs (Tiger & Shepher, 1975).

CONCLUSION

The present orientation of the kibbutz child-rearing system should be described as more individualistic than ever before. The decline of collectivistic ideology has led to this change in educational orientation, which is likely to lead to further changes in the communal education system, especially in education for the early years. The most important change is likely to be a decline in communal sleeping arrangements for infants, which will change mother–child relationships significantly.

Psychologists should now write about the "classical" or "historical" kibbutz, as opposed to the present one, which is certainly a paradox for a movement that seemed to embody a breakdown of some basic human traditions and a rebellion against all of history. One can no longer speak of the "kibbutz" in general but must be more specific. If the kibbutz is to continue as a child-rearing laboratory, experimental conditions have to be specified and monitored. The kibbutz is no longer a single, child-rearing laboratory, but it includes several different laboratories (or experimental conditions). What we observe is a general pattern of departures from the original kibbutz ideology, a pattern that encompasses all areas of life in the kibbutz. The changes in child-rearing patterns make up one component in this wider historical trend.

If a specific child-rearing pattern is assumed to lead to a certain personality pattern, then a change in child-rearing methods in any direction should lead to differences in the previously established pattern. The historical changes should lead to differences between the "baseline" personality and the present one that are important both factually and theoretically. Generalizations about the "kibbutz personality" should be kept close to empirical findings. Moreover, the changes in child-rearing practices give us an opportunity to test again our theoretical notions. Historical changes have set up a natural experimental design. Children growing up now under the communal sleeping arrangements can be compared to children growing up under the family-based sleeping arrangement in a neighboring kibbutz.

Findings regarding "orthodox" kibbutz child rearing can be compared with data based on current practices, and the first steps in this direction are being taken (Regev, Note 1). The differences we have pointed to between the "classical" and the "modern" kibbutz may come as a surprise to psychologists who have preferred the simplicity of the textbook and the easy psychological generalization to the complexity of history and living organizations. The kibbutz has its own dynamics of development that are bound up with wider historical changes. One might say that the days of the kibbutz as a simple experiment are over. Those studying it must face more complexity and variety than before, but they also have greater opportunities to answer some significant psychological questions.

REFERENCE NOTES

1. Regev, E., *Sleeping arrangements and psychological development in the kibbutz.* Unpublished research proposal, Haifa University, 1976.
2. Rabin, A. I., & Beit-Hallahmi, B. *Family and communally reared (Kibbutz) children 20 years later.* Unpublished manuscript, Michigan State University, 1976.
3. Rabin, A. I. *Changing times in the kibbutz.* Unpublished manuscript, Michigan State University, 1971.

REFERENCES

Amir, Y. The effectiveness of the kibbutz-born soldier in the Israel Defense Forces. *Human Relations,* 1969, *22,* 333–344.
Bettelheim, B. *The children of the dream.* New York: Macmillan, 1969.
Buber, M. *Paths in utopia.* Boston: Beacon Press, 1958.
Caplan, G. Clinical observations on the emotional life of children in the communal settlements of Israel. In M. S. E. Senn (Ed.), *Problems of infancy and childhood.* New York: Josiah Macy, Jr., Foundation, 1954.
Crandall, V. C., & Gozali, J. The social desirability responses of children of four religious-cultural groups. *Child Development,* 1969, *40,* 751–762.
Devereux, E. C., et al. Socialization practices of parents, teachers and peers in Israel: The kibbutz versus the city. *Child Development,* 1974, *45,* 269–281.
Etzioni, A. Solidaric work groups in the kibbutz. *Human Organization,* 1957, *16,* 2–7.
Fried, Y. [Psychomotor development of kibbutz children.] *Ofakim,* 1960, *41,* 303–312.
Gewritz, J. L. The course of infant smiling in four child rearing environments in Israel. In B. M. Foss (Ed.), *Determinants of infant behavior III.* London: Methuen, 1965.
Golan, S. *Hchinukh hameshutaf* [Communal education]. Merhavia, Israel: Sifriat Poalim, 1961.

Handel, A. [Self-concept of the kibbutz adolescent.] *Metgamot*, 1961, 11, 142–159.

Irvine, E. E. Observations on the aims and methods of child-rearing in communal settlements in Israel. *Human Relations*, 1952, 5, 247–276.

Kaffman, M. A comparison of psychopathology: Israeli children from kibbutz and from urban surroundings. *American Journal of Orthopsychiatry*, 1965, 35, 509–520.

Katz, F., & Lewin, G. Early childhood education. In A. I. Rabin & B. Hazan (Eds.), *Collective education in the kibbutz*. New York: Springer, 1973.

Kohen-Raz, R. Mental and motor development of kibbutz, institutionalized, and home-reared infants in Israel. *Child Development*, 1968, 39, 489–504.

Leon, D. *The kibbutz*. New York: Pergamon, 1969.

Luria, Z., Goldwasser, M., & Goldwasser, A. Response to transgression in stories by Israeli children. *Child Development*, 1963, 34, 271–280.

Nevo, B. Personality differences between kibbutz born and city born adults. *American Journal of Psychology*, in press.

Rabin, A. L. The Israeli kibbutz (collective settlement) as a "laboratory" for testing psychodynamic hypotheses. *Psychological Record*, 1957, 7, 111–115.

Rabin, A. I. Kibbutz adolescents. *American Journal of Orthopsychiatry*, 1961, 31, 493–504.

Rabin, A. I. Kibbutz mothers view "collective education." *American Journal of Orthopsychiatry*, 1964, 34, 140–142.

Rabin, A. I. *Growing up in the kibbutz*. New York: Springer, 1965.

Rabin, A. I. The sexes: Ideology and reality in the Israeli kibbutz. In G. M. Seward & L. C. Williamson (Eds.), *Sex roles in a changing society*. New York: Random House, 1970.

Rabin, A. I. *Kibbutz studies*. East Lansing: Michigan State University Press, 1971.

Rabin, A. I., & Goldman, H. The relationship of severity of guilt to intensity of identification in kibbutz and non-kibbutz children. *Journal of Social Psychology*, 1966, 69, 159–163.

Rabin, A. I., & Hazan, B. (Eds.). *Collective education in the kibbutz*. New York: Springer, 1973.

Rapaport, D. The study of kibbutz education and its bearing on the theory of development. *American Journal of Orthopsychiatry*, 1958, 28, 587–597.

Rettig, K. S. Relation of social systems to intergenerational changes in moral attitudes. *Journal of Personality and Social Psychology*, 1966, 4, 400–414.

Sharabany, R. *Intimate friendship among kibbutz and city children and its measurement*. Unpublished doctoral dissertation, Cornell University, 1974.

Sharabany, R. Socialization in the Israeli kibbutz—Bibliography. JSAS *Catalog of Selected Documents in Psychology*, 1975, 5, 185. (Ms. No. 847).

Shepher, J. *Hishtakfut sidrei hahalana bamivneh hahaevrati shel hakibbutz*. Tel-Aviv: Ihud Hakibbutzim vehakvutzot, 1967.

Shepher, J. Familism and social structure: Case of the kibbutz. *Journal of Marriage and the Family*, 1969, 31, 567–573.

Shepher, J. [Sleeping arrangement for children in the kibbutz.] In *Yalkut Hahinuh Hameshutaf bagil Harakh*. Merhavia, Israel: Hakibbutz Haartzi, 1971.

Spiro, M. Education in a communal village in Israel. *American Journal of Orthopsychiatry*, 1953, 23, 120–130.

Spiro, M. *Children of the kibbutz*. Cambridge, Mass.: Harvard University Press, 1958.

Talmon, Y. *Family and community in the kibbutz*. Cambridge, Mass.: Harvard University Press, 1974.

Tiger, L., & Shepher, J. *Women in the kibbutz*. New York: Harcourt Brace Jovanovich, 1975.

16

INFANT DAY CARE AND ATTACHMENT BEHAVIORS TOWARD MOTHERS AND TEACHERS

Dale C. Farran and Craig T. Ramey

University of North Carolina at Chapel Hill

The growing trend toward placing infants in group day care at very early ages may have serious effects on the development of the mother-child attachment bond. Twenty-three black infant-day-care-reared children were observed in a situation designed to heighten attachment behaviors; both their mothers and an infant-day-care teacher were present. Children overwhelmingly preferred to be near and to interact with their mothers rather than their teachers, indicating that the attachment bond to the mother had indeed been formed. Moreover, they perceived their mothers as the help giver when faced with a mildly difficult problem.

Day-care placement involves separating the child for long periods from his mother. The effect of daily separations on the development

---

Reprinted with permission from *Child Development,* 1977, 48, 1112-1116, Copyright 1977 by the Society For Research in Child Development, Inc.

This research was funded in part by National Institute of Child Health and Human Development grants HD-03110 and HD00424-02. The assistance of Art Cross, Kitty Wilson, and Clyde Dent is gratefully acknowledged. In addition, we are grateful to Eleanor Richardson and Fannie Edwards of the teaching staff.

of the attachment bond between mother and child must be addressed by infant-day-care practitioners and researchers. Specifically, does day-care placement in infancy affect the developing bond between mother and child so that the child forms a stronger, alternative bond to his day-care teacher? Does the child's behavior toward these two primary caregivers indicate a differential understanding of the roles they play in his life?

Evidence indicates that children do form various attachment bonds: to their fathers (Cohen & Campos 1974; Lewis, Weinraub & Ban, Note 1), to caregivers in a day-care situation (Ricciuti 1974), to their blankets (Passman & Weisberg 1975), and to relative strangers on short acquaintance (Fleener 1973). These attachment objects perform functions similar to the mother'; they serve to promote exploration in a novel environment, and the child seeks to be near them in times of stress.

The present investigation of day-care children explored the child's responsiveness to two important attachment figures—his mother and his day-care teacher. A situation was designed to investigate the child's attachment behaviors toward each of the two people (with both present), and the same situation was used to assess his choice of a help giver when faced with a mildly difficult problem. Measures of proximity, time in contact, and initiations by the child were used as the primary indicators of attachment as they are considered more reliable and less age specific than measures of crying, smiling, and exploration in the mother's absence (Clarke-Stewart 1973; Cohen 1974; Cohen & Campos 1974; Feldman & Ingham 1975; Masters & Wellman 1974).

METHOD

Subjects.—Children in the study were 23 black infants and toddlers in daily attendance at a day-care center. All could locomote with ease. There were 11 males and 12 females, ranging in age from 9 to 31 months ($M = 19.5$ months; SD = 7.3 months).[1]

Infants attending the center were selected from families of low socioeconomic status, determined by level of parental income and education. Infants attended the center for approximately 6 hours per day, beginning in the second or third month of life. At 12–14 months, infants are moved from the "nursery" to the "toddler" program on a different floor of the building, where they join older children. Ten children were in the nursery program; 13 were in the toddler pro-

---

[1]More detailed information on the sample is available from the authors.

gram. The staff-child ratio in the nursery is 1:3; in the toddler program, the ratio is 1:4. Children were not assigned to specific caretakers in either setting but had free access to all the teachers. (At the time of this study, there were a total of 13 children in the nursery and 14 in the toddler program.)

Procedure.—Children were observed in a room (3.2 m × 2.9 m) furnished with a carpet, three chairs, a wall-mounted television camera, a table lamp placed in the "blind" corner under the camera, and four toys placed in the center of the room. All sessions were videotaped.

Each child was observed for 14 min with his mother, teacher, and a stranger in the room. The stranger (a white male graduate student, unfamiliar to the children) sat directly across the room from where the child was initially placed by the experimenter; the child's mother and the teacher sat on either side. Left-right positions of the mother and teacher were counterbalanced across subjects. (A schematic of the room is provided in fig. 1.)

Mother and teacher had been instructed not to gesture to or initiate picking up the child but were asked to respond to any overtures the child made to them. An attempt was made by the stranger and teacher to maintain conversation among the adults so that the situation would seem as natural as possible.

At the end of 12 min, the experimenter reentered the room with an attractive cookie which she showed to the child and then placed in a clear plastic "lock-top" box. The mother was instructed to open the box if the child became distressed but otherwise to let the child try alone for approximately 2 min. In all cases, the mother ended the session by opening the box for the child, either at her own initiative or at the experimenter's instruction, and the cookie was given to the child.

The role of the teacher was played by two black female teachers from the day-care center, one from the nursery and one from the toddler program. Each was chosen because she was considered by her supervisor to have the best overall realtionship with the children to be observed. Each teacher had been in her position with the center for more than 5 years prior to the study.

Data recording.—The child's proximity to each of the three adults in the room was scored from the videotapes after the session by means of an acetate overlay placed on the monitor. This overlay divided the observation room into four quadrants: (1) the stranger side of the mother, (2) the open side of the mother, (3) the stranger side of the teacher, and (4) the open side of the teacher (see fig. 1).

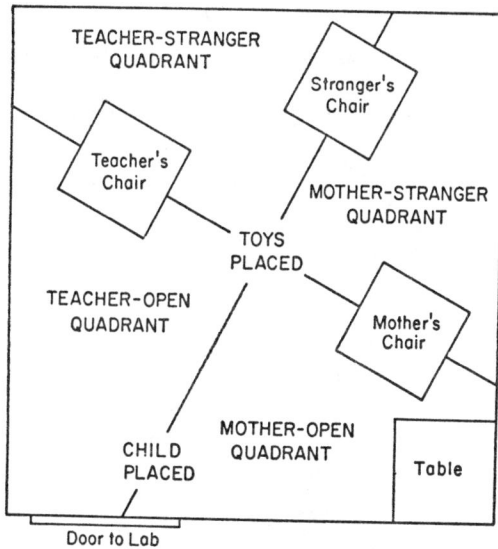

FIG. 1.—Schematic of observational room

Frequencies and durations of the following behaviors of the child were scored from videotapes in continuous recording: (1) the amount of time and frequency of visits in each of the four quadrants, (2) solitary play with toys, (3) extending toys—child gestures with or holds toy toward an adult, (4) sharing toys—child and adult are both in physical contact with toy, (5) physical contact with adults, (6) being held, (7) manipulating cookie box, (8) extending cookie box, and (9) sharing cookie box.

Interobserver reliability (assessed by percentage of agreement with a 2-sec criterion for onset) was established for each observational session and for each behavior. Agreement for both duration and frequency across all categories was 85% or better.

RESULTS

Effect of person on child's proximity behaviors.—On being placed in the room, children could move either to the mother-open or teacher-open quadrant; 17 of 23 children moved first to the mother's side of the room. This initial quadrant choice was significant by a test of proportions ($p < .01$). Children moved to the initial quadrant with an average latency of 10.8 sec. Table 1 provides a breakdown of the percentage of time spent in the four quadrants of the room.

TABLE 1

% TIME SPENT IN EACH QUADRANT
FOR 14-MIN OBSERVATION

Quadrant	Mean % Visitation	SD (%)
Mother-open...........	68.16	32.50
Teacher-open..........	19.63	27.26
Mother-stranger........	6.77	11.02
Teacher-stranger.......	5.44	17.21

A repeated measures multivariate analysis of variance (see McCall & Appelbaum 1973) revealed that children spent significantly more time in the mother-open quadrant than in all three other quadrants combined, $F(1,21) = 10.85$, $p < .003$. The children also stayed significantly longer on the open side of the room, $F(1,21) = 72.10$, $p < .001$, and in fact spent only 12% of the session on the side of the room near the stranger.

Comparing the halves of the room by mother's and teacher's presence, it is clear that a significantly greater percentage of time, 74.9%, was spent near the mother than near the teacher, $F(1,21) = 9.64$, $p < .005$.

Effect of person on child's behavior.—A repeated measures analysis of variance was performed on each interactive behavior, comparing (a) responses to mother and teacher and (b) responses to teacher and stranger. Children engaged in interactive behaviors significantly more with their mothers than with the teacher or stranger. Table 2 depicts the mean duration of time children spent in each interactive behavior with the three adults in the room. Children spent more time with their mothers than with their teachers extending and sharing toys; in physical contact and being held; and extending and sharing the cookie box, F's $(1,19) \geq 4.80$, p's $< .04$. There were no significant differences in their interactions with the teacher and stranger. These means are based on the total sample of 23 children. As the standard deviations make clear, not all children displayed each behavior. Table 2 includes the numbers of children who displayed each response.

During the cookie-box problem, 20 of the 23 children approached and manipulated the box. Of these, 15 indicated a need for help in opening it by extending the box or placing it in an adult's lap. Of these 15 children, all asked their mothers for help. No child extended the box or initiated sharing the box with the teacher or the stranger.

TABLE 2

INTERACTIVE BEHAVIOR BY PERSON

Target	Extending Toy	Sharing Toy	Physical Contact	Held	Extending Cookie Box	Sharing Cookie Box
Mother:						
M..............	5.4[16]	85.3[16]	119.4[20]	156.5[9]	4.95[11]	14.5[19]
SD.............	7.1	134.1	142.3	288.2	9.5	16.0
Teacher:						
M..............	2.3[7]	14.4[6]	3.8[6]	8.0[2]	0.0[0]	0.04[1]
SD.............	6.3	36.8	8.7	33.6	0.0	0.91
Stranger:						
M..............	1.0[5]	3.4[4]	1.9[1]	0.0[0]	0.0[0]	0.26[2]
SD.............	2.3	11.5	5.7	0.0	0.0	0.91
Total:						
M..............	8.9[16]	104.8[16]	125.8[20]	163.4[9]	4.9[11]	14.7[19]
SD.............	12.7	151.7	138.5	286.3	9.5	15.9

NOTE.—All time given in number of seconds duration over 840 sec. Bracketed figures indicate number of children displaying the response.

(The sharing which did occur with teacher and stranger was at their initiation at the end of the session.)

Exploration of the room.—Seventeen children moved into two or more quadrants during the session; 11 children visited three of the four quadrants in the room. Frequency of quadrant changes was significantly correlated with manipulating toys, $r = .47$, $p < .023$; with extending toys to adults, $r = .71$, $p < .001$; and with the number of times toys were shared, $r = .80$, $p < .001$.

Spending a great deal of time in the mother-open quadrant correlated negatively with all exploration measures: manipulating toys, interacting with adults, and manipulating the cookie box. The percentage of time spent in the mother-open quadrant correlated with maternal IQ, $r = -.55$, $p < .004$, and the maternal-involvement scale, $r = -.67$, $p < .001$, of the Home Observation for Measurement of the Environment (Caldwell, Wright, Honig, & Tannenbaum 1970) obtained when the children were 6 months old.

DISCUSSION

The data from this study indicate that these 23 infant-day-care-reared children clearly displayed more attachment behavior toward their teachers. These differences in behavior were present even though the children spent at least half of their waking time each day with their teachers in a pleasant, stimulating, and reinforcing environment. Therefore we conclude that these infants were more attached to their mothers than to their teachers. In addition, the children appeared to perceive their mothers as the preferred help giver in a problem situation. Although much help with daily problems was provided by their day-care teachers, when given a choice, day-care children asked their mothers for help.

The possibility that the child's day-care teacher might have been the preferred attachment figure was a plausible one for this sample of children. A majority of the children lived in an extended-family situation, some with extended families and transient family friends as well. Only nine children left the center to go home to their mothers on a daily basis; the rest went home to relatives or neighbors because their mothers worked or were in school at night or were not home for some other reason. Seventeen children had lived in three or more homes prior to the study, and one child had experienced 11 moves before she was 2½. It is precisely for this type of population that day care has been suggested as a method of preventing developmental delay. Yet no studies of attachment had been conducted previously with children raised in similar circumstances. These findings therefore have both practical and theoretical implications.

In this study the stranger's presence created a mildly stressful situation for the purpose of energizing a choice among alternative attachment figures. The 23 children in this sample reacted variably to the level of stress provided. Seventeen children appeared to perceive the situation as not terribly stressful; they made contact with their mothers and then proceeded to explore the room, to play with the materials provided, and to interact with the adults in the room (particularly the mother) by inviting the adults to join in their play. During their explorations, the children maintained periodic contact with their mothers either by moving near them or physically touching them. Mothers appeared to serve as an important resource (i.e., a positive attachment figure) for them. Six of the 23 children, however, seemed to find the same situation so stressful that they stayed near or were held by their mothers for the entire observational session.

The variability in this sample did not seem to relate to any particular factor in the children themselves such as sex, age or intelligence. Rather, it appeared to be linked to factors which may describe how competent their mothers were and thus how consistent and reassuring the relationship was between mother and child. Mothers who were less involved and less intelligent had children who reacted to the situation with distress, whereas mothers who were involved and interactive with their children in the home environment had children who explored the room in this novel situation.

It is difficult to make a case for the general effects of any kind of rearing condition on the attachment bond; in all studies of different care conditions including the present one, there is great variation among children in their responses to the measurement situation. Clearly more than day care or home rearing alone is affecting the developing bond between mother and child. What those other factors are—and, more important, how to measure them—are questions which need to be explored in greater depth.

The questions addressed in the current study were the following: (1) Do children who have been placed in day care since infancy prefer to be near and to interact more with their mothers or teachers when given a choice between the two? (2) To whom do these children turn when they need help with a specific problem? The answers are clearly that (1) these children are attached more intensely to their mothers than to their teachers and (2) they perceive their mothers as help givers. Moreover, for most of the children the relationship with their mothers seemed secure enough to allow them to "detach" from her to make developmentally appropriate independent explorations of a novel environment.

REFERENCE NOTE

1. Lewis, M.; Weinraub, M.; & Ban, P. Mothers and fathers, girls and boys: attachment behavior in the first two years of life (ETS RB 72-60). Princeton, N.J.: Educational Testing Service, 1972.

REFERENCES

Caldwell, B. M.; Wright, C. M.; Honig, A. S.; & Tannenbaum, J. Infant day care and attachment. *American Journal of Orthopsychiatry,* 1970, **40**, 397–412.

Clarke-Stewart, K. A. Interactions between mothers and their young children: characteristics and consequences. *Monographs of the Society for Research in Child Development,* 1973, **38** (6–7, Serial No. 153).

Cohen, L. J. The operational definition of human attachment. *Psychological Bulletin,* 1974, **81**, 207–217.

Cohen, L. J., & Campos, J. J. Father, mother, and stranger as elicitors of attachment behaviors in infancy. *Developmental Psychology,* 1974, **10**, 146–154.

Feldman, S. S., & Ingham, M. E. Attachment behavior: a validation study in two age groups. *Child Development,* 1975, **46**, 319–330.

Fleener, D. E. Experimental production of infant-maternal attachment behaviors. *Proceedings of the 81st Annual Convention of the American Psychological Association,* 1973, **8**, 57–58.

McCall, R. B., & Appelbaum, M. I. Bias in the analysis of repeated measures designs: some alternative approaches. *Child Development,* 1973, **44**, 401–415.

Masters, J. C., & Wellman, H. M. The study of human infant attachment: a procedural critique. *Psychological Bulletin,* 1974, **81**, 218–237.

Passman, R. H., & Weisberg, P. Mothers and blankets as agents for promoting play and exploration by young children in a novel environment: the effects of social and nonsocial attachment objects. *Developmental Psychology*, 1975, **11**, 170–177.

Ricciuti, H. N. Fear and the development of social attachments in the first year of life. In M. Lewis & L. Rosenblum (Eds.), *The origins of human behavior*, Vol. **2**. *The origins of fear*. New York: Wiley, 1974.

17

THE MOTHER-CHILD RELATION-SHIP AND THE DEVELOPMENT OF AUTONOMY AND SELF-ASSERTION IN YOUNG (14-30 MONTHS) ASTHMATIC CHILDREN

Y. Gauthier, C. Fortin, P. Drapeau, J.-J. Breton,
J. Gosselin, L. Quintal, J. Weisnagel,

Hôpital Sainte-Justine pour les Enfants

L. Tetreault, and G. Pinard

Hôpital Sainte-Jean-de-Dieu, Montreal

This study had a threefold purpose: (1) to focus on the very young asthmatic (14–30 months) and to evaluate his autonomous and self-assertive strivings; (2) to study the mother-child rela-tionship *as a transactional, reciprocal process of mutual adapta-tion; and (3) to look for a possible relationship between allergic factors and the psychological variables. We evaluated 40 asthmatic children and their mothers, following an observational methodol-ogy, both at home and in the hospital. The results led us to question*

Reprinted with permission from *Journal of the American Academy of Child Psychiatry,* Vol. 16, 1977, 109–131.

This work was made possible through a grant from the Department of National Health and Welfare, Ottawa, 1971–1974 (#604-7-773).

the theory of a "psychosomatic type" of mother-child relationship in childhood asthma as well as the inverse reciprocity between allergy and psychopathology which has been described in the literature. The implications of this study for pediatric and child psychiatric practice and for future research are also described.

Among the psychosomatic diseases of childhood, asthma is probably still the most prevalent, as several epidemiological studies have demonstrated (Brown, 1958; Thomas, 1971; Weisnagel and Rivard, 1971). In spite of numerous and varied studies carried out in several countries, asthma remains a complex symptom, at the levels of both etiology and therapy. Moreover, if the psychogenic effect of the recognized psychological factors is still a matter of debate, the pathophysiological mechanisms involved are no more accounted for: there is a standing controversy between allergists, with their pragmatic viewpoint, and the pneumologists who are searching for answers in the nervous system pathways.

The interrelationship between multiple concomitant factors has led to the elaboration of a great number of theories, a fact which only adds to the confusion. We agree with Pinkerton and Weaver (1970) who say, "Asthma is perhaps the example 'par excellence' of psychosomatic illness, the clearest demonstration of that complex interrelationship of body, intellect and emotion, which links patient, family, doctor and nurse in the elusive quest for etiology and therapeutic efficacity" (p. 81).

REVIEW OF LITERATURE

In spite of the theoretical controversy and conflicting viewpoints, there now appears to be a trend, largely due to a concerted effort of clinical and experimental research, toward more objective data gathering and evaluation of better identified and selected groups of patients and controls, for a unified view of psychosomatic illness. Turning away from the fruitless dichotomy of psyche and soma, researchers have come to recognize the need for reconciling divergent findings and accept the "principle of a summation of various factors underlying the etiology of childhood asthma" (Pinkerton, 1973, p. 461).

At present, there seems to be a consensus of opinion about the etiology of asthma, which is based on "convincing evidence in favor of an immuno-physiological substrate: its nature is an inherent instability [hyperreactivity] of the bronchial system . . . which is presumably inherited and blocked by the specific antiallergic action of disodium cromoglycate . . . it overreacts to infective, allergenic, physiologic and psychologic challenge" (Pinkerton, 1973, p. 461).

Dolovich et al. (1973) also recognize this bronchial hyperreactivity which they explain with the Szentivanyi (1968) theory of partial blocking of the beta-adrenergic receptors of the autonomic nervous system. These authors consider emotional disturbances not as psychogenic agents but as potential aggravating factors among various others, e.g., infectious, allergic.

Recent psychosomatic research has gradually evolved toward the study of the relationship between emotional and somatic causes and implications of the asthmatic symptom: its purpose is to find the link between objective data (with measures of ventilatory dysfunction, allergy potential, severity of physical impairment) and the psychodynamic factors in childhood asthma (McNicol et al., 1973). In such a perspective, Purcell and his research team at the Children's Asthma Research Institute and Hospital in Denver have used the study of subgroups of rapidly remitting and persistently steroid-dependent asthmatic children, hospitalized for purposes of "parentectomy" (Peshkin, 1963). The results of their numerous studies (Purcell, 1973; Purcell and Metz, 1962; Purcell and Weiss, 1970; Purcell et al., 1962, 1969a, 1969b) seem to indicate that the rapidly remitting group has less evidence of somatic involvement, but more disturbed emotional reactions and family relationships.

Following this trend, Block et al. (1964) have found a phenomenon of negative reciprocity between allergic and psychopathological factors in a group of asthmatic children, subdivided into two groups of high and low allergy potential score. Although their findings have been challenged by two studies (Jacobs et al., 1966; Hirt et al., 1968), the discrepancy in methods and patient population that the latter have used do not in fact adequately disprove Block's views.

As to the nature of the psychopathological factors involved, there has been, since French and Alexander (1941), the pioneer psychosomaticists, a plethora of theories. These have emerged largely from psychoanalytic concepts, and have been identified as conflicts centering on dependence-independence tendencies, separation anxiety, and repressed aggression. Most investigators have emphasized the etiological significance of an early disturbance in the mother-child relationship.

Sperling (1968), on the basis of her therapeutic experience with a number of asthmatic patients and their mothers, has masterfully unified these psychodynamic processes in a global synthesis which could be summarized as follows:

1. There is a "psychosomatic type" of mother-child relationship, the specific quality of which is that the child is rejected by his mother only when he is healthy and evidences strivings toward independence, but is in fact rewarded for being sick and helpless by the special care and attention given to him at such time.

2. The child's aggression and rebellion against the controlling mother are discharged together with other forbidden and dangerous impulses through the somatic symptom. The cessation of asthmatic attacks will be followed by overt aggressive behavior.

3. The psychogenic etiology of asthma is situated during the anal phase of development (1 to 3 years) when the child abandons his passive-dependent role and as a toddler strives for self-assertion.

4. There is a phenomenon of reverse reciprocity between somatic and psychological symptoms: i.e., the sicker the patient is somatically, the less apparent will be the underlying personality disturbance and vice versa.

Sandler (1964, 1965) and Wenar et al. (1962) have carried out two independent objective studies of asthmatic children (4 to 7 years; 6 to 11 years) and their mothers in order to test the hypothesis of a particular mother-child tie in psychosomatic infantile diseases. Sandler found in her group of mothers a characteristic childrearing attitude of using the threat of removal of love as an instrument of discipline, while Wenar et al. found mothers of asthmatics to be lacking in "motherliness" and engaging in a close but mutually frustrating relationship with their children.

While reviewing a mass of theoretical papers based on clinical material and observations of a few cases, in addition to more objective comparative and longitudinal research reports,[1] we have not been able to find one study which focused on very young children at the toddler stage when, according to so many of these researchers, the particular mother-child relationship is established and will eventually result in a psychosomatic illness. This, we believe, is a major deficiency in infantile asthma research.

To emphasize this need even further, we should mention the results of a small epidemiological survey which we carried out at l'Hôpital Sainte-Justine pour les Enfants in Montreal, before starting our own research effort. For the year 1968, 348 children with asthma were hospitalized and in 250 of those, the first asthmatic attack or manifestation of the symptom had appeared between the ages of 8 months

---

[1]A review article, as yet unpublished, includes 157 references since 1941.

and 2 years. Other studies have reported similar findings (Ghory, 1973).

PURPOSE OF THIS STUDY

If asthma appears frequently at an early age, it is at this privileged moment that we should try to observe the early manifestations of the illness, and the relationship which is established (or in the process of establishing itself) between mother and child. Since Sperling (1968), among others, suggests a close link between asthma and unacceptable (to the mother) tendencies toward autonomy and assertion, we have chosen to study children from 14 months (when walking has been mastered) to 30 months (the anal-sadistic stage appearing between 18–24 months).

In this study we mainly wanted to verify the following working hypotheses:

During this developmental (anal) stage, the normal child has acquired his autonomy and becomes more and more assertive against the demands of mother and family. To what extent does the asthmatic child correspond to this pattern? Will he still be overly dependent and have difficulty in expressing his oppositional tendencies?

The asthmatic child's mother does not easily accept such tendencies toward autonomy and assertion; she tends to foster dependency in him by gratifications of special attention when he is sick and to reject him when he is well, independent, and expressing oppositional tendencies. Will we find these maternal attitudes of alternating overprotection and rejection if our asthmatic children do manifest dependency or normal strivings for independence and opposition?

Finally, does Block's (1964) theory of a negative reciprocity between allergic and psychopathological factors apply in the case of young asthmatics? If so, the greater the allergy potential score, the more harmonious will be the mother-child relationship; conversely, if the allergy potential score is low, the greater will be the disturbance in the relationship.

PROCEDURE

Selection of Sample

From the daily admission list of the hospital, we retained those who had been hospitalized with a tentative diagnosis of asthma and who were between the age range of 14 to 30 months. In a preliminary perusal of the medical file, we excluded three categories of patients: (1) those who were suffering from any other severe physical illness; (2) those whose history showed a major developmental retardation of organic origin, suspected mental deficiency, etc.; and (3) those who resided outside a radius of 20 miles: a greater distance would have made the evaluation difficult for both the family and the research team.

Then a pediatrician[2] and an allergist independently confirmed the diagnosis of asthma after agreeing beforehand on these criteria: (a) an analysis of hereditary antecedents; (b) attacks characterized by episodes of dyspnea with polypnea, wheezing, and sibilance; (c) attacks that responded well to sympathicomimetic medication; (d) recurring attacks: only after the second attack with those clinical signs was a child considered asthmatic for our purposes.

Our sample was made up of 40 of these asthmatic children whose parents, first contacted by phone, then receiving an official explanatory letter, were willing to collaborate in our subsequent evaluation. Only four families refused to collaborate as research subjects to our proposal during the 3 years that we carried out our project.

Schedule and Methods of Data Collection

Our research team of six members was subdivided into two teams made up of one psychologist and two psychiatrists, one acting as an observer; three clinicians thus evaluated each case for the psychological variables.

In a first *home visit* the psychologist established contact with the family and filled out a *questionnaire*[3] with factual material obtained from the mother on the developmental history of the child and the evolution of the asthmatic symptoms.

In the two following weeks, the child with his parents came to the hospital for two half-day periods of observation. Each time there was a *psychiatric interview* recorded on videotape, one psychiatrist acting as interviewer, the other observing on a closed-circuit television screen. They alternately took up one or the other role in successive cases. The interview was of a semistructured type and followed a definite

---

[2]We are grateful to Gloria Jeliu, M.D., who helped in the diagnostic work with our subjects.

[3]The questionnaire was elaborated from the schedule by Sears et al. (1957) of patterns of child-rearing and Gouin-Décarie's (1969) psychological developmental history of thalidomide children. We take this opportunity to thank Dr. Décarie, whose help in developing our methodology was much appreciated.

scheme, probing for reported facts as well as affects, and observing behavior in such areas as feeding, sleeping, contact, toilet training, motor and play activities, manifestations of autonomy and opposition, type of communication, reaction to separation, and reactions of the parents to the illness.

At the first visit to the hospital, the psychologist tested the child, in the presence of the mother, on the *Griffiths Developmental Scale* (1954).

On the subsequent visit, child and mother were observed alone in the playroom in a *structured play session* by the psychologist and a student in psychology,[4] both observing through a one-way mirror. Elaborated for the purposes of this research, this session consisted of six 3-minute periods, some with shared play activities, one during which the mother was busy with a task, leaving the child on his own, and another in which she left the room entirely. The observers dictated a running commentary of observation on a dual recorder with a pre-recorded signal each 10 seconds. The transcripts were coded following B. Merrill Bishop's (1951) list of behavior categories for child and mother.

On a second *home observation visit*, which lasted 3 hours during the time of day including the lunch hour, the psychologist observed and made a continuous record of the mother-child interactions in their natural setting. These notes served as a basis for a detailed report following David and Appell's (1966) model of observation.

Independently from our own observations, the allergist evaluated the allergy potential of the child. Based on Block's (1964) *Allergy Potential Scale* with slight modifications, the allergist's score was summed on 5 variously weighted items: hereditary antecedents, personal antecedents, associated manifestations of allergy, blood eosinophile count, skin test reactivity, both intradermic and by scarification.

Data Analysis

In order to render all this clinical material, gathered from different sources, amenable to comparison between each child-mother pair we developed seven ordinal 5-point scales measuring the psychological variables implied in our working hypotheses. Five of these were entered on autonomy, two on opposition.

For purposes of evaluating these abstract concepts from concrete observable behaviors, we operationally defined *autonomy* under four

---

[4]We are grateful to Miss Suzanne Douesnard, B.A., who gave many hours of her time in the observation itself and the coding of the material. She also collaborated in the review of literature.

headings: capacity for independent activity: direction, vigor, control; capacity for autonomous satisfaction of needs: frustration tolerance; capacity for separation from mother; level of communication: capacity for social exchange. A fifth scale concerning autonomy was a maternal variable: reaction of the mother to the child's manifestations of autonomy.

Self-assertion which straddles both autonomous strivings and oppositional tendencies was operationally defined as: capacity for accepting demands and prohibitions. Again we had the corresponding maternal variable of: reaction of the mother to manifestations of opposition. We used still two other 3-point scales to evaluate the *quality of the mother-child relationship* in both areas of autonomy and opposition: (1) harmonious relationship: in which the child manifests age-adequate strivings for autonomy and opposition and the mother accepts them well; (2) vulnerable relationship, potentially pathogenic: in which the child remains timid about expressing these strivings and the mother has an ambivalent attitude; in such cases we could not predict what the outcome would be; (3) pathological relationship: in which an open conflict between mother and child around these strivings was already present.

The mother-child couples were first rated independently on these scales, the two psychiatrists using the interview material, and the psychologist using the home observational material. All three then discussed the case and, if there was any discrepancy in their individual ratings, they arrived at a final consensual rating which was used for statistical analysis.

The other measures used for statistical treatment were the Allergy Potential Scale score and the General Development quotient, as well as the quotients on the six subscales of the Griffiths test. The frequency measures for the play session have not yet been analyzed. The Spearman method of rank-order correlations for nonparametric data was used by our statistical consultants.

FINDINGS

Characteristics of Population

Our 40 subjects consisted of 22 male and 18 female asthmatic children of whom 2 were in the 14–18 months range, 22 in the 18–24 months range, and 16 in the 24–30 months range. They were the offspring of young parents (M age of the fathers: 28.2 years; M age of the mothers: 25.7 years). They mostly came from small families: 15

were the only child, 19 were from families of two to three children, and only 6 had more than two siblings. Leaving out the 15 only children, their sibling rank was as follows: eldest, 2; youngest, 20; and 3 in the middle position.

The socioeconomic status of the families was evaluated according to number of years of schooling of both parents and occupation of the father, and was distributed as follows: high-middle class, 7; low-middle class, 19; lower class, 14. There were no broken homes in our sample at the time of evaluation. An exception was an adopted child (who had been living with the adoptive parents for 10 months and adopted as an infant); one other boy was living with his young (18 years) unmarried mother who resided with her own parents, but the young father made frequent visits and provided for the child, both parents planning for an eventual marriage.

If we now look at the asthmatic condition itself, we note that the *age of onset* of the first respiratory symptoms was set in the following way: 0–6 months, 21; 7–12 months, 9; 13–18 months, 8; over 18 months, 2.

Only 4 out of the 40 subjects had never been hospitalized but were frequent visitors of the emergency clinic of the hospital; 17 had been hospitalized once or twice, and 19, three times or more. Of the latter, 5 had been hospitalized more than five times. The *duration of hospitalization* varied from less than 2 weeks (N = 10) to more than 2 weeks (N = 26); of these, 10 children had remained at the hospital 9 weeks or more on different occasions during their short life span. These last two factors in spite of their importance could not be retained for statistical analysis since they are linked to personal outlook and idiosyncrasies of the attending physicians.

We have not been able to assess properly the factor of severity of the illness since, in our opinion, only pulmonary function tests can give a rigorous measure; and these cannot be used with such young children who are unable to offer full cooperation in the testing situation.

On the general development quotient, only 2 subjects were below the mean, 22 at the mean level, and 16 above, of whom 8 were at the superior level. This same pattern holds for the subscales, indicating that our asthmatic children have a normal development in all its aspects. On the locomotor scale, all are at or above the mean, which may be explained by the fact that at the age of evaluation, the locomotor tasks have preference over others for most children who take pleasure in mastering their bodies after having discovered the freedom of walking and exploring. On the verbal scale, 8 are below the mean, on the eye-and-hand coordination, 6, and on both the social

Figure 1

Capacity for Independent Activity

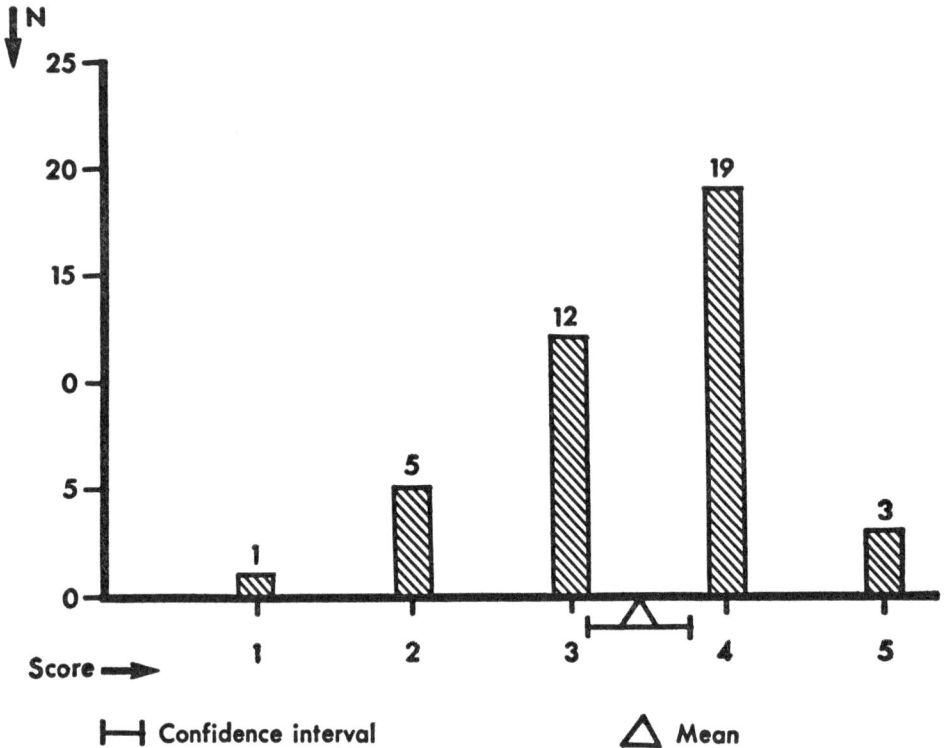

and performance scales, 4. If we take into account our clinical observations and the facts reported in the anamneses of these low scorers, the developmental lag seemed due mostly to outside causes: lack of stimulation of the low socioeconomic environment, adoption, or conflict-laden mother-child relationship rather than to the illness itself.

Psychological Variables

We have evaluated two main dimensions of the young asthmatic child, autonomy and opposition, which we have judged to be in the forefront at the developmental stage and time corresponding to the chronological age selected for our sample.

Figure 2

Frustration Tolerance

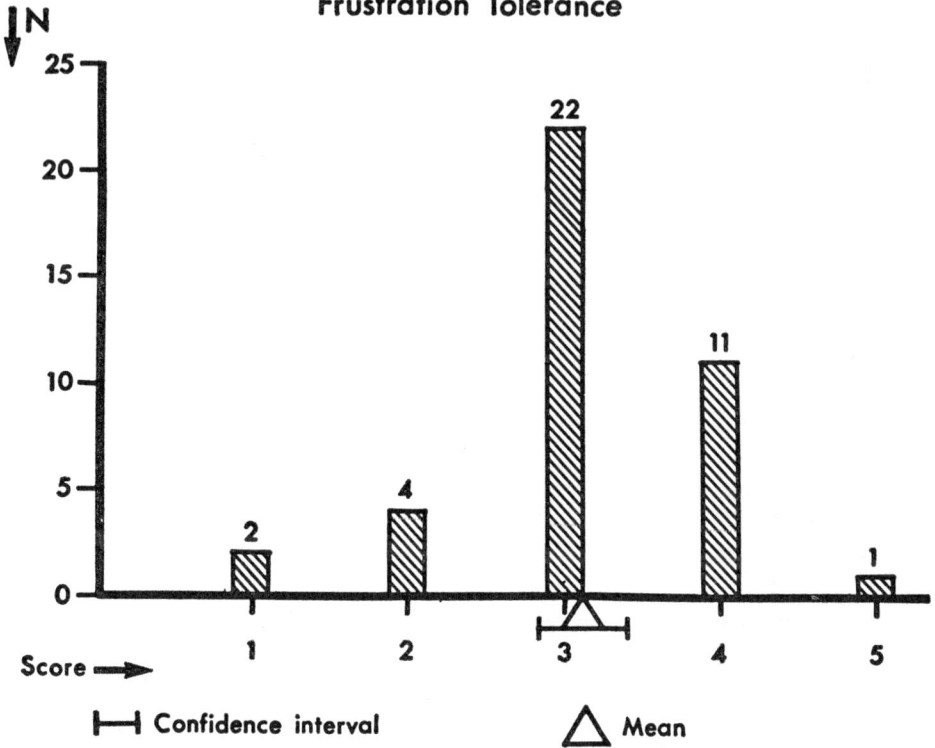

├─┤ Confidence interval   △ Mean

As a first step in reporting our results, we shall give a general description of the psychological characteristics according to the ratings
obtained on the different scales of autonomy and opposition. As regards three aspects of the *autonomy dimension*, i.e., independent activity, frustration tolerance, and communication, all our children seem to
follow a healthy pattern of development and have been rated as average on our scales (see figs. 1, 2, and 3).[5] Yet, on the fourth scale, (see
fig. 4), that of the ability to separate from the mother, although a
majority have been rated at the level of 3 on our 5-point scale, i.e.,
"visual contact replaces physical contact; protests when mother leaves,
but is easily comforted; plays at a distance; physical presence of the
mother still essential on certain occasions," a fair number (15/40) still

───────────

[5]All confidence intervals have been calculated at 0.05.

Figure 3

Mode of Communication

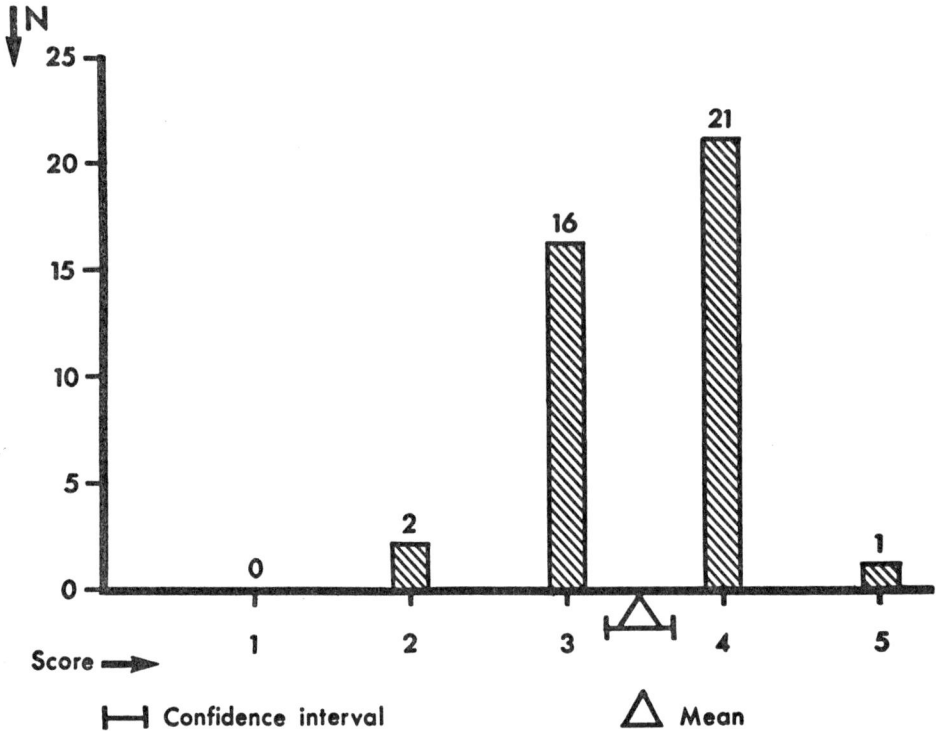

cling to more immature patterns and are rated at level 2 of the scale, which reads: "intense if not exclusive attachment; accepts care from a mother substitute; emotional dependency shown in seeking reassurance, approbation, caresses; jealous when mother's attention given to others or to her own tasks; tries to follow her when she leaves the room; some separation anxiety." We may then surmise a greater sensitivity to separation in our asthmatic population, but we cannot conclude a true separation anxiety common to all cases.

Faced with these autonomous strivings in their children, half of our group of mothers (19) react favorably (see fig. 5); at the level of 4 on our scale, they are described as "fosters autonomy; respects individuality of her child; stimulates locomotion and manipulation; lets the child

Figure 4

Capacity for Separation from Mother

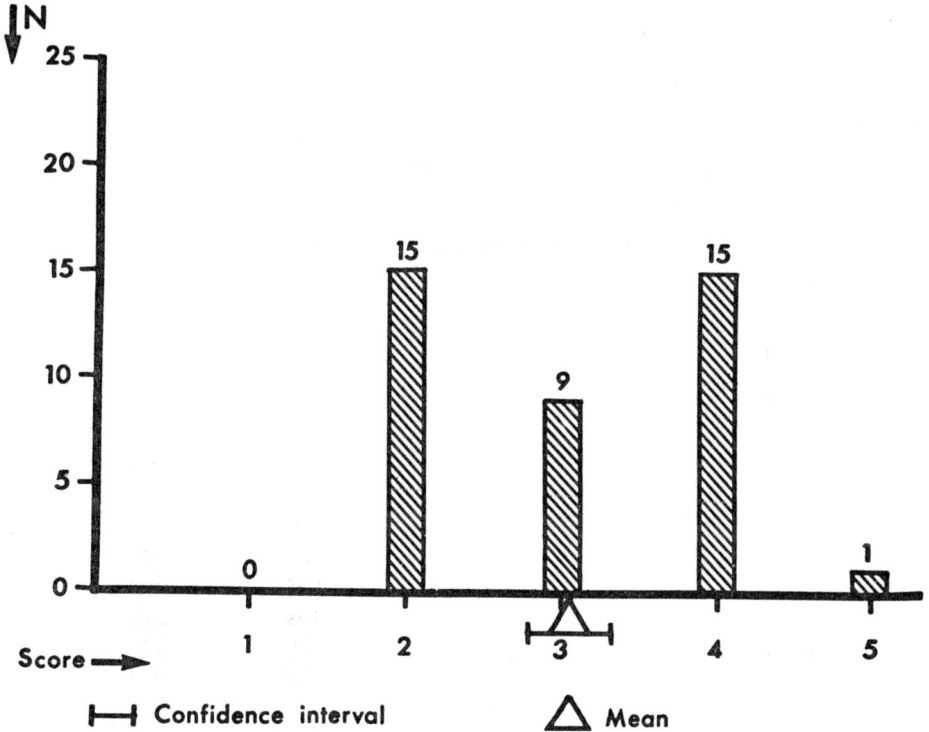

explore while watching at a distance; facilitates separation by entrusting him to the care of a babysitter." Only 14 mothers are "perplexed and surprised" (level 3) by these autonomous tendencies, and an even smaller number (6) generally ignore them because of a reluctance to modify their mothering role. None can really be identified as overprotective, engulfing, the "asthmatogenic mother" (Block et al., 1966) who opposes all autonomous manifestations in her child while keeping him in a state of dependency in order to satisfy her own needs.

When we consider the *opposition dimension* (see fig. 6), most of our asthmatic children can express freely these normal tendencies in age-appropriate behaviors, such as "saying a flat 'no' and showing occasional verbal and physical aggressivity: throwing toys, biting, etc." A

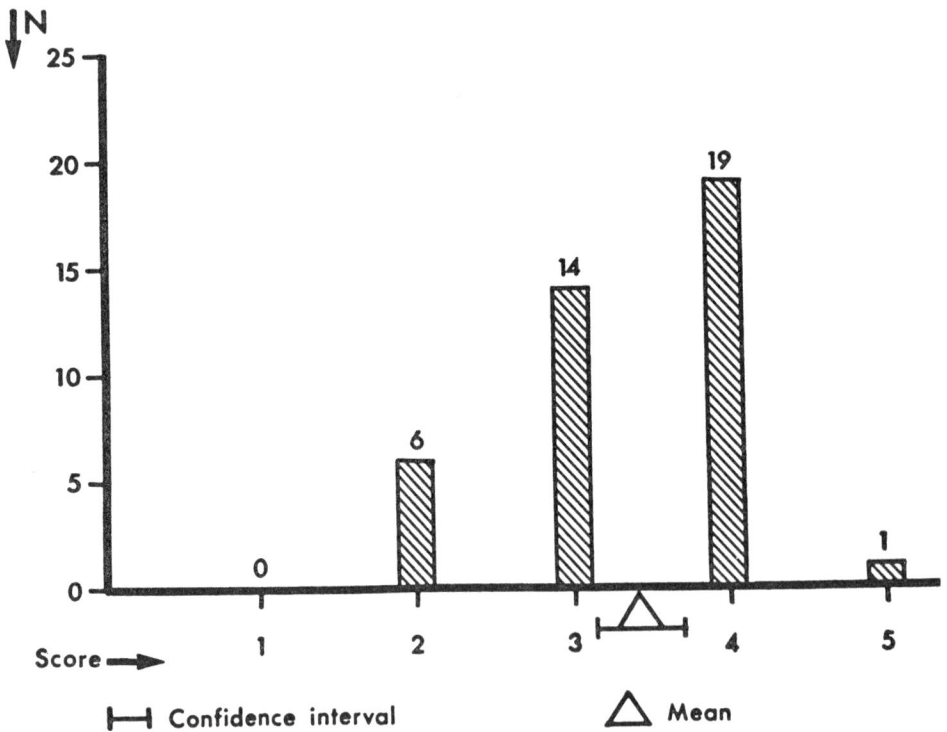

Figure 5

Reactions of the Mother to the Child's
Manifestations of Autonomy

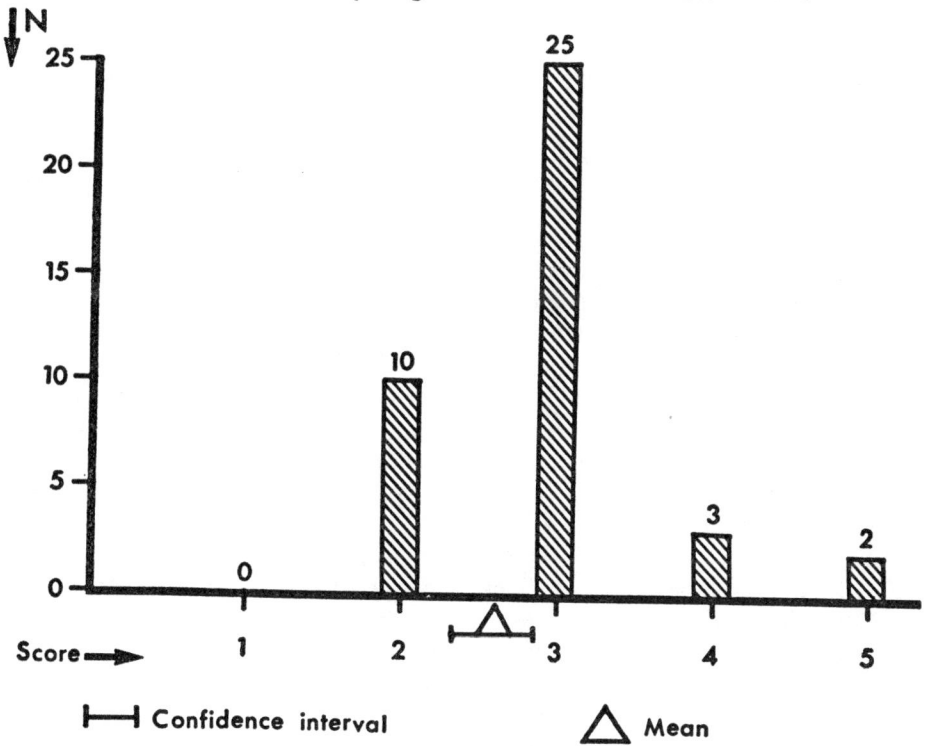

Figure 6

Capacity for Accepting Demands and Prohibitions

small minority (5) manifest more uncontrolled aggression and provocative or stubborn behaviors, while none are rated as passive and inhibited. Faced with these new aggressive tendencies (see fig. 7), 18 of our mothers are able to cope with a firm, no-nonsense attitude; 11 are rated as hesitant, lacking confidence in their exercise of authority; 6 are entirely too permissive; and 5 are at the other end of the scale with rigid or punitive attitudes.

If we turn now to our evaluation of the *quality of the relationship* between mother and child around the dimension of autonomy, on a 3-point scale we found: 23 normal situations, i.e., harmonious relationship in which the child develops well and the mother fosters his autonomous tendencies; 10 cases of what we identified as a vulnerable relation with possible pathogenic overtones; 7 cases in which the situation was already severely conflictual.

We are inclined to interpret these results as highly interesting, since they tend to show a much more harmonious mother-child relationship than has been implied in the generally accepted concepts of infantile asthma. Yet here again we must be cautious, since in a fair number of cases (17), already at this early age we found either the potentiality for psychopathology or definite signs of at least severe conflict.

The results are somewhat similar when we consider the mother-child relationship around the oppositional tendencies. Although we have a majority (22) of the mother-child pairs living through this period in a harmonious way, 7 show some vulnerability, and a stronger number (11) are already experiencing open conflict.

We have also studied statistically how these psychological variables correlate with one another.

Autonomy. There is a high positive correlation (p < .001) between the autonomous manifestations of the child and the mother's reaction to her child's autonomy: the more the child is able to be autonomous, the better the mother is able to foster these strivings in her child. This positive correlation applies in his capacity for independent activity, his frustration tolerance, and his capacity for separation. Only in the communication sector did we not find a significant degree of correlation, which might indicate that in this sphere the child develops at his own pace and is not influenced by the mother's attitudes. And finally, there is a negative correlation (p < .001) between conflict in the mother-child relationship and the positive reaction of the mother to her child's autonomy: the more the mother favors autonomy in her child, the less we see conflict in the mother-child relationship within this area.

Opposition. We were surprised to find that no correlation of statisti-

Figure 7

Reactions of the Mother to Manifestations of Opposition

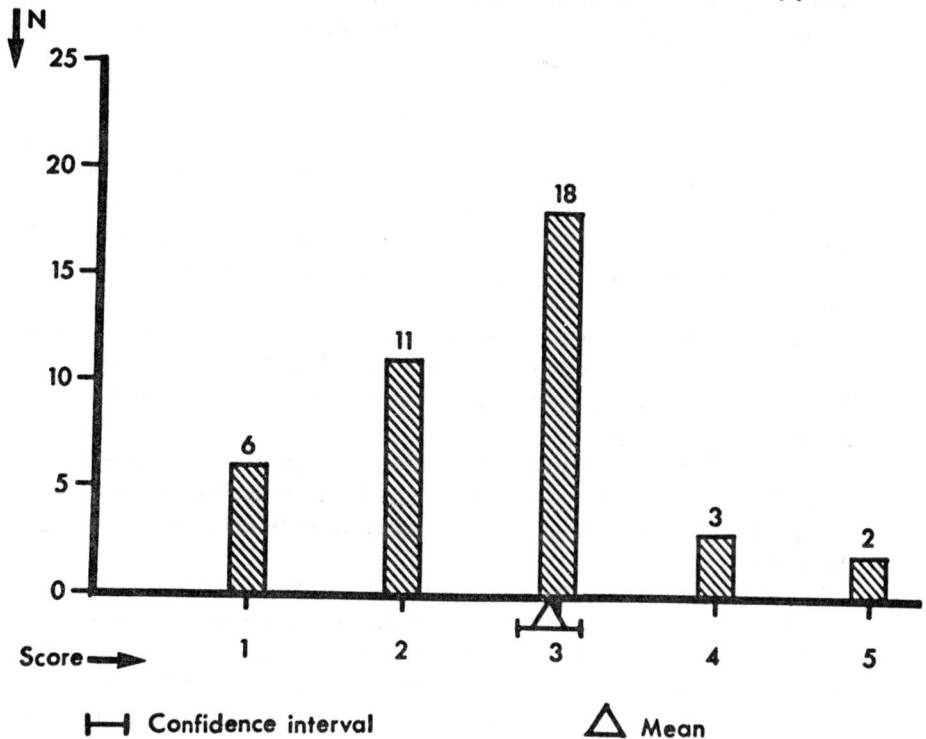

cal significance could be established between the oppositional behaviors of the child and his mother's reaction to them. It seems that
both these variables are two distinct phenomena that evolve independently from one another. One explanation could be that the child's
self-assertive needs are basically of the "instinctual type," and manifest
themselves whether or not the mother accepts or rejects them. Although there is an associative negative link between conflict in the
mother-child relationship in this area and the mother's reactions, the
correlation does not attain a statistical level of significance.

Autonomy and Opposition. It is interesting to note that we did not find
any statistically significant correlation between our measures of autonomy and opposition. It might mean that both these dimensions
evolve independently. But it definitely indicates that our scales were
evaluating two independent sets of phenomena, which is a comforting

and rewarding thought and brings validity to these research instruments. Finally, the mother's reactions to autonomy and opposition both evolve in the same direction, to a statistically significant degree (p < .05). This is logical enough and self-explanatory.

The Allergy Potential Scale

In order to assess the relative value of this scale, we have established correlations between each item and the total score; the results show definite coherence in the sense that all elements are related in a positive way, thus showing that they measure an identical substratum. We have then evaluated the weight of each item within the total score with the following results: hereditary factors, 21.52%; eosinophile count, 13.53%; personal antecedents, 14.44%; associated allergic manifestations, 25.26%; allergy tests, 25.23%. These weights correspond to the clinical importance allergists give to each item when making their diagnosis.

Finally, when comparing our results, obtained by the simple addition of the raw scores, to those obtained using the Block formula of standard scores, we arrive at a correlation of 0.9425, which is more than satisfactory.

On a frequency distribution of the Allergy Potential Score (APS) of our 40 subjects (see fig. 8), we find a definite asymmetry in the curve which is slightly skewed to the left of the mean. This is why instead of breaking up our population into two distinct groups of high and low allergy potential score, we have used the Spearman rank-order correlations with the purpose of preserving all important information when comparing the allergic factor with the psychological variables.

We then proceeded to correlate the APS with other factors, such as age of onset of respiratory symptoms and the Griffiths developmental score, as well as with the psychological variables previously described.

The only statistically significant correlations established between these sets of variables are grouped in figure 9.

We thus found a positive correlation between age of onset of symptoms and the APS: the higher the APS, the later is the age of onset of respiratory symptoms (p < 0.10). But since we found no correlation between the age of onset and the age at which the APS was evaluated, and, even more important, no correlation between age of onset and the psychological variables, we must then look for other factors besides allergic ones to account for the early appearance of symptoms in the first year of life.

When we correlated the child's developmental score on the Griffiths

Figure 8

Index of Allergy Potential

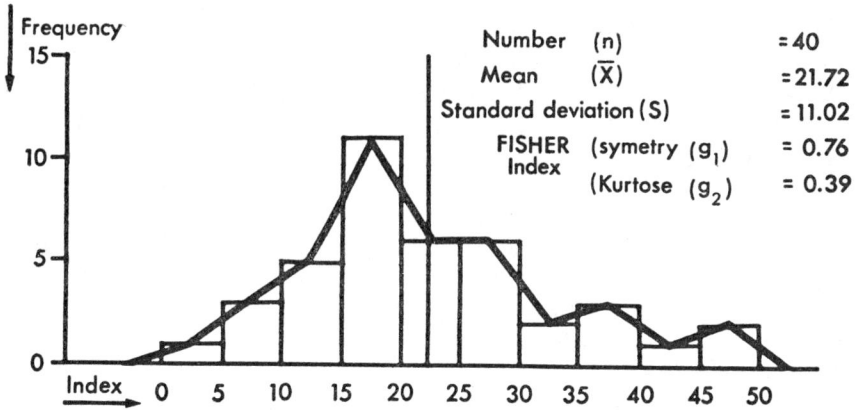

Number	(n)	= 40
Mean	($\overline{X}$)	= 21.72
Standard deviation	(S)	= 11.02
FISHER Index	(symetry (g_1)	= 0.76
	(Kurtose (g_2)	= 0.39

Figure 9

Significant Correlations Between Allergy Potential and Other Factors

CORRELATION

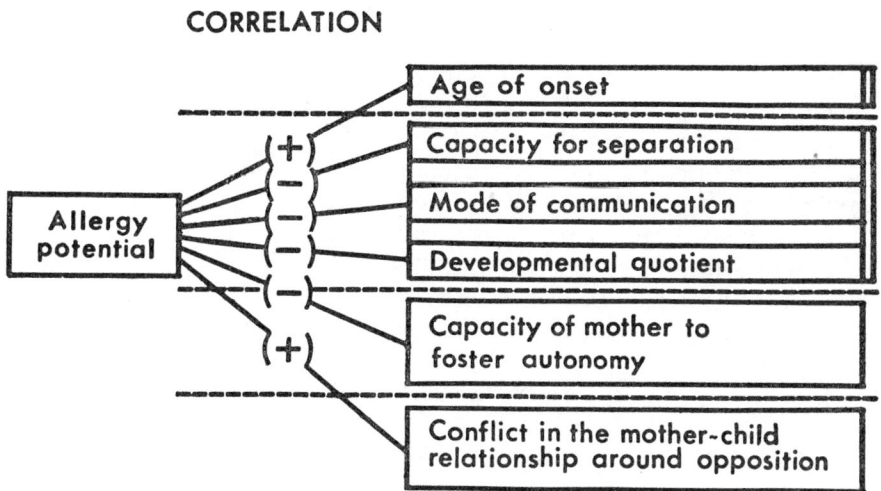

Test and the APS, we found that the higher the AP, the lower were results on all scales of the developmental test (p < 0.10). But we could not establish any link between age of onset or number and length of hospitalizations and the developmental quotients; we could have assumed that those children who were sick earlier and more often would have had a slower development, but this was not the case.

Analyzing now the statistically significant correlations between the different psychological variables and the APS proves a little more complex.

Autonomy. Although no correlation could be established between the APS and scales I, "capacity for independent activity," and scale II, "frustration tolerance," we found a negative correlation between the APS and the two scales, III, "capacity for separation" (p < 0.10), and IV, "level of communication" (p < 0.05): the higher the APS, the less the asthmatic child is able to communicate in social exchange, and the less is he able to separate from the mother. Moreover, we also found a negative correlation (p < 0.10) between the APS and the mother's reaction to the child's manifestations of autonomy (scale V): the higher the APS, the less the mother tends to foster his autonomy. But we were not able to demonstrate any relation between the AP and conflict in the mother-child relationship around the autonomy dimension.

If we study further the directions of all these correlations, we notice that only the scale "capacity for distanciation" is related both to the APS and to the maternal reactions: the higher the APS, the less the child is able to separate, and when the asthmatic child evidences these separation difficulties, the mother manifests them also.

This phenomenon is of interest especially since it is only on this scale that a fair number (15/40) of our cases were rated under the mean (see fig. 4), even though the majority were adequate in accepting separation from the mother. We could be tempted to interpret this as the first sign of the separation anxiety so often described in the literature; but at this point, we cannot explain the mechanism which links these three elements, nor can we assess the influence of such other factors as severity of the illness,[6] nature of the treatment, or quality of the experiences of separation on their common movement.

Opposition. Looking now at the oppositional tendencies, we have not found any statistically significant correlation with the APS. Nevertheless, we did find that when the APS is high, there is more conflict in

---

[6]The AP is not equivalent to the severity of the illness.

the mother-child relationship around the asthmatic child's expression of opposition.

These findings are not in accordance with the findings of Block et al. (1964); instead of showing a negative reciprocity between allergic and psychopathological variables, our results point in an opposite direction. In fact, *our asthmatic children who had a higher APS were also those who presented the most psychological disturbances.* But we are conscious of the fact that our young age group is very different from Block's latency age group.

Our study also challenges certain a priori ideas about the relation of asthma to allergy. For instance, we cannot accept the point of view of Kreisler et al. (1973), who consider asthma an essentially allergic illness. The fact that in our sample, those children who manifested respiratory symptoms earlier are the same who have a low APS is hard to reconcile with their hypothesis.

CONCLUSIONS

It is obvious that our results do not confirm the hypotheses of Sperling (1968) and Block et al. (1964); they seem, on the contrary, to invalidate their theories. We may also question the tendency of so many authors to generalize their findings on latency children to very young asthmatics: to us, it was a pleasant surprise to observe in our sample a majority of mothers and their asthmatic children functioning so adequately.

Generally, our asthmatic children were developing satisfactorily according to their age; they were autonomous, independent, coping well with the demands and limits imposed by the environment. Even in their capacity to separate from the mother, the majority were doing well.

The mother-child relationship which Sperling and others have described as disturbed and of a particular "psychosomatic type" has not proven to be quite as frequent as we had been led to believe. Instead, we have been struck by the fact that a majority of our mothers were very adequate indeed: only a few exceptions conformed to the cliché of the "asthmatogenic mother," in spite of the everyday presence of a severe, anxiety-producing, and handicapping illness.

On the other hand, we have to note that a minority of cases already showed potential or actual signs of psychopathology. It may be that during the course of evolution of the asthmatic illness, those will be the more complex psychiatric problems we often encounter when asked in consultation by pediatricians, and who may have led to the clinical description we so often read in the literature on asthma. We are not questioning the observations that Sperling and others have made; it is their generalization to the early mother-child relationship that our results seem to challenge.

The inverse relationship between allergy and psychopathology described by Block et al. may be reopened for questioning by our own findings. However useful and seductive her dichotomous explanation of the phenomena conducive to childhood asthma, we tend to abandon this simple logic and rally behind the multifactorial summative etiology of Pinkerton (1973) and McNicol et al. (1973).

At the moment, our findings make us lean toward a theory which ties in with the current concept of vulnerability: certain mothers are probably more sensitive than others to the sudden outbreak of an illness such as asthma, whose symptom manifestations are undoubtedly anxiety-producing and whose constant menace is very disturbing at the precise moment when the mother-child relationship is being established and is highly vulnerable to the vicissitudes of everyday living. The latent ambivalence of certain mothers may be activated by such a high-risk illness as asthma. We suggest that these vulnerable mothers or mother-child couples might become the difficult clinical problems we will later meet in consultation.

Our results point to two avenues for further research: (1) longitudinal observations of young asthmatic children in order to verify at what point in the course of their development and the evolution of their illness the psychopathological factors invoked by so many authors settle in and exert their influence: some authors (Kreisler et al., 1973) have stated that when the age of onset is in infancy, asthma tends to disappear before the age of 6; a continuous observation of such cases, similar to our sample, would enable us to verify these allegations. (2) It would also be of the utmost interest to replicate our observations on very young asthmatic children and compare them with control groups of normal or other chronically ill children (e.g., congenital cardiopathy). Only then could we confirm our hypothesis of *vulnerable* mothers who are unable to cope with such illnesses at the critical period of the establishing of the mother-child relationship.

Our study also holds important implications for the practice of both pediatricians and child psychiatrists. It is clear to us that clinicians should become more aware of the impact of recent research and avoid the traditional dichotomous view of disease in childhood psychosomatic ailments; emphasis should be placed on the recognition of *multiple factors*, operating *simultaneously* and *with varying influence*. In the case of infantile asthma, for instance, pediatricians should be open to the thought that certain mothers will react with ambivalence to their child's illness, the illness being responsible for revealing this ambivalence and the resulting pathological mother-child relationship. Similarly, child psychiatrists should abandon their pervasive concept of the "bad mother" in childhood asthma which often makes the mothers of asthmatic children feel unjustifiably guilty.

REFERENCES

Bishop, B. M. (1951), Mother-child interaction and the social behavior of children. *Psychol. Monogr.*, vol. 65, no. 328.

Block, J., Jennings, P. H., Harvey, E., & Simpson, E. (1964), Interaction between allergic potential and psychopathology in childhood asthma. *Psychosom. Med.*, 26:307–320.

———— ———— ———— ———— (1966), Clinicians conceptions of the asthmatogenic mother. *Arch. Gen. Psychiat.*, 15:610–618.

Brown, F. (1968), A clinical psychologist's perspective on research in psychosomatic medicine. *Psychosom. Med.*, 20:173–180.

David, M. & Appell, G. (1966), La relation mère-enfant. *Psychiat. l'enf.*, 9:455–531.

Dolovich, J., Hargreave, F. E., & Kerigan, A. T. (1973), Réponses asthmatiques tardives. *Méd. Mod. Canad.*, 28:1075–1079.

French, T. M. & Alexander, F. (1941), Psychogenic factors in bronchial asthma. *Psychosom. Med. Monog.* 4. Washington, D.C.: Nat. Res. Council.

Ghory, J. (1973), The pre-school child in an asthma rehabilitation program. *J. Asthma Res.*, 11:37–42.

Gouin-Décarie, T. (1969), A study of the mental and emotional development of the thalidomide child. In: *Determinants of Infant Behaviour*, ed. B. M. Foss. London: Methuen, 4:167–187.

Griffiths, R., ed. (1954), *The Abilities of Babies*. London: McGraw-Hill.

Hirt, M., Goldberg, R., & Bernstein, L. (1968), Interaction of personality variables and allergic predisposition in asthma. *Psychosomatics*, 9:340–343.

Jcabos, M. A., Friedman, S., Franklin, M. J., Anderson, L. S., Muller, J. S., & Eisman, H. D. (1966), Incidence of psychosomatic predisposing factors in allergic disorders. *Psychosom. Med.*, 28:679–695.

Kreisler, L., Amado, G., Cahn, R., & Soule, M. (1973), Asthme du nourrisson. *Clin. psychosom. de l'enf.*, 15:15–38.

McNicol, K., Williams, H., Allan, J., & McAndrew, I. (1973), Spectrum of asthma in children. *Brit. Med. J.*, 4:7–16.

Peshkin, M. M. (1963), Diagnosis of asthma in children. In: *The Asthmatic Child*, ed. H. I. Schneer. New York: Harper & Row, pp. 1–15.

Pinkerton, P. H. (1973), The enigma of asthma. *Psychosom. Med.*, 35:461–463.

———— & Weaver, C. (1970), Childhood asthma. In: *Modern Trends in Psychosomatic Medicine*, ed. O. Hill. London: Butterworth, 6:81–104.

Purcell, K. (1973), Distinction between subgroups of asthmatic children. *J. Abnorm. Child Psychol.*, 1:2–15.

———— Brady, K., Chai, H., Muser, J., Mook, L., Gordon, M., & Means, J. (1969a), The effect on asthma in children of experimental separation from the family. *Psychosom. Med.*, 31:144–164.

—— & Metz, R. (1962), Distinctions between subgroups of asthmatic children. *J. Psychosom. Res.*, 6:251–258.

—— Muser, J., Miklich, D., & Dietiker, K. E. (1969b), A comparison of psychologic findings in variously defined asthmatic subgroups. *J. Psychosom. Res.*, 13:67–75.

—— Turnbull, J. W., & Bernstein, L. (1962), Distinctions between subgroups of asthmatic children. *J. Psychosom. Res.*, 6:283–291.

—— & Weiss, J. (1970), Emotions and asthma. In: *Symptoms of Psychopathology*, ed. C. G. Costello. New York: Wiley, pp. 597–623.

Sandler, L. (1964), Child rearing practices of mothers of asthmatic children, I. *J. Asthma Res.*, 2:109–116.

—— (1965), Child rearing practices of mothers of asthmatic children, II. *J. Asthma Res.*, 2:215–256.

Sears, R. R., Maccoby, E., & Levin, H. (1957), *Patterns of Child-rearing*. New York: Row & Peterson, 491–501.

Sperling, M. (1968), Asthma in children. *This Journal*, 7:44–58.

Szentivanyi, A. (1968), The Beta adrenergic theory of the atopic abnormality in bronchial asthma. *J. Allergy*, 42:203–232.

Thomas, R. (1971), Asthma and the school child. *Spec. Educ.*, 60:23–25.

Weisnagel, J. & Rivard, G. (1971), L'asthme chez l'enfant. *L'Union méd. Canad.*, 100:1176–1184.

Wenar, C., Handlon, M. W., & Garner, A. M. (1962), *Origins of Psychosomatic and Emotional Disturbances*. New York: Hoeber.

Part VI

THE HYPERACTIVE CHILD

The problem of hyperactivity in children has engaged the attention of many investigators and clinicians in recent years. The symptom complex is frequently clear-cut and relatively easy to diagnose. The deviant behaviors of these children create many difficulties for themselves, their peers, their parents and their teachers. As a consequence normal emotional, social and educational development is impaired in these children.

A number of studies on the etiology and pathophysiology of the hyperactive child syndrome have been reprinted in this Annual Progress series in the last few years. The two articles reprinted here are concerned with reviews of the literature on treatment. One deals with the use of stimulant drugs, the other with behavioral intervention.

The discovery that stimulant drugs such as dexedrene and ritalin produced quick and dramatic therapeutic effects in many hyperactive children soon gave rise to widespread use. Unfortunately, it became evident that the treatment was being abused. Large numbers of school children were given these potent drugs to control obstreperous behavior in the classroom which should have been more properly managed by pedagogic techniques. Even when clinically indicated, the stimulant drug was often prescribed as the sole therapeutic agent, and the use of more time-consuming and expensive but essential measures such as tutoring and parent and teacher counseling ignored. Finally, little attention was given, in the initial enthusiasm for this drug treatment, to the possibility of long-term harmful side effects, an issue which must be of concern in the use of any drug over a prolonged period of time with children.

The review of the literature by Barkley brings these *caveats* regarding stimulant drug treatment into sharp focus. The short-term effectiveness is confirmed but the results of follow-up studies suggest that stimulant drug treatment is not a panacea in the treatment of hyper-kinesis.

Prout takes up the issue of behavioral approaches for the management and treatment of the hyperactive child. The literature is reviewed critically with the limitations in the research data thus far emphasized. Directions for future research are suggested.

18

A REVIEW OF STIMULANT DRUG RESEARCH WITH HYPERACTIVE CHILDREN

Russell A. Barkley

Medical College of Wisconsin

Stimulant drugs have, for some time now, been the drug of choice for the treatment of hyperkinesis in children. Although some (Eisenberg, 1966; Fish, 1971) have warned that the stimulants are not appropriate for all hyperactive children, they are the most popular drugs used with this population (Krager and Safer, 1975). Of the drug treatments for hyperkinesis, or hyperactivity, the stimulant compounds appear to be by far the most widely studied. It would therefore seem useful to attempt to bring this vast body of literature together for the purposes of drawing conclusions on the effects of stimulant drugs on hyperkinesis.

While others have reviewed various portions of this literature (Cantwell, 1975; Conners, 1970, 1972b; Douglas, 1972; Fish, 1975; Freeman, 1966; Greenspoon and Singer, 1973; Kornetsky, 1970; Lambert *et al.*, 1976; Millichap, 1973; Werry, 1970), the present review differs from most in having a greater breadth of coverage, espe-

Reprinted with permission from the *Journal of Child Psychology and Psychiatry*, Vol. 18, 1977, 137–165.

The comments of Donald K. Routh on an earlier version of this manuscript are gratefully acknowledged.

cially of the more recent research, in addition to providing summaries of the research designs of these studies. Furthermore, it also examined the long-term results of follow-up studies on the prolonged use of these drugs with hyperactive children.

This review has two general aims. First, to review the results of a vast number of research reports on stimulant drugs and hyperkinesis. And second, to attempt to formulate conclusions and generalizations regarding a number of specific questions, such as: (1) How effective are these drugs in treating hyperkinesis? (2) What side effects are generally found to accompany stimulant drug therapy with hyperactive children? (3) What effects do these drugs have on various biochemical and psychophysiological characteristics of these children? (4) What effects do the drugs have on the behavior and test performance of hyperactive children? And (5) what are the long-term effects of maintaining hyperactive children on stimulant drugs for a prolonged period of time?

DRUG RESPONSE RATES

A number of studies were found which reported the percentage of hyperkinetic children responding or not responding to stimulant drug treatment as judged by various social agents, such as parents, teachers, clinicians, etc. The studies and their response rates are listed in Table 1 according to the type of stimulant drug evaluated (amphetamines, methylphenidate, or magnesium pemoline). Where a study had two different social agents judge the treatment outcome, both sets of response rates are reported. As Table 1 shows, on the average 74% of the hyperkinetic children given amphetamines improved while 26% did not change or were exacerbated by the drugs. Similar improvement rates are seen for methylphenidate and magnesium pemoline in that 77 and 73%, respectively, of the children taking these drugs improved. By collapsing the results across drug type, an average of 75% of the children treated with stimulants improve while 25% remain unchanged or are made worse by them.

These figures clearly exceed the 39% average improvement rate noted for placebo treatments. However, the fact that studies using placebos found improvement rates ranging from 8 to 67% suggests that future studies which fail to use placebo conditions may be sorely limited in interpreting their results.

An obvious problem with the data reported in Table 1 is that of defining what is meant by "improvement". This has been discussed elsewhere (Loney and Ordona, 1975; Sprague and Werry, 1971) and it need only be said that judges probably disagree to some extent on just what is "improvement" in a drug study (Zrull et al., 1966). Thus, it is no longer adequate, as in early studies, to report merely the percentage of various degrees of improvement. It is necessary to measure objectively a variety of specific variables to ascertain just how the hyperactive child's behavior is or is not altered by stimulant drugs. A number of studies have already examined certain variables for the effects of stimulant drugs and their results will be reviewed later in this paper. However, before doing so, it is important to first review the side effects which are known to accompany treatment with these drugs.

STIMULANT DRUG SIDE EFFECTS

Those studies which were found to report the side effects resulting from stimulant drug treatment are listed in Table 2 along with the types of side effects cited in each report. If the number of studies reporting various side effects can be taken as a gauge of their frequency, the most frequently noted are insomnia, or sleep disturbances, and decreased appetite. The next most frequent appear to be weight loss, irritability and abdominal pains. Other side effects of lesser frequency are headaches, drowsiness, sadness, dizziness, nausea, proneness to crying, euphoria, nightmares, tremor, dry mouth, constipation, lethargy, depression, dazed appearance, nervous tics, anxiety and others. Many investigators found these side effects to be temporary and easily modified by adjusting dosages downward (Bradley, 1937–38, 1950; Werry and Sprague, 1974).

However, one side effect which has not been observed to disappear so readily is suppressed height and weight gain. Safer, Allen and Barr (1972) reported that d-amphetamine inhibited weight gain significantly more than methylphenidate but that both drugs were capable of suppressing weight gain during prolonged treatment with these drugs. Children removed from medication for the summer months displayed a "rebound" effect in that abnormally high weight increases were noted. However, it did not entirely compensate for the suppressed weight gain experienced over the previous nine months of therapy. No tolerance to these effects was observed over the more than two years of drug treatment. The results were essentially replicated at a later time (Safer and Allen, 1973) with the exception that tolerance to the weight suppression effect was observed. However, suppressed height gain continued to be problematic. The authors concluded that children should be removed from stimulant drugs over

TABLE 1

Drug Response Rates by Drug Type

Author(s)	No. of Subjects	Judge	Percentage Improved	Percentage Unchanged or Worsened
		Amphetamines		
Bradley, 1937-38	30	Hospital Staff	76	24
Bradley, 1950	275	Hospital Staff	73	27
Bradley & Bowen, 1941	100	Hospital Staff	79	21
Comly, 1971	40	Teacher	78	22
Conners, 1972a	81	Clinician	96	4
Conners et. al., 1967	37	Teacher	81	19
Conners et. al., 1972	27	Clinician	96.3	3.7
	22	Teacher	77.3	22.7
Epstein et. al., 1968	10	Parent	70	30
	10	Clinician	70	30
Knopp et. al., 1973	22	Clinician	64	36
	22	Parent	67	33
Rapoport et. al., 1971	16	Teacher	69	31
Steinberg et. al., 1971	46	Teacher	79	21
Weiss et. al., 1968	26	Parent	85	15
Winsberg et. al., 1972	32	Parent	44	56
Winsberg et. al., 1974	18	Teacher	78	22
Zrull et. al., 1963	91	Clinician	57	43
Total: 15 studies	915	18 Judges	74 (Mean)	26 (Mean)
		Methylphenidate		
Comly, 1971	134	Parent	88	22
Hoffman et. al., 1974	34	Physician	84	16
	34	Parent	77	23
Knights and Hinton, 1969	40	Teacher	88	12
	40	Parent	73	27
Knobel, 1962	150	Clinician	90	10
Lytton & Knobel, 1959	20	Clinician	75	25

TABLE 1 Continued

Rapoport et. al., 1974	27	Psychologist	69	31
	29	Physician	94	6
Satterfield et. al., 1973	57	Teacher	68	32
Schain and Reynard, 1975	98	Parents and Teachers	79	21
Schnackenberg and Bender, 1971	10	Parent	60	40
Seger and Hallum, 1974	29	Parent	86	14
	29	Teacher	90	10
Weiss et. al., 1971	26	Parent	94	6
Werry and Sprague, 1974	37	Physician	51	49
Winsberg et. al., 1974	18	Teacher	61	39
Zimmerman et. al., 1958	54	Clinician	65	35
Total: 14 studies	866	18 Judges	77 (Mean)	23 (Mean)

Magnesium Pemoline

Conners, 1972a	81	Clinician	77	23
Conners et. al., 1972	26	Clinician	77	23
	22	Teacher	63.7	36.4
Total: 2 studies	105	3 Judges	73 (Mean)	27 (Mean)

Placebo

Conners, 1972a	81	Clinician	30	70
Conners et. al., 1972	27	Clinician	29.6	80.4
	23	Teacher	30.4	69.6
Knights and Hinton, 1969	40	Teacher	67	33
	40	Parent	54	46
Rapoport et. al., 1971	18	Psychologist	38	61
	18	Physician	33	66
Schain and Reynard, 1975	48	Parents and Teachers	8	92
Weiss et. al., 1968	12	Parent	50	50
Weiss et. al., 1971	26	Parent	50	50
Zrull et. al., 1963	84	Clinician	37	63
Total: 8 studies	417	11 Judges	39 (Mean)	61 (Mean)

TABLE 2

Stimulant Drug Side Effects

Author(s)	Insomnia	Decreased Appetite	Weight Loss	Irritability	Abdominal Pain	Headaches	Drowsiness	Sadness	Other
Arnold et. al., 1976	X	X			X	X			
Arnold et. al., 1972	X	X	X						
Bradley, 1937-38	X								Proneness to crying, euphoria
Bradley, 1950	X	X	X	X	X				Anxiety, tic-like behavior, proneness to crying, fine hand tremor
Bradley and Bowen 1941	X	X							Dizziness, nausea, fine hand tremor
Claghorn et. al., 1971	X								
Comly, 1971	X		X						
Conners, 1972a	X	X							Dazed appearance, nail biting, facial tics
Conners et. al., 1969	X	X							
Conners et. al., 1972	X	X		X				X	
Epstein et. al., 1968	X	X	X	X	X	X			Proneness to crying
Garfinkel et. al., 1975		X		X					
Greenberg et. al., 1972	X	X	X		X	X			Depression, 1 case of induced psychosis
Hoffman et. al., 1974	X	X	X	X		X			
Knights and Hinton, 1969	X	X			X	X			Bed wetting, 1 case of induced psychosis
Knobel, 1962	X	X			X	X			
Lucas and Weiss, 1971	X				X	X	X		3 cases of induced psychosis
Mackay et. al., 1973									Euphoria
McConnell et. al., 1964				X	X			X	Excessive clinging to others
Millichap and Boldrey, 1967	X	X				X	X		

Table 2 Continued

Author(s)	Insomnia	Decreased Appetite	Weight Loss	Irritability	Abdominal Pain	Headaches	Drowsiness	Sadness	Side Effects Other
Montagu and Swarbrick, 1975							X		
Rapoport et. al., 1971		X		X					
Rapoport et. al., 1974	X	X		X	X	X	X	X	Nausea, dizziness, constipation, and dry mouth
Rie et. al., 1976a, 1976b									Decreased humor, range of emotion, and responsiveness to the environment
Schain and Reynard, 1975				X	X				Lethargy
Schleifer et. al., 1975	X	X							Increased solitary play
Schnackenberg and Bender, 1971	X	X							
Schnackenberg, 1973	X	X	X						
Seger and Hallum, 1974		X			X				
Steinberg et. al., 1971	X		X						
Weiss et. al., 1971	X	X	X	X		X		X	
Werry and Sprague, 1974	X		X	X		X	X		Nausea and many others – See article
Winsberg et. al., 1972				X					Anxiety, 1 case of induced psychosis
Winsberg et. al., 1974	X	X					X		Dizziness, nightmares, tremor
Zimmerman et. al., 1958	X	X							
Total: 29 Studies	26	23	12	13	11	10	4	4	6 cases of induced psychosis

the summer months so as to permit partial compensation for the suppressed weight and height gain experienced during the previous nine months of treatment.

Several reports of stimulant induced psychosis were noted in this review and are deserving of further attention. Three reports occurred during treatment with amphetamine (Millichap and Boldrey, 1967; Ney, 1967; Winsberg et al., 1972) while four were observed during treatment with methylphenidate (Knights and Hinton, 1969; Lucas and Weiss, 1971). All included symptoms of visual and tactile hallucinations with the psychotic episodes subsiding once drug treatment was discontinued.

Needless to say, these side effects strongly argue for caution in the prescribing of these medications for hyperactive children. Once prescribed, close monitoring of the child's drug response over the course of treatment is needed.

STIMULANT DRUG EFFECTS

At this point, there have been a sufficient number of studies demonstrating that stimulant drugs generally "improve" the behavior of most hyperactive children. Just exactly what behavioral changes occur in the child during stimulant drug treatment are not precisely understood. Most investigators agree that attention span has been enhanced (Conners, 1972b; Douglas, 1972, 1974; Werry, 1970) although effects on other variables are less conclusive. The research to be cited has been set forth in Table 3. The results of these studies are presented under the general types of dependent measures utilized in the investigations. These are: (1) biochemical, (2) psychophysiological, (3) behavior rating scales, and (4) objective psychological tests and measures. A number of these studies attempted to examine predictors of drug responding. These have been reviewed elsewhere (Barkley, 1976) and little attention will be paid to those findings in this paper. Some studies are less methodologically rigorous than others thereby limiting the comparability of their results. A well controlled drug study should conform to the guidelines set forth by Sprague and Werry (1971) although the majority of those reviewed do not. Despite these methodological differences, some general conclusions regarding the effects of stimulants on hyperkinesis can be drawn.

Biochemical Effects

Rapoport et al. (1974b) studied changes in plasma dopamine-β-hydroxylase (DBH) levels in hyperkinetic children in response to methylphenidate administration. Results revealed that methylphenidate significantly increased DBH levels but that this did not correlate with changes in behavioral ratings of hyperactivity or conduct problems. More recently, methylphenidate has been observed to have little influence on 5-hydroxyindole (5–HI) blood levels in hyperactive children (Greenberg and Coleman, 1976). In any event, biochemical studies of this type are to be encouraged as a means of revealing a possible biochemical basis for hyperkinesis. Currently, this area is receiving considerable attention in animal research which may hopefully shed more light on the mechanisms involved.

Knights and Hinton (1969) found no change in urine pH values as a result of 6 weeks of stimulant drug treatment. Rapoport *et al.* (1974a) did not find any changes in liver functioning due to treatment with methylphenidate nor were changes in blood count noted in this study or in one by Bradley (1950). More biochemical studies are needed before any conclusive statements can be made regarding the physiological effects of stimulant drugs.

Psychophysiological Effects

Several studies have examined various measures of psychophysiological functioning. Three studies measured changes in respiration during drug and no-drug periods and none found an effect for the stimulant drugs (Barkley and Jackson, 1976; Epstein *et al.*, 1968; Zahn *et al.*, 1975). As for skin temperature, only one report monitored this variable with significant decreases being observed during drug treatment (Zahn *et al.*, 1975). Several studies reported increases in pulse and/or blood pressure during drug therapy (Arnold *et al.*, 1976; Arnold *et al.*, 1972; Epstein *et al.*, 1966; Knights and Hinton, 1969; Rapoport *et al.*, 1974; Rie *et al.*, 1976a, 1976b) although several others have failed to find such results (Bradley, 1950; Conners *et al.*, 1972).

Rapoport *et al.* (1974) did not find any change in the electrocardiograms of hyperactive children on methylphenidate but changes in heart rate have been frequently reported in the literature on stimulant drugs (Cohen *et al.*, 1971; Knights and Hinton, 1969; Porges *et al.*, 1975; Zahn *et al.*, 1975). While this suggests an energizing effect on the autonomic nervous system, the effect may be occurring directly on the cardiovascular system itself. Porges *et al.* (1975) reported a significant reduction in heart rate variability due to methylphenidate while Sroufe *et al.* (1973) and Zahn *et al.* (1975) observed significant changes in heart rate deceleration during a reaction time task. Heart rate deceleration has been considered to be a psychophysiological correlate of attentional processes (Sroufe *et al.*, 1973), suggesting that the stimul-

TABLE 3

Stimulant Drug Research with Hyperactive Children

Authors & Year	No. of Children	Drug Type	Daily Dosage	Time on Drug[1]	Use of Placebo	Design Type[2]	Double Blind
Alexandris and Lundell, 1968	21	amphetamine	7.5 to 75 mg.	6 months	Yes	Uncrossed	Yes
Aman and Sprague, 1974	18	d-amphetamine methylphenidate	.2 mg./kg. .5-1.0 mg./kg.	75 min. before testing	Yes	Uncrossed	Yes
Anderson et. al., 1974	18	amphetamines methylphenidate	?	?	No	On - Off Drug Counterbalanced	No
Arnold et. al., 1976	31	l-amphetamine d-amphetamine	∨ 35 mg. ∨ 25 mg.	4 weeks	Yes	Crossed	Yes
Arnold et. al., 1973 (See also Arnold et. al., 1972)	11	l-amphetamine d-amphetamine	5 mg. - 30 mg.	3 weeks	Yes	Crossed	Yes
Barkley and Jackson, 1976	14	methylphenidate	10 mg.	1 day	Yes	Crossed	Yes
Barkley et. al., 1976	18	methylphenidate	10 mg.	1 day	Yes	Crossed	Yes
Blacklidge & Ekblad, 1971	31	methylphenidate	20 mg.	2 months	Yes	Crossed	Yes
Bradley, 1937-38	30	amphetamine	10-30 mg.	1 week	No	On - Off Drug	No
Bradley, 1950	275	amphetamine	10-40 mg.	1 week to several months	No	On - Off Drug	No
Bradley and Bowen, 1940	19	amphetamine	20-30 mg.	At least 1 month	No	On - Off Drug	No
Bradley and Bowen, 1941	100	amphetamine	10-40 mg.	1-4 weeks	No	On - Off Drug	No
Bradley and Green, 1940-41	21	amphetamine	10-20 mg.	1-3 hours before testing	No	On - Off Drug	No
Buchsbaum and Wender, 1973	24	amphetamine	10-20 mg.	4-8 months	No	On - Off Drug Counterbalanced	No
Burks, 1964	43	amphetamine	?	?	No	On - Off Drug	No
Butter and Lapierre, 1974	32	methylphenidate	10-30 mg.	2 weeks	Yes	Crossed	Yes
Butter and Lapierre, 1975	32	methylphenidate	10-30 mg.	2 weeks	Yes	Crossed	Yes

Table 3 continued

Reference		Drug	Dose	Duration			
Campbell et. al., 1971	22	methylphenidate	10-100 mg.	2 weeks	Yes	Crossed	Yes
Carpenter and Sells, 1974	1	d-amphetamine	2.5-5 mg.	6 days	Yes	Crossed	Yes
Christensen, 1975	16	methylphenidate	.3 mg./kg.	4 weeks	Yes	Crossed	Yes
Christensen and Sprague, 1973	12	methylphenidate	.3 mg./kg.	1.5 hours before testing	Yes	Uncrossed	Yes
Claghorn et. al., 1971	27	amphetamine	15 mg.	1 week	Yes	Crossed	?
Cohen et. al., 1971	22	methylphenidate	10-100 mg.	2 weeks	Yes	Crossed	Yes
Comly, 1971	48	d-amphetamine	5, 10, & 15 mg.	1 week	Yes	Crossed	Yes
Conners, 1966	32	d-amphetamine	Mean: 20 mg.	8 weeks	Yes	Uncrossed	Yes
Conners, 1969	97	d-amphetamine	5-25 mg.	4 weeks	Yes	Uncrossed	Yes
Conners, 1971	69	d-amphetamine / methylphenidate	15 mg. / 30 mg.	3 weeks	Yes	Uncrossed	Yes
Conners, 1972a	75	d-amphetamine / methylphenidate	15 mg. / 30 mg.	8 weeks	Yes	Uncrossed	Yes
Conners and Eisenberg, 1963 (See Also Conners et. al., 1964)	81	methylphenidate	20-60 mg.	10 days	Yes	Uncrossed	Yes
Conners et. al., 1967	52	d-amphetamine	10 mg.	1 month	Yes	Crossed	Yes
Conners and Rothschild, 1968	31	amphetamine	15-25 mg.	1 month	Yes	Uncrossed	Yes
Conners et. al., 1969	42	d-amphetamine	5-25 mg.	4 weeks	Yes	Uncrossed	?
Conners et. al., 1972	81	d-amphetamine magnesium pemoline	5-40 mg. / 25-125 mg.	8 weeks	Yes	Uncrossed	Yes
Conrad et. al., 1971	68	d-amphetamine	10-20 mg.	4-6 months	Yes	Uncrossed	Yes
Conrad and Insel, 1967	31	amphetamine	?	?	No	Review of records	No
Creager and Van Riper, 1967	30	methylphenidate	20 mg.	3 days	Yes	Crossed	Yes
Cutts and Jasper, 1939	12	amphetamine	20 mg.	6 days	No	On - Off Drug	No
Denhoff et. al., 1971	42	d-amphetamine	10 mg.	3 weeks	Yes	Crossed	Yes
Ellis et. al., 1974	9	methylphenidate	.1-1.0 mg./kg.	1 month	Yes	Crossed	Yes

Table 3 Continued

Epstein et. al., 1968	10	d-amphetamine	10-15 mg.	2 weeks	Yes	Crossed	Yes
Finnerty et. al., 1971	20	d-amphetamine	5-15 mg.	3 weeks	Yes	Uncrossed	Yes
Garfinkel et. al., 1975	8	methylphenidate	20 mg.	10 days	Yes	Crossed	Yes
Greenberg and Coleman, 1976	30	methylphenidate	?	1 month	Yes	Incomplete Crossover for 22 Subjects	?
Greenberg et. al., 1972	76	d-amphetamine	Mean: 25 mg.	8 weeks	Yes	Uncrossed	Yes
Greenwold and Jones, 1971	3	methylphenidate	?	?	No	On - Off Drug	No
Huestis et. al., 1975	18	d-amphetamine methylphenidate	5-25 mg. 30-60 mg.	3 weeks	Yes	Crossed	Yes
Hoffman et. al., 1974	31	methylphenidate	20-80 mg.	12 weeks	No	On - Off Drug	No
Knights and Hinton, 1968	40	methylphenidate	20-40 mg.	6 weeks	Yes	Uncrossed	Yes
Knobel, 1962	150	methylphenidate	20-40 mg.	8 months	No	On - Off Drug	No
Knopp et. al., 1973	22	d-amphetamine	At least 5 mg.	?	No	On - Off Drug	No
Laufer et. al., 1958	13	amphetamine	5-15 mg.	?	No	On - Off Drug Counterbalanced	No
Levy, 1959	100	amphetamine	10-40 mg.	?	No	On - Off Drug	No
Lindsley and Henry, 1942	13	amphetamine	20 mg.	7 days	No	On - Off Drug	No
Loney et. al., 1975	50	methylphenidate	?	?	No	On - Off Drug	No
Lytton and Knobel, 1959	20	methylphenidate	15-200 mg.	8-20 weeks	No	On - Off Drug	No
Mackay et. al., 1973	10	methylphenidate	10-60 mg.	?	No	Case Studies	No
McConnell et. al., 1964	57	d-amphetamine	7.5-15 mg.	6 days	Yes	Crossed	Yes
Millichap et. al., 1968	30	methylphenidate	.3-2.3 mg./kg.	3 weeks	Yes	Uncrossed	Yes
Millichap and Boldrey, 1967	13	methylphenidate	?	24 hours	Yes	Uncrossed	?
Molitch and Eccles, 1937	93	amphetamine	10-30 mg.	40 days	Yes	Uncrossed	Yes
Montagu and Swarbrick, 1975	6	l-amphetamine d-amphetamine	10 mg./m^2	1 day	Yes	Crossed	?
Porges et. al., 1975	16	methylphenidate	.3 mg./kg.	3 weeks	Yes	Crossed	?

Table 3 continued

Reference	N	Drug	Dose	Duration			
Rapoport et. al., 1970	19	d-amphetamine	10 mg.	2 weeks	Yes	Crossed	?
Rapoport et. al., 1971	19	d-amphetamine	10 mg.	3 weeks	Yes	Crossed	No
Rapoport et. al., 1974	76	methylphenidate	30 mg.	6 weeks	Yes	Uncrossed	Yes
Rie et. al., 1976a	28	methylphenidate	5-40 mg.	12 weeks	Yes	Crossed	Yes
Rie et. al., 1976b	18	methylphenidate	5-20 mg.	15 weeks	Yes	Crossed	Yes
Safer and Allen, 1975	84	d-amphetamine methylphenidate	5-20 mg. 10-40 mg.	years	No	On - Off Drug	No
Saletu et. al., 1973	12	d-amphetamine	Mean: 18.6 mg.	4 weeks	Yes	On - Off Drug	?
Satterfield and Dawson, 1971	24	d-amphetamine methylphenidate	5-10 mg. 10 mg	1 hour	No	Uncrossed	No
Satterfield et. al., 1973a See Also Satterfield et. al., 1973b	57	methylphenidate	?	3 weeks	No	On - Off Drug	Yes
Satterfield et. al., 1972	31	methylphenidate	?	90 minutes	Yes	On - Off Drug	Yes
Schain and Reynard, 1975	98	methylphenidate	10-60 mg.	16 weeks	Yes	Uncrossed	Yes
Schleifer et. al., 1975	26	methylphenidate	2.5-20 mg.	3 weeks	Yes	Crossed	Yes
Schnackenberg, 1973	11	methylphenidate	?	4 months	No	On - Off Drug	No
Schnackenberg and Bender, 1971	14	methylphenidate	20 mg.	2 weeks	Yes	Crossed	Yes
Seger and Hallum, 1974	29	methylphenidate	10-60 mg.	8 weeks	No	On - Off Drug	No
Shetty, 1971	28	d-amphetamine methylphenidate	10 mg. 20 mg.	15 min.	Yes	Crossed	Yes
Sleator et. al., 1974	42	methylphenidate	20.5 mg.	11 months	Yes	Crossed	Yes
Sprague et. al., 1970	12	methylphenidate	.25-.35 mg./kg.	6 days	Yes	Crossed	Yes
Sprague and Sleator, 1973	23	methylphenidate	.1-.7 mg./kg.	4 weeks	Yes	Crossed	Yes
Spring et. al., 1973	39	methylphenidate	Mean: 14.5 mg.	1.5 hours	No	Uncrossed	No
Spring et. al., 1974	38	methylphenidate	Mean: 13 mg.	1.25 hours	No	Uncrossed	No
Sroufe et. al., 1973	21	methylphenidate	1 mg./kg.	6 weeks	Yes	Uncrossed	Yes
Stableford et. al., 1976	2	methylphenidate d-amphetamine	15 mg. 25 mg.	1 week 50 weeks	Yes Yes	Crossed Crossed	Yes Yes

Table 3 Continued

Sykes et. al., 1972	23	methylphenidate	10-100 mg.	2 weeks	Yes	Crossed	Yes
Sykes et. al., 1971	40	methylphenidate	30-40 mg.	5-7 weeks	Yes	Uncrossed	Yes
Steinberg et. al., 1971	46	d-amphetamine	10-15 mg.	4 weeks	Yes	Crossed	Yes
Weber and Sulzbacher, 1975	12	d-amphetamine	.12-.62 mg./kg.	?	Yes	Crossed	Yes
Weiss et. al, 1971	51	methylphenidate	up to 50 mg.	4-6 weeks	Yes	Uncrossed	Yes
Weiss et. al., 1968	40	d-amphetamine	5-20 mg.	3-5 weeks	Yes	Uncrossed	Yes
Werry and Aman, 1975	24	methylphenidate	.3 mg./kg.	3 weeks	Yes	Crossed	Yes
Werry & Sprague, 1974	37	methylphenidate	.1-1.0 mg./kg.	4 weeks	Yes	Crossed	Yes
Winsberg et. al., 1972	41	d-amphetamine	15-30 mg.	7-10 days	Yes	Crossed	Yes
Winsberg et. al., 1974	18	d-amphetamine methylphenidate	20 mg. 30 mg.	9-10 days	Yes	Crossed	Yes
Zahn et. al., 1975	42	d-amphetamine methylphenidate	?	2.5 months	No	On - Off Drug	No
Zimmerman and Burgemeister, 1958	108	methylphenidate	20-40 mg.	6 months	No	On - Off Drug	No
Zrull et. al., 1963	16	d-amphetamine	.5 mg. b.i.d.	2 weeks	Yes	Crossed	Yes

[1]This column indicates the total length of time the child spent on each type of drug, or placebo if one was used, during each of the drug conditions. Where such a time was not reported, the time after oral ingestion or injection of the drug until testing is reported instead.

[2]In this column are listed the types of methodological designs employed in each study. On - Off Drug means a design in which all children received the drug and were evaluated both on and off drug. Where "Counterbalanced" follows this design type, it indicates that approximately half of the children were evaluated off the drug first while the other half were evaluated on the drug first. Uncrossed means a design in which children were assigned to either a drug or placebo group, or to a no drug group if no placebo was used. Crossed means a complete crossover design in which each subject served as his own control, receiving all of the possible drug and placebo conditions in a randomized order.

[?]indicates that the information in this column was either not provided or was so ambiguously stated in the report   as to make for uncertainty.

ants are altering these processes in hyperactive children—a conclusion strongly supported by studies using psychological measures of attention span as well (Douglas, 1972).

Several studies found measures of basal skin conductance to be significantly increased by stimulant drugs (Cohen *et al.*, 1971; Satterfield and Dawson, 1971; Zahn *et al.*, 1975) while Spring *et al.* (1974) did not. In contrast, Montagu and Swarbrick (1975) found a decrease in palmar skin admittance in hyperactive children on amphetamines, possibly suggesting a paradoxical response to these drugs. However, palmar skin admittance is not necessarily a reliable indicant of central nervous system functioning and has been noted to be confounded by changes in skin temperature (Zahn *et al.*, 1975). Further study of this phenomenon is therefore required.

Other parameters of skin conductance studied include nonspecific and specific skin conductance responses. The findings to date are equivocal as to the effects of stimulant drugs on these variables. Several studies (Satterfield and Dawson, 1971; Spring *et al.*, 1974) found more nonspecific GSRs (galvanic skin responses) in hyperactive children on stimulants as compared to those not receiving drugs while others did not (Cohen *et al.*, 1971; Zahn *et al.*, 1975). However, Zahn *et al.* (1975) did find the stimulants to decrease the amplitude of nonspecific GSRs in hyperactive children. Both Spring *et al.* (1972) and Zahn *et al.* (1975) also found significant increases in the amplitude of specific skin conductance responses, while Zahn *et al.* (1975) observed increases in the latency and rise rate of these responses. These findings suggest that the stimulants are energizing or increasing the arousal levels of hyperkinetic children.

Cutts and Jasper (1939) did not find any effect from benzedrine on the alpha activity in the EEG of hyperactive children. However, Lindsley and Henry (1942) later reported that benzedrine significantly increased alpha activity in the parietal and occipital areas with decreases in amplitude of both alpha rhythm and two abnormal EEG patterns. Shetty (1971) also observed increases in EEG alpha wave activity following stimulant drug therapy. These findings suggest that the stimulants may be increasing the cortical inhibitory mechanisms of the central nervous system and probably result in a filtering out of irrelevant stimuli (Shetty, 1971). Stimulants have also been noted under some circumstances to reduce the abnormality of EEG patterns (Mackay *et al.*, 1973) but this finding requires more controlled investigation.

Buchsbaum and Wender (1973) found differences in averaged evoked responses (AER) in the EEG of hyperactive children who responded well to drugs as opposed to those who did not. The AERs of responders were reduced by the stimulant drugs while those of the poor responders were augmented. Similar results were reported by Saletu *et al.* (1973) and Satterfield *et al.* (1972), indicating that, again, perhaps the stimulants are arousing cortical inhibitory mechanisms which screen out irrelevant stimuli. However, Weber and Sulzbacher (1975) found the stimulants to lower the thresholds of AERs, thereby suggesting a sensitizing or augmenting effect on the auditory AERs. This would indicate an increase in the excitatory systems of the brain responsible for these auditory AER patterns. Thus, taken together these results suggest that the stimulants may increase the level of functioning of both excitatory and inhibitory systems. This is, however, a matter of speculation at the moment.

Several studies have examined the influence of stimulants on the electropupillograms (EPG) of hyperkinetic children (Knopp *et al.*, 1973; Yoss, 1975; Yoss and Moyer, 1971). The most elaborate was conducted by Knopp *et al.* (1973) who measured changes in the dark adapted pupil diameter in response to light both before and after stimulant drug treatment. Changes in EPGs during drug treatment correlated significantly with parental and clinician ratings of behavioral improvement. These children could be categorized into five groups on the basis of their baseline EPG patterns and response to drugs. Thus, Knopp *et al.* (1973) find hyperactive children to be heterogeneous with respect to EPG arousal patterns both before and while taking stimulant drugs. Additionally, they appear to have found a promising method for categorizing hyperactive children into more homogeneous subgroups and are thereby better able to predict their drug responses. Similar results have been reported by Yoss (1975) who finds many of these children to be underaroused in their EPG patterns with the stimulant drugs serving to increase these arousal levels.

On a quite different measure, Laufer, Denhoff and Solomons (1957) observed that hyperactive children had photo-metrazol thresholds which were significantly lower than normal children and that stimulants served to increase the thresholds up to those characteristic of normal children. They concluded that stimulant drugs may in some way be raising the level of diencephalic inhibition of the cortex thus preventing the cortex from being bombarded by a stream of impulses from irrelevant stimuli. Unfortunately, the results have yet to be replicated and little or no attention has been paid to this issue in the recent literature.

In summary, the following conclusion seems warranted: in most cases, hyperkinetic children are stimulated or energized by the stimulant drugs, rather than being sedated. These results suggest that CNS inhibitory systems may be stimulated by these drugs thereby enhancing the ability of the cortex to screen out distracting stimuli. Excitatory systems may also be stimulated thereby augmenting the impact of certain stimuli on the cortex. As a result, the hyperactive child is better able to focus his attention upon a task while inhibiting impulsive responding.

Behavioral Rating Scales

By far, the vast majority of drug research with hyperactive children has utilized some type of rating scale completed by parents, teachers, etc. Virtually all of this research has found such ratings to be sensitive to stimulant drug use. This research will now be briefly reviewed under the type of rater used in judging the child's response to stimulant drugs—that is, parents, teachers and other agents.

Parental rating scales. Two of the most frequently used rating scales for parents are the Conners Parent Symptom Questionnaire (Conners *et al.*, 1969) and the Werry–Weiss–Peters Activity Rating Scale (Werry, 1968). Research on the Conners scale indicates that the factors of hyperkinesis and neurotic symptoms account for most of the variance in drug response ratings (Conners *et al.*, 1969). Reductions in the ratings of hyperkinetic symptoms in response to drug treatment have been reported by some investigators (Arnold *et al.*, 1972; Conners *et al.*, 1972; Hoffman *et al.*, 1974; Rapoport *et al.*, 1974) while others have not found such results (Finnerty *et al.*, 1971; Werry and Sprague, 1974).

All of the research conducted on the Werry–Weiss–Peters Activity Rating Scale to date has found significant improvement in scores due to stimulant drug therapy (Barkley *et al.*, 1976; Conners and Rothschild, 1968; Conners *et al.*, 1969; Hoffman *et al.*, 1974; Knights and Hinton, 1969; Rapoport *et al.*, 1971; Schleifer *et al.*, 1975; Weiss *et al.*, 1971; Zahn *et al.*, 1975).

Other studies have also found parental opinion to be significantly altered by stimulant drug treatment of hyperactive children (Arnold *et al.*, 1976; Blacklidge and Ekblad, 1971; Greenberg *et al.*, 1971; Huestis *et al.*, 1975; Knopp *et al.*, 1973; Rie *et al.*, 1976a, 1976b). However, the Peterson–Quay Symptom Checklist as completed by parents has not proven useful in stimulant drug research (Knights and Hinton, 1969; Millichap *et al.*, 1968). In general, then, parents appear to be attuned to changes in their children's behavior as a function of treatment with stimulant drugs. A question to be raised later is whether or not the parental ratings are accurately reflecting actual changes in the child's behavior.

Teacher rating scales. A similar state of affairs exists for rating scales for teachers. The most frequently used scale is the Conners Teacher Rating Scale (Conners, 1969), composed of five factors, for which separate scores can be obtained. While Conners has reported in some instances that all five factors are sensitive to stimulant drug treatment (Conners *et al.*, 1967; Conners and Rothschild, 1968; Conners, 1969), the most reliable factor to improve in response to drugs has been the hyperactivity scale, while other factors are less consistently altered (Arnold *et al.*, 1976; Arnold *et al.*, 1972; Conners, 1972a; Conners *et al.*, 1972; Huestis *et al.*, 1975; Garfinkel *et al.*, 1975; Rapoport *et al.*, 1971, 1974; Safer and Allen, 1975; Schleifer *et al.*, 1975; Werry and Sprague, 1974; Winsberg *et al.*, 1974).

Research using less commonly employed teacher rating scales have also found them to be responsive to changes brought about by stimulant drug treatment (Arnold *et al.*, 1976; Blacklidge and Ekblad, 1971; Comly, 1971; Denhoff *et al.*, 1971; Greenberg *et al.*, 1972; Hoffman *et al.*, 1975; Lindsley and Henry, 1942; Rie *et al.*, 1976a, 1976b; Satterfield *et al.*, 1972; Schnackenberg, 1973; Sleator *et al.*, 1974). Only the Peterson–Quay Behavior Checklist as completed by teachers has not revealed significant drug changes over those noted on the scale during placebo conditions (Knights and Hinton, 1969).

Rating scales for other agents. A number of studies have used rating scales completed by clinicians, ward attendants, nurses, etc. Ratings are found to improve significantly during drug manipulations, especially if the scales appear to be assessing activity level, inattentiveness, or aggressiveness (Alexandris and Lundell, 1968; Arnold *et al.*, 1976; Burks, 1964; Claghorn *et al.*, 1971; Conrad *et al.*, 1971; Greenberg *et al.*, 1972; Weiss *et al.*, 1971).

Problems with rating scales. Although the rating scale has been the most frequently used measure in drug research with hyperactive children, serious problems exist in its use. First, there are simply too many rating scales in use with little regard to their construction and relationship to others already in use. Second, there is little or no information available on most scales as to their reliability, either test-retest or inter-rater. But, the third and more important issue involves validity. Most of these scales are said to assess activity level, attention span, or aggression and they are interpreted as if they did so. Yet, for most of them, there is virtually no information available on the relationship of the scale to more empirical correlates of the same construct. Thus, future drug studies need to use objective measures of the constructs under study in addition to rating scales so as to elucidate the relationships among these measures.

Objective Psychological Tests and Measures

A number of tests and measures have been used to assess a variety of behavioral and psychological constructs. The results are discussed under the particular type of construct evaluated. These are: (1) intelligence tests, (2) achievement tests, (3) tests and measures of attention span, (4) measures of drawing and copying ability, (5) measures of activity level, and (6) other tests and measures.

Intelligence tests. Studies using intelligence test scores have generally found equivocal results. The test most frequently used has been the Wechsler Intelligence Scale for Children (Wechsler, 1949). Several studies have found significant improvement in Full Scale I.Q. (Conners, 1972a; Hoffman *et al.*, 1974; Weiss *et al.*, 1973), while others have found changes in either Verbal (Epstein *et al.*, 1968; Conners, 1972a; Weiss *et al.*, 1968; Weiss *et al.*, 1971) or Performance I.Q.s (Epstein *et al.*, 1968; Finnerty *et al.*, 1971; Greenberg *et al.*, 1972; Hoffman *et al.*, 1974; Knights and Hinton, 1969). In some instances, only one or a limited number of subtest scores were affected by the drugs (Conners, 1972a; Conrad *et al.*, 1971; Seger and Hallum, 1974; Weiss *et al.*, 1968; Weiss *et al.*, 1971). However, others have not found significant changes in I.Q. estimates as measured by this test (Alexandris and Lundell, 1968; Conners and Rothschild, 1968; Conners *et al.*, 1969; Conners *et al.*, 1972; Conrad *et al.*, 1971; Rapoport *et al.*, 1974; Rie *et al.*, 1976a, 1976b; Werry and Sprague, 1974). Similarly, some investigators have not found significant drug effects on other tests of intelligence (Bradley and Green, 1940; Molitch and Eccles, 1937; Weiss *et al.*, 1968).

Given the inconsistency of findings in this area, it is likely that these changes in I.Q. or subtest scores probably do not reflect significant changes in basic intellectual or cognitive processes but are due to improvement in concentration and attention span (Conners, 1972b; Douglas, 1972; Weiss *et al.*, 1971).

Achievement tests. The most frequently used test is the Wide Range Achievement Test (WRAT) (Jastak and Jastak, 1965). Several investigators reported finding significant improvement in one or more of the WRAT subtests (Conners *et al.*, 1969; Conners *et al.*, 1972) although most have not (Blacklidge and Ekblad, 1971; Conners, 1972a; Conrad *et al.*, 1971; Finnerty *et al.*, 1971; Hoffman *et al.*, 1974;

Rapoport *et al.*, 1974). Weiss *et al.* (1971) found significant improvement on a measure of oral reading while Werry and Sprague (1974) did not. Nor did Conners *et al.* (1969) or Blacklidge and Ekblad (1971) find improvement on the Gray Oral Reading Test (Gray, 1963), although in a later report, Conners *et al.* (1972) found such improvement during drug treatment. In two recent studies, Rie *et al.* (1976a, 1976b) evaluated the effects of stimulant drugs on several tests of achievement skills. Results indicated very few changes on these measures as a function of drug treatment. These equivocal results suggest that the few reports of positive findings are probably due to increased concentration or attention span in response to stimulant drugs (Weiss *et al.*, 1971).

Measures of attention span. A number of various tests and measures have been used to assess attention span. These have included measures of reaction time (Douglas, 1972, 1974), continuous performance tests (Anderson *et al.*, 1974), the Porteus Mazes (Porteus, 1965), Kagan's Matching Familiar Figures Test (Kagan *et al.*, 1964), and such playroom measures as the number of toy or activity changes made by a child during free play (Barkley and Routh, 1974; Barkley and Ullman, 1975; Shaffer *et al.*, 1974). While it is obvious that these tests measure a number of other variables besides attention span, some research (Douglas, 1972) suggests that they have a common source of variance which can be labeled as concentration or attention span. For ease and brevity, then, these tests and measures will be reviewed with respect to this common attentional component.

Several investigators (Kupietz *et al.*, 1976; Barkley *et al.*, 1976) have used reaction time as a measure of attention span in research with hyperactive children. Virtually every stimulant drug study that used this measure found reaction time to be significantly improved, or reduced, by stimulant drugs (Barkley *et al.*, 1976; Cohen *et al.*, 1971; Conners *et al.*, 1967; Conners and Rothschild, 1968; Sprague *et al.*, 1970; Spring *et al.*, 1973; Sroufe *et al.*, 1973; Sykes *et al.*, 1972; Zahn *et al.*, 1975), or found trends in that direction (Porges *et al.*, 1975). Only Bradley and Bowen (1940) found no significant changes in reaction time while Campbell *et al.* (1971) observed reaction times to increase, or become slower, while the hyperactive children were on stimulants.

Another type of test believed to measure attention span is the continuous performance or vigilance test (Anderson *et al.*, 1974). Most studies using this task have observed significant reductions in error scores as a function of stimulant drug treatment (Anderson *et al.*, 1974; Conners, 1966, 1972a; Conners and Rothschild, 1968; Sykes *et al.*, 1972; Sykes *et al.*, 1971; Weiss *et al.*, 1971; Werry and Aman, 1975). Only a few studies have not found such improvement (Conners *et al.*, 1972; Sprague and Sleator, 1973). In a recognition task similar to the continuous performance task, both Werry and Aman (1975) and Sprague *et al.* (1970) found drugs to significantly improve scores for correct responding.

Performance on the Porteus Mazes has also been considered as a measure of attention span or concentration (Douglas, 1972), as well as of the ability to plan, reason and control impulsive responding (Conners and Rothschild, 1968). Almost every study using this test found it to be sensitive to stimulant drug effects (Conners, 1972a; Conners and Eisenberg, 1963; Conners and Rothschild, 1968; Conners *et al.*, 1969; Conners *et al.*, 1972; Epstein *et al.*, 1968; Greenberg *et al.*, 1972; Hoffman *et al.*, 1974; Rapoport *et al.*, 1974). Only two studies did not (Blacklidge and Ekblad, 1971; Winsberg *et al.*, 1972).

Using a maze coordination test (Reitan and Davison, 1974), several investigators found that stimulant drugs significantly reduced the number of errors made during the performance of this task (Barkley *et al.*, 1976; Garfinkel *et al.*, 1975; Knights and Hinton, 1969). This has been interpreted (Sroufe *et al.*, 1973) as reflecting improvement in the ability to concentrate rather than simply improved motor coordination during drug treatment.

Other tests believed to assess concentration or attention span are the Kagan Matching Familiar Figures Test and the Early Childhood Familiar Figures Test (Banta, 1968). Scores on both tests have been found to improve significantly after stimulant drug treatment (Campbell *et al.*, 1971; Garfinkel *et al.*, 1975; Rapoport *et al.*, 1974; Schleifer *et al.*, 1975).

Besides these tests, others (Barkley and Routh, 1974; Barkley and Ullman, 1975; Routh *et al.*, 1973; Shaffer *et al.*, 1974) have used the number of toy or activity changes made by a child during free play as a measure of attention span. Rapoport *et al.* (1971) and Barkley *et al.* (1976) reported significant reductions in toy change activity following stimulant drug treatment in hyperactive children. Similarly, on measures of attention to classroom tasks, several investigators also found improvement resulting from stimulant drug treatment (Greenwald and Jones, 1971; Sprague *et al.*, 1970; Stableford *et al.*, 1976). Further, Barkley *et al.* (1970) noted improvement in the amount of time hyperactive children spent watching a televised school lesson and in the amount of material they recalled from that lesson.

It is apparent from these results that the primary impact of the stimulant drugs on hyperactive children is increased concentration or attention span (Conners, 1972b; Douglas, 1974; Werry, 1970) or improvement in the ability to "stop, look, and listen" (Douglas, 1972). While the measures reviewed above assess a number of different abilities, they appear to have in common the fact that each is strongly influenced by the child's ability to concentrate on the task and to inhibit impulsive responding. Improvement in these abilities by the stimulants probably accounts for the equivocal findings on other tests, such as intelligence tests or tests of achievement skills. Hence, improved test performance on other variables is likely to occur in some situations using some types of tests while not in others using different tests depending on the extent to which the setting and test are sensitive to changes in attentional processes.

Tests of drawing and copying ability. In general, tests of drawing or copying have not typically been found to be affected by the stimulant drugs. One of the most frequently used of these tests is the Bender Visual–Motor Gestalt Test (Bender, 1946). Most stimulant drug studies employing this test, especially the more rigorously controlled ones, do not find the test to be improved by drugs (Alexandris and Lundell, 1968; Conners and Rothschild, 1968; Conners et al., 1969; Conners et al., 1972; Conrad et al., 1971; Epstein et al., 1968; Garfinkel et al., 1975; Greenberg et al., 1972; Knights and Hinton, 1969; Rapoport et al., 1974; Rie et al., 1976a, 1976b; Schnackenberg and Bender, 1971; Weiss et al., 1968; Weiss et al., 1971; Winsberg et al., 1971). Only a relatively few studies of a less well controlled nature found improvement in test scores by hyperactive children receiving stimulant drugs (Conners, 1972a; Millichap et al., 1968; Seger and Hallum, 1974).

Similarly, only a few studies have found improvement in performance by hyperactive children on the frequently used Goodenough Draw-A-Man Test (Goodenough, 1926) during stimulant drug treatment (Conners, 1971, 1972a; Millichap et al., 1968) while most have not (Alexandris and Lundell, 1968; Conners and Rothschild, 1968; Conners et al., 1969; Conners et al., 1972; Rapoport et al., 1974; Schnackenberg et al., 1971; Weiss et al., 1968; Weiss et al., 1971).

Additionally, Schleifer et al. (1975) did not find any significant drug effects on a draw-a-line test nor did Schnackenberg and Bender (1971) on the Benton Visual Retention Test (Benton, 1963). Thus, once again, where a few positive effects of drugs on drawing tests have been found, they are probably due to improved concentration or attention span rather than to changes in other cognitive or intellectual abilities (Conners, 1971).

Measures of activity level. The results of studies using rating scales of activity level strongly suggest that the major impact of the stimulant drugs is the reduction of activity level across all situations. However, the results of studies using more objective measures of activity level reveal a far more complex picture. It seems that drug effects on activity level are due to several factors: (1) the situation in which the measures are taken (free play or structured settings), (2) the type of activity measured (wrist, ankle, locomotor, etc.), and (3) the type of instrument used to assess that type of activity (actometers, pedometers, ultrasonic generators, grid-marked playrooms, etc.).

One measure frequently used to assess activity level in structured settings is the stabilimetric cushion. This device yields a score for seat movements made by the child while completing a given task. All but one (Christensen, 1975) of the studies which used the device reported significant reductions in seat movement activity during stimulant drug treatment (Barkley et al., 1976; Christensen and Sprague, 1973; Sprague et al., 1970; Sprague and Sleator, 1973; Sroufe et al., 1973; Werry and Aman, 1975). However, in a study in which hyperactive children were required to sit in a ballistograph chair (McConnell et al., 1964), no drug effects on this type of seat activity were observed.

Although the reliability of the device has been questioned (Johnson, 1971), Millichap et al. (1968) observed a trend for reduced wrist actometer scores during stimulant drug treatment while Barkley et al. (1976) found both wrist and ankle actometer scores in several types of structured settings to be significantly reduced by methylphenidate. Thus, measures of seat restlessness, and arm and ankle activity have been found to be significantly reduced by the stimulants during structured situations.

In free play, where no demands are placed on the child to channel his activity in any direction, the results are not so clearcut. Montagu and Swarbrick (1975) observed significant reductions in full body movement as measured by the ultrasonic generator while Claghorn et al. (1971), using a similar device, did not. Montagu and Swarbrick (1975) also used electric pressure mats on the floor of a playroom to measure locomotor activity in free play and found significant reductions in this measure during drug treatment. Another measure of locomotor activity involves dividing the floor of a playroom into several parts by tape or electric eye beams and then counting the number of grid-lines the child crosses during a certain period. Here, too, significant reductions in locomotor activity have been found in response to stimulant drug therapy (Barkley et al., 1976; Rapoport et al., 1971).

Several studies have reported reductions in wrist and ankle actometer scores during free play as a function of drug treatment (Barkley et *al.*, 1976; Millichap and Boldrey, 1967; Rie *et al.*, 1976a). Rapoport *et al.* (1971) placed actometers on the backs of hyperactive children in free play and found a trend for this type of torso activity to be reduced by stimulant drugs. However, Ellis *et al.* (1974) derived nine measures of free play activity from videotaped play sessions of hyperactive children and found none of these to be significantly influenced by stimulant drugs. They concluded that in informal settings, stimulant drugs may not alter the activity level of hyperactive children.

These results for free play activity suggest that wrist, ankle and locomotor activity may be significantly reduced by stimulant drugs while changes in total body activity, such as that measured by body actometers or ultrasonic generators, are less predictable. Additionally, under some circumstances, different measures of free play activity, such as those used by Ellis *et al.* (1974), may not show alterations during drug therapy.

Three studies were found which observed the classroom activity of hyperactive children during drug treatments (Christensen, 1975; Schleifer *et al.*, 1975; Sprague *et al.*, 1970) and none found the stimulants to significantly reduce activity as measured by the number of times the child got out of his seat. Schliefer *et al.* (1975) also found no reduction in the number of times the child was away from his desk during drug treatment. Thus, in this type of classroom setting, changes in some forms of activity do not occur in response to drug treatment.

In summarizing these results, it appears that in comparison to measures of attention span, changes in measures of activity level during drug treatment are less predictable. Such changes appear to depend on a number of factors, such as type of setting, type of activity being measured, type of measuring instrument being used, and cross-situational variability in the types of activity level being studied (Barkley and Ullman, 1975; Shaffer *et al.*, 1974).

Other tests and measures. Improved test performance has been observed during treatment on measures of quickness and decisiveness (Conners *et al.*, 1967), paired associate learning (Conners, 1972a; Conners and Eisenberg, 1963; Conners and Rothschild, 1968; Conners *et al.*, 1969) and verbal productivity (Conners, 1972a; Creager and Van Riper, 1967).

A number of measures showed inconsistent effects during stimulant drug treatment. These were: the Frostig Test of Visual Perception (Frostig, 1961) (Conners, 1972a; Conners *et al.*, 1969; Conners *et al.*, 1972; Conners and Rothschild, 1968; Conrad *et al.*, 1971; Garfinkel *et al.*, 1975; Hoffman *et al.*, 1974; Millichap *et al.*, 1968; Weiss *et al.*, 1971), the Lincoln–Oseretsky Test of Motor Development (Doll, 1946) (Conners *et al.*, 1972; Weiss *et al.*, 1968; Weiss *et al.*, 1971), measures of visual and auditory perception and discrimination (Butter and Lapierre, 1974, 1975; Conners, 1972a; Conners *et al.*, 1969; Millichap *et al.*, 1968; Weiss *et al.*, 1971), measures of short-term memory (Carpenter and Sells, 1974; Conners and Rothschild, 1968; Sprague and Sleator, 1973; Werry and Aman, 1975), the Illinois Test of Psycholinguistic Ability (McCarthy and Kirk, 1968) (Butter and Lapierre, 1974, 1975; Rie *et al.*, 1976a, 1976b; Weiss *et al.*, 1971; Conners *et al.*, 1972), the Reitan holes test of steadiness (Reitan and Davison, 1974), (Garfinkel *et al.*, 1975; Knights and Hinton, 1969), and embedded figures types of tests (Karp and Konstadt, 1963) (Campbell *et al.*, 1971; Conners, 1972a; Conners *et al.*, 1967; Schleifer *et al.*, 1975; Winsberg *et al.*, 1972).

Negative findings in drug research with hyperactive children have been reported for the following tests and measures: measures of left–right orientation (Conrad *et al.*, 1971; Weiss *et al.*, 1971), anxiety (Conners and Eisenberg, 1963), motor control and inhibition (Bradley and Green, 1940; Conners, 1966; Conners *et al.*, 1969; Conners and Rothschild, 1968; Conners *et al.*, 1972; Hoffman *et al.*, 1974), body boundary perception (Hoffman *et al.*, 1974), tapping speed and accuracy (Bradley and Green, 1940), repeating a motor pattern and pegboard tests (Knights and Hinton, 1969; Winsberg *et al.*, 1972), behavioral measures of aggression (Schleifer *et al.*, 1975), measures of body orientation in space (Zahn *et al.*, 1975), and the Leiter International Performance Scale (Arthur, 1952) (Carpenter and Sells, 1974).

As noted earlier, these scattered reports of positive findings on some tests and equivocal results on others are probably due to increased concentration or attention span rather than to any dramatic change in cognitive, intellectual, sensory, or motor skills (Conners, 1971; Weiss *et al.*, 1971).

FOLLOW-UP STUDIES OF HYPERACTIVE CHILDREN ON STIMULANT DRUGS

In addition to attempting to understand their more immediate effects, it is also important to determine what the long-term effects are for prolonged treatment with stimulant drugs. In a follow-up study of 67 children with learning problems, Hinton and Knights (1971) reported that 19 of these children had received stimulant drugs over an average of 3 years. About two-thirds of these children were reported as improved (unspecified) at follow-up.

A similar result was reported by Mendelson *et al.* (1971) in a 2–5 yr follow-up of 83 hyperactive children, 92% of whom had received stimulant drug therapy sometime during the follow-up interval. Of these children, 60% were said to have improved (unspecified) for at least 6 months while receiving drugs, 12% worsened, and 28% had "doubtful" results. Despite the large percentage of children receiving stimulant drugs, at follow-up the vast majority of children were still described as more active, inattentive, impulsive, defiant, rebellious, difficult to discipline, incorrigible, and failing one or more grades in school as compared to peers. In view of these results, the extent to which stimulant drugs may have helped these children seems relatively minimal.

In a later study, Minde *et al.* (1972) reported the results of a 5-yr follow-up of 91 children. All of the children had received phenothiazines or *d*-amphetamine at one time or another during the 5 years. At the end of follow-up, only 12 of the children remained on medication with the remainder ceasing the drug treatment for reasons such as ineffectiveness of medication, side effects, sufficient improvement, or inability to come for supervision. The authors concluded that at follow-up, "psychological adjustment did not appear to be dependent on the duration of drug taking" (p. 602). Although a significant reduction in symptoms was observed over the 5 years, these hyperactive children still scored significantly higher than normal children on ratings of hyperactivity, distractibility and aggressiveness.

Huessy *et al.* (1974) reported an 8–10 yr follow-up of 84 hyperactive children placed on pharmacotherapy when first seen. Many of the children were receiving stimulants. Results indicated that of the 75 children who could be reached, 18 had been institutionalized in various correctional or mental health facilities, only 25 had satisfactory academic levels, 37 had satisfactory family relations, and only 24 had a satisfactory work record. The authors were unable to relate length of drug treatment to final outcome and concluded that "this study gives little encouragement to the hope that temporary symptom control with medication alters prognosis" (p. 234).

Quinn and Rapoport (1975) conducted a 1 yr follow-up of 76 hyperactive children who had been placed on methylphenidate, imipramine or placebo in a drug study 1 year earlier. "The striking clinical impression at 1 yr follow-up was that the boys in all three groups continued to have difficulties" (p. 242). At the end of the second year of follow-up for 72 of these children (Riddle and Rapoport, 1976), they continued to have behavioral and academic difficulties despite their maintenance on stimulant drugs. Although declines in ratings of hyperactivity and conduct problems were evidenced, these children continued to differ from normal children on such ratings. In addition, little improvement in tested achievement skills occurred over the 2 years with math scores actually declining during this time. It was concluded that while medication may have suppressed impulsive and hyperactive behavior, peer status and academic achievement were not improved.

Weiss et al. (1975) reported a 5 yr follow-up of 24 hyperactive children treated with methylphenidate. While the drug was helpful in making the children more manageable at home and school, it did not significantly affect their outcome at the end of treatment. Compared to children not receiving medication, children on drugs did not differ significantly at follow-up in emotional adjustment, delinquency, academic performance, quality of mother–child relations, ratings of hyperactivity, or ratings of family diagnosis.

In summary, almost all of these studies reported little change in outcome at time of follow-up as a function of stimulant drug therapy. Yet, a dramatic improvement in attention span and activity level has been observed as the short-term effect of these drugs in innumerable studies. As Weiss et al. (1975) have noted, these differences in short-term and long-term drug studies are difficult to reconcile. While it is possible that tolerance to the medication may have developed, this does not seem to account for these differences as parents and teachers have been able to recognize a worsening of symptoms as soon as medication was discontinued even if the child had been on drugs for several years (Sleator et al., 1974; Weiss et al., 1971). Rie et al. (1976a, 1976b) proposed that these discrepant findings may be due to the fact that some children lose the spontaneity and interest in their surroundings believed to be necessary to adequate learning experiences while on their drugs. Thus, while concentration may be improved, decreased interest in and affective reactions to the environment may cancel out the short-term effects thus making long-term gain from drug therapy essentially nil (Rie et al., 1976a, 1976b).

It seems then that the stimulant drugs offer an effective treatment for the short-term management of hyperactivity but are not the answer to long-term treatment of these children. They are unlikely to alter the prognosis of the disorder and the overall findings show that a treatment "package" of drugs and some other form of intervention is needed. Stimulant drugs appear to facilitate management of the hyperkinetic children but do not provide the necessary influences to alter later social and academic adjustment.

Several factors must be noted as limiting, to some degree, the extent to which the results of the studies reviewed are comparable. Briefly, these are: (1) the variety of definitions used by the investigators to define hyperkinesis, (2) differences in the methodology of the studies, (3) differences in the types of drugs, the drug dosages and time the children were on drugs in these studies, (4) variations in the criteria of improvement used by those studies citing drug response rates, and (5) differences in the measures used to assess the same construct when such measures may not be comparable. To the extent that the studies reviewed differed in these areas, the conclusions drawn from pooling their findings are also limited to some extent.

CONCLUSIONS

Based upon the more than 110 studies reviewed above, the following conclusions regarding the effects of stimulant drugs on the more than 4200 hyperactive children studied in these reports seem warranted:

1. On the average, about 75% of the hyperactive children placed on stimulant medication appear to be judged as improved while about 25% remain unchanged or are worsened by the drugs. There is some evidence (Barkley, 1976) to suggest that those who respond well to these drugs are more inattentive than those who do not.

2. The primary side effects noted for the stimulants appear to be insomnia, anorexia or loss of appetite, weight loss and irritability. These and other side effects are reported to be transitory and to disappear with a reduction in drug dosage. However, some research suggests that suppression of weight and height gain over the course of treatment may be problematic.

3. The psychophysiological research on stimulant drug effects indicates that they are generally not acting paradoxically or sedatively on the CNS of hyperactive children but are indeed having their typical energizing effect on CNS responsivity. These results further suggest that the stimulants may be arousing CNS inhibitory systems thereby permitting the hyperactive child to screen out distracting stimuli and to concentrate more fully on assigned tasks.

4. The primary behavioral or cognitive impact of the stimulant drugs on hyperactive children is increased concentration or attention span and decreased impulsiveness in responding. It is not unusual, then, for these drugs to be the drug of choice for most hyperactive children since inattentiveness, or the inability to "stop, look, and listen" (Douglas, 1972, 1974), appears to be the major problem in these children. While these drugs also appear to reduce activity level, such

findings are less predictable and are dependent upon such factors as the setting in which the measures are taken, the type of measures being employed, and the type of activity being assessed, among others. It has been suggested that these changes in activity level are simply an indirect result of the changes in attentional processes resulting from drug treatment (Barkley et al., 1976; Conners, 1972b; Douglas, 1972; Sroufe et al., 1973). Effects on other tests and measures of cognitive, intellectual, achievement, sensory, or motor abilities, when observed, are also likely to be due to this increased concentration or attentiveness rather than to dramatic changes in these various abilities (Weiss et al., 1971; Werry, 1970).

5. The results of follow-up studies suggest that stimulant drug therapy is not a panacea for treating hyperkinesis. While the drugs seem to facilitate the short-term management of hyperactive children, they have little impact on the long-term social, academic, or psychological adjustment of these children. Obviously, more research on the long-term effects of these drugs is needed. Nevertheless, the results of these follow-up studies are disappointing and lead to the inescapable conclusion that the stimulant drugs are simply not enough for the treatment of hyperactivity in children (Eisenberg, 1966; Fish, 1971; Werry, 1970). In addition, they call into question the practice of wantonly prescribing these drugs to most hyperactive children without due consideration for other modes of intervention that might be used in conjunction with or as alternatives to drugs (Greenspoon and Singer, 1973). Physicians should not allow themselves to be pressured into prescribing these drugs and, when prescribed, should take adequate steps to see that the drugs are properly monitored and administered. Furthermore, parents should not be permitted to "juggle" the dosage of these drugs as they see fit (Solomons, 1973).

In view of these results, future research should concentrate on the efficacy of using stimulants in combination with other modes of therapy, such as with behavior modification (Christensen, 1975). As others have warned (Eisenberg, 1966; Werry, 1970), the value of pharmacotherapy with children lies only in the ability of drugs to facilitate changes in the child such that certain responses become more or less likely to occur. However, whether or not such responses actually occur must rely on additional efforts at restructuring the crucial environmental variables which greatly influence the child's long-term psycho-social adjustment (Werry, 1970).

SUMMARY

A number of studies using stimulant drugs with hyperactive children are reviewed. Results indicated that most children are judged as improved on the drugs while a small percentage are not. Although most side effects are transitory, suppressed weight and height gain may remain problematic throughout treatment. The drugs appear to energize the central nervous system of these children while increasing their ability to concentrate without responding impulsively. Changes in other abilities are occasionally observed but appear to result from improvement in attentional processes. In contrast, follow-up studies find the long-term psychosocial adjustment of these children to be essentially unaffected by stimulant drug treatment.

REFERENCES

Alexandris, A. and Lundell, F. (1968) Effect of thioridazine, amphetamine, and placebo on the hyperkinetic syndrome and cognitive area in mentally deficient children. *Can. Med. Ass. J.* **98**, 92–96.

Aman, M. and Sprague, R. (1974) The state-dependent effects of methylphenidate and dextroamphetamine. *J. Nerv. Ment. Dis.* **158**, 268–279.

Anderson, R., Halcomb, C., Gordon, W., Jr. and Ozolins, D. (1974) Measurement of attention distractibility in LD children. *Acad. Ther.* **9**, 261–266.

Arnold, E., Huestis, R., Smeltzer, D., Scheib, J., Wemmer, D. and Colner, G. (1976) Levoamphetamine vs dextroamphetamine in minimal brain dysfunction. *Arch. Gen. Psychiat.* **33**, 292–301.

Arnold, E., Kirilcuk, V., Corson, S. and Corson, E. (1973) Levoamphetamine and dextroamphetamine: differential effect on aggression and hyperkinesis in children and dogs. *Am. J. Psychiat.* **130**, 165–170.

Arnold, E., Wender, P., McCloskey, K. and Snyder, S. (1972) Levoamphetamine and dextroamphetamine: comparative efficacy in the hyperkinetic syndrome. *Arch. Gen. Psychiat.* **27**, 816–822.

Arthur, G. (1952) *The Arthur Adaptation of the Leiter International Performance Scale.* Psychological Services Center Press, New York.

Banta, T. (1968) Tests for the evaluation of early childhood education. In *Cognitive Studies*, Vol. 1., Helmuth, J. (Ed.). Special Child Publications, Seattle, Washington.

Barkley, R. (1976) Predicting the response of hyperkinetic children to stimulant drugs: a review. *J. Abn. Child Psychol.* **4**, 327–348.

Barkley, R. and Jackson, T., Jr. (1976) The effects of methylphenidate on autonomic arousal and its relationship to improvement in activity and attention in hyperactive children. Unpublished manuscript, Bowling Green State University, Ohio.

Barkley, R. and Routh, D. (1974) Reduction of children's locomotor activity by modeling and the promise of contingent reward. *J. Abn. Child Psychol.* **2**, 117–131.

Barkley, R. and Ullman, D. (1975) A comparison of objective measures of activity and distractibility in hyperactive and nonhyperactive children. *J. Abn. Child Psychol.* **3**, 231–244.

Barkley, R., Ullman, D. and Brown, H. (1976) The effects of methylphenidate on multiple measures of activity and attention in hyperactive children. Unpublished manuscript, Bowling Green State University, Ohio.

Bender, L. (1946) *The Bender Visual–Motor Gestalt Test*. Psychological Corp., New York.

Benton, A. (1963) *The Revised Visual Retention Test*. Psychological Corp., New York.

Blacklidge, V. and Ekblad, R. (1971) The effectiveness and methylphenidate hydrochloride (Ritalin) on learning and behavior in public school educable mentally retarded children. *Pediatrics* **47**, 923–926.

Bradley, C. (1937–38) The behavior of children receiving benzedrine. *Am. J. Psychiat.* **94**, 577–585.

Bradley, C. (1950) Benzedrine and dexedrine in the treatment of children's behavior disorders. *Pediatrics* **5**, 24–37.

Bradley, C. and Bowen, M. (1940) School performance of children receiving amphetamine (benzedrine) sulfate. *Am. J. Orthopsychiat.* **10**, 782–788.

Bradley, C. and Bown M. (1941) Amphetamine (benzedrine) therapy of children's behavior disorders. *Am. J. Orthopsychiat.* **11**, 92–103.

Bradley, C. and Green, E. (1940–41) Psychometric performance of children receiving amphetamine (benzedrine) sulfate. *Am. J. Psychiat.* **97**, 388–394.

Buchsbaum, M. and Wender, P. (1973) Average evoked responses in normal and minimally brain dysfunctioned children treated with amphetamine: a preliminary report. *Arch. Gen. Psychiat.* **29**, 764–770.

Burks, H. (1964) Effects of amphetamine therapy on hyperkinetic children. *Arch. Gen. Psychiat.* **11**, 604.

Butter, H. and Lapierre, Y. (1974) The effect of methylphenidate on sensory perception and integration in hyperactive children. *Int. Pharmopsychiat.* **9**, 235–244.

Butter, H. and Lapierre, Y. (1975) The effects of methylphenidate on sensory perception in varying degrees of hyperkinetic behavior. *Dis. Nerv. Syst.* **36**, 286–288.

Campbell, S., Douglas, V. and Morgenstern, G. (1971) Cognitive styles in hyperactive children and the effect of methylphenidate. *J. Child Psychol. Psychiat.* **12**, 55–67.

Cantwell, D. (Ed.) (1975) *The Hyperactive Child*. Spectrum Publications, New York.

Carpenter, R. and Sells, C. (1974) Measuring effects of psychoactive medication in a child with a learning disability. *J. Learn. Dis.* **7**, 545–550.

Christensen, D. (1975) Effects of combining methylphenidate and a classroom token system in modifying hyperactive behavior. *Am. J. Ment. Defic.* **80**, 266–276.

Christensen, D. and Sprague, R. (1973) Reduction of hyperactive behavior by conditioning procedures alone and combined with methylphenidate. *Behav. Res. Ther.* **11**, 331–343.

Claghorn, J., Neblett, G., Sutter, E., Farrell, G. and Kraft, I. (1971) The effect of drugs on hyperactivity in children with some observations of changes in mineral metabolism. *J. Nerv. Ment. Dis.* **153**, 118–125.

Cohen, N., Douglas, V. and Morgenstern, G. (1971) The effect of methylphenidate on attentive behavior and autonomic arousal in hyperactive children. *Psychopharmacologia* **22**, 282–294.

Comly, H. (1971) Cerebral stimulants for children with learning disorders. *J. Learn. Dis.* **4**, 484–490.

Conners, C. (1966) The effects of dexedrine on rapid discrimination and motor control of hyperkinetic children under mild stress. *J. Nerv. Ment. Dis.* **142**, 429–433.

Conners, C. (1969) A teacher rating scale for use with drug studies with children. *Am. J. Psychiat.* **126**, 884–888.

Conners, C. (1970) The use of stimulant drugs in enhancing performance and learning.

In *Drugs and Cerebral Function*, Smith, W. L. (Ed.). Charles C. Thomas, Springfield, Illinois.

Conners, C. (1971) The effect of stimulant drugs on human figure drawings in children with minimal brain dysfunction. *Psychopharmacologia* 19, 329–333.

Conners, C. (1972a) Psychological effects of stimulant drugs in children with minimal brain dysfunction. *Pediatrics* 49, 702–708.

Conners, C. (1972b) Pharmacotherapy of psychopathology in children. In *Psychopathological Disorders of Childhood*, Quay, H. and Werry, J. (Eds.). Wiley, New York.

Conners, C. and Eisenberg, L. (1963) The effects of methylphenidate on the symptomatology and learning in disturbed children. *Am. J. Psychiat.* 120, 458–464.

Conners, C., Eisenberg, L. and Sharpe, L. (1964) Effects of methylphenidate (Ritalin) on paired-associate learning and Porteus Maze performance in emotionally disturbed children. *J. Consult. Psychol.* 28, 14–22.

Conners, C., Eisenberg, L. and Barcai, A. (1967) Effect of dextroamphetamine on children. *Arch. Gen. Psychiat.* 17, 478–485.

Conners, C. and Rothschild, G. (1968) Drugs and learning in children. In *Learning Disorders*, Vol. 3, Special Child Publications, Seattle, Washington.

Conners, C., Rothschild, G., Eisenberg, L., Stone, L. and Robinson, E. (1969) Dextroamphetamine sulfate in children with learning disorders. *Arch. Gen. Psychiat.* 21, 182–190.

Conners, C., Taylor, E., Meo, G., Kurtz, M. and Fournier, M. (1972) Magnesium pemoline and dextroamphetamine: a controlled study in children with minimal brain dysfunction. *Psychopharmacologia* 26, 321–336.

Conrad, W. (1967) Anticipating the response to amphetamine therapy in the treatment of hyperkinetic children. *Pediatrics* 40, 96–98.

Conrad, W., Dworkin, E., Shai, A. and Tobiessen, J. (1971) Effects of amphetamine therapy and prescriptive tutoring on the behavior and achievement of lower class hyperactive children. *J. Learn. Dis.* 4, 509–517.

Creager, R. and Van Riper, C. (1967) The effect of methylphenidate on the verbal productivity of children with cerebral dysfunction. *J. Speech Hearing Res.* 10, 623–628.

Cutts, K. and Jasper, H. (1939) Effects of benzedrine sulfate and phenobarbital on behavior problem children with abnormal electroencephalograms. *Arch. Neurol. Psychiat.* 41, 1138–1145.

Davids, A. (1971) An objective instrument for assessing hyperactivity in children. *J. Learn. Dis.* 4, 499.

Denhoff, E., Davids, A. and Hawkins, R. (1971) Effects of dextroamphetamine on hyperkinetic children: a controlled double-blind study. *J. Learn. Dis.* 4, 491–498.

Doll, E. (1946) *The Oseretsky Tests of Motor Proficiency*. American Guidance Service Inc., Minnesota.

Douglas, V. (1972) Stop, look, and listen: the problem of sustained attention and impulse control in hyperactive and normal children. *Can. J. Behav. Sci.* 4, 259–282.

Douglas, V. (1974) Are drugs enough?—To treat or to train the hyperactive child. In *Clinical Use of Stimulant Drugs in Children*, Conners, C. (Ed.). Excerpta Medica, New York.

Eisenberg, L. (1966) The management of the hyperkinetic child. *Dev. Med. Child Neurol.* 8, 593–598.

Ellis, M., Witt, P., Reynolds, R. and Sprague, R. (1974) Methylphenidate and the activity of hyperactive children in the informal setting. *Child Dev.* **45**, 217–220.

Epstein, L., Lasagna, L., Conners, C. and Rodriguez, A. (1968) Correlation of dextroamphetamine excretion and drug response in hyperkinetic children. *J. Nerv. Ment. Dis.* **146**, 136–146.

Fish, B. (1971) The "one child, one drug" myth of stimulants in hyperkinesis. *Arch. Gen. Psychiat.* **25**, 193–203.

Fish, B. (1975) Stimulant drug treatment of hyperactive children. In *The Hyperactive Child*, Cantwell, D. (Ed.). Spectrum Publications, Inc., New York.

Finnerty, R., Soltys, J. and Cole, J. (1971) The use of dextroamphetamine with hyperkinetic children. *Psychopharmacologia* **21**, 302–308.

Freeman, R. (1966) Drug effects on learning in children: a selective review of the past thirty years. *J. Spec. Educ.* **1**, 17–33.

Frostig, M. (1961) *Developmental Tasks of Visual Perception*. Consulting Psychologist Press, Palo Alto, California.

Garfinkel, B., Webster, C. and Sloman, L. (1975) Methylphenidate and caffeine in the treatment of children with minimal brain dysfunction. *Am. J. Psychiat.* **132**, 723–727.

Goodenough, F. (1926) *Measurement of Intelligence by Drawings*. World Book Co., New York.

Gray, W. (1963) *Gray Oral Reading Tests*. Bobbs–Merrill Co., Indianapolis, Indiana.

Greenberg, A. and Coleman, M. (1976) Depressed 5-hydroxyindole levels associated with hyperactive and aggressive behavior. *Arch. Gen. Psychiat.* **33**, 331–336.

Greenberg, L., Deem, M. and McMahon, S. (1972) Effects of dextroamphetamine, chlorpromazine, and hydroxyzine on the behavior and performance of hyperactive children. *Am. J. Psychiat.* **129**, 532–539.

Greenspoon, S. and Singer, S. (1973) Amphetamines in the treatment of hyperkinetic children. *Harv. Educ. Rev.* **43**, 515–555.

Greenwold, W. and Jones, P. (1971) The effect of methylphenidate on behavior of three school children: a pilot investigation. *Except. Child.* **38**, 261–262.

Hinton, G. and Knights, R. (1971) Children with learning problems: academic history, academic prediction, and adjustment 3 years after assessment. *Except. Child.* **37**, 513–519.

Huessy, H., Metoyer, M. and Townsend, M. (1974) 8–10 year follow-up of 84 children treated for behavioral disorder in rural Vermont. *Acta Paedopsychiat.* **10**, 230–235.

Huestis, R., Arnold, E. and Smeltzer, D. (1975) Caffeine versus methylphenidate and *d*-amphetamine in minimal brain dysfunction. *Am. J. Psychiat.* **132**, 868–870.

Hoffman, S., Engelhardt, D., Margolis, R., Polizos, P., Waizer, J. and Rosenfeld, R. (1974) Response to methylphenidate in low socioeconomic hyperactive children. *Arch. Gen. Psychiat.* **30**, 354–359.

Jastak, J. and Jastak, S. (1965) *The Wide Range Achievement Test Manual*. Guidance Associates, Wilmington, Delaware.

Johnson, C. (1971) Hyperactivity and the machine: the actometer. *Child Dev.* **42**, 2105.

Kagan, J., Rosman, B., Day, D., Albert, J. and Phillips, W. (1964) Information processing in the child: significance of analytic and reflective attitude. *Psychol. Monogr.* **78** (1, Whole No. 578).

Karp, S. and Konstadt, N. (1963) *Manual for Children's Embedded Figures Test*. Cognitive Tests, New York.

Knights, R. and Hinton, G. (1969) The effects of methylphenidate on the motor skills and behavior of children with learning problems. *J. Nerv. Ment. Dis.* **148**, 643–653.

Knobel, M. (1962) Psychopharmacology for the hyperkinetic child—dynamic considerations. *Arch. Gen. Psychiat.* **6**, 198–202.

Knopp, W., Arnold, E., Andras, R. and Smeltzer, D. (1973) Predicting amphetamine response in hyperkinetic children by electronic pupillography. *Pharmakopsychiatry* **6**, 158–166.

Kornetsky, C. (1970) Drugs and the immature organism. *Psychopharmacologia* **17**, 105–136.

Krager, J. and Safer, D. (1974) Type and prevalence of medication used in treating hyperactive children. *New Engl. J. Med.* **291**, 1118–1120.

Kupietz, S., Camp, J. and Weissman, A. (1976) Reaction time performance in behaviorally deviant children: effects of prior preparatory interval and reinforcement. *J. Child Psychol. Psychiat.* **17**, 123–131.

Lambert, N., Windmiller, M., Sandoval, J. and Moore, B. (1976) Hyperactive children and the efficacy of psychoactive drugs as a treatment intervention. *Am. J. Orthopsychiat.* **46**, 335–352.

Laufer, M., Denhoff, E. and Solomons, G. (1957) Hyperkinetic impulse disorder in children's behavior problems. *Psychosom. Med.* **19**, 38–49.

Levy, S. (1959) Post-encephalitic behavior disorder—a forgotten entity. A report of 100 cases. *Am. J. Psychiat.* **115**, 1062–1067.

Lindsley, D. and Henry, C. (1942) The effect of drugs on behavior and the electroencephalogram of children with behavior disorders. *Psychosom. Med.* **4**, 140–149.

Loney, J., Comly, H., Hunter, H. and Simon, B. (1975) Parental management, self-concept, and drug response in minimal brain dysfunction. *J. Learn. Dis.* **8**, 187–190.

Loney, J. and Ordona, T. (1975) Using cerebral stimulants to treat minimal brain dysfunction. *Am. J. Orthopsychiat.* **45**, 564–572.

Lucas, A. and Weiss, M. (1971) Methylphenidate hallucinosis. *J. Am. Med. Ass.* **217**, 1079–1081.

Lytton, G. and Knobel, M. (1959) Diagnosis and treatment of behavior disorders in children. As cited in Knobel, M., Wolman, M. and Mason, E. Hyperkinesis and organicity in children. *Arch. Gen. Psychiat.* **1**, 310–321.

Mackay, M., Beck, L. and Taylor, R. (1973) Methylphenidate for adolescents with minimal brain dysfunction. *N.Y. State J. Med.* **73**, 550–554.

McCarthy, J. and Kirk, S. (1968) *Illinois Test of Psycholinguistic Ability.* University of Illinois Press.

McConnell, T., Cromwell, R., Bialer, I. and Son, C. (1964) Studies in activity level—VII. Effects of amphetamine drug administration on the activity level of retarded children. *Am. J. Ment. Defic.* **68**, 647–651.

Mendelson, W., Johnson, N. and Stewart, M. (1971) Hyperactive children as teenagers: a follow-up study. *J. Nerv. Ment. Dis.* **153**, 273–279.

Millichap, J. (1973) Drugs in the management of minimal brain dysfunction. *Ann. N.Y. Acad. Sci.* **205**, 321–334.

Millichap, J., Aymat, F., Sturgis, L., Larsen, K. and Egan, R. (1968) Hyperkinetic behavior and learning disorders. *Am. J. Dis. Child.* **116**, 235–244.

Millichap, J. and Boldrey, E. (1967) Studies in hyperkinetic behavior. *Neurol.* **17**, 467–471.

Millichap, J. and Fowler, G. (1967) Treatment of "minimal brain dysfunction" syndromes. *Ped. Clin. N. Am.* **14**, 767–777.

Minde, K., Weiss, G. and Mendelson, N. (1972) A 5 yr follow-up study of 91 hyperactive school children. *J. Am. Acad. Child Psychiat.* **11**, 595–610.

Molitch, M. and Eccles, A. (1937) The effect of benzedrine sulfate on the intelligence scores of children. *Am. J. Psychiat.* **94**, 587–590.

Montagu, J. and Swarbrick, L. (1975) Effect of amphetamines in hyperkinetic children: stimulant or sedative? A pilot study. *Dev. Med. Child Neurol.* **17**, 293–298.

Ney, P. (1967) Psychosis in a child associated with amphetamine administration. *Can. Med. Ass. J.* **97**, 1026–1029.

Porges, S. Walter, G., Korb, R. and Sprague, R. (1975) The influence of methylphenidate on heart rate and behavioral measures of attention in hyperactive children. *Child Dev.* **46**, 727–733.

Porteus, S. (1965) *Porteus Maze Tests: Fifty Years Application.* Pacific Books, Palo Alto, California.

Quinn, P. and Rapoport, J. (1975) One-year follow-up of hyperactive boys treated with imipramine and methylphenidate. *Am. J. Psychiat.* **132**, 241–245.

Rapoport, J., Lott, I., Alexander, D. and Abramson, A. (1970) Urinary noradrenaline and playroom behavior in hyperactive boys. *Lancet* **2**, 1141.

Rapoport, J., Abramson, A., Alexander, D. and Lott, I. (1971) Playroom observations of hyperactive children on medication. *J. Am. Acad. Child Psychiat.* **10**, 524–534.

Rapoport, J., Quinn, P., Bradbard, G., Riddle, D. and Brooks, E. (1974) Imipramine and methylphenidate treatments of hyperactive boys. *Arch. Gen. Psychiat.* **30**, 789–793.

Rapoport, J., Quinn, P. and Lambrecht, F. (1974) Minor physical anomalies and plasma dopamine–beta–hydroxylase activity in hyperactive boys. *Am. J. Psychiat.* **131**, 386–390.

Reitan, R. and Davison, L. (Eds.) (1974) *Clinical Neuropsychology: Current Status and Applications.* Wiley, New York.

Riddle, D. and Rapoport, J. (1976) A 2-yr follow-up of 72 hyperactive boys. *J. Nerv. Ment. Dis.* **162**, 126–133.

Rie, H., Rie, E., Stewart, S. and Ambuel, J. (1976a) Effects of methylphenidate on underachieving children. *J. Consult. Clin. Psychol.* **44**, 250–260.

Rie, H., Rie, E., Stewart, S. and Ambuel, J. (1976b) Effects of Ritalin on underachieving children: a replication. *Am. J. Orthopsychiat.* **46**, 313–322.

Routh, D., Schroeder, C. and O'Tuama, L. (1973) Development of activity level in children. *Dev. Psychol.* **10**, 163.

Safer, D. and Allen, R. (1973) Factors influencing the suppressant effects of two simullant drugs on the growth of hyperactive children. *Pediatrics* **51**, 660–667.

Safer, D. and Allen R. (1975) Stimulant drug treatment of hyperactive adolescents. *Dis. Nerv. Syst.* **36**, 454–457.

Safer, D., Allen, R. and Barr, E. (1972) Depression of growth in hyperactive children on stimulant drugs. *New Engl. J. Med.* **287**, 217–220.

Saletu, B., Saletu, M. and Itil, T. (1973) The relationship between psychopathology and evoked responses before, during and after psychotropic drug treatment. *Bio. Psychiat.* **6**, 45–74.

Satterfield, J., Cantwell, D., Lesser, L. and Podosin, R. (1972) Physiological studies of the hyperkinetic child—I. *Am. J. Psychiat.* **128**, 1418–1424.

Satterfield, J., Cantwell, D., Saul, R., Lesser, L. and Podosin, R. (1973) Response to stimulant drug treatment in hyperactive children: prediction from EEG and neurological findings. *J. Autism Childhood Schizophrenia* **3**, 36–48.

Satterfield, J. and Dawson, M. (1971) Electrodermal correlates of hyperactivity in children. *Psychophysiology* **8**, 191–197.

Satterfield, J., Lesser, L., Saul, R. and Cantwell, D. (1973) EEG aspects in the diagnosis and treatment of minimal brain dysfunction. *Ann. N.Y. Acad. Sci.* **205**, 274–282.

Schain, R. and Reynard, C. (1975) Observations on effects of a central stimulant drug (methylphenidate) in children with hyperactive behavior. *Pediatrics* **55**, 709–716.

Schleifer, M., Weiss, G., Cohen, N., Elman, M., Cvejic, H. and Kruger, E. (1975) Hyperactivity in preschoolers and the effect of methylphenidate. *Am. J. Orthopsychiat.* **45**, 38–50.

Schnackenberg, R. (1973) Caffeine as a substitute for schedule II stimulants in hyperkinetic children. *Am. J. Psychiat.* **130**, 796–798.

Schnackenberg, R. and Bender, E. (1971) The effect of methylphenidate hypochloride on children with minimal brain dysfunction syndrome and subsequent hyperkinetic syndrome. *Psychiat. Forum* **2**, 32–36.

Seger, E. and Hallum, G. (1974) Methylphenidate in children with minimal brain dysfunction: effects on attention span, visual-motor skills and behavior. *Curr. Ther. Res.* **16**, 635–641.

Shaffer, D., McNamara, N. and Pincus, J. (1974) Controlled observations on patterns of activity, attention, and impulsivity in brain-damaged and psychiatrically disturbed boys. *Psychol. Med.* **4**, 4–18.

Shetty, T. (1971) Alpha rhythms in the hyperkinetic child. *Nature, Lond.* **234**, 476.

Sleator, E., Von Neumann, A. and Sprague, R. (1974) Hyperactive children: a continuous long-term placebo-controlled follow-up. *J. Am. Med. Ass.* **229**, 316–317.

Solomons, G. (1973) Drug therapy: initiation and follow-up. *Ann. N.Y. Acad. Sci.* **205**, 335–344.

Sprague, R., Barnes, K. and Werry, J. (1970) Methylphenidate and thioridazine: learning, reaction time, activity, and classroom behavior in disturbed children. *Am. J. Orthopsychiat.* **40**, 615–628.

Sprague, R. and Sleator, E. (1973) Effects of psychopharmacological agents on learning disabilities. *Ped. Clin. N. Am.* **20**, 719–725.

Sprague, R. and Werry, J. (1971) Methodology of psychopharmacological studies with the retarded. *Int. Rev. Res. Ment. Retard.* **5**, 147–219.

Spring, C., Greenberg, L., Scott, J. and Hopwood, J. (1973) Reaction time and the effects of Ritalin on children with learning problems. *Percept. Motor Skills* **36**, 75–82.

Spring, C., Greenberg, L., Scott, J. and Hopwood, J. (1974) Electrodermal activity in hyperactive boys who are methylphenidate responders. *Psychophysiology* **11**, 436–442.

Sroufe, A., Sontes, B., West, W. and Wright, F. (1973) Anticipatory heart rate deceleration and reaction time in children with and without referral for learning disability. *Child Dev.* **44**, 267–273.

Stableford, W., Butz, R., Hasazi, J., Leitenberg, H. and Peyser, J. (1976) Sequential withdrawal of stimulant drugs and use of behavior therapy with two hyperactive boys. *Am. J. Orthopsychiat.* **46**, 302–312.

Steinberg, G., Troshinsky, C. and Steinberg, H. (1971) Dextroamphetamine responsive behavior disorder in school children. *Am. J. Psychiat.* **128**, 174–179.

Sykes, D., Douglas, V. and Morgenstern, G. (1972) The effect of methylphenidate (Ritalin) on sustained attention in hyperactive children. *Psychopharmacologia* **25**, 262–274.

Sykes, D., Douglas, V., Weiss, G. and Minde, K. (1971) Attention in hyperactive children and the effect of methylphenidate (Ritalin) . *J. Child Psychol. Psychiat.* **12**, 129–139.

Weber, B. and Sulzbacher, S. (1975) Use of CNS stimulant medication in averaged electroencephalic audiometry with children with MBD. *J. Learn. Dis.* **8**, 300–303.

Wechsler, D. (1949) *Manual for the Wechsler Intelligence Scale for Children.* The Psychological Corp., New York.

Weiss, G., Kruger, E., Danielson, U. and Elman, M. (1975) Effect of long-term treatment of hyperactive children with methylphenidate. *Can. Med. Ass. J.* **112**, 159–165.

Weiss, G., Minde, K., Douglas, V., Werry, J. and Sykes, D. (1971) Comparison of the effects of chlorpromazine, dextroamphetamine, and methylphenidate on the behaviour and intellectual functioning of hyperactive children. *Can. Med. Ass. J.* **104**, 20–25.

Weiss, G., Werry, J., Minde, K., Douglas, V. and Sykes, D. (1968) Studies on the hyperactive child—V. The effects of dextroamphetamine and chlorpromazine on behavior and intellectual functioning. *J. Child Psychol. Psychiat.* **9**, 145–156.

Werry, J. (1968) Developmental hyperactivity. *Ped. Clin. N. Am.* **15**, 581.

Werry, J. (1970) Some clinical and laboratory studies of psychotropic drugs in children: an overview. In *Drugs and Cerebral Function,* Smith, W. L. (Ed.). Charles C. Thomas, Springfield, Illinois.

Werry, J. and Aman, M. (1975) Methylphenidate and haloperidol in children. Effects on attention, memory, and activity. *Arch. Gen. Psychiat.* **32**, 790–795.

Werry, J. and Sprague, R. (1974) Methylphenidate in children: effect of dosage. *Aust. N.Z.J. Psychiat.* **8**, 9–19.

Winsberg, B., Bialer, I., Kupietz, S. and Thomas, J. (1972) Effects of imipramine and dextroamphetamine on behavior of neuropsychiatrically impaired children. *Am. J. Psychiat.* **128**, 1425–1431.

Winsberg, B., Press, M., Bialer, I. and Kupietz, S. (1974) Dextroamphetamine and methylphenidate in the treatment of hyperactive/aggressive children. *Pediatrics* **53**, 236–241.

Yoss, R. (1975) Personal communication, Mayo Clinic, Rochester, Minnesota.

Yoss, R. and Moyers, N. (1971) The pupillogram of the hyperkinetic child and the underachiever. *Abstracts of the 7th Colloquium on the Pupil.* The Mayo Clinic, Rochester, Minnesota.

Zahn, T., Abate, F., Little, B. and Wender, P. (1975) Minimal brain dysfunction, stimulant drugs, and autonomic nervous system activity. *Arch. Gen. Psychiat.* **32**, 381–387.

Zimmerman, F. and Burgemeister, B. (1958) Action of methylphenidate (Ritalin) and reserpine in behavior disorders of children and adults. *Am J. Psychiat.* **115**, 323–328.

Zrull, J., Westman, J., Arthur, B. and Bell, W. (1963) A comparison of chlordiazepoxide, *d*-amphetamine, and placebo in the treatment of the hyperkinetic syndrome in children. *Am. J. Psychiat.* **120**, 590–591.

Zrull, J., Westman, J., Arthur, B. and Rice, D. (1965) An evaluation of methodology used in the study of psychoactive drugs for children. *J. Am. Acad. Child Psychiat.* **5**, 284–291.

19

BEHAVIORAL INTERVENTION WITH HYPERACTIVE CHILDREN: A REVIEW

H. Thompson Prout

James Madison University, Harisonburg, Va.

This paper reviews behavioral (nonmedical) approaches for the management and treatment of the hyperactive child. A variety of approaches are discussed, including both those interventions which have and have not been systematically evaluated. A critique of the current state of research in this area is offered with suggestions for future investigations.

In recent years, the treatment of the hyperactive or hyperkinetic child has received much attention in education, medicine, and psychology. This article reviews behavioral intervention approaches employed with hyperactive children and summarizes issues and trends in this area.

"Behavioral interventions" are any nonmedical treatments which have as a goal the reduction of hyperactive behaviors or a more satisfactory adjustment of the child and/or his family. Issues in drug and medical management of the hyperactive child have been dealt with by other authors (Conners 1971, Bosco 1972, Grinspoon & Singer 1973). In fact, many of the cautions raised in these reviews of drug therapy suggest that more emphasis should be placed on nondrug interven-

Reprinted with permission from *Journal of Learning Disabilities*, Vol. 10, No. 3, 141–146, 1977. Copyright 1977, Professional Press, Inc.

tions. Although symptoms may disappear as the child approaches puberty (Laufer & Denhoff 1957, McFarlane, Allen, & Honzik 1954), data on the prognosis of hyperactive children as they become older provide evidence that hyperactive children have lower chances for successful adjustment in adolescence and adulthood (Menkes, Rowe, & Menkes 1967, Stewart 1970, Mendelson, Johnson, & Stewart 1971, Weiss, Minde, Werry, Douglas, and Nemeth 1971). This further suggests that we need to know more about dealing with the psychological problems of these children, in promoting optimal development, and in behavioral management. Included in this review are discussions of general considerations, psychotherapy, operant approaches, environmental manipulations, self-control skill training, and biofeedback.

Many authors suggest that it is essential to work with the parents in a counseling or guidance relationship (Wender 1971, Stewart & Olds 1973, Laufer & Denhoff 1957). Weiss (1971) suggests that work with the parents focus on structuring the home environment. Schrager and Lindy (1970), noting that hyperactive children in kindergarten show indications of potential school failure, suggest anticipatory parental guidance and teacher consultation early in the child's school career. Stewart, Pitts, Craig, and Dierfel (1966) suggest that the physician begin treatment before the child starts school, if possible. Waldrop and Goering (1971), after finding that hyperactive boys display more minor physical anomalies than normals, recommend early pediatric anomaly assessment to screen for early intervention. Stewart (1970) recommends educating parents and teachers about the disorder to prevent the child from suffering consequences of his behavior which are often beyond his control. Remedial education is often suggested to treat the associated learning disabilities (Weiss 1971, Wender 1971, Van Osdol & Carlson 1972).

PSYCHOTHERAPY

Wender (1971) notes that the child with minimal brain dysfunction is often referred for psychotherapy when treated in a mental health or psychiatric clinic. Wender recommends against psychotherapy in most cases unless the disorder has resulted in additional psychological problems for the child. Weiss (1971) comments that extensive individual therapy is rarely indicated, while Laufer and Denhoff (1957) recommend therapy only after the child is on medication and is "able to simmer down and participate in the psychotherapeutic process" (p. 473). Marwit and Stenner's (1972) delineation of two patterns of hyperkinesis suggests two different interventions. Pattern I, "hyperactive," is caused by organic brain damage, maturational lag, or constitutional predisposition. Pattern II, "hyperreactive," would appear to be caused by anxiety. The hyperactive child (pattern I) might best be treated medically, while the hyperreactive child (pattern II) should be treated psychotherapeutically or with a behavioral approach. Eisenberg, Gilbert, Cytryn, and Molling (1961) studied the effectiveness of psychotherapy with neurotic and hyperactive children. The treatment was oriented toward brief therapy and the therapy appeared to help the neurotics, but did little for the hyperactive children. The neurotic group reported a 60–70% improvement rate and the hyperkinetic group showed a 15–40% improvement rate. Levitt (1971) has noted that many outcome studies of child psychotherapy do not indicate that therapy is beneficial. Levitt includes hyperactivity as a problem behavior that tends to disappear with development and, as in many cases of developmental problems, treatment may have been unnecessary. It would appear that psychotherapy for hyperactive children should only be instituted when the child's hyperactivity does not interfere with the process and when there are indications that there are psychological problems beyond the hyperactivity.

OPERANT PROCEDURES

Operant procedures have been used with hyperactive children for shaping new behaviors and eliminating undesirable behaviors. Alabiso (1972) has suggested conditioning attention or attending behavior for mentally retarded populations. He notes that attention is incompatible with hyperactive behavior and performs an inhibitory function for a variety of off-task behaviors. Patterson, Jones, Whittier, and Wright (1965) used a token system and rewarded attending behavior in a hyperactive child, and used no conditioning in a control child. Prior to starting conditioning, several weeks of baseline data were obtained. The experimental child was rewarded with a token for every 10-second interval of attending behavior, and could also earn points for his classmates (i.e., the classmates were also rewarded for the experimental child's attending behavior). The conditioning resulted in a significant increase in attending behavior as judged by the observers. This study has limitations in the number of subjects and the failure to use blind observations. The observers knew which child was the experimental subject and which was the control subject. Allen, Henke, Harris, Baer, and Reynolds (1967) report on a case study of a hyperactive child. They focused on attending behavior or attention span and chose as the target behavior the time spent on an activity.

Systematic programming of adult social reinforcement resulted in a decrease in the number of activity changes to half of the preconditioning number. Krop (1971), in another case study, used systematic operant procedures with an 8-year-old brain-damaged, emotionally disturbed child whose intelligence test scores were in the retarded range. Initially using primary reinforcers (candy) and then switching to secondary reinforcers (praise), Krop was able to shape attending behavior. A 4-week follow-up showed that the changes were maintained. Both of these studies have limited generalizability since they are case studies.

Doubrous and Daniels (1966) employed a token system with six overactive, mentally retarded children between the ages of 6 and 13. Observers tallied hyperactive behaviors on a checklist which included stationary body movements, locomotive behavior, destructive acts, and communication. The children were placed in 15-minute play situations where baseline observations and conditioning took place. A clicking noise informed the child that he had earned a token for doing well in the play situations. The tokens could be exchanged for candy. Hyperactive behaviors were reduced to one-third during the extinction phase and maintained in a 2-week follow-up.

Hamblin and Buckholdt (1967) focused on children who were reported to be the most severe behavior problems in a local school system. In the first phase of the project, teachers were instructed to conduct their classrooms as they would normally. Observational reports showed chaotic classrooms with teachers actually rewarding aggressive behavior through attention and social reinforcement. Token exchange systems were introduced focusing on cooperative behavior, and structured according to the needs of the classroom. Anecdotal records and observational data showed substantial reduction of hyperactive behavior and destructive acts, with a resulting significant increase in attention level and class cooperation. Removal of the token system resulted in a return to baseline and the reinstatement of the system returned the classes to the levels of the first treatment situation. The authors noted that it was necessary to restructure the reward systems for several of the students before the program was effective with them.

Mitchell and Crowell (1973) report the use of tangible and social reinforcers (praising and ignoring) with three boys who "tended" to be hyperactive. The boys, all in the same classroom, showed significant drops in hyperactive behaviors when reinforcement contingencies were instituted. Two of the boys showed only slight increases in hyperactive behavior when contingencies were removed, while the third boy returned to the original baseline level of activity. When reinforcement was begun again, all three displayed few hyperactive behaviors.

Parents have been trained successfully to use behavioral management techniques with their hyperactive children. Furman and Feighner (1973) present a preliminary report on the use of videotape feedback in teaching parents behavior modification skills. Parents of hyperkinetic children were instructed in operant techniques and then videotaped interacting with their children. The parents worked on specific target behaviors and also emphasized improvement in communication. The parents then viewed the tape and were given feedback by the therapists. A subjective analysis of three case studies suggested that feedback sessions on the tapes were beneficial. Wiltz and Gordon (1974) worked with a 9-year-old hyperactive and aggressive boy and his parents. The family spent five consecutive days in an apartment-like setting with observation facilities. Training included instructional materials, prompting, modeling, and feedback. Follow-up via telephone showed significant reductions in noncompliance and destructive acts.

In general, these approaches to the treatment of hyperkinetic behaviors appear to have considerable potential. However, the literature to date is dominated by case studies and studies employing small numbers of subjects. It is difficult at this time to determine the effects of these programs.

MANIPULATING THE ENVIRONMENT AND SELF-REGULATION

Environmental manipulations involve changing, structuring, or initiating new activities within the various aspects of the child's school or home setting. Wunderlich (1970), who views hyperactivity as an absence of or breakdown in control over one's behavior, suggests that when a child's internal control is low, there must be considerable external control over the child which can be lessened gradually as the child learns or develops internal control. Krauch (1971) has suggested an engineered classroom concept for the hyperactive child in school. In this system, the day is divided into 15- or 20-minute intervals, with a structured schedule and the child changing activities at each interval. The schedule should be structured so that the child is not forced to maintain attention for periods longer than he is able to do so. For example, the child should not have three consecutive intervals in which he is involved in an activity sitting at his desk. The engineered classroom employs a cue system to signal times when activities change.

No grades are given, but the child receives check marks for completing work, and a token reward system is used. Cermark, Stein, and Abelson (1973) describe a structured activity group therapy model for treatment of hyperactive children. Self-regulation is the focus, with the children in the group monitoring each other's behavior. The authors note that there are six aspects of treating hyperactivity: space or physical environment; time or the sequencing of activities to account for the short attention span; level of readiness for activities; multiplicity of the child's problems; relationship including self-concept; and relationships with peers and teachers or therapists. Arnold (1972) discusses a case study in which a bright hyperactive and aggressive child with satisfactory achievement was advanced one grade with a resulting decrease in hyperactivity and aggressive acts. Arnold states: "In other cases, also, children have reported that they feel better able to control themselves in the presence of larger children with whom they could not get away with impulsive outbursts" (p. 459). The author lists seven guidelines for this procedure: (1) the problem should be behavior rather than academic; (2) the behavior should be noticeably worse around smaller or younger children and better around larger or older children (playground observations are helpful in gathering this information); (3) the child should be intelligent enough to permit advancement; (4) the receiving teacher should be flexible; (5) placement should not be with a problem group in the class; (6) concomitant medical or psychiatric problems should be considered; and (7) the possible advancement should be explored with the child. While this approach appears to have a logical base, one must wonder if the approach could be instituted on a mass or system basis since bad behavior is apparently being rewarded. That is, the child's bad behavior results in an advanced placement, which could possibly be a positive reinforcer and be a vicariously reinforcing experience for other children.

Scott (1970) used recordings of the Beatles in a program for four hyperactive boys. The boys were placed in 10-minute arithmetic test situations. Three conditions (music in the classroom, sitting in a booth, and music in the booth) all produced significant increases in the number of correctly solved problems as compared with performance in a normal classroom setting. Edson (1969) suggests physical education programs can provide an energy release and sense of success for the hyperactive child.

Palkes, Stewart, and Kahana (1968) conducted a study in which they instructed hyperactive boys to utilize self-directed verbal commands. Both the experimental and control groups were given the Porteus

Maze Test on Day 1 of the experiment. Following this, the experimental group was given training in self-directed verbal commands while the control group was given practice work on other tests for the same amount of time. The command training instructed the children to be less impulsive and employed cue cards with slogans like "Stop!" and "Think!" with appropriate cartoon illustrations. On Day II, the subjects were retested with the Porteus Maze, and the verbal training group did significantly better. Flynn and Hopson (1972) describe a program in which they attempt to teach hyperactive children to inhibit or control motor responses. The program is a sequence of motor exercises designed to follow the natural development of the child and remediate deficits that have developed. The authors theorize that the program reduces the imbalance between the excitatory and inhibitory processes, but they present no data concerning the efficacy of their program.

BIOFEEDBACK

The recent interest in biofeedback approaches to behavior change have led some authors to suggest biofeedback in the treatment of hyperactive children. Mulholland (1973), in a call "to try the hardware in the classroom" (p. 103), suggests that biofeedback is appropriate for hyperactive or overactive children. He feels that these children have too much tension in their muscles, but could learn to bring muscle relaxation under voluntary control. Nall (1973), after informally observing what appeared to be positive effects of alpha training with hyperactive children in a special school for children with behavior problems, conducted a study using an alpha training group, a placebo group, and a control group. Comparisons between the training and placebo groups were inconclusive, although Nall noted that the training appeared to be very beneficial with particular children. Simpson and Nelson (1972) report a preliminary study on breathing control and attention training for hyperactive children. The three experimental children were placed in a cubicle in which they received feedback concerning their breathing rate and the amount of discrepancy from a desired rate. The experimental children were also given attention training, while the control group only worked on tasks in the cubicles. The experimental group showed less breathing irregularity, better performance on tasks, and better attending behavior. However, these differences were noticed only in the cubicles and there was no transfer to the classroom setting.

CONCLUSIONS

Behavioral interventions for hyperactivity have included a wide variety of techniques. Due to limitations in the research data, the question of the effectiveness of these various approaches remains largely unresolved. The results of many studies must be viewed with caution due to inappropriate design, lack of control groups, differences in subject populations, various intervening variables, small numbers of subjects, and the use of the case study approach. However, it must be considered that research on treating hyperactivity encounters many of the same problems of research on behavioral interventions for other specific disorders. That is, identification of adequate and representative samples and the use of rigid experimental control often is not possible in research of this nature. Future studies need to employ more refined experimental methods so that results would be more generalizable and definitive.

Given the above limitations, it is still possible to draw some tentative conclusions. In general, psychotherapy does not appear to be the treatment of choice for the hyperactive child. In some cases, psychotherapy or counseling may be beneficial as an adjunct to medical interventions if there are additional emotional or behavior problems. Further, if it can be determined that the hyperactivity has an emotional or learned base, psychotherapy might be indicated. Other interventions, however, would appear to have greater chances for success. In particular, operant, behavioral, parent interventions, and self-control training approaches have considerable potential.

One area that appears to have been ignored in the literature is that of interventions with pre-adolescents, adolescents, and adults who were hyperactive as children. As noted previously, although the symptoms can disappear at puberty, later adjustment of these groups is generally poorer than normal populations. Interventions emphasizing supportive counseling, acquisition of social skills that may not have been developed in childhood (e.g., peer interaction skills), and facilitation of school adjustment, should be studied at pre-adolescent and early adolescent levels. This period would appear to be extremely critical for the hyperactive child, since the adolescent period is even difficult for normal children. This period could be potentially a period of rapid development for the hyperactive child, if appropriate encouragement and experiences are provided.

REFERENCES

Alabiso, F.: Inhibitory functions of attention in reducing hyperactive behavior. *Amer. J. Ment. Defic.*, 1972, 77(3), 259–282.

Allen, K. E., Henke, L. B., Harris, F. B., Baer, D. M., and Reynolds, N. J.: Control of hyperactivity by social reinforcement of attending behaviors. *J. Educ. Psychol.*, 1967, 58(4), 231–237.

Arnold, L. E.: Control of aggression by advanced grade placement: Criteria and case history. *J. School Health*, 1972, 42(8), 458–459.

Bosco, J.: The use of Ritalin for the treatment of minimal brain dysfunction and hyperkinesis in children. Kalamazoo, Mich.: Western Michigan Univ., 1972. (ERIC Document Reproduction Service No. ED076540)

Cermark, S. A., Stein, F., and Abelson, C.: Hyperactive children and activity group therapy model. *Amer. J. Occup. Ther.*, 1973, 27(6), 311–315.

Conners, C. K.: Recent drug studies with hyperkinetic children. *J. Learning Disabil.*, 1971, 4, 476–483.

Doubrous, S. G., and Daniels, G. J.: An experimental approach to the reduction of overactive behavior. *Behav. Res. Ther.*, 1966, 4, 251–258.

Edson, T.: Physical education: A substitute for hyperactivity and violence. *J. Health, Phys. Educ., and Recreation*, 1969, 40(7), 79–81.

Eisenberg, S., Gilbert, A., Cytryn, L., and Molling, P.: The effectiveness of psychotherapy alone and in conjunction with peraphenazine or placebo treatment of neurotic and hyperkinetic children. *Amer. J. Psychiat.*, 1961, 117, 1088–1093.

Flynn, R., and Hopson, B.: Inhibitory training: An alternative to development of controls in hyperactive children. Paper presented at the National Association of School Psychologists meeting, Chicago, March 1972.

Furman, S., and Feighner, A.: Video feedback in treating of hyperkinetic children: A preliminary report. *Amer. J. Psychiat.*, 1973, 130, 792–796.

Grinspoon, L., and Singer, S. B.: Amphetamines in the treatment of hyperkinetic children. *Harvard Educ. Rev.*, 1973, 43, 515–555.

Hamblin, R. L., and Buckholdt, D.: Structured exchanges and childhood learning: Hyperaggressive children. St. Ann, Mo.: Central Midwestern Regional Educational Laboratory, 1967. (ERIC Document Reproduction Service No. ED004797)

Krauch, V.: Hyperactive engineering. *Amer. Educ.*, 1971, 7(5), 12–16.

Krop, H.: Modification of hyperactive behavior of a brain-damaged, emotionally disturbed child. *Training School Bull.*, 1971, 68, 49–54.

Laufer, M. W., and Denhoff, E.: Hyperkinetic behavior syndrome in children. *J. Pediat.*, 1957, 50, 463–474.

Levitt, E. E.: Research on psychotherapy with children. In A. E. Bergin, and S. L. Garfield (Eds.) *Handbook of Psychotherapy and Behavior Change.* New York: John Wiley, 1971.

Marwit, S. J., and Stenner, A. J.: Hyperkinesis: Delineation of two patterns. *Exceptional Child.*, 1972, 38(5), 401–406.

McFarlane, J. W., Allen, L., and Honzik, M.: A Developmental Study of the Behavior Problems of Normal Children Between 21 Months and 14 Years. Berkeley and Los Angeles: Univ. of California Press, 1954.

Mendelson, W., Johnson, N., and Stewart, M. A.: Hyperactive children as teenagers: A follow-up study. *J. Nerv. Ment. Dis.*, 1971, 153(4), 273–279.

Menkes, M. M., Rowe, J. S., and Menkes, J. H.: A 25-year follow-up on the hyperkinetic child with minimal brain dysfunction. *Pediatrics,* 1967, 39, 393–399.

Mitchell, D. W., and Crowell, P. J.: Modifying inappropriate behavior in an elementary art class. *Elementary School Guidance and Counseling*, 1973, 8(1), 34–42.

Mulholland, T. B.: It's time to try the hardware in the classroom. *Psychol. Today*, 1973, 7, 103–104.

Nall, A.: Alpha training and the hyperkinetic child: Is it effective? *Acad. Ther.*, 1973, 9(1), 5–19.

Palkes, H., Stewart, M., and Kahana, B.: Porteus Maze performance of hyperactive boys after training in self-directed verbal commands. *Child Develop.*, 1968, 39, 817–826.

Patterson, G. R., Jones, R., Whittier, J., and Wright, M. A.: A behavior modification program for the hyperactive child. *Behav. Res. Ther.*, 1965, 2, 217–220.

Schrager, J., and Lindy, J.: Hyperkinetic children: Early indicators of potential school failure. *Community Mental Health J.*, 1970, 6, 447–454.

Scott, T. J.: The use of music to reduce hyperactivity in children. *Amer. J. Orthopsychiat.*, 1970, 40, 677–680.

Simpson, D. D., and Nelson, A. E.: Breathing control and attention training: A preliminary study of a psychophysiological approach to self-control of hyperactive behavior in children. Fort Worth, Tex.: Texas Christian Univ. Inst. of Behav. Res., 1972.

Stewart, M. A.: Hyperactive children. *Sci. Amer.*, 1970, 222, 94–98.

Stewart, M. A., and Olds, S. W.: *Raising a Hyperactive Child*. New York: Harper & Row, 1973.

Stewart, M. A., Pitts, F. N., Craig, A. G., and Dierfel, W.: The hyperactive child syndrome. *Amer. J. Orthopsychiat.*, 1966, 36, 861–867.

Van Osdol, B. M., and Carlson, L.: A study of developmental hyperactivity. *Ment. Retardat.*, 1972, 10(3), 18–24.

Waldrop, M. F., and Goering, J. D.: Hyperactivity and minor physical anomalies in elementary school children. *Amer. J. Orthopsychiat.*, 1971, 41, 602–607.

Weiss, G.: Treatment of hyperactivity in children. *Curr. Psychiat. Ther.*, 1971, 10, 26–29.

Weiss, G., Minde, K., Werry, J. S., Douglas, V., and Nemeth, E.: Studies on the hyperactive child, VIII: Five-year follow-up. *Arch. Gen. Psychiat.*, 1971, 24, 409–414.

Wender, P. H.: Minimal Brain Dysfunction in Children. New York: Wiley-Interscience, 1971.

Wiltz, N. A., and Gordon, S. B.: Parental modification of a child's behavior in an experimental residence. *J. Behav. Therap. Exper. Psychiat.*, 1974, 5(1), 107–109.

Wunderlich, R. C.: Hyperkinetic disease. *Acad. Ther.*, 1970, 5, 99–108.

Part VII

MENTAL RETARDATION

In the past, the diagnosis of mental retardation was a global, grab-bag label based on measures of cognitive competence, skill acquisition and social adaptation. It was clear, however, that the diagnosis was an umbrella characterization for a heterogeneous group of conditions of widely varying etiologies. This concept has been affirmed by the identification of a series of genetic, metabolic, congenital and environmental conditions which can produce retardation in intellectual development.

The paper by Crandall reviews the genetic disorders which are responsible for nearly 50 percent of the cases of moderate and severe mental retardation. The advances in knowledge in this area are indeed spectacular. Precise categories of pathology have been defined, and refined methods of diagnosis developed. This knowledge is of great importance for the development of programs of prevention by genetic counseling and prenatal diagnosis.

An important contribution to the care and management of chronically handicapped children came with the identification of the harmful consequences that often resulted from long-term institutional placement. Inevitably, this resulted at first in the generalization that all institutions were bad. In recent years, a number of careful research workers have gone beyond this generalization to study the specific characteristics of different institutions, and their differential impact on specific groups of children. A leading research unit in this area is that of Zigler and his colleagues. In the present section, Zigler and Balla review and summarize the work of their group over a 20-year period on the impact of institutional experiences on the behavior and development of retarded persons. Their findings have important implications for child development theory, for the care of the mentally retarded, and for social policy.

PART VII: MENTAL RETARDATION

20

GENETIC DISORDERS AND MENTAL RETARDATION

Barbara F. Crandall

UCLA School of Medicine

Genetic disorders are responsible for nearly 50 percent of the half million moderately and severely mentally retarded. These include chrōmosomal abnormalities, those due to single genes, and others resulting from a combination of genetic and environmental factors. With the exception of specific metabolic diseases, most are not treatable so that prevention by genetic counseling and prenatal diagnosis becomes imperative. Neither of these can be accomplished without an accurate diagnosis underlining the importance of a diagnostic evaluation for all moderately and severely retarded individuals.

Mental retardation is a common problem and, based on intelligence alone, affects 3 percent of the population or 6 million individuals in the U.S. The accepted clinical definition, however, requires that there be a concurrent impairment of general adaptation (Grossman, 1973); with this added criterion there are 2 million retardates or about 1 percent of the population. This population can be further subdivided into a larger group (1.5 million) who are minimally retarded (IQ

Reprinted with permission from *Journal of the American Academy of Child Psychiatry*, Vol. 16, 1977, 88–108.

This research was supported in part by: University of California at Los Angeles; PHS Grants MCH-927, HD-04612, HD-00345, and HD-05615.

50–70) and generally lack physical stigmata. The fact that parents and siblings frequently are similarly impaired suggests a genetic etiology, but the known social class and economic dependency make this difficult to identify; perhaps this is best considered as multifactorial (genetic and environmental). It may well be that several subgroups with distinct genetic and environmental etiologies will emerge. With the exception of the sex-chromosome abnormalities and certain other genetic syndromes, most of the known genetic disorders affect the smaller group comprising about half a million retardates. It is this group which will be considered in more detail.

The moderately and severely retarded individuals (IQ < 50) frequently show clinical and laboratory pathology and come from all socioeconomic levels. In one study, nearly 50 percent of this group had a genetically related disorder (Kaveggia et al., 1972). Some of the genetic types of mental retardation to be discussed include: (1) *chromosome abnormalities* which account for about 45 percent of cases; (2) *single gene mutations* are responsible in about 35 percent and can be further subdivided into: (a) *metabolic disorders*; (b) *structural disorders* affecting several systems; (c) *multiple congenital anomaly/mental retardation* syndromes; and (3) *malformations of the central nervous system (CNS)*, which often result from a combination of genetic and environmental factors.

DIAGNOSTIC EVALUATION OF THE MENTALLY RETARDED

While genetically related disorders are responsible for nearly 50 percent of moderate mental retardation, an accurate diagnosis is essential for possible treatment and prevention by genetic counseling and prenatal diagnosis. This evaluation includes:

Family pedigree. This includes the patient, siblings and their children, the parents and their siblings and children, and grandparents. Names and birthdates are noted together with spontaneous abortions and their gestational ages, stillbirths, deaths in those under 30 and causes. Consanguinity is specifically stated. Relevant family history and comments concerning mental retardation, malformations, and neurological diseases are noted.

Pregnancy and neonatal history of the patient. These are compared in general to siblings; there are specific questions concerning diseases, drugs, and X-rays during and just prior to the pregnancy, weight gain during pregnancy, fetal movement, bleeding, delivery and presentation at delivery, length, head circumference, and neonatal problems.

Developmental history. A general comparison to siblings is helpful to-

Table 1

Indications for Urinary Screening and Amino-Acid Chromatography

1. Psychomotor retardation
2. Failure to thrive or vomiting in newborns
3. Unusual odor
4. Cutaneous changes such as unusual skin color, texture or rash, hair abnormalities
5. Eye abnormalities such as cataracts, corneal clouding, retinal degeneration, blindness
6. Enlargement of liver or spleen
7. Neurological deficits, seizures, or behavioral abnormalities

gether with the parents' concept of when and why they first became concerned. Was the condition progressive or nonprogressive? Developmental milestones are noted together with behavioral problems.

Past Illnesses, Trauma, Seizures.

Physical examination. This includes height, weight, head circumference, careful observation of anomalies; pigmentary and other changes of the skin, dermatoglyphics and neurological examination.

Physical examination of siblings and parents where indicated.

Additional diagnostic studies such as verbal and auditory tests, EMI brain scans, IVPs and immunologic tests to identify possible prenatal infection.

Metabolic studies including urinary screening and amino-acid chromatography form part of the work-up unless the condition is clearly secondary to an environmental insult. These studies are particularly important in the conditions listed in table 1. Additional studies on blood, bone marrow, and fibroblasts may follow.

Chromosome analyses are usually indicated where more than two physical defects are found together with retardation. Unless a simple trisomy is likely, differential banding studies using one of the recently developed stains is indicated. However, although most but not all autosomal changes result in some physical stigmata, it is our belief that chromosome studies should be included in the work-up of all moderately retarded individuals unless the findings result from a simple defect of the brain or clearly represent a known nonchromosomal disorder.

CHROMOSOME ABNORMALITIES

It is estimated that 10 percent of all conceptuses carry a chromosome abnormality, the majority arising from nondisjunction at 1st or 2nd meiotic metaphase (Boué et al., 1965). The majority of these fetuses are spontaneously aborted, and chromosome studies of abortuses show that about 60 percent of those lost in the first trimester have a chromosome abnormality (Carr, 1967). Most are sporadic events. Chromosome studies indicate that nearly 1 percent of all newborns show a chromosome change, of which some are rearrangements without loss or addition of chromosome material such as balanced translocations or certain normal variants (Walzer et al., 1969). Just over 0.5 percent have an abnormal amount of chromosome material. Where these changes affect the sex chromosomes, mental retardation is unusual, but it is nearly always present when one of the nonsex chromosomes or autosomes is affected. The absence of an entire autosome is rarely compatible with survival, but loss of part of such a chromosome may be tolerated and results in physical and mental changes. The use of the newer chromosome stains allows the identification of each chromosome by the position of its bands and has enabled us to associate specific chromosomes with specific physical changes and confirm previously unrecognized chromosome changes (figs. 1 and 2). Further progress in this area should enable us to identify chromosome changes in previously undiagnosed cases of mental retardation. Several of the commoner chromosome syndromes will now be described.

AUTOSOMAL ABNORMALITIES

Trisomy 21 (Down's Syndrome)

Trisomy 21 is one of the commonest malformation syndromes known and accounts for 15 to 20 percent of institutionalized patients.

Some of the clinical findings in Down's syndrome are well known and include hypotonia, brachycephaly, obliquity of the palpebral fissures, epicanthal folds, flat facies, abnormal and low-set ears, short neck, large furrowed tongue, simian lines, abnormal dermatoglyphics, and fifth finger clinodactyly. No single sign is pathognomonic of the malformation; the clinical impression results from the presence of several of these findings. Mental retardation, although variable in degree, appears to be present in every case, and the majority show a moderate degree of retardation (IQ 30–50). In the severely retarded, mental development may cease, or appear to deteriorate, after the age of 10 or 11 years. Sixteen percent of the higher-grade retardates reach a peak between 11 and 15 years, 35 percent at age 18, and 48 percent after the age of 20 (Darling and Benda, 1952). Approximately 40 percent of Down's syndrome patients have a cardiac malformation;

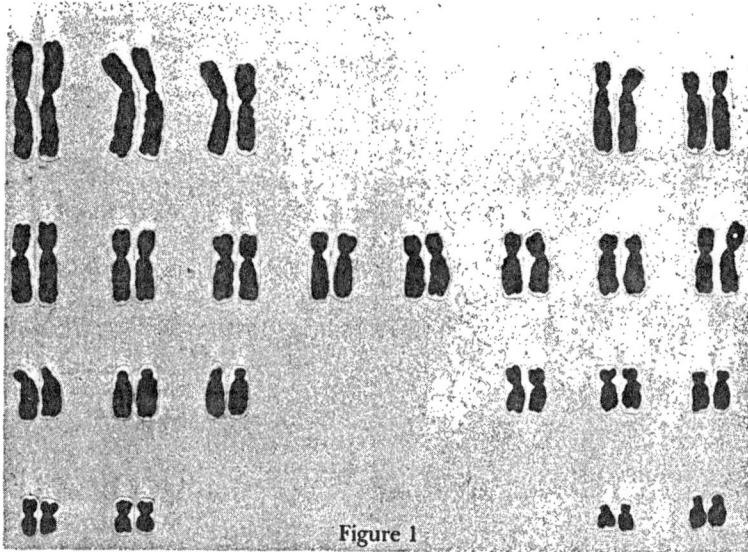

Figure 1

Routine karyotype

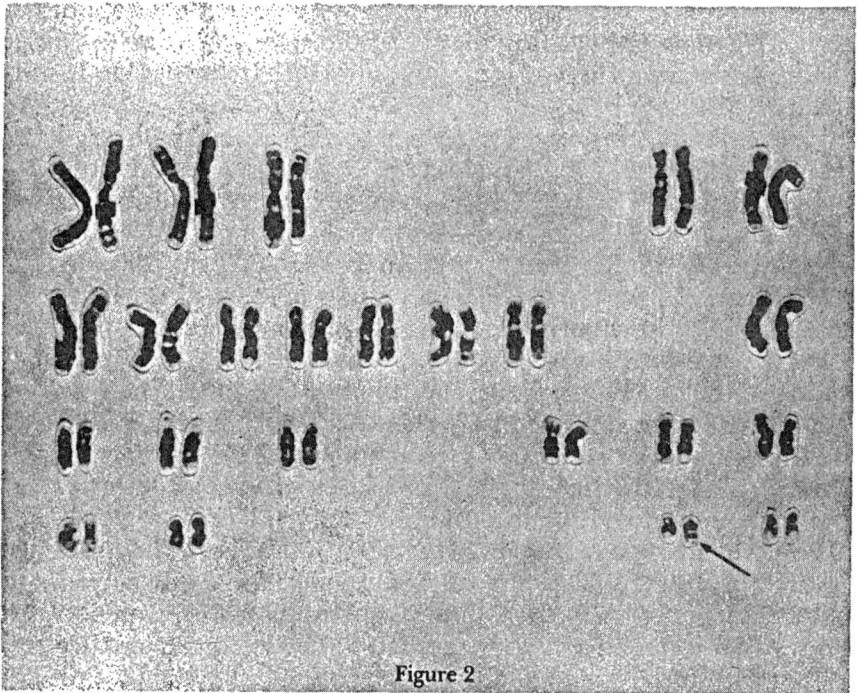

Figure 2

Trypsin-Giemsa banded karyotype of same patient. Note that the differential banding study identifies additional material on the no. 21 chromosome which was not seen on the routine study; the latter was interpreted as normal.

ventricular and atrial septal defects are the most common, followed by patent ductus arteriosus and atrioventricularis communis (Berg et al., 1960). Other malformations sometimes found in Down's syndrome include tracheoesophageal fistula, duodenal atresia, exomphalos, and Hirschsprung disease.

Down's syndrome occurs once in about 700 births. The incidence increases from 1/2,000 births when the maternal age is 20 years to about 1/25 by age 45 years. The majority (94%) of patients with Down's syndrome have trisomy 21, but 2.4 percent are mosaics and 3.6 percent have translocations (Richards et al., 1965). Primary trisomy probably results from nondisjunction of chromosomes 21, usually at the first meiotic division. The maternal age relationship suggests that the nondisjunction occurred in the mother. The mechanism for this is not known, but studies in rodents have shown reduced chiasma counts in "older" eggs, and this may lead to irregular distribution of homologous chromosomes in meiosis. Some cases of trisomy 21 result from mosaicism in either parent, the trisomic cells being too limited in number or distribution to produce phenotypic changes. The increased incidence of thyroid antibodies in young mothers (under 35 years) of a Down's syndrome child suggests that an immunologic mechanism could be an etiologic factor in nondisjunction (Fialkow, 1967).

There have been several studies concerning mortality in Down's syndrome. Carter (1958) found that of 700 patients with Down's syndrome, 30 percent died within 1 month of birth, 53 percent by 1 year, and 60 percent by 10 years. The highest mortality was between the ages of 1 and 5 years, and after 40 years (Forssman and Akesson, 1965); between 5 and 40 years it was little above normal. Females had a higher mortality than males. Collman and Stoller (1963) found that the infant mortality rate (deaths under 1 year per 1,000) was 311 for Down's syndrome, as compared with 20.8 in the general population. The commonest cause of death in the neonatal period was congenital heart disease, and respiratory infections accounted for the majority by the end of the first year (Richards et al., 1965). The increased mortality from acute leukemia in children under 2 years of age with Down's syndrome is between 15 and 20 times that of the general population (approximately 1 percent). All patients with Down's syndrome may show the neuropathologic changes of Alzheimer disease after 35 years of age and this presenile dementia probably accounts for the increased mortality after age 40 (Malamud, 1972).

Ideally, the diagnosis of Down's syndrome should be made at birth or shortly thereafter. A routine chromosome analysis is important in every case, both to confirm the diagnosis and to identify those with translocations. If trisomy 21 is found in the propositus, we do not arrange for parental chromosome studies unless other cases of Down's syndrome have been reported in the family. It is true that chromosomal mosaics and minor variants of etiologic importance could go undetected, but we believe that the chance of finding these is very small. If one child is born with trisomy 21, the risk for another is approximately 1 percent (Carter and Evans, 1961), and amniocentesis is recommended in all succeeding pregnancies. When translocation Down's syndrome is detected in a patient, chromosome analysis is indicated in both parents. Translocations account for 9 percent of Down's syndrome cases when the mother is less than 30 years old (Stein et al., 1973). Approximately one third of translocations are inherited, and the remainder arise de novo in the patient. When one parent is found to be a translocation carrier, the carrier's sibs and children are studied in order of reproductive risk. The observed risk for a second child with Down's syndrome is 10–15 percent when the mother carries the translocation and 4 percent when the father carries it (Hamerton, 1971). Amniocentesis is therefore strongly indicated if either parent carries a translocation.

Trisomy 18 (Edwards Syndrome)

Trisomy 18 was first described in 1960 by Edwards et al. The incidence is 1/3,000 newborns, and many are spontaneously aborted early in pregnancy. Like trisomy 21, this chromosome abnormality shows a maternal age relationship. The sex ratio at birth favors females by 3 to 1. A large group of abnormalities have been ascribed to trisomy 18 and include growth deficiency; hypertonicity; prominent occiput; low-set, malformed, rotated ears; small palpebral fissures; micrognathism; 2nd finger overriding the 3rd; congenital heart defect; and unusual dermatoglyphic patterns. All are severely retarded, and 75 percent die within 6 months after birth. While the majority of these children have an additional chromosome 18, a few have partial trisomies (resulting from translocations) or mosaicism. For this reason, as well as for diagnostic confirmation, all suspected trisomy 18 patients have a routine chromosome analysis. Parental chromosome studies are indicated, particularly if a translocation is detected. Although most cases of trisomy 18 are sporadic, a second chromosome abnormality in a succeeding pregnancy has prompted us to recommend amniocentesis for succeeding pregnancies in these mothers (Crandall and Ebbin, 1973).

Trisomy 13 (Patau Syndrome)

This chromosome abnormality occurs once in 5,000 births. The findings noted in 50 percent include: polydactyly, congenital heart defect, microphthalmia, simian line, cleft lip and palate, apneic spells, hyperconvex nails, low-set ears with or without malformation, scalp defects, and skin folds around the neck. Approximately 75 percent of these patients die by 6 months of age, and the rest are profoundly retarded. Most commonly, chromosome analysis reveals an additional D-group chromosome, identified as a no. 13 by differential banding studies. A few patients have only 46 chromosomes, with a sporadic translocation involving two no. 13s or one no. 13 and another chromosome; a few others have an inherited translocation. D-D translocations are the commonest chromosomal rearrangement in the general population (1/1,000) but have rarely resulted in a child with trisomy 13.

Trisomy 8

Trisomy 8 was identified by Caspersson et al. (1972) using differential chromosome stains, and the phenotypic changes are characteristic enough to form a recognizable syndrome. Three patients with this syndrome have been seen at UCLA, and the physical findings in all were sufficiently specific to allow the diagnosis to be made prior to the chromosome study (Crandall et al., 1974). All were mosaics, as were 2 of Caspersson's patients. Clinical findings include mental retardation (usually moderate), strabismus, prominent ears, vertebral anomalies, absent patellas, progressive contractures, and abnormalities of the hands and feet. One of Caspersson's patients had no reported physical or mental defects but a history of two spontaneous abortions. Trisomy 8 appears to carry the largest reduplicated autosome compatible with survival.

Partial Trisomy 15

Another trisomy, a partial one of chromosome 15, is of interest because both the children we have described with this anomaly lack physical malformations (Crandall et al., 1973). They are of normal height, but both are moderately retarded (IQ 40–50) and very hyperkinetic. The additional no. 15 (approximately two thirds of this chromosome) was present in all cells examined. The absence of malformations with this autosomal abnormality has caused us to revise our indications for chromosome studies so that moderate or severe retardation alone is sufficient.

Chromosome Deletion Syndromes

While additional chromosome deletion syndromes continue to be described, those affecting chromosomes nos. 9, 13, 21, 4, 5, and 18 identify the more consistent syndromes. Of these, loss of part of the short arm of chromosomes no. 4 (4p-), 5 (5p-), and the long arm of no. 18 (18q-) will be described here. Deletions may result from a familial balanced translocation and require chromosome studies of both parents.

· *4p- (Wolf syndrome).* Clinical findings include moderate to severe mental retardation, seizures, cleft lip and/or palate, and depressed angles of the mouth.

5p- (Cri du chat syndrome). The most specific symptom here is a high-pitched cry due to laryngeal hypoplasia in the first year of life. These individuals are moderately retarded and tend to have rounded facies, large corneas, and moderate mental retardation.

18q-. Moderate to severe mental retardation with a poorly developed midface, depressed angles of the mouth, and unusual ears with prominent antihelices suggest this chromosome change.

SEX CHROMOSOME ABNORMALITIES

Sex chromosome anomalies are relatively common and are found in about 0.25 percent of newborns. The resulting physical changes are often minimal. The majority of these patients have normal intelligence; a small proportion are retarded, but usually only minimally. The sex chromatin, Barr body test, or buccal smear is a simpler and older test than a chromosome analysis. Its use, however, is limited to a screening procedure with additional chromosome studies if the result is at variance with the anatomical sex. The normal female has a single Barr body, the normal male none. However, this test will fail to identify a structurally abnormal X chromosome, may be negative in normal newborn female infants, and technical artifacts are common and make interpretation difficult.

Turner's Syndrome (45, X)

In 1938, Turner first described a syndrome of short stature, sexual infantilism, webbed neck, and cubitus valgus. The chromosome abnormality was not found until 1959 (Ford et al., 1959). The incidence is 1 in 3,000 female births, and a large number are aborted spontaneously, particularly late in pregnancy. Probably only 1 in 40 affected fetuses survive to term.

Infants with Turner's syndrome are frequently of low birth weight and may have edema of the dorsum of the hands and feet and webbing of the neck. The only consistent findings, however, are short stature and failure to develop secondary sex characteristics. Ninety percent of these patients have gonadal dysgenesis. Twenty-five percent of patients have cardiac abnormalities, of which the commonest is a coarctation. Fifty percent have a neural type hearing loss, and 60 percent have urinary tract anomalies. All of these patients are sterile. The majority (90%) are not retarded, although learning problems, particularly in space-form cognition, appear to be common and may lead to difficulties in school (Money, 1963). IQ tests reveal a statistically significant difference between the verbal and performance scores. About 30 percent of clinically diagnosed Turner's syndrome patients have positive sex chromatin tests due to mosaicism, a structural defect of an X chromosome, or an XX complement. The rest have only one X chromosome. Turner's syndrome has no relationship to increased maternal age, and genetic studies using the Xg blood group have shown that about 74 percent of patients have received their single X from their mother.

Klinefelter's Syndrome (47, XXY)

Klinefelter's syndrome occurs once in 500 births and is due to the presence of an additional X chromosome in a male. The only consistent physical finding is hypogonadism, and all such males are sterile; thus, most patients are referred after puberty or because of infertility. Thirty percent of patients have gynecomastia; long limbs, eunuchoid proportions, and lack of pubic hair have also been noted.

There are a number of reports of psychiatric studies in Klinefelter's syndrome, and the variable conclusions probably reflect biased sampling. Emotional immaturity, apathetic behavior, failure to participate in classroom activities, and difficulties in establishing relationships with peers have frequently been noted. A relationship between this sex chromosome abnormality and antisocial behavior is suggested by some reports and denied by others (Court Brown, 1962; Neilsen, 1964a, 1964b). Likewise, the predisposition to schizophrenia is supported by some and denied by others. Raphael and Shaw (1963) suggest that sex chromosome anomalies are commoner in schizophrenic patients than in the general population, but this was not supported by Nielsen's study. Although figures vary in different studies, approximately 25 percent of Klinefelter males are retarded and usually minimally.

Genetic studies have shown that in 60 percent of cases the additional X is maternally derived. This chromosome abnormality occurs more commonly in children of older mothers. Cases with multiple X's (e.g., 49, XXXXY) have been described, but are less common than one additional X chromosome. Nearly all of these patients are retarded; the degree of retardation tends to increase with the multiplicity of X's, and physical malformations also occur.

XYY Syndrome (47, XYY)

Generally, patients with an XYY pattern are not retarded, but they tend to be of increased stature. An insufficient number of patients have been studied to be certain that aggressive, unpredictable behavior is characteristic of this syndrome. XYY individuals are fertile, and the majority produce sons with a normal complement of Y chromosome.

XXX Syndrome (47, XXX)

The incidence of females with an additional X chromosome is about 1 in 1,500 births. A few of these patients are retarded, usually minimally, and there is no characteristic physical abnormality. Menstrual irregularities and secondary amenorrhea have been reported, but most are fertile and their children are chromosomally normal.

SINGLE GENE MUTATIONS RESULTING IN MENTAL RETARDATION

Metabolic disorders may be the result of enzymatic disorders leading to the absence of the products of that enzyme through failure to metabolize small circulating molecules but without intracellular storage. Storage diseases normally result from a defect in a catabolic pathway with accumulation of products within a cell. Other metabolic disorders result from defects in transport mechanisms.

Enzymatic Disorders without Storage

Enzymatic abnormalities in this category result in accumulation of the substrate prior to the block (as in PKU), failure to produce an end product (as in hypothyroidism), or diversion of products to an alternate pathway. Mental retardation probably results from one or more of these effects, but not from the abnormal storage of metabolites. Metabolic errors affecting amino acids account for the majority of the disorders in this category, and PKU is the commonest of these (Stanbury et al., 1960).

Phenylketonuria (PKU). This disease, transmitted as an autosomal recessive, occurs once in 10,000 to 13,000 births and results from a deficiency of liver phenylalanine hydroxylase. Many states now require screening of all newborn babies, and this has contributed to the early identification of a number of affected infants. However, tests done before discharge from the hospital (i.e., prior to 3 days of age) fail to identify some infants with a late rise in phenylalanine. Untreated children are frequently, but not always, retarded and may exhibit hyperkinetic or autistic behavior; seizures and an unusual odor are additional complaints. The low phenylalanine diet necessary to control this disorder is usually continued until 5 years of age, but opinions differ as to the need for the diet after this age.

Women who have discontinued their low phenylalanine diets or who have a variant form of PKU have a high risk for children with mental retardation. Although the elevated phenylalanine level has no effect on the mother, it may compromise the developing fetal brain and other organs. It appears that a large number of the children of PKU mothers who are untreated during their pregnancies are retarded and about 25 percent have congenital malformations in addition (Perry et al., 1973). This speaks for the continuation of the diet in affected people, routine ferric chloride urine tests for all pregnant women (with therapeutic abortion, where acceptable, when the phenylalanine level appears to be greater than 10 mg%) and routine urinary screening of women who have more than one retarded child or more than one child with a learning problem. Although all the children of an affected individual will be PKU carriers, the risk that they will also have PKU is 1/50 (the frequency of carriers in the general population) x ½ or 1/100. Phenylalanine hydroxylase, a liver enzyme, cannot be detected in amniotic fluid cells.

Homocystinuria, tyrosinemia, and methylmalonic aciduria are other metabolic disorders affecting amino acids. The best known metabolic disorder to affect carbohydrates is galactosemia, and early recognition with prompt elimination of lactose from the diet can often prevent the defects. Untreated cases show mental retardation, cataracts, cirrhosis, seizures, and early death. This disease is inherited as an autosomal recessive and can be detected prenatally in amniotic fluid cells.

Storage Diseases

These may involve several large classes of compounds of which a few examples will be described.

Sphingolipids. This large group of compounds is derived from a base sphingosine with the addition of a long-chain fatty acid and either phosphorylcholine (sphingomyelin), glucose, or galactose. All these substitutions result in different sphingolipids and lipid storage diseases have consequently been classified according to the compounds stored.

Tay-Sachs disease results from the absence of the enzyme hexoseaminidase-A and the accumulation of ganglioside, particularly in the central nervous system. This disease is particularly common among Ashkenazi Jews, where the incidence of carriers is 1/30. It is now possible to detect carriers by a simple serum estimation of hexoseaminidase. By identifying all carriers prior to pregnancy, it should be possible to eliminate this disorder. When both parents are found to be carriers, there is a 25 percent risk for an affected child, and amniocentesis with assay of hexoseaminidase-A in the amniotic fluid cells is necessary to identify the affected fetus.

Tay-Sachs disease usually develops in the first year of life, with loss of motor milestones and voluntary movement in a previously normal baby. Hyperacusis is common, and blindness develops with spasticity and terminal seizures. A cherry-red spot on the macula is frequently noted, although it is not confined to this disease. Death usually occurs by 3 to 4 years of age. The late infantile and juvenile forms of amaurotic family idiocy are less common than Tay-Sachs disease. Sandhoff's disease produces a similar clinical picture but affects non-Jewish infants.

Mucolipids. The mucolipidoses are a newly described group of disorders once thought to be variants of Hurler's syndrome. The specific enzyme defect is not known, but lysosomal enzymes are depleted in the cells which become filled with granular inclusions. Mucopolysaccharides are not excreted in the urine. In Type I, hypotonia is followed by hypertonicity, the coarse features resemble Hurler's syndrome, and there is mental retardation. Type II, I-cell or Leroy's disease, shows considerable variation in severity. Typically, it causes progressive mental retardation with coarse features, minimal corneal clouding, gingival hypertrophy and skeletal abnormalities. A third and fourth type have since been described. All of these disorders are inherited as autosomal recessive traits, and the abnormality can usually be detected in amniotic fluid cells.

Mucopolysaccharides

The large group of disorders in this category include three which result in mental retardation: Hurler's and Sanfilippo's syndromes are transmitted as autosomal recessives, while Hunter's is an X-linked disorder. Characteristically, mucopolysaccharides are excreted in the urine. In addition to mental retardation, these children develop coarse facies with large heads, hernias, corneal clouding, short stature, joint limitations by about 6 months of age, and hepatosplenomegaly. The defective enzymes have now been identified and can be detected in amniotic fluid cells.

Polysaccharides

A number of disorders of glycogen metabolism are included in this group, but Pompe's disease is the one which results in mental retardation. Glycogen is deposited in the central nervous system and heart with death usually prior to 2 years of age, but variants with longer survival have been described. This autosomal recessive disease can be identified prenatally by demonstrating the absence of the enzyme alpha-1-4-glucosidase in amniotic cells.

Defects in Transport

Defects in transport may block the absorption of substances, prevent their transport to target organs, and affect their excretion.

Menke's syndrome appears to be due to a defect in copper transport across the intestinal wall and results in abnormal hair, failure to thrive, seizures, and spasticity. This disease is transmitted as an X-linked recessive. Amniocentesis can be offered to couples who have had an affected son and who wish to have further children. The test is for sex determination only to identify the male fetus.

Hartnup's disease appears to be due to a defect in intestinal and renal transport of specific neutral amino acids. Cerebellar ataxia, a pellagralike rash, mental retardation, and amino aciduria can be reversed by nicotinamide therapy.

Wilson's disease is included in this category because there is an abnormality of ceruloplasmin, a serum protein involved in the transport and/or transfer of copper. Copper is deposited in the liver, brain, and spleen. Mental deterioration may be quite late in onset and very variable in degree; some forms of the disease present as cirrhosis with very little mental abnormality. Tremors, ataxia, and rigidity are usually present and progressive. The pathognomic finding is the Kayser-Fleischer ring due to deposition of copper in the cornea. This autosomal recessive disease may be detected prior to the onset of symptoms by measuring the ceruloplasmin levels in siblings of an affected individual. Penicillamine administration can prevent or reverse early symptoms.

Single Gene Mutations Causing Structural Disorders of Several Systems

A group of diseases with neurocutaneous lesions sometimes called the phacomatoses are probably responsible for as many cases of mental retardation as the metabolic diseases. An abnormal overgrowth of several tissues occurs with hemangiomata, neural tumors, and abnormal skin pigmentation. Many of these are genetic, and some of the commoner diseases will be discussed.

Tuberous sclerosis. Of this group of diseases, tuberous sclerosis is the one most frequently seen in institutionalized mentally retarded individuals. A study of 2,000 retarded children reported 20 children with one of the phacomatoses, of whom 75 percent had tuberous sclerosis (Berg and Crome, 1963). Infantile spasms followed by myoclonic seizures and later grand mal epilepsy may be the first evidence of the disease. Mental retardation may be absent, mild, or moderate. All those with retardation develop seizures. Vitiliginous cutaneous spots which fluoresce with a Wood's lamp are helpful in diagnosis. The typical butterfly facial rash is often angiomatous at first and later becomes fibroangiomatous. Intracranial calcification can be seen on skull films, but may not be present until 10 years of age. Retinal phacomas are present in 50 percent of patients and subungual fibromas are also common. Sixty percent of patients have cystic changes in their phalanges. Renal tumors probably affect nearly all such patients. Cardiac rhabdomyomas develop in 5 percent of patients with this disease, and 5 to 10 percent die of brain tumors.

The incidence of tuberous sclerosis is approximately 1/30,000, but as a proportion of mild cases probably remain undiagnosed, this figure is certainly an underestimate. The disease is inherited as an autosomal dominant trait, but expressivity is extremely variable. Not uncommonly, a family with only one affected child requests genetic counseling. In addition to a detailed family history, it is important to examine all siblings, parents, and if possible grandparents for evidence of seizures and mental retardation, intracranial calcification, retinal phacomas, and vitiliginous skin lesions. If all of these are negative, the family is advised that the affected child probably represents a new mutation and the risk for further affected siblings is low. At least one third of cases appear to be the result of a new mutation. However, the affected child has a 50 percent risk for affected children. Any evidence of the disease in parents or siblings is indicative of the inherited form, and the risk then for another affected child to these parents is 50 percent. It is important to point out that the severity of the disease may show a wide range of variability even in members of the same family.

The *Sturge-Weber syndrome* is probably not genetic and rarely affects other family members. Cutaneous hemangiomata are distributed over areas of the face supplied by divisions of the trigeminal nerve. Involvement of the eye may lead to buphthalmos and of the meninges to seizures, mental retardation, and paresis.

Multiple Neurofibromatosis (Van Recklinghausen's Disease)

Neurofibromatosis with an incidence of 1 in 3,000 is one of the commonest genetic diseases. About 30 percent of these patients are retarded, but this is frequently minimal. The expressivity is exceedingly variable, and the most reliable diagnostic evidence of this disease is the presence of 6 or more cafe-au-lait spots of 1.5 cm. or more at their widest diameter (Crowe et al., 1956). When confronted with one affected child, examination of both parents and any other siblings for 6 or more cafe-au-lait spots, subcutaneous neurofibromatoses, scoliosis, deafness, and retinal changes is essential. If none of these are found, the parents are advised of the probability of a new mutation with the same counseling as for tuberous sclerosis. At least one third of cases appear to represent new mutations. Positive physical signs in another family member imply a 50 percent risk for other affected children, and the disease may be severely handicapping or mild. The risk to the children of the one affected individual is 50 percent.

Multiple Congenital Anomaly/Mental Retardation Syndromes

Some of these syndromes appear to be familial and are listed in table 2 together with their more consistent physical anomalies. While others appear to be sporadic, they may represent new mutations. Recognition of these disorders is helpful for prognosis and particularly for genetic counseling. A careful history of drugs taken during a pregnancy is important as an increasing number of multiple congenital anomaly/mental retardation syndromes may be attributed to specific medications. Some of these are listed in table 3.

MALFORMATIONS OF THE CNS

This group of disorders includes those which result from genetic and environmental factors, i.e., multifactorial disorders. Those most likely to result in mental retardation are CNS malformations such as spina bifida with hydrocephalus and encephalocele. Approximately half of all spina bifidas are associated with mental retardation. Before genetic counseling can be given, it is essential to be sure that this is

Table 2

Examples of Genetic Multiple Congenital Anomaly (MCA)/MR Syndromes

Syndrome	Common Physical Findings	Inheritance
1. Smith Lemli Opitz	Failure to thrive, ptosis, syndactyly of toes 2 and 3 and abnormalities of external genitalia	A/R *
2. De Sanctis-Cachione	Xeroderma pigmentosa, microcephaly, hypogonadism	A/R
3. Seckel	Prenatal growth deficiency, microcephaly, prominent nose	A/R
4. Cockayne	Growth failure with senility, retinal degeneration, deafness, and photosensitivity	A/R
5. Sjogren-Larsson	Ichthyosis, spasticity, shortness	A/R
6. Congenital Myotonic Dystrophy	Mother affected, severe hypotonia, clubfeet, myopathic facies	A/D †
7. Craniosynostosis syndromes	Synostosis of cranium, maxillary hypoplasia ± syndactyly, and thumb anomalies or polydactyly	A/D or A/R
8. Multiple lentigines	Cutaneous lentigines, deafness, pulmonic stenosis, hypertelorism, growth failure	A/D

* AR = autosomal recessive
† AD = autosomal dominant

Table 3

Malformations Attributed to Specific Drug Exposure in Pregnancy

Drug	MR	Physical Findings
Alcohol (fetal alcohol syndrome) (Jones et al., 1974)	+	Prenatal growth deficiency, microcephaly, short palpebral fissures, joint anomalies.
Tridione (German et al., 1970)	+	Growth deficiency, maxillary hypoplasia, ptosis or strabismus, heart defect
Hydantoin (Monson et al., 1973)	±	Growth deficiency, cleft lip and palate, dysplasia of terminal phalanges, occasional cardiac abnormalities
Progesterone (Nora et al., 1976)	±	Limb defects, congenital heart defects
Warfarin (Janerich et al., 1974; Shaul et al., 1975)	+	Hypoplastic nasal cartilage, stippled epiphyses, hypotonia, seizures

the only malformation. Empiric risk figures have been collected from several large studies and show that after one child with anencephaly or spina bifida, the risk for a second with either is 5 percent. After two children with either or both malformations, the risk becomes 15 percent. In addition, defects confined to the developing brain are frequently sporadic, while others (simple microcephaly and X-linked hydrocephalus) are inherited as Mendelian traits.

PREVENTION AND TREATMENT

Genetic Counseling

Genetic counseling consists of the presentation of data to an individual, couple, or family so that they can learn the risks for a specific disease or malformation within a family, the clinical picture and prognosis of a disease, and the possibilities of prevention and treatment. For adequate scientific genetic counseling, the following basic information is essential: a specific diagnosis, detailed family pedigree, knowledge of the inheritance pattern, and familiarity with recent literature.

Autosomal traits are determined by genes that are not carried on the X chromosome; they may be dominant or recessive. Autosomal dominant traits are manifested when only one of a pair of genes is mutant and are frequently inherited through a number of generations within a family. Males and females are affected in equal proportions, and the risk for each child of an affected individual is 50 percent. This group of diseases sometimes develops in adulthood and shows much variability in degree of severity.

Autosomal recessive disorders are the result of a pair of mutant genes, indicating both parents are obligate carriers. Families often show several affected siblings, and the risk for each successive child is 25 percent. However, an affected individual or his unaffected sibling who marries a normal individual rarely has affected children. As many of these diseases are rare, a history of parental consanguinity is common.

Sex-linked traits are carried only on an X chromosome, as the Y appears to contribute sex-determining genes only. The transmission of a disease from father to son excludes X linkage. X-linked dominant diseases are transmitted to 50 percent of the offspring of an affected woman, and all the daughters of an affected male will also be affected. X-linked recessive diseases are transmitted by normal females; 50 percent of their daughters will be carriers, and 50 percent of their sons will be affected.

The ultimate goal of the diagnostic evaluation, other than treatment, is to identify a specific disorder as genetic or nongenetic. The former includes chromosomal, Mendelian, and multifactorial diseases; the latter may have a recognizable etiologic basis (prenatal infection or drugs) or suggest a known and usually sporadic condition. Where the diagnosis is not known, genetic counseling with regard to recurrence risks becomes exceedingly difficult.

Table 4

Indications for Amniocentesis

Category	Reason	Risk
Chromosome abnormality	Maternal age greater than 35 years;	1% or greater
	previous child with Down's syndrome;	1%
	parents known translocation carriers	12–50% for mother
		4–50% for father
	Previous child with chromosome	
	abnormality (sporadic);	Less than 1%
	multiple anomalies—undiagnosed	?
Sex-linked disorders:		
a. Specific enzyme assay		
available	Hunter's, Fabry's, Lesch-Nyhan	50% of males
b. For sex only	Duchenne muscular dystrophy,	
	hemophilia	50% of males
Autosomal recessive disorders	i.e., Galactosemia, Gaucher's,	
	Tay-Sachs	25%
CNS malformation	for α fetoprotein estimation	5%

Amniocentesis

Amniocentesis is an extension of genetic counseling and is included in that discussion. It is important to identify situations where amniocentesis is inappropriate and the reasons. The indications for amniocentesis are shown in table 4. By far the largest proportion are now done for maternal age because of the increasing risk of a chromosome abnormality. This increase is irrespective of parity. Approximately 6 percent of births occur to women who are 35 years of age or more, yet about one third of all Down's syndrome infants are born to them. Despite efforts to publicize amniocentesis, only about 5 percent of women in this age group obtain the test (Crandall and Lebherz, 1976). We prefer to perform it at 16 weeks, dated from the last menses. A complete genetic history and pedigree are an initial requirement followed by ultrasonography to confirm the gestational age and identify the placental position. Amniocentesis is an outpatient procedure requiring but a short time to aspirate 20 ml of amniotic fluid. It is a safe procedure with a risk of 1 percent or less of spontaneous abortion. The accuracy is high, but approximately three weeks are required to culture sufficient cells for the necessary studies. Other than Tay-Sachs disease, where a simple blood test on both parents identifies the need for amniocentesis if both parents are carriers, the diagnosis of a previously affected child identifies the specific metabolic disorder to be tested. Alpha-fetoprotein measurement should identify 90 percent of neural tube defects (spina bifida, anencephaly, and encephalocele), and is particularly indicated where a previous child has had one of these malformations.

Treatment in genetic disorders is limited to some of the metabolic disorders. Accurate diagnosis of the enzymatic defect is essential, and rather few respond to treatment. This may involve elimination of a particular substance from the diet (phenylalanine in PKU or lactose in galactosemia), the use of specific compounds such as penicillamine in Wilson's disease, or high doses of co-factors to stimulate enzymatic activity such as vitamin B6 in some cases of homocystinuria. Tissue and organ replacement (kidney transplant in Fabry's disease) are possible forms of treatment in specific conditions, and therapy may include direct enzyme replacement in the future.

FUTURE PROSPECTS

Only a few examples of some genetic types of mental retardation have been presented. As technological improvements continue, the large group of individuals with mental retardation, etiology unknown, can be expected to diminish. Improved chromosome stains and biochemical studies will certainly play a role here. Clearly, many causes of mental retardation, genetic and nongenetic, have their origin during pregnancy, and improved noninvasive studies such as ultrasonography may be used to identify some of these. The extension of amniocentesis for the diagnosis of additional abnormalities can be expected to continue with the use of fetal blood and tissue to identify abnormalities not possible in amniotic cells. Greater availability of diagnostic and genetic counseling services, particularly for the parents and siblings of the mentally retarded, should be given priority together with financial support for these services.

REFERENCES

Berg, J. M. & Crome, L. (1963), Les phakomatoses dans la deficience mentale. In: *Les phakomatoses cerebrales*, ed. L. Michaux & M. Feld. Paris: Spei-editeurs, pp. 297–304.

——— ——— & France, N. E. (1960), Congenital cardiac malformations in mongolism. *Brit. Heart J.*, 22:331–346.

Boué, J. G., Boué, A., & Lazar, P. (1965), Les aberrations chromosomiques dans les avortements. *Ann. Genet., Semaine Hop.*, 10:179–187.

Carr, E. H. (1967), Chromosome anomalies as a cause of spontaneous abortion. *Am. J. Obs. Gyn.*, 97:283–293.

Carter, C. O. (1958), A life-table for mongols with the causes of death. *J. Ment. Defic. Res.*, 2:64–74.

——— & Evans, K. A. (1961), Risk of parents who have had one child with Down's syndrome (mongolism) having another child similarly affected. *Lancet*, 2:785–787.

Caspersson, T., Lindsten, J., Zech, L., Buckton, E., & Price, W. H. (1972), Four patients with trisomy 8 identified by the fluorescence and Giemsa banding techniques. *J. Med. Genet.*, 9:1–7.

Collmann, R. D. & Stoller, A. (1963), Data on mongolism in Victoria, Australia. *J. Ment. Defic. Res.*, 7:60–68.

Court Brown, W. M. (1962) Sex chromosomes and the law. *Lancet*, 2:508–509.

Crandall, B. G., Bass, H. N., Marcy, S. M., Glovsky, M., & Fish, C. H. (1974). The trisomy 8 syndrome. *J. Med. Genet.*, 11:393–398.

———— & Ebbin, A. (1973), Trisomy 18 and 21 in two siblings. *Clin. Genet.*, 4:517–519.

———— & Lebherz, T. B. (1976), Prenatal genetic diagnosis in 350 amniocenteses. *Obs. & Gyn.*, 48:158–162.

———— Muller, H. M., & Bass, N. H. (1973), Partial trisomy of chromosome no. 15 identified by trypsin-Giemsa banding. *Amer. J. Ment. Defic.*, 77:571–578.

Crowe, F. W., Schull, W. J., & Neel, J. V. (1956), *A Clinical, Pathological and Genetic Study of Multiple Neurofibromatosis*. Springfield, Ill.: Charles C. Thomas.

Darling, D. & Benda, C. E. (1952), Mental growth curves in untreated institutionalized mongoloid pattients. *Amer. J. Ment. Defic.*, 56:578–788.

Edwards, J. H., Harnden, D. G., Cameron, A. H., Crosse, V. M., & Wolff, O. H. (1960), A new trisomic syndrome. *Lancet*, 1:787–789.

Fialkow, J. (1967), Thyroid antibodies, Down's syndrome and maternal age. *Nature*, 214:1253–1254.

Ford, C. E., Jones, K. W., Polani, P. E., de Admeida, J. C., & Briggs, J. H. (1959), A sex-chromosome anomaly in a case of gonadal dysgenesis (Turner's syndrome). *Lancet*, 1:711–713.

Forssman, H. & Akesson, H. O. (1965), Motility in patients with Down's syndrome. *J. Ment. Defic. Res.*, 9:146.

German, J., Kowal, A., & Ehlers, K. H. (1970), Trimethadione and human teratogenesis. *Teratology*, 3:349–361.

Grossman, H. J. (1973), *Manual on Terminology and Classification in Mental Retal Retardation: 1973 Revision*. Washington: American Association on Mental Deficiency, Special Publication Series no. 2.

Hamerton, J. L. (1971), *Human Cytogenetics*, Vol. 1. New York: Academic Press, p. 279.

Janerich, D. T., Piper, J. M., & Glebatis, D. M. (1974), Oral contraceptives and congenital limb-reduction defects. *New Eng. J. Med.*, 291:697–700.

Jones, K. L., Smith, D. W., Streissguth, A. P., & Myrianthopoulos, N. C. (1974), Outcome in offspring of chronic alcoholic women. *Lancet*, 1:1076–1078.

Kaveggia, E. G., Opitz, J. M., & Pallister, P. D. (1972), Diagnostic genetic studies in severe mental retardation. In: *The Proceedings of the 2nd Congress of the International Association for the Scientific Study of Mental Retardation*. Primrose: Swets & Zeilingen, pp. 305–312.

Malamud, N. (1972), Neuropathology of organic brain syndromes associated with aging. In: *Advances in Behavioral Biology*, Vol. 3, ed. C. M. Gaitz, New York: Plenum Press, pp. 63–87.

Money, J. (1963), Cytogenetics and psychosexual incongruities with a note on space-form blindness. *Amer. J. Psychiat.*, 119:820–827.

Monson, R. R., Rosenberg, L., Hartz, S. C., Shapiro, S., Heinonen, O., & Slone, D. (1973), Diphenylhydantoin and selected congenital malformations. *New Eng. J. Med.*, 289:1049.

Nielsen, J. (1964a), Klinefelter's syndrome and behavior. *Lancet*, 2:587–588.

—— (1964b), Prevalence of Klinefelter's syndrome in patients with mental disorders. *Lancet*, 1:1109.

Nora, J. J., Nora, A. H., Perinchief, A. G., Ingram, J. W., Fountain, A. K., & Peterson, M. J. (1976), Congenital abnormalities and first-trimester exposure to progestagen/estrogen. *Lancet*, 1:313–314.

Perry, T. L., Hansen, S., Tischler, B., Richards, F. M., & Sokol, M. (1973), Unrecognized adult phenylketonuria. *New Eng. J. Med.*, 289:395–398.

Raphael, T. & Shaw, M. W. (1963), Chromosome studies in schizophrenia. *J. Amer. Med. Assn.*, 183:1022–1028.

Richards, B. W., Stewart, A., Sylvester, P. E., & Jasiewicz, V. (1965), Cytogenetic survey of 225 patients diagnosed clinically as mongols. *J. Ment. Defic. Res.*, 9:245–259.

Shaul, W. L., Emery, H., & Hall, J. G. (1975), Chondrodysplasia punctata and maternal Warfarin use during pregnancy. *Amer. J. Dis. Child.*, 129:360.

Stanbury, J. B., Wyngaarden, J. B., & Fredrickson, D. S., eds. (1960), *The Metabolic Basis of Inherited Disease*, New York: McGraw-Hill.

Stein, Z., Susser, M., & Guterman, A. V. (1973), Screening program for prevention of Down's syndrome. *Lancet*, 1:305–309.

Turner, H. H. (1938), A syndrome of infantilism, congenital webbed neck, and cubitus valgus. *Endocrinology*, 23:566–574.

Walzer, S., Breau, G., & Gerald, P. S. (1969), A chromosome survey of 2,400 normal newborn infants. *J. Pediat.*, 74:438–448.

21

IMPACT OF INSTITUTIONAL EXPERIENCE ON THE BEHAVIOR AND DEVELOPMENT OF RETARDED PERSONS

Edward Zigler and David A. Balla

Yale University

A program of research on the effects of institutional experience on retarded persons was described. The importance of such research for theory construction, use by clinicians, and construction of social policy was discussed, as was the value of both longitudinal and cross-institutional studies. We stressed that any comprehensive understanding of the effects of institutional experience requires a consideration of: (a) the characteristics of the retarded person, (b) his preinstitutional life experience, (c) the nature of the institution, and (d) a range of criterion behavior on the part of the resident.

Our purpose in the present paper is to present a discussion of a longstanding research commitment by ourselves and our colleagues; namely, investigating the impact of institutional experiences on the behavior and development of retarded persons. As will soon become clear, much less is known about the impact of institutions than would be expected, considering the importance of the issue. Reliable knowledge concerning the effects of institutions is important for several

Reprinted with permission from *American Journal of Mental Deficiency*, Vol. 82, 1–11, 1977.

reasons. At a theoretical level, many investigations of retarded persons' behavior have involved comparisons of noninstitutionalized nonretarded individuals and institutionalized retarded individuals. In this kind of study it is impossible to determine which effects are attributable to institutionalization as contrasted to mental retardation per se (Baumeister, 1967; Hagen & Huntsman, 1971; Katz & Rosenberg, 1969). Indeed, several of our colleagues are now trying to separate these two factors.

Second, increased knowledge about the effects of institutions would be extremely helpful to parents and professionals. The decision of whether to institutionalize a retarded person is one of the most painful that parents can face. Many professionals hold strong views on this subject, but they are often contradictory or too simplistic. Depending on the expert approached, a parent might be informed that (a) the degree of retardation is such that institutionalization is the only possible solution, (b) institutionalization is necessary so the development of the other children in the family will not be prejudiced, or (c) institutionalization should be avoided at all costs because it is either unnecessary or so demeaning to the retarded person that no parent should permit it. If the effects of institutionalization were known, a great deal of parental conflict and pain would be alleviated.

Perhaps of greatest importance, though, is that reliable knowledge concerning institutionalization effects—especially differences between large central institutions vs. community-based regional centers or group homes—would be extremely helpful when formulating social policy in the field of mental retardation. For almost 15 years, the predominant thrust of social policy in the mental retardation area has been a movement away from large central institutions to a community-based regionalization model in which retarded persons are treated in small, residential, community settings. This social policy has evolved almost completely without an empirical base. The almost total lack of data on what constitutes the most adequate care setting for retarded individuals is potentially disastrous for those involved in the creation of social policy, whatever their persuasions as to what is the best care setting. For example, in this day of drastic budget-cutting at all levels of government, it is entirely possible that the large central institution will be rediscovered: expensive professional services can be consolidated, there would be savings in administrative costs, and the economies of scale would operate. If policymakers cannot demonstrate that regional centers or group homes are cost-effective, it would be difficult to resist such arguments for central institutions.

With this background as to the importance of the issue, we will discuss a program of research that we and our collaboraters have conducted for almost 20 years. To anticipate, we have become convinced that any comprehensive understanding of the effects of institutionalization must require a consideration of three classes of variables. The first is the characteristics of the person. The effects of institutionalization have been found to be different as a function of such factors as the person's sex, diagnosis, developmental level, and chronological age (CA). Of particular importance is the preinstitutional life experience of the individual. We have found again and again that a retarded person's response to institutionalization is partially determined by the nature of his experiences prior to institutionalization.

The second important class of variables concerns the nature of the institution. We have found that it is crucial to go beyond the simple question of size. We must look at other demographic variables, e.g., cost, number of staff per resident, and employee-turnover rate. We must go even further than this examination of multiple demographic variables and investigate the social-psychological characteristics of institutions—administrative structure, employee attitudes, and the actual way in which the residents are cared for. We consider this class of variables to be especially important. The view that institutions with enlightened administrators, employees with positive attitudes concerning retarded persons, and humane caretaking practices will promote more adequate adaptation and competence in the residents is certainly a plausible one. However, we feel that investigations concerned with the quality of life of retarded persons are valuable in and of themselves. Retarded individuals have a right to humane care and treatment whether or not such care ultimately results in greater behavioral growth. The final class of variables of importance is, of course, measures of the behavioral status and growth of retarded individuals, including both cognitive and motivational factors.

Our work on institutional effects can be traced back to the senior author's doctoral dissertation (Zigler, 1958) concerning the phenomena of perseveration and dependency so often seen in institutionalized retarded persons. Based on the work of Lewin, it was widely believed at the time that this perseveration was somehow an inherent characteristic of retarded individuals (Kounin, 1941a, 1941b; Lewis, 1936). In this study, an alternate view was proposed. Zigler (1958, 1961) hypothesized that many institutionalized retarded persons had been deprived of supportive contact with adults both before they were institutionalized and while they were in the institutions. Consequently, it seemed reasonable to assume that they would be extremely responsive to supportive contacts with adults when such contacts were available. In this context perseveration was viewed as being a consequence of such a heightened responsiveness to social reinforcement. To test this idea, a group of retarded individuals who had been institutionalized for approximately 2 years played an extremely boring and repetitive game involving simply dropping marbles in the hole of a box. However, when they dropped the marbles they were frequently told that they were doing very well, with additional frequent reinforcement in the form of nods and smiles. Two experienced clinical psychologists were asked to rate the social histories of the individuals as to how much social deprivation they had experienced before coming to the institution. It was found that people who had been rated as more deprived persevered longer on the Marble-in-the-Hole game than individuals rated as less deprived. It seemed that the perseveration to often seen in retarded persons was due to a lack of contact with supportive adults rather than somehow being intrinsic to mental retardation. Additional support for this view was found in a study of responsiveness to social reinforcement in institutionalized and noninstitutionalized nonretarded and retarded children (Zigler, 1963). The institutionalized nonretarded children were just as responsive to social reinforcement as the institutionalized retarded children. There were also no differences between the noninstitutionalized nonretarded and retarded groups.

At this point, our interest in institutionalization led us in several different directions. Probably the most important was the choice of a research strategy that has been characteristic of our work for many years—the longitudinal study. It is apparent that there are difficulties in any study involving institutionalized persons on a one-time basis. If the behavior of institutionalized retarded individuals is found to be different from that of noninstitutionalized retarded persons, we really have difficulty in saying that these differences are solely due to the effects of institutionalization. It may be that institutionalized individuals are different in many crucial respects from those who remain in their homes. Consequently, we came to believe early, along with others, that longitudinal studies are necessary in order to understand fully the effects of institutions. When the growth of a group of individuals is mapped over time, we can be on more confident grounds in attributing any changes to the effects of institutional experience.

The first longitudinal study was conducted by Zigler and Williams (1963). In this study, the individuals tested in a previous study (Zigler, 1961) were retested after 3 additional years of institutional experience. In addition to changes in responsiveness to social reinforcement, we also looked at changes in intelligence test scores. We found that, over the 3-year period, individuals became significantly more motivated to receive the attention and support of a friendly adult. However, the increase in motivation for social reinforcers was related to the amount of preinstitutional deprivation that the individuals had experienced. Individuals who came from relatively good homes showed a much greater increase in their motivation for social reinforcers than did individuals coming from more socially deprived homes. It seemed that the effects of institutionalization depended on the preinstitutional history of the individual, with such institutionalization being more socially depriving for individuals from relatively good homes than for individuals from extremely deprived backgrounds.

We were surprised to find a general decrease in IQ between the first and second testing. We also found that this finding was reminiscent of those in a study done in England by Clarke and Clarke (1954). They discovered that individuals coming from extremely poor homes showed an increase in IQ following institutionalization, with no increase observed in individuals coming from relatively good homes. Indeed, in the Zigler and Williams (1963) study, the only persons showing increase in IQ were in the highly deprived group, as defined by the clinical psychologists who had rated the social histories.

Zigler, Butterfield, and Capobianco (1970) studied these same individuals after 7 years and after 10 years of institutional experience. After both 7 and 10 years of institutionalization, highly deprived individuals became much less responsive to social reinforcement than did less deprived individuals. This finding certainly supported the view that institutionalization was less depriving for individuals from poor homes than for those from good homes. Even more important was our discovery that the effects of preinstitutional social deprivation were still in evidence after 10 years of institutionalization. The importance of this point cannot be overemphasized. Social deprivation is a phenomenon that, once experienced, is built into the motivational structure of the individual and subsequently mediates his interactions with his environment.

At about this time, we conducted another longitudinal study of changes in responsiveness to social reinforcement and IQ in a group if institutionalized retarded persons (Zigler, Balla, & Butterfield, 1968). We tested individuals approximately 3 weeks following institutionalization and then again approximately 3 years after institutionalization. The individuals were residents in what was considered to be one of the finest public institutions in the country. In contrast to the findings in the Zigler and Williams (1963) study, the individuals in this institution became less responsive to social reinforcement over 3 years and increased in IQ. Furthermore, individuals from relatively good homes showed a smaller decrease in responsiveness to social reinforcement than did individuals from relatively poor homes. It seemed most reasonable to conclude that the differences in findings between the two studies were due to the differences in the quality of the two institutions. It seemed that the institution employed in the first study was a depriving one, while the one employed in the second study actually ameliorated the effects of preinstitutional deprivation. In a further study of this group of individuals, we found that after 6 years of institutional life the tendencies towards psychological growth found after 3 years were still in evidence (Balla & Zigler, 1975). There was a further significant increase in IQ, while the individuals' responsiveness to social reinforcement stabilized. Just as in the Zigler et al. (1970) study, the effects of preinstitutional life experience were still in evidence after 6 years, in that organically retarded subjects who came from homes characterized by marital discord and/or mental illness were more responsive to social reinforcement over all 6 years than less deprived organically retarded subjects.

We then conducted a study of the developmental course of responsiveness to social reinforcement in institutionalized retarded and noninstitutionalized nonretarded children (Zigler & Balla, 1972). Groups with mental ages (MAs) of approximately 7, 9, and 12 were investigated. We found that both retarded and nonretarded children of higher MAs were less responsive to social reinforcement than those of lower MAs. This finding was certainly consistent with a common observation that children become less dependent and more autonomous as they grow older. However, at every MA level the retarded subjects were far more dependent than their nonretarded counterparts. There was no tendency for the retarded individuals to catch up in their autonomy as they became older. In fact, the oldest retarded group persisted at the Marble-in-the-Hole game almost twice as long as the youngest nonretarded group. Thus, institutionalized retarded children seem to be severely deficient in the development of the reliance upon internal resources that determines much of their effectiveness in the adult world.

As in our previous studies, we found that those individuals who had experienced greater preinstitutional social deprivation were more responsive to social reinforcement than less deprived children. Of special interest was our finding that the retarded individuals who maintained contact with their parents or parent-surrogates either by being visited at the institution or by going home on vacations were more likely to display the type of autonomous behavior characteristic of nonretarded children. Thus, we found clear empirical evidence that an institutional policy of encouraging many contacts with the community does promote psychological growth.

By this time, we were demonstrating in our research that the effects of institutionalization are extremely complex, dependent on the individuals' preinstitutional life experience and the particular institution under consideration. While this point should almost be self-evident, it is all too often overlooked. Institutions for retarded persons continue to be seen as uniform entities producing monolithic behavioral consequences.

As it became increasingly apparent that there were important differences between institutions, we planned cross-institutional studies. The first of these was conducted by Butterfield and Zigler (1965). Two nearby large central institutions with which we were familiar impressed us as having very different social climates. In the first institution, every effort was made to provide a home-like atmosphere: no buildings were locked, and all of the residents could freely move around the grounds. It was organized on a cottage system with a large number of relatively small residential units. In the second institution, little effort was made to provide a home-like atmosphere. The residents ate in a large central dining room with virtually no individual supervision. All of the buildings were locked, and no individual could move around the grounds unattended by an employee. The institution was organized on a dormitory system with very large living units. We expected and found that the second institution was much more socially depriving than the first one, and the effects of such deprivation would be seen in the responsiveness to social reinforcement of the individuals.

The next cross-institutional study was a good deal more ambitious (Balla, Butterfield, & Zigler, 1974). We used a longitudinal design and investigated four institutions in different parts of the country. In this study, we tried to take a much more fine-grained look at the nature of the institutions: size, number of residents per living unit, cost per resident per day, employee-turnover rate, number of direct care personnel per resident, number of professional staff per resident, and number of volunteer hours per resident per year. We felt that an examination of these factors, in conjunction with our general impressions, would provide a reasonable framework from which to evaluate residents' behavior change. Indeed, the institutions varied in size from approximately 400 to 2,000 residents. There was also considerable variation in cost, number of aides per resident, and employee-turnover rate.

Residents in each of the institutions were examined within 6 months of their admission date and again after 2.5 years of institutional experience. In addition to the measure of responsiveness to social reinforcement used in previous studies, we also obtained measures of MA, IQ, verbal dependency, extent of imitation of adults, and variability in behavior. Contrary to our most pessimistic views concerning the effects of institutionalization, we found considerable evidence of psychological growth on the part of the residents. Over the course of 2.5 years, in all of the institutions the residents became less verbally dependent, less imitative, and more variable in their behavior. IQ level did not change and MA level increased. To our surprise, very few of the findings were related to any of the characteristics of the institutions. Residents in the largest of the institutions were more responsive to social reinforcement than residents in the other three institutions. With this exception, none of the other demographic characteristics of the institutions were found to be related to the behavior or development of the residents. Our subjective impressions were equally inaccurate in relating to the behavior of the development of the residents. At this point, it seemed clear to us that as even more detailed measure of institutional characteristics was needed.

We were extremely fortunate in that King, Raynes, and Tizard (1971) had conducted extensive and sensitive cross-institutional studies of resident-care practices in institutions for retarded persons in England. They developed a Resident Management Practices Inventory that was an excellent measure of the social-psychological characteristics of the institutions. This inventory was conceptualized as tapping institution-oriented care practices, at one extreme, vs. resident-oriented practices at the other. In their view, the items in the inventory could be grouped along four dimensions. The first item was called Rigidity of Routine and concerned the inflexibility of management practices, so that at one extreme, neither individual differences among residents nor unique circumstances are taken into account by the staff in their interactions with residents. The second dimension was called Block Treatment and concerned the regimentation of residents before, during, and after specific activities, e.g., meal time. The third dimension was referred to as Depersonalization, a measure of the presence of absence of opportunities for residents to have personal possessions, privacy, or situations allowing self-expression and initiative. The fourth dimension was referred to as Social Distance and concerned the limitation of interaction between staff and resident to formal and specific activities and the use of physically separate areas of congregation between the staff and those who cared for them.

Using this inventory, King et al. (1971) investigated three types of facilities for retarded persons: mental deficiency hospitals, ranging in size from 121 to 1,650 residents; voluntary homes, from 50 to 93 residents; and local authority hostels (group homes), from 12 to 41 residents.

The care practices were found to be more resident- than institution-oriented in the group homes and more institution-oriented in the mental deficiency hospitals, with the voluntary homes falling between. Of particular interest was the finding that, once type of institution was taken into account, there was no tendency for management practices to be associated with institution size. In other words, type rather than size of institution was the important determinant of care practices. The importance of this point is underscored when it is recalled that the mental deficiency hospitals ranged in size from approximately 100 to 1,600 residents, yet no differences in care practices were found within this type of institution. When type of institution was taken into account, no association was found between the number of residents in each living unit and the care practices observed nor was a relationship found between resident-to-staff ratios and care practices. Finally, King et al. (1971) found that the level of retardation of residents in the individual living units was not an overriding determinant of care practices. This result was of some surprise in view of the findings that child-rearing practices are so much determined by the characteristics of the child as by the characteristics of the adult (Bell, 1968; Yarrow, Waxler, & Scott, 1971). More severely retarded children are less responsive and provide less feedback than children of higher cognitive competence. It would seem quite easy to become mechanical and unresponsive while caring for children when responsiveness to such care is not immediately evident.

We felt that the investigations by King et al. (1971) were important for several reasons. First, they studied different types of institutions at a time when far too little attention had been paid to the relative adequacy of central institutions, regional centers, and group homes. Second, they were directly concerned with the quality of life of institutionalized retarded persons, a matter that has been grossly neglected in empirical research. Finally, they underscored the importance of the living unit as a unit of analysis.

We decided that just such a study was needed for institutions in the United States and were also quite fortunate in having the opportunity to study institutions in a Scandinavian country world-renowned for its humane care of retarded persons. We studied the resident-care practices in 166 living units from 19 institutions in the United States and

11 institutions in the Scandinavian country (McCormick, Balla, & Zigler, 1975). A number of institutional demographic variables were examined: institution type, i.e., large, central, regional center and group home; institution size; average number of residents per living unit; cost per resident per day; number of aides per resident; number of professional staff per resident; annual employee-turnover rate; volunteer hours per resident per year; and mean institutional IQ. We also obtained additional information on level of retardation in each unit—i.e., mild, moderate, or severe-profound—and the age level of the residents in each unit—i.e., child, adolescent, or adult.

We found that living units in the Scandinavian country were more resident-oriented than were living units in the United States. In both countries, large central institutions were characterized by the most institution-oriented care practices and group homes by the most resident-oriented care practices, with regional centers falling between. This finding was consistent with that of King et al. (1971). Living units for more severely retarded residents were found to be more institution-oriented. We then determined which of the demographic variables were most closely associated with care practices by employing multiple regression analyses, with the demographic characteristics of both institution and individual living unit as predictor variables and the Resident Management Practices Inventory as the dependent variable. The findings of these analyses were particularly interesting. Large living-unit size and level of retardation were found to be predictive of institution-oriented care practices. Cost per resident per day, number of aides per resident, or number of professional staff per resident, *did not* predict care practices.

The lack of association of either financial or human factors—as measured by cost per resident per day and by number of aides and professional staff per resident, respectively—came as a considerable surprise to us. Apparently, simply increasing expenditures or personnel will not necessarily guarantee better care for retarded persons. Rather, it is how these personnel are utilized in the settings. The finding that living-unit size was predictive of care practices is of special practical interest. One way of creating more humane settings for institutionalized retarded persons may well be to design living units small enough so that each resident is, of necessity, seen as an individual. It is encouraging to note that it may be possible to pursue such a policy with existing resources. The reader will recall that the most resident-oriented care practices were found in group homes, which were operated at less cost than either the regional centers or the large central institutions. It may well be that part of the lower cost for group homes can be accounted for by the fact that these facilities, for the most part, serve mildly retarded residents who require less care and supervision. However, as mentioned above, number of aides or professional staff per resident were not found to be predictive of care practices.

We did find one exception to the general lack of association of such "human variables" as number of aides per resident and employee-turnover rate and care practices. In group homes in the United States, low employee-turnover rate and a high ratio of professional staff per resident were found to be predictive of more resident-oriented care practices. It may well be that such human factors as continuity of staffing can only become operative in certain settings.

The results of this study, as well as the findings of King et al. (1971), convinced us that we had a sensitive method of characterizing the social-psychological milieu of residential settings for retarded persons. What was lacking in both our work and that of King et al. (1971) was a study in which both care practices and the actual behavior of the residents were investigated. We decided to conduct just such a study (Balla, Kossan, & Zigler, Note 1). A total of 114 retarded persons in 20 living units in seven institutions were examined. Five of the facilities were regional centers and two were large central institutions. In each living unit, King et al.'s Resident Management Practices Inventory was administered to the charge aide. We also obtained a measure of attitudes concerning the retarded residents from each aide in each living unit. We looked into such institutional demographic variables as cost per resident per day, employee-turnover rate, and number of aides per resident. The association of preinstitutional life experience, CA, MA, IQ, sex, and length of institutionalization with behavior was also examined. On the behavioral side, we obtained indicies of responsiveness to social reinforcement or dependency, wariness of adults, and imitation. Our previous work has suggested that these three factors are particularly important in retarded individuals' daily competence.

Before discussing the findings concerning the determinants of the behavior of the subjects in the study, one major result with the demographic institutional variables should be mentioned. Large-institution size was found to be very significantly related to larger living-unit size, high employee-turnover rate, low cost per resident per day, a low ratio of aides to residents, a low proportion of professional staff to resident, a low number of volunteer hours per resident per year, more adverse opinions concerning retarded persons, and more institution-oriented care practices. This pattern of interrelationships is especially important in discussions concerning social policy and residential facilities, which most often focus solely on institution size. If our findings have generality beyond the state in which the study was conducted, discussions could as easily focus on lack of professional staff, lack of aides, or lack of continuity of care, as measured by turnover rate. We should certainly display considerable caution when interpreting relationships between institution size and some other variable, since any such empirically discovered relationship may be due to the common relationship that these two measures have with a third measure.

Turning now towards findings concerning behavior, there were no differences between persons residing in central institutions and persons residing in regional centers on any of our behavioral measures. This lack of findings was of some surprise in view of the fact that the average size of the large central institutions was 1,633, while the average size of the regional centers was 111. The central institutions also housed more residents per living unit and had a higher employee-turnover rate. The cost per resident per day was twice as high in the regional centers as in the central institutions. The number of aides per resident was twice as high in the regional centers as in the central institutions. The proportion of professional staff per resident and the number of volunteer hours per resident per year was almost six times as great in the regional centers as in the central institutions. Such findings lend credence to the view that simply increasing cost and/or increasing staff will not, in and of itself, ensure greater behavioral competency on the part of residents in institutions. The findings also suggest that more intensive efforts need to be made to discover what particular kinds of programs enhance the behavioral competency of residents in institutions. The mere placement of a retarded person in a regional center did not seem to suffice as a means for increasing competency.

With one exception, no behavioral differences were found between persons residing in the two central institutions or five regional centers. There were also no behavioral differences between persons residing in the largest regional center (population 290) and the smallest regional center (population 12). It seems most reasonable to conclude that the behavior of the residents in all of the institutions was similar.

A series of multiple-regression analyses were performed in which all of the characteristics of the residents (e.g., MA or length of institutionalization) and all of the institutional characteristics (e.g., cost per resident per day or Resident Management Practices Inventory score) were used to predict the scores on our measures of behavior.

We should note that in this kind of analysis, the effect found for any one variable is independent of the effects of all other variables.

We found that several of the characteristics of the institutions were associated with the behavior of the residents. The larger the size of the institution, the greater the motivation of the individuals to receive adult attention and support. In large institutions, individuals appear to be relatively deprived of this class of social reinforcer. This finding was the single instance in which institution size was predictive of the resident's behavior. To this point, we had been assuming that depriving socializing experiences lead retarded individuals to be excessively dependent upon adults when the adults are reinforcing their behavior by making supportive comments. However, there is a body of work in the tradition of Spitz (Spitz, 1945; Spitz & Wolf, 1946) and Bowlby (1951) suggesting that extreme forms of deprivation can result in apathy, withdrawal, and a lack of responsivity to supportive adults. In order to develop attachments to adults and thus become responsive to their attention and support, it seems as if the child must have some minimal number of positive encounters with them. Children extremely deprived of such encounters would be expected to show greatly attenuated responsivity to adult attention and support. On the other hand, if children experience some minimum of support and attention at the hands of adults within a general socializing history of deprivation, we would expect these children to show atypically high responsivity to attention and support. We found some support for this formulation: large professional staffs and active volunteer programs were associated with higher responsiveness to social reinforcement.

We found considerable evidence that depriving socializing conditions produce wariness of adults. The larger the number of individuals in a living unit, the greater the wariness of the individuals who lived in the unit. Increased wariness was found in settings with high employee-turnover rates and a high proportion of aides to residents. Thus, it would seem that the response to a large number of noncontinuous adult caretakers—and, therefore, nonpredictable adult caretaking—is the development of wariness. We also found that aides' adverse attitudes concerning retarded persons, was related to greater wariness on the part of the residents.

There was evidence suggesting that some institutions socialize their residents in the direction of reduced behavioral spontaneity and/or conformity. We found high levels of imitation in individuals institutionalized a relatively long period of time and in individuals who were the recipients of institution- as opposed to resident-oriented care practices. Thus, many of the institutionalized retarded persons appear to live in a highly predictable environment that emphasizes conformity. Such conformity may be a form of adjustment to the institution. The value of living in a well-organized and predictable environment can be seen in a finding that less wariness was displayed by residents receiving institution- as opposed to resident-oriented caretaking practices. However, such conformity was probably purchased at too high a psychological cost. The conforming and imitative child distrusts spontaneous solutions to problems and may be ill-equipped to function in the much less organized and predictable environment outside the institution.

We have come to view either too little or too much imitation as negative psychological indicators, with some intermediate level of imitation being viewed as a positive developmental phenomenon reflecting a person's healthy attachment to adults and responsivity to cues adults emit that can be used in problem-solving efforts. Consistent with this view was our finding that retarded individuals whose caretakers had negative attitudes concerning them were less imitative. Persons consistently reacted to in a negative manner may respond by ignoring the cues provided by adults and thus become less imitative.

In addition to these effects of institutions upon behavior, we found several characteristics of the persons to be predictive of their behavior. Consistent with earlier findings (Balla et al., 1974; Zigler & Balla, 1972), residents of high MA were found to be less motivated for social attention and support than were residents of low MA. Thus, retarded children, like their peers of average IQ, seemed to move from dependency to autonomy as their cognitive level became higher. Evidence was also found indicating that the higher the MA level, the greater the wariness. This finding is consistent with the body of work indicating that the higher the developmental level of the child, the greater his sensitivity to depriving events and his capacity to construct such self-defeating mechanisms as wariness and avoidance of adults (Katz & Zigler, 1967; Katz, Zigler, & Zalk, 1975; Zigler, Balla, & Watson, 1972). Consistent with earlier findings, MA was negatively related to imitation (Balla et al., 1974; Balla, Styfco, & Zigler, 1971; Ruble & Nakamura, 1973; Yando & Zigler, 1971; Zigler & Yando, 1972). This finding was in keeping with two facets of our outerdirectedness formulation (Zigler, 1972; Zigler & Balla, 1976). The higher the cognitive level of the child, the less he employs imitation in problem-solving efforts, and the lower the IQ of the child, the more failure experiences he has when employing his own cognitive resources and, thus, the greater tendency for imitativeness.

Finally, we found that individuals who had experienced frequent changes of parenting figures before they were institutionalized were both more motivated to attain the attention and support of an adult and more wary of doing so. These findings provided additional evidence for our view that deprived retarded individuals have both atypically high positive and negative reaction tendencies (Zigler, 1971; Zigler & Balla, 1976). The subjects in this study had been institutionalized for an average of over 8 years and the fact that the effects of preinstitutional life experience were still in evidence after so long a time is consistent with our general position that social deprivation experienced relatively early in life can affect the behavior of retarded persons when it is assessed many years later (Balla & Zigler, 1975; Zigler et al., 1968; Zigler et al., 1970).

In conclusion, if there is a consistent theme to this 20 years of work on the effects of institutionalization on retarded persons, it is a continuing and increasing emphasis on the social-policy implications of our research. We are convinced that any comprehensive program of research must take into account not only the behavioral functioning of residents but the quality of life they experience, the extent to which they maintain contact with the community, and whether they are successfully discharged to community placement. We believe that only by means of such a multifaceted research program will it be eventually possible to determine empirically the optimal residential setting at the optimal cost.

REFERENCE NOTE

1. Balla, D., Kossan, N., & Zigler, E. *Effects of preinstitutional history and institutionalization on the behavior of the retarded.* Unpublished manuscript, Yale University, 1976.

REFERENCES

Balla, D., Butterfield, E. C., & Zigler, E. Effects of institutionalization on retarded children: A longitudinal cross-institutional investigation. *American Journal of Mental Deficiency*, 1974, 78, 530–549.

Balla, D., Styfco, S. J., & Zigler, E. Use of the opposition concept and outerdirectedness in intellectually-average, familial retarded, and organically retarded children. *American Journal of Mental Deficiency*, 1971, 75, 663–680.

Balla, D., & Zigler, E. Preinstitutional social deprivation and responsiveness to social reinforcement in institutionalized retarded individuals: A six-year follow-up study. *American Journal of Mental Deficiency*, 1975, 80, 228–230.

Baumeister, A. A. Problems in comparative studies of mental retardates and normals. *American Journal of Mental Deficiency*, 1967, 71, 869–875.

Bell, R. Q. A reinterpretation of the direction of effects in studies of socialization. *Psychological Review*, 1968, 75, 81–95.

Bowlby, J. *Maternal care and mental health.* Geneva: World Health Organization, 1951.

Butterfield, E. C., & Zigler, E. The influence of differing institutional social climates on the effectiveness of social reinforcement in the mentally retarded. *American Journal of Mental Deficiency*, 1965, 70, 48–56.

Clarke, A. D. B., & Clarke, A. M. Cognitive changes in the feebleminded. *British Journal of Psychology*, 1954, 45, 173–179.

Hagen, J. W., & Huntsman, N. J. Selective attention in mental retardates. *Developmental Psychology*, 1971, 5, 151–160.

Katz, P. A., & Rosenberg, S. Effects of labels on the perception and discrimination learning of retardates. *Journal of Abnormal Psychology*, 1969, 74, 95–99.

Katz, P., & Zigler, E. Self-image disparity: A developmental approach. *Journal of Personality and Social Psychology*, 1967, 5, 186–195.

Katz, P., Zigler, E., & Zalk, S. Children's self-image disparity: The effects of age, maladjustment, and action-thought orientation. *Developmental Psychology*, 1975, 11, 546–550.

King, R. D., Raynes, N. V., & Tizard, J. *Patterns of residential care: Sociological studies in institutions for handicapped children.* London: Routledge & Kegan Paul, 1971.

Kounin, J. Experimental studies of rigidity: I. The measurement of rigidity in normal and feebleminded persons. *Character and Personality*, 1941, 9, 251–272. (a)

Kounin, J. Experimental studies of rigidity: II. The explanatory power of the concept of rigidity as applied to feeblemindedness. *Character and Personality*, 1941, 9, 273–282. (b)

Lewin, K. *A dynamic theory of personality.* New York: McGraw-Hill, 1936.

McCormick, M., Balla, D., & Zigler, E. Resident-care practices in institutions for retarded persons: A cross-institutional, cross-cultural study. *American Journal of Mental Deficiency*, 1975, 80, 1–17.

Ruble, D. N., & Nakamura, C. Outer-directedness as a problem-solving approach in relation to developmental level and selected task variables. *Child Development*, 1973, 44, 519–528.

Spitz, R. A. Hospitalism: An inquiry into the genesis of psychiatric conditions in early childhood. In A. Freud (Ed.), *The psychoanalytic study of the child* (Vol. I). New York: International Universities Press, 1945.

Spitz, R. A., & Wolf, K. M. Analytic depression. In A. Freud (Ed.), *The psychoanalytic study of the child* (Vol. II). New York: International Universities Press, 1946.

Yando, R., & Zigler, E. Outerdirectedness in the problem-solving of institutionalized normal and retarded children. *Developmental Psychology.* 1971, 4, 277–288.

Yarrow, M. R., Waxler, C. Z., & Scott, P. M. Child effects on adult behavior. *Developmental Psychology*, 1971, 5, 300–311.

Zigler, E. *The effect of preinstitutional social deprivation on the performance of feebleminded children.* Unpublished doctoral dissertation, University of Texas, 1958.

Zigler, E. Social deprivation and rigidity in the performance of feebleminded children. *Journal of Abnormal and Social Psychology*, 1961, 62, 413–421.

Zigler, E. Rigidity and social reinforcement effects in the performance of institutionalized and noninstitutionalized normal and retarded children. *Journal of Personality*, 1963, 31, 258–269.

Zigler, E. The retarded child as a whole person. In H. E. Adams & W. K. Boardman, III, (Eds.), *Advances in experimental clinical psychology* (Vol. 1). New York: Pergamon Press, 1971.

Zigler, E. Rigidity in the retarded: A re-examination. In E. Trapp & P. Himelstein (Eds.), *Readings on the exceptional child: Research and theory* (2nd ed.). New York: Appleton-Century-Crofts, 1972.

Zigler, E., & Balla, D. Developmental course of responsiveness to social reinforcement in normal children and institutionalized retarded children. *Developmental Psychology*, 1972, 6, 66–73.

Zigler, E., & Balla, D. Motivational factors in the performance of the retarded. In R. Koch & J. C. Dobson (Eds.), *The mentally retarded child and his family: A multidisciplinary handbook* (2nd ed.). New York: Brunner/Mazel, 1976.

Zigler, E., Balla, D., & Butterfield, E. C. A longitudinal investigation of the relationship between preinstitutional social deprivation and social motivation in institutionalized retardates. *Journal of Personality and Social Psychology*, 1968, 10, 437–445.

Zigler, E., Balla, D., & Watson, N. Developmental and experimental determinants of self-image disparity in institutionalized and noninstitutionalized retarded and normal children. *Journal of Personality and Social Psychology*, 1972, 23, 81–87.

Zigler, E., Butterfield, E. C., & Capobianco, F. Institutionalization and the effectiveness of social reinforcement: A five- and eight-year follow-up study. *Developmental Psychology*, 1970, 3, 255–263.

Zigler, E., & Williams, J. Institutionalization and the effectiveness of social reinforcement: A three-year follow-up study. *Journal of Abnormal and Social Psychology*, 1963, 66, 197–205.

Zigler, E., & Yando, R. Outerdirectedness and imitative behavior of institutionalized and noninstitutionalized younger and older children. *Child Development*, 1972, 43, 413–425.

Part VIII

CHILDHOOD PSYCHOSIS

Earlier concepts of the etiology of autism and childhood schizophrenia emphasized a purely psychogenic etiology, with such formulations as "the schizophrenogenic mother," "refrigerator parents," and "the double bind." Recent research has not validated this position, but, to the contrary, emphasized the role of biological factors. As always, these factors must be viewed as integrated with environmental influences in the production of the final behavioral outcome.

The three contributions to this section deal with biological data, but all are by workers who have consistently emphasized the organism-environment interactional model in their influential studies. Folstein and Rutter report a study of 21 pairs of same-sexed twins, one or both of whom had autism. Their findings indicate the significance of a genetic factor in the etiology of autism, as well as the importance of brain injury, especially in the perinatal period.

Fish provides a detailed summary of the evidence for the existence of a neurobiologic disorder in children antedating the onset of childhood schizophrenia. She concludes that preschizophrenic infants show a fluctuating dysregulation of maturation, a "pandevelopmental retardation," which is significantly related to a genetic history for schizophrenia.

Chess reports a study on autism in congenital rubella, a follow-up of her previous finding of a strikingly high prevalence of this psychosis in a sample of 243 children with congenital rubella. In the follow-up, an unexpectedly larger proportion of children had recovered relatively quickly in childhood from their autistic symptoms, as compared to other follow-up reports on autistic children. In addition, four new cases were identified with onset after 2.5–5 years of age, again an unusual finding. She concludes that these data are best explained in terms of the effect of a chronic viral encephalitis.

435

22

GENETIC INFLUENCES AND INFANTILE AUTISM

Susan Folstein and Michael Rutter

Institute of Psychiatry, London

In his original description of infantile autism, Kanner suggested an "inborn defect," because symptoms were often present from early infancy. Despite the rarity of a family history of autism and lack of a known increase in parental consanguinity, there are two reasons for suspecting hereditary influences: the 2% rate of autism in siblings is 50 times that of the general population[1], and a family history of speech delay is found in about a quarter of families[2]. Reports of single pairs of twins with autism have not added much to our knowledge of genetic effects because of a bias toward reporting monozygotic (MZ) concordant pairs and because few reports contain both adequate clinical descriptions and evidence of zygosity[1]. We therefore undertook a study of a systematically collected sample of 21 pairs of same-sexed twins, one or both of whom had autism as diagnosed by the criteria of Kanner[3] and Rutter[4]. The results reported here indicate the importance of hereditary influences in the aetiology of autism.

The names of twins were collected from consultants, schools and units for autistic children, the National Society for Autistic Children and two hospital twin registers. Apart from two pairs in which dermatoglyphics were used, zygosity was determined by blood grouping in all cases not markedly different in physical appearance. Case notes

Reprinted with permission from *Nature* Vol. 265, No. 5596, 726–728, 1977. Copyright 1977, Macmillan Journals, Ltd.

of the 33 pairs thus obtained were reviewed and eight pairs were rejected on diagnostic grounds. The remaining 25 pairs and their families were extensively interviewed, tested and examined at home or in the hospital. Obstetric records and case notes were also studied. On the basis of all information, a further four pairs were excluded as not meeting diagnostic criteria.

The adequacy of our sampling is shown by the MZ:DZ ratio (11 : 10) which was about that expected for same-sexed twin pairs surviving the first year (6 : 7); and by the number of autistic twin pairs found. In the English twin population of school age who would meet our diagnostic criteria, between 19 and 27 autistic children would be expected and 20 were found. Our sampling of children over school age was less complete, but not likely to be biased as to zygosity or concordance since most cases came from twin registers.

The diagnoses were made from case summaries, numbered randomly to prevent sorting by pair and from which name, exact age, and zygosity had been deleted.

At least one member of 21 same-sexed pairs of twins met the diagnostic criteria for autism. In all, the 11 MZ and 10 DZ pairs gave rise to 25 autistic children. Apart from being twins, these were similar to other reported series of autistic children with respect to sex ratio (3.4 : 1), social class (57% from I and II), and IQ (about ½ severely retarded but ¼ with normal non-verbal IQ). Affective disorder was described in four families, but schizophrenia did not occur. One sibling suffered from autism (a rate of 2.8%). Delayed speech was reported in three families (Table 1).

Four of the 11 MZ pairs but none of the 10 DZ pairs were concordant for autism ($P = 0.055$). All concordant pairs were male. Because autism is a rare condition (about 4 per 10,000 children), the MZ concordance rate is equivalent to a very high correlation in liability (over 0.9) using the multifactorial model[5,6].

If, using this model, it is hypothesised that autism reflects some form of continuously distributed, abnormal characteristic, the question arises whether the non-autistic co-twins showed any other abnormality. We found that very few did in the DZ pairs but in most MZ pairs the co-twins showed some form of cognitive disorder (see Tables 1 and 2).

Thus, in addition to the autistic twins, 6 non-autistic co-twins (5 MZ and 1 DZ) showed a cognitive abnormality as defined by the criteria of no phrase speech until 3 years (three cases), IQ 70 or below (two cases), severely abnormal articulation after 5 years (two cases), or scholastic difficulties requiring special schooling (two cases). Four non-autistic twins showed only one of the above features and none were severely hand-

439

Table 1 Pair-wise concordance by zygosity

	MZ pairs (n = 11)	DZ pairs (n = 10)	MZ−DZ difference (exact test)
Concordance for autism	36%	0%	P = 0.055
Concordance for cognitive disorder (including autism)	82%	10%	P = 0.0015

Table 2 Summary of findings for MZ pairs

	First-born twin	Second-born twin
1	Autism + severe MR	Autism + severe MR
2	Autism + mild MR	Autism
3	Autism + severe MR	Autism + severe MR
4	Autism	Autism + mild MR
5	Mild MR	Autism + severe MR
6	Autism	Educational difficulties (ESN school)
7	Severe articulation defect	Autism
8	Autism + severe MR	Language disorder
9	Mild MR	Autism + severe MR
10	Autism + mild MR	Normal
11	Normal	Autism

MR, Mental retardation.
ESN, Educationally subnormal.

icapped. All the autistic twins met at least two of the criteria. Thus, 9 (82%) of the 11 MZ pairs were concordant for cognitive disorder/autism compared with only 1 (10%) of the DZ pairs (P = 0.0015). The findings strengthen the suggestion of genetic determination and indicate that what is inherited is a form of cognitive abnormality which includes but is not restricted to autism.

Twins have a raised rate of perinatal difficulties leading to brain injury and it was necessary to check that the concordance was not an artefact of these. We found that it was not. In none of the four pairs concordant for autism did both twins have a history of brain injury. Furthermore, no twin with cognitive disorder in the absence of autism showed evidence of perinatal brain injury (Table 3).

Brain injury was, however, relevant to discordance regarding autism. We identified five features known to be associated with brain injury: kernicterus, perinatal apnoea of more than 6 minutes, neonatal convulsions, multiple congenital anomalies, and a second birth delayed by at least 30 minutes. In 6 of the 17 pairs discordant for au-

Table 3 Summary of biological hazards in discordant pairs

Hazard	MZ pairs	
	Autistic twin	Non-autistic twin
Definite	Multiple congenital anomalies	—
	Neonatal convulsions	
Possible	Severe febrile illness	—
	Pathologically narrow cord	—
None	—	—
	—	—

Hazard	DZ pairs	
	Autistic twin	Non-autistic twin
Definite	Apnoea	—
	Delay second birth	
	Delay second birth	—
	Delay second birth	—
Possible	Severe haemolytic disease + apnoea	Delay second birth
or		
Difference in severity	Severe haemolytic disease + apnoea	Mild haemolytic disease
	Birth weight 1 and ¾ pounds lower	—
	Birth weight 1 and ¾ pounds lower	
None	—	—
	—	—

tism, the autistic child but not the non-autistic co-twin had experienced one or more of these biological hazards in the perinatal period.

A wider definition of biological hazard was then applied to the 11 cases not differentiated on the stricter criteria. Using the wider definition (lower birth weight by 1 pound or more, pathological narrow umbilical cord, a more severe kernicterus with apnoea and a severe febrile illness—possibly encephalitis—just before onset), a further six discordant pairs were differentiated. Thus, in 12 of 17 pairs discordant for autism, the autistic member probably or possibly suffered a brain injury, whereas in none of the discordant pairs did this occur only in the non-autistic member.

To summarise the results: the markedly higher rate of concordance in MZ, compared with DZ, pairs for both autism and cognitive abnormalities indicates the importance of genetic factors in the aetiology of autism. Indeed, the concordance rates in conjunction with the very low prevalence of autism in the general population point to a strong genetic determination. Nevertheless, the finding of an association between biological hazards in the perinatal period and autism also demonstrates the important role of environmental influences for the causation of autism (but not cognitive disorder).

In some cases, genetic factors seem to be both necessary and sufficient causes. Among the eight autistic children in the four concordant MZ pairs, biological hazards (even using the broader criteria) occurred in only one child. He was more severely affected than his twin. On the other hand, brain injury alone seems to be a sufficient cause in some cases. In one of the two completely discordant MA pairs, the autistic twin had experienced neonatal convulsions, whereas the non-injured co-twin was normal in every way. The importance of brain damage is also indicated by the finding in other studies of autism in children with congenital rubella or infantile spasms.

Finally, some cases seem to result from the combination of an inherited cognitive defect plus brain damage. In three of the five MZ pairs discordant for autism but concordant for cognitive deficit, the autistic child had experienced a biological hazard whereas the cognitively impaired nonautistic co-twin had not.

Determining the mode of inheritance is difficult since autistic children rarely reproduce. It would be helpful to know what happens to the offspring of the non-autistic twins with cognitive impairment, but no such information is available.

In summary, we conclude that this systematic study of 21 same-sexed twin pairs in which at least one twin showed the syndrome of infantile autism, indicates the importance of a genetic factor in the aetiology of autism. It also indicates the importance of brain injuries, especially during the perinatal period, which may operate either by themselves or in combination with a genetic predisposition involving language. Both the mode of inheritance and exactly what is inherited remain uncertain.

We thank our many colleagues whose collaboration made the study possible.

REFERENCES

1. Rutter, M. in *Recent Developments in Schizophrenia* (ed. Coppen, A. J. & Walk, D.) (Royal Medico-Psychological Association, London, 1967).
2. Bartak, L., Rutter, M. & Cox, A. *Br. J. Psychiat.* **126**, 127–145 (1975).
3. Kanner, L. *Nervous Child* **2**, 217–250 (1943).
4. Rutter, M. in *Infantile Autism* (ed. Churchill, D. W. *et al.*) (Charles C. Thomas, Springfield, Illinois, 1971).
5. Smith, C. *Am. J. Hum. Genet.* **26**, 454–466 (1974).
6. Curnow, R. N. & Smith, C. *J. R. Statist. Soc.* **A138,** 131–169 (1975).

23

NEUROBIOLOGIC ANTECEDENTS OF SCHIZOPHRENIA IN CHILDREN

Barbara Fish

University of California at Los Angeles

In chronic schizophrenics, disordered motor development in childhood is followed by more early cognitive and social impairment and poorer outcome; childhood schizophrenics represent the most extreme variants of this. Pre-schizophrenic infants show a fluctuating dysregulation of maturation—or "pandevelopmental retardation" (PDR)—that involves physical growth; gross motor, visual-motor, and cognitive development; proprioceptive and vestibular responses; muscle tone; and possibly arousal. Pandevelopmental retardation was significantly related to a genetic history for schizophrenia ($<$ .05), but not to obstetric complications. The severity of PDR was significantly related to the severity of later psychiatric and cognitive disorder ($<$ .01). Pandevelopmental retardation provides a "marker" in infancy for the inherited neurointegrative defect in

Reprinted with permission from *Archives of General Psychiatry,* 34:1297–1313, 1977. Copyright 1977, American Medical Association.

This study was supported in part by a grant from the Harriett Ames Charitable Trust, New York. The New York State Department of Mental Hygiene cooperated with this study.

An earlier version of this article appeared in *Res. Publ. Assoc. Res. Nerv. Ment. Dis.* 54:49–80, 1975. Figures 2 and 3 are reprinted with permission from the American Psychiatric Association.

*schizophrenia. These disordered functions should be studied by any-
one interested in the biology of the schizophrenic genotype or in
specific early interventions for children at risk.*

If we could study the antecedents of schizophrenic and manic-
depressive disorders, we would be able to isolate the biology of the
genotype from nonspecific correlates of the psychotic state. The different genetic histories of the two disorders suggest that one should
find different biologic antecedents. "No case of a child with manic-
depressive psychosis has yet been reported in the adoption studies of
schizophrenia," and "no instance has ever been reported of clear-cut
schizophrenia in one twin and clear-cut manic-depressive psychosis in
his monozygotic co-twin."[1] To some extent, the studies of children lend
support to the concept of two diseases.

There is considerable evidence that a neurobiologic disorder exists
in children before the onset of the more chronic forms of *schizophrenic*
psychosis. This material is reviewed in the body of this article. These
chronic schizophrenic patients, with more early cognitive and social
impairment, lie at the opposite end of the "schizophrenia spectrum"
from the schizo-affective disorders,[1] and clinically are the most unlike
manic-depressives.[2] In contrast to schizophrenic patients, manic-
depressives typically do not show cognitive impairment before their
psychosis, and so far no gross neurobiologic or behavioral disorders
have turned up in their childhood histories. A comparison of the
Army intelligence test scores at induction showed that the pre-illness
scores of those who developed manic-depressive psychosis were significantly high compared to controls who remained well, whereas the
scores of the preschizophrenics were significantly low.[3] Within the
schizophrenic group, those later diagnosed as having simple schizophrenia had even lower pre-illness scores than the hebephrenics,
whereas there was no significant lowering of the scores of the
paranoid and catatonic schizophrenics.

Robins' study[4] demonstrated that male preschizophrenics had
symptoms that required psychiatric attention in childhood, but adult
manic-depressive patients did not. Seven percent of boys brought to a
child guidance clinic for a variety of antisocial and non-antisocial
symptoms were found to be schizophrenic as adults, whereas none of
their matched controls were. However, the former clinic patients did
not have a higher rate of manic-depressive disease than did the controls. The biologic antecedents of schizophrenia in children may
therefore represent one aspect of the biology of schizophrenia that is
distinct from the biology of manic-depressive disorder.

Several bodies of evidence in children that bear on the biology of schizophrenia are reviewed briefly in this article. First, there is evidence that childhood schizophrenia is continuous with adult schizophrenia, and that it probably represents the subgroup with the most severe biologic disorder. Then, there is evidence of abnormal neurologic development in infants who were later diagnosed as childhood schizophrenics. Similar but less severe disorders occurred in infants who were diagnosed as having severe behavior disorders as children, and who later became adult schizophrenics.

The occurrence of neurologic deviations from the first day of life certainly implies the presence of a biologic disorder in some infants who manifest schizophrenia later. Characteristics of the disorder in preschizophrenic infants raise questions about the nature of the underlying brain dysfunctions. Finally, the infant disorders suggest a strategy for studying biochemical and neurophysiologic disorders in infants at risk, without waiting 30 to 40 years for the final adult outcome.

CHILDHOOD SCHIZOPHRENIA, THE MOST SEVERE SUBGROUP OF SCHIZOPHRENIA

Neurologic antecedents of childhood schizophrenia are only relevant to the broader problem of schizophrenia if a continuity exists between this condition and schizophrenia in adults. Data from several sources support this continuity.

Similar Clinical Phenomenology: Thought Disorder
in Childhood and Adult Schizophrenia

First are the similarities in clinical phenomenology. Schizophrenics of all ages share the critical symptoms of autistic withdrawal and formal thought disorder. Since Bleuler's historic description,[5] most authors have viewed "the fragmentation of the thinking as the most significant schizophrenic symptom."[2] The loosening of associations and the interpenetration of personal preoccupations, the difficulties in formulating and using precise abstract categories, and the peculiar fragmentation and distortion of syntax, have been demonstrated experimentally in adult schizophrenics by many authors since Vigotsky's work 50 years ago[6-9].

The profound disorders of speech, language function, and thought also have been considered critical diagnostic characteristics of childhood schizophrenia by all authors, starting with the early descriptions of Potter,[10] Despert,[11,12] Bemder,[13,14] and Kanner.[15,16] Goldfarb's recent review[17] of the major reports of childhood schizophrenia concluded that all the behavioral symptoms used for diagnosis were encompassed in the nine points of the British working party.[18] Gross impairment in human relationships and noncommunicative speech were among the four major symptoms found in all the schizophrenic children. A parsimonious list of diagnostic criteria shows these to be the only two symptoms that can be considered both necessary and sufficient to make the diagnosis of childhood schizophrenia.[19]

The differences in the way these cardinal symptoms are expressed by adults and children depend on the degree of immaturity. The form of the children's psychotic speech is limited by their mental age and can be analyzed quantitatively.[20-23] The words children acquire gradually replace the earlier grunts, babble, and jargon. In the schizophrenic child, unintelligible speech is retained longer and persists alongside of more mature forms.[20] The higher the percentage of unintelligible speech, the more retarded is the child compared to age norms and the worse his prognosis.[23]

Normally, a child's noncommunicative speech, including expressive speech and echoing, diminishes rapidly during the second year. The schizophrenic child's echoing is retained longer and is pathologically rigid.[21] Unlike the imitative echoing of the normal child acquiring speech, the schizophrenic child regurgitates accumulated fragments just as they were heard; he does not reorganize and transform old phrases into new creative sentences, adapted for use in new contexts.[21,24] This results in distorted syntax and fragmented speech, which are analogous to the formal thought disorder, with incoherence, in adult schizophrenia.[25] Furthermore, words and sentences are triggered by adventitious and idiosyncratic associations and emitted in inappropriate contexts.[16,22] The greater the percentage of such noncommunicative speech, the worse the outcome.[23] In the most severe childhood schizophrenics, even the communicative portion of speech is rigid, stereotyped, and limited to the simplest here-and-now categories.[22]

This molecular analysis of their speech reveals a central cognitive disorder in childhood schizophrenia that involves disturbances of association and conceptualization, and idiosyncratic and irrelevant referents, a peculiar impairment of the cognitive functions underlying flexible language organization and use. The pattern of speech is primitive in these retarded schizophrenic children under 5 years of age, but the disturbed organization of thought that is revealed appears analogous in many respects to characteristics found in older schizophrenics.

When a severe psychotic process begins in the first two years of life, as in early infantile autism, the severity of the underlying disorder and the absence of any normal experience understandably lead to mental retardation. The severe cognitive disorder reflected in the beginnings of his speech indicate that the 2- to 3-year-old, severely schizophrenic child does not respond to the meaningful patterns and relationships in the world around him in the same way the normal child does. This is also seen in his fragmented play sequences with inanimate objects and in his frequent disregard for their physical properties and normal use.[19]

Hermelin and O'Connor[26] demonstrated experimentally that autistic children were impaired in their ability to process and interpret visual patterns. There was an analogous deficit in their ability to appreciate the grammatically structured aspects of language and to associate words semantically. These impairments went beyond what was found in nonautistic children who were equally retarded. The autistic child's inability to comprehend the meaning of other's speech, to reason logically, and to communicate with others cuts him off still further from normal learning. The wonder is not that his performance is retarded on many tests of mental functioning, but that he manages to achieve any islands of normality.

This greater cognitive impairment does not necessarily mean that early infantile autism is a separate disease entity from childhood schizophrenia or that childhood schizophrenia is distinct from the adult form. Kanner[27] himself emphasized this in his review over 20 years ago: "It has been generally agreed that the earliest form of childhood schizophrenia is probably represented by . . . early infantile autism. . . . The clinical manifestations (of childhood schizophrenia) depend upon the time and mode of onset, and the later the onset, the more does the symptom combination resemble that of adult schizophrenia."

In the schizophrenic children who are more advanced in their use of language, the formal thought disorder is indistinguishable from that in severely ill schizophrenic adults. There are disturbances in conceptualization and in the logic of thought and association that render the speech more or less incomprehensible to others. This is readily seen in verbatim samples of their spontaneous speech[14] and in their responses to psychologic tests.[28,29] The content necessarily reflects not only the distorted perceptions and thinking of the schizophrenic, but the special experiences of childhood and the particular child.[14] One therefore finds preoccupations with movement and aggression, with the child's own body and its functioning, and with his disturbed identification and relationships to others. In the prepuberty schizophrenic child, paranoid ideas are more fragmentary and diffuse than adults' or adolescents' delusions; projection and hallucinations are less significant phenomena than are introjection and the preoccupation with fantasized objects and persons the child experiences as being inside his own body. In childhood schizophrenics, as in adults, the content reflects the individual's unique history and dynamics, but an analysis of the formal structure of the thoughts reveals a disorganizing process characteristic of schizophrenia.

Genetic Continuity Between Childhood and Adult Schizophrenia

Genetic evidence also supports the continuity with adult schizophrenia (Table 1). There is good agreement that childhood schizophrenia that begins after 5 years of age, and that has clinical features similar to adult schizophrenia, has the same genetic predisposition as adult schizophrenia (Table 1). In Kallman and Roth's,[30] Bender and Feretra's,[31] and Kolvin et al[32] studies, the rates for schizophrenia in the parents of childhood schizophrenics are as high or higher than the rates (4.2% to 4.4%) for parents of adult schizophrenics.[1,33] The incidence of parents hospitalized with schizophrenia was as high for Bender and Feretra's children with onset between ages 2 and 7 (12.2%) as for those with onsets after age 8 (11.5%).

Kallman and Roth's[30] is the only major study of childhood schizophrenic twins. Children with mental retardation, or onsets before age 7, were excluded. The 70.6% uncorrected concordance rate for childhood schizophrenia in monozygotic pairs is raised to 88.2%, if one includes co-twins with a later onset. Similarly, the rates for dizygotic pairs (17.1% with childhood schizophrenia and 22.9% with total schizophrenia) and siblings are higher when one includes those with adult schizophrenia. In other words, adult schizophrenia tends to cluster in the families of childhood schizophrenics, although most of the illness in siblings and co-twins resembles that in the index cases and occurs before puberty. Rosenthal[1] concluded that "these findings considered collectively make a strong case for the biologic unity" of preadolescent and adult schizophrenia, and suggested that "preadolescent schizophrenia is a more virulent form which has virtually complete penetrance."

The studies of infantile psychosis (Table 1) appear contradictory at first glance. Bender and Faretra[31] (details in an oral communication from L. Bender, MD, July 1976) found that 7% of the parents were schizophrenic. This is less than that for children with later onsets, but it is significantly higher than the prevalence in the general population.

Table 1.—Schizophrenic Relatives of Psychotic Children

Source	Probands				Parents Hospitalized for Schizophrenia		Siblings with Autism (A) or Schizophrenia (S)	
	Age at Onset, yr	% With Organic Brain Syndrome		% In SES Class V	N	% Schizophrenic	N*	% Affected
		Definite	Possible					
Schizophrenia								
Kallman & Roth,[30] 1956	7-11	..†	...	...	204	8.8	234	7.7 (S)
	7-11	...	...				35 Dz	22.9 (S)‡
	7-11	...	...				17 Mz	88.2 (S)‡
Kolvin et al,[32] 1971	5-15	27	31	19	64	9.4	56	1.8 (S)
Bender & Faretra,[31] 1972, 1976§	2-10	2	12	52	100	12.0	87	13.8 (S)
Infantile psychosis								
Bender & Faretra,[31] 1972, 1976§	< 2	8	16	38	100	7.0	131	2.3 (A)
Kanner,[33] 1953	≤ 2	1	1	10 (IV & V)	200	0		
Meyers & Goldfarb,[37,45,47] 1961, 1962, 1968	< 5	4	15	18	84	2.4 (−21?)	48	8.3 (S)
Fish et al,[34] 1968, 1976||	< 2	3	3	24	70	5.7	44	4.5 (A,S)
	< 2	0	0				2 Mz	100 (A)
Creak & Ini,[43,44] 1960, 1963	...	14	14	2	120	1.7 (−2.5?)	135	0 (2.2?)
Rutter & Lockyer,[41,42] 1967, 1970	< 5	35	63	3	126	0	85	0 (2.4?) (A)
Kolvin et al,[32] 1971	< 3	39	54	2	92	1.1	68	0
Lotter,[38] 1967	≤ 4.5	19	31	13 (IV & V)	60	0 (1.7-8.3?)‡	62	0 (4.8?)‡

*Mz indicates monozygotic twins; Dz, dizygotic twins.
†Psychotic children with mental retardation excluded.
‡See text for details.
§Parents with nonschizophrenic psychoses in earlier report (1972) eliminated (Bender, oral communiction, 1976).
||Includes additional unpublished (1976) data.

Fish et al[34] found a somewhat lower rate (5.7%) in parents of 2- to 5-year-old schizophrenic children (also shown by unpublished data).

On the other hand, six studies have failed to find an increased prevalence of schizophrenia in the parents of infantile psychotics (Table 1). The low rate in Kanner's study[35] is not consistent with the relative absence of organic brain syndrome (OBS) in his group and the 44% of his "speaking" group who were psychotic on follow-up.[36] Meyers and Goldfarb[37] reported that 21% of parents were schizophrenic, but only 2.4% were hospitalized. The remainder included "borderline, pseudoneurotic, and compensated schizophrenics" whom others might consider "schizoid personalities."

Lotter[38] provided some data on the relatives not officially diagnosed schizophrenic in hospitals. From his brief vignettes, 4.8% of the siblings appear to be very possibly schizophrenic. They required chronic treatment or hospitalization for "psychotic," "bizarre," and "very autistic-like" symptoms that began before 6 years, but were milder than the autistic probands' symptoms. While no parent "was known to be schizophrenic," hospital notes were available on only four of six, and Lotter warns of "the difficulty of obtaining reliable information" on disorders not requiring hospitalization. A careful reading of their vignettes suggests that one to five (eg, 1.7% to 8.3%) of these parents might be suspected of having acute psychotic or chronic borderline disorders in the "schizophrenia spectrum."[39] Given the small sample size and the dilution by an indeterminate number with neurologic disorder, the data are insufficient to make a strong case either for *or* against an increased risk for schizophrenia in these relatives.

These apparent contradictions are not too difficult to understand. Hanson and Gottesman[40] reviewed these data and concluded that most groups of infantile psychotics seem unrelated to schizophrenia and probably are associated with OBS. It is clear from Table 1 that the populations are dissimilar in ways other than their genetic histories. Rutter and Lockyer's[41,42] and Kolvin et al's[32] populations have high rates (35% to 63%) of organic brain disorders (toxoplasmosis, CNS lues, spastic diplegia, epilepsy, etc). The rates are somewhat lower in the groups of Lotter[38] and Creak and Ini,[43] but they are still two to six times higher than the OBS in the series of Bender and Faretra and Fish. One would not expect children with OBS to have families with increased rates of schizophrenia. Hence, it is misleading to calculate familial rates of schizophrenia with populations diluted by a large but indeterminate number of children with OBS. One should not be surprised to find more familial schizophrenia in populations in which organic brain disorders have been excluded more successfully.

These populations also differ with regard to their socioeconomic class composition. The families of the infantile psychotics described by Bender and Faretra[31] and Fish (unpublished data) have two to three more class V families than the general population, and more than Goldfarb's[45] and Lotter's[38] groups. The groups studied by Kanner,[35] Creak,[43] Rutter and Lockyer,[41] and Kolvin[32] have almost no families in class V. It has been well established[46] that there is an increased prevalence of schizophrenia in this lowest socioeconomic group. The large number of such families in the series of Bender and Faretra and Fish is consistent with the family incidence of schizophrenia. The exclusion of class V families from the other studies, whatever the reasons, has apparently eliminated one source of families with high rates of schizophrenia that was available to the Bellevue studies (Bender and Faretra, and Fish).

Continuity of Childhood and Adult Schizophrenia in Follow-up Studies

Direct evidence that childhood schizophrenia is continuous with adult schizophrenia comes from the follow-up of schizophrenic children into adulthood (Table 2). Unfortunately, few authors have followed up psychotic children into adulthood. Rutter's[42] report of a mail follow-up, at a mean age of 21.7 years, provided information on social adjustment and additional cases of epilepsy, but no other neurologic and no psychiatric diagnoses. Kanner[48] followed up on the first 11 cases but gave no diagnoses. Bennett and Klein[49] followed up the severe childhood schizophrenics whose conditions were originally diagnosed by Potter.[10] On reexamination in their 40s, all 12 were indistinguishable from chronic adult schizophrenics (Table 2). Only one maintained himself outside a hospital; most were severely deteriorated.

The most detailed information is available on 100 childhood schizophrenics followed up by Bender[31,50] to ages 22 to 45 years. Other psychiatrists had diagnosed 94 as adult schizophrenics. One had psychosis with psychopathic personality, and five were considered to be organically defective (Table 2). Annell's[51] findings were similar, although her follow-up extended only to 23 years and used stricter European criteria for the diagnosis. Almost all of the 19 that she diagnosed as clearly schizophrenic in childhood proved to be schizophrenic as adults. Of the 43 children she diagnosed as having "schizophreniform psychosis," only one third were later diagnosed as schizophrenic; one third of the milder group adapted as schizoid personality disorders at 15 to 23 years of age.

Table 2.—Childhood Schizophrenics Independently Diagnosed Schizophrenic as Adults

Source	Age at Onset, yr	N	% Schizophrenic as Adults (Age Range, yr)
Annell,[51] 1963	<2-9	19	85 (15-23)
Bennett & Klein,[49] 1966	3.5-10	12	100 (40-45)
Bender & Faretra,[21] 1972	<2-10	100	94 (22-45)
	<2	50	90 (22-45)
Dahl,[52] 1976	<2-<14	17	53* (20-40)
	<2	10	50 (—90?)† (20-40)

*One third of these diagnosed as having chronic "atypical psychosis." "Same characteristics as the schizophrenics," including hallucinations, but less florid symptoms and lower intellectual function.
†See text for details.

The incidence of schizophrenia in adulthood was almost as high for the children in the series with infantile psychosis of Bender and Faretra[31] (onsets before 2 years of age), as it was for those with later onsets (Table 2). While only 50% of the infantile psychotics in Dahl's[52] series were diagnosed unquestionably schizophrenic in hospitals as adults, four additional pateints (40%, for a possible total of 90%) appear to be in the "schizophrenia spectrum." Their independent hospital diagnoses were as follows: one with "schizophreniform psychosis" (at age 15) and "schizophrenia (pseudoneurosis)" (at 18); one with psychosis secondary to oligophrenia (at 15 to 22) and schizophrenia (at 28); one with schizoid character disorder; and one with "psychosis infantilis antea" (whom Dahl personally diagnosed as having borderline schizophrenia [written communication, December 1976]).

Bender's[50] detailed report of outcome attests to the severity and chronicity of the disease when schizophrenic symptoms begin early. Twice as many childhood schizophrenics (63%) remain chronically disabled and institutionalized compared to schizophrenics first admitted as adolescents or adults (33%). Children with an onset of psychosis before 2 years of age had the highest rate (72%) of chronicity (Fig 1). To some extent, this increased chronicity resulted from the larger number of early-onset schizophrenics whose verbal intelligence quotients remained below 70. But, children with higher and more variable IQs also required continual institutional care.

When this life course was viewed from the other end, it was found that only 15% of adult schizophrenics who had been brought to a child guidance clinic for a variety of problems had been diagnosed as schizophrenic in childhood.[53] The rest had been diagnosed as having severe behavior disorders. An undetermined number go unrecognized. When elementary and high school records of schizophrenic adults were compared to matched classroom controls, only half of the preschizophrenics could be distinguished by the teachers' comments on their behavior, most of these by 12 to 15 years.[54] Either the unrecognized preschizophrenics have symptoms that are ignored by families and schools because they are less troublesome, or they have no clinical features that could have distinguished them from other children. This question can only be answered by very large long-term prospective studies, with direct investigation of the children, rather than postdictive studies of records.[53]

Childhood Schizophrenia: A Biologically More Severe Subgroup

Linguistic, genetic, and longitudinal studies, therefore, all indicate that childhood schizophrenia is continuous with the most severe,

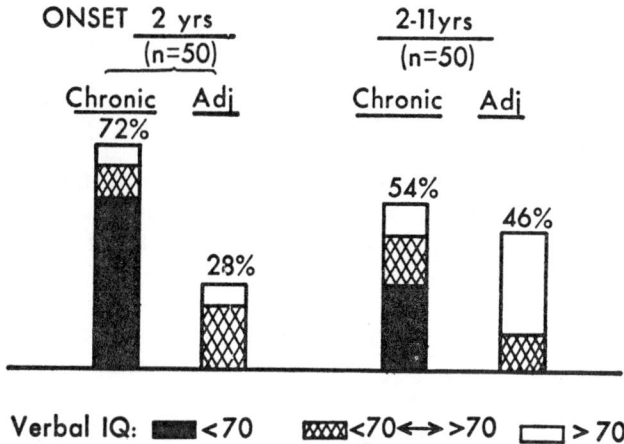

Fig 1.—Verbal IQ and outcome of childhood schizophrenics with onset before or after 2 years of age. Chronic indicates chronically institutionalized; Adj, some adult adjustment in community, from "complete psychotic dependency in a tolerant home to various degrees of independence, emotionally, socially, and economically"; verbal IQ < 70 ⟷ > 70, IQ sometimes below and sometimes above 70 (adapted from Bender[50]).

chronic, adult schizophrenia, which presumably has the largest biologic component. The high concordance rate in twins suggests that the childhood form of schizophrenia has a higher degree of penetrance.[1] The long-term course indicates that when schizophrenic thought disorder is present during childhood, and particularly before 2 years of age, it is much more likely to result in a permanently disabled individual who is likely to show a permanent cognitive deficit. All the differences between the childhood and adult forms of the disease point to the greater severity associated with an earlier onset of psychosis.

Earlier symptoms might produce some greater disability secondarily through the distortion and deficit of early learning. However, the early-onset, poor-outcome childhood schizophrenics all had a later onset of speech or early regression,[31] indicating that language and cognition were seriously affected in the first two years of life, at the very beginning of the illness, however much they may have been additionally depressed by later experiences. The increased genetic penetrance also supports the view that early-onset schizophrenia reflects a biologically more severe form of the disease that primarily produces a greater disruption of CNS functioning and more severe developmental deviations, including greater language and cognitive disability.

The greater genetic penetrance and more severe cognitive deficit in childhood schizophrenics parallel the differences between "process" and "reactive" schizophrenics, in an exaggerated form. "Process" schizophrenics have a more insidious onset, with greater cognitive and social impairment by the time they are seen as adults.[55] Rosenthal[1] pointed out that "the more benign forms of schizophrenic-like illness belong in the same genetic spectrum as the more malignant forms, since the occurrence of schizophrenia often occurs in relatives at rates that are comparable for both groups," but that there are some data suggesting "a slightly higher heritability for the more typical forms," whether these are categorized as "process" vs "reactive," or as catatonic and hebephrenic vs paranoid. This higher heritability has been confirmed by others.[33]

The evidence indicates that childhood schizophrenia, that is, schizophrenia with an early onset, belongs at the most severe extreme of chronic adult schizophrenia in a spectrum of biologic continuity, and that within childhood schizophrenia the severity also increases the earlier the onset.

DISORDERS OF EARLY MOTOR DEVELOPMENT IN PRESCHIZOPHRENIC CHILDREN AND CHILDREN GENETICALLY AT RISK FOR SCHIZOPHRENIA

Evidence from several sources points to early disorders of motor development, especially in chronic schizophrenics. Large-scale controlled studies have found motor symptoms in the histories of children with severe personality disorders who later turned out to be schizophrenic. In O'Neal and Robins' follow-up,[56] difficulty in walking was among the early developmental symptoms that significantly differentiated preschizophrenic children from the others. Less than 25% of these schizophrenics were chronically hospitalized as adults. Only 10% had been suspected of possibly being psychotic when they were seen at a mean age of 14 years (range, 7 to 17). Watt[57] found that severe organic handicaps, including "neurologic disorders," significantly differentiated the preschizophrenics from their classroom controls and constituted one of the five factors that postdicted a schizophrenic outcome.

Similarly, Ricks and Nameche[58] found slow motor development and other "symptoms suggesting neurologic impairment" in 20% of the preschizophrenics compared with 10% of the controls. Because of missing information, they considered these rates to "underestimate the actual frequencies of neurologic deficit in both groups." Furthermore, in the preschizophrenics there was "less evident external or clearly traceable causation" in the form of birth and subsequent neurologic trauma. These neurologic symptoms and estimates of probable brain damage based on neurologic examinations were more frequent in the chronic preschizophrenic group than in the "released" preschizophrenics.[59] In the chronic, withdrawn preschizophrenics, the neurologic symptoms included hypoactivity, rigidity, abnormal gait, poor coordination, and impaired attention. Hyperactivity occurred more frequently in the chronic, delinquent preschizophrenics.

Ricks and Berry[59] concluded that "brain damage, although not essential to the genesis of schizophrenia, is related to its *chronicity*." They believed that these children were more vulnerable to disorder because of "disorganization and low competence, suggesting poor functioning of the higher integrative brain centers." Regression and chronic hospitalization depended on IQ and on social and vocational success. The "best predictors of recovery are measures of competency and integration, including neurological integration."

Children genetically at risk for schizophrenia, as well as preschizophrenics, may show similar early disorders. From the Rosenthal-Nagler project,[60] Marcus[61] reported significantly more "soft" neurologic signs in the 7- to 10-year-old male offspring of schizophrenics compared to controls who were matched for rearing environments. The population consisted of 50 children, 7½ to 14 years of age, who were born to schizophrenic mothers or fathers, and matched controls whose parents had no mental disease. Half of the children in each group lived in the city. Half lived in kibbutzim and had less contact with their parents. The items that were significant in differentiating the younger offspring of schizophrenics from their controls were facial asymmetry, fine motor coordination, left-right orientation, the Bender-Gestalt Test, and auditory-visual integration. Poor overall neurologic functioning characterized half of the schizophrenic offspring, but only those under 11 years of age, suggesting that these functions matured after 11 years, even in the neurologically immature children at risk. Moreover, this younger group consisted mostly of boys reared in cities who presumably had had more contact with their disturbed families.

In a study of obstetric records, Mednick, et al[62] found that retarded motor development at 5 days of age and at 1 year differentiated the offspring of schizophrenics from controls. All of this adds up to convincing documentation that disorders and delays of motor development occur more often in preschizophrenics, especially in chronic schizophrenics, and in children at greater genetic risk for schizophrenia than in controls.

CHARACTERISTICS OF PANDEVELOPMENTAL DISORDER
IN PRESCHIZOPHRENIC INFANTS
AND INFANTS AT RISK FOR SCHIZOPHRENIA

In order to understand the nature of this early neurologic disorder, one must plot the course of development in the first two years of life in more detail. Frequent measurements of several functions yield peculiar curves that reflect a disruption of the normal pattern of neurologic maturation. The disorganization is far more complex than the simple retardation revealed by one or two points on the curve, and it affects not only motor development, but visual-motor, perceptual, and cognitive development, and even physical growth. The major findings from my infant studies that illustrate this point are discussed in the following section. The subjects, methods, predictions, and detailed findings have been reported in earlier papers for the children born in 1952 and 1953[63-66] and in 1959 and 1960[67-70] and are not repeated here.

SUBJECTS

Briefly, the infants born in both periods compose a group of 24 individuals, of whom over half are now 24 years old (Table 3). The 1952–1953 infants were randomly selected from the Bellevue Hospital well-baby clinic, which served a lower-class neighborhood with high rates of social and psychiatric disorders.[65] Recent immigrants who spoke too little English to give the necessary detailed history had to be excluded from the study. This undoubtedly eliminated many psychiatrically normal parents who moved to the neighborhood because of external social circumstances. Because almost all of the 1959–1960 schizophrenic mothers were chronically hospitalized, their offspring were generally reared in carefully selected, permanent adoptive or foster homes, and more of them grew up in stable and supportive homes than in the 1952–1953 group.

There was also a high incidence of pregnancy and birth complications in the 1952–1953 infants[65] compared to the 1959–1960 group (Table 3). However, adequate antepartum records for the first trimester were not available for several mothers in both groups.

Method, Tests, and Measurements in Infancy

The analysis of infant development was based on standard infant tests and measurements and was repeated at key ages ten times between birth and 2 years of age. Height, weight, head circumference,

Description	Infants Born In 1952-1953	Infants Born in 1959-1960
Subjects		
Random first admissions to NYC "well-baby" clinic	16	0
Consecutive infants born to schizophrenic mothers in 2 New York State hospitals	0	13
Followed up to present time	14	10
White	9	3
Black	1	4
Puerto Rican	4	3
Boys	5	5
Current age, yr	24	17
Mothers with chronic schizophrenia	2	9*
Mothers with schizophrenia in remission	0	1
Mothers with illegitimate pregnancy	5	10
Pregnancy or birth complications		
Severe (two with toxemia; one with three-day labor, five days after ruptured membranes, with high forceps, cyanosis)	3†	0
Moderate (one with bleeding in first trimester, one with thyroidectomy for hyperthyroidism in first trimester and infant born with cord around neck)	2	0
Mother under age 15	0	1
Rearing families of current group		
Psychotic mother + social agency placements	2	1
Stable home, one parent with paranoid or schizoid personality disorder	3	0
Stable, but frequent open derogation of child (after age 6)	3	1‡
Stable, generally supportive	6	8§

Table 3.—Subjects and Families in Infant Studies

*One father was a hospitalized schizophrenic. Most fathers unknown.
†One schizophrenic mother with toxemia ("Conrad").
‡Maternal grandmother ("Pia").
§One maternal grandmother, one paternal grandmother, six permanent adoptive/foster homes.

and overall body growth ("auxodrome") were plotted on the Wetzel grid,[71] which enables one to plot changes in the infant's growth curve compared to his own earlier "channel" pattern. Separate developmental quotients (DQs) were obtained for postural-motor, visual-motor, and language development, using the Gesell examination.[72] Visual-motor items were analyzed for specific "integrative functions."[70] The analysis of the serial DQs in different functions is comparable to following serial changes in IQs in older individuals.

In the 1959–1960 study, behavioral state was recorded through 16 weeks of age for 1½ hours during the presentation of a standard series of stimuli and the Gesell examination.[67,68] Caloric vestibular responses were also tested in this study,[69,73] using the maximal stimulus of one minute of cold air at 10°C, which is equivalent to instilling 30 ml of ice water for one minute.[74] The duration of nystagmus or tonic deviation after the end of the stimulus was measured in seconds and analyzed according to the initial state of arousal and the infants's age.[73]

Independent Psychologic and Psychiatric Evaluations at Follow-up

Independent psychologic and psychiatric assessments were made first when the children were 10 and again at 18 years of age. In addition to a standard psychiatric diagnosis, the children were given a global severity rating and were ranked in order of severity. The psychologic tests included the Weschler Intelligence Scale for Children (WISC) or the Weschler Adult Intelligence Scale (WAIS), Rorschach, Thematic Apperception Test, human figure drawings, Bender-Gestalt Test, and a perceptual-motor battery. Informed consent was obtained from parents or guardian and the children.

The distribution of the diagnoses and severity ratings is shown in Table 4. The two schizophrenic children, and one of those with severe personality disorders ("Conrad"),[63,65,66] were the only schizophrenic offspring who had any significant contact with their psychotic mothers. Conrad was the only schizophrenic offspring with pregnancy or birth complications (Table 3).

Brief summaries of the two schizophrenic children have been published. "Peter" was born in 1952[63,66] and leads a marginal, dependent existence at age 24, but has never been hospitalized. His diagnosis of schizophrenia was again independently confirmed at 18 years of age by a second psychologist. "Linda" was born in 1959,[70] was hospitalized from 7 to 10 years of age, and has been slowly improving in a residential treatment center from age 10 to 17 years.

The children diagnosed as having severe personality disorders had pathologic disorders of thinking, identification, and personality organization resembling schizophrenia, but without gross psychotic disruption.[66,70] In today's terminology, they would fit Meehl's[75] characterization of severe "schizotypic personality disorders," who have so

Table 4.—Independent Psychiatric Diagnoses, at 10 Years, of Schizophrenic Offspring and Controls		
Children's Diagnoses	Schizophrenic Mothers	Nonpsychotic Mothers
Childhood schizophrenia	2	0
Personality disorder Severe	3	1
Moderate	5	2
Mild or no symptoms	2	9
Total	12	12

far remained compensated, or the severely schizoid, paranoid or inadequate personalities in the "schizophrenia spectrum" described by Kety et al.[39]

EVIDENCE OF A NEUROBIOLOGIC DISORDER: PANDEVELOPMENTAL RETARDATION

Analysis of the developmental curves points to an early biologic disorder in the two childhood schizophrenics. Both infants had a major disorganization of neurologic maturation that involved postural-motor, visual-motor, and physical development as early as the first month of life. There was no fixed neurologic defect, but rather a disorder of the timing and integration of neurologic maturation.

Several features distinguish this from the usual forms of retardation and precocity. First, there was an unusual fluctuation in the rate of development, with marked acceleration and marked retardation succeeding one another (Fig 2). Peter's postural-motor development dropped to 45% of normal at 9 months of age and then, without any change in his external circumstances, suddenly accelerated to achieve five months' development in the next two months, and reached normal levels by 13 months.

Other features differed from the usual patterns in chronic organic brain syndromes. Sometimes there was a temporary loss of a previously acquired ability.[64,73] At times, they showed a reversed cephalocaudal gradient of postural development, with head control lagging months behind the control of trunk and legs. At times, a "higher" function, such as Peter's visual-motor ability,[64] remained relatively intact at a time when postural-motor ability was severely retarded. This is the reverse of the pattern in diffuse, chronic brain damage.[76] In infants with brain damage, higher cognitive functions

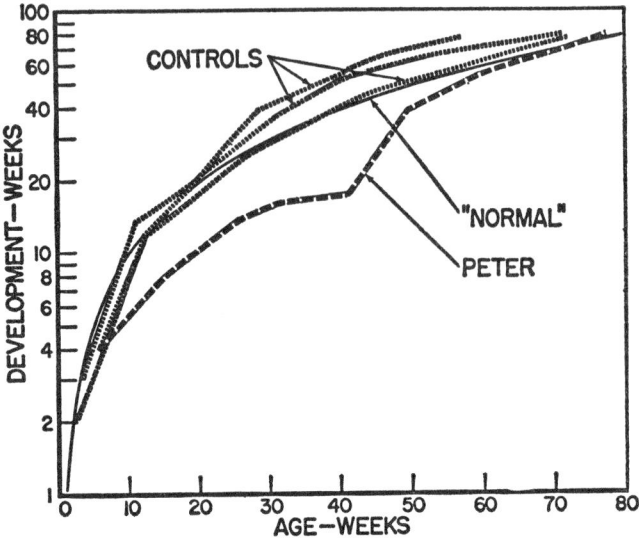

Fig 2.—Comparison between mean postural-motor development of schizophrenic child (Peter) and controls. Development—Weeks indicates age at which postural-motor performance occurs in normal standardization sample[72]; "Normal", development—weeks equals chronologic age in weeks; controls, offspring of nonpsychotic mothers (from Fish[64]).

are usually affected first, whereas postural development and physical growth become retarded only when the damage is more severe.

The erratic functioning of these preschizophrenic infants is analogous to the disturbance of older schizophrenic patients, who fail easy items on an intelligence test and then succeed on more advanced items during the same session.

In adult schizophrenics, it is difficult to determine which aspects of their peculiar test performance might be disturbances in attention or cognitive function that are specific to schizophrenia, and which might be nonspecific results of anxiety or disturbed motivation.[8] However, when one sees this disorganized pattern in the first month of life, it is clear that such temporary states of poorly integrated CNS functioning can occur in schizophrenia, long before complex motivational and defensive behaviors have developed.

Pandevelopmental Retardation, Psychiatric Morbidity, and Genetic Risk

The most severe, overall retardation involved physical growth, as well as postural-motor or visual-motor development or both (Fig 3).

Table 5.—Comparison of Developmental Deviations in Two Schizophrenic Children		
Description	"Peter"	"Linda"
Ages with pandevelopmental retardation, mo	6-18	6-13
Lowest postural-motor DQ	45	75
Lowest visual-motor DQ	64	59
Age at onset of schizophrenic symptoms	3	6
IQ at 10 years (WISC)		
Full-scale	65	84
Verbal	75	92
Performance	61	78
IQ at 18 years (WAIS)		
Full-scale	81	...
Verbal	87	...
Performance	76	...

This "pandevelopmental retardation" was related to psychiatric morbidity at 10 years of age. It was most severe in the two preschizophrenic infants, and was most extreme in Peter (Table 5). His onset was earlier and his subsequent cognitive and perceptual disturbances were more severe than Linda's. Children in whom pandevelopmental retardation was milder and shorter were ranked just below the schizophrenic children in the severity of their psychiatric disturbance at 10 years (Table 6). Children who had no associated retardation of physical growth had still milder psychiatric disorders at ten years, although one ("Carol")[65] had moderately severe symptoms between 16 and 21 years. Pandevelopmental retardation in infancy was significantly related to the appearance of severe to moderate psychiatric disorder at 10 years of age ($\chi^2, P < .01$).

The offspring of schizophrenic mothers were exposed to fewer pregnancy and birth complications, but they had a higher incidence of pandevelopmental retardation in infancy ($\chi^2, P < .05$) and of severe to moderate personality disorders at 10 years ($\chi^2, P < .025$) (Table 7). Another sequel of early developmental disorder was the occurrence of *specific reading disabilities* with perceptual disorders at 10 years of age.[70] These were usually associated with failure on the block-design subtest of the WISC and failures on the perceptual battery, including high Koppitz scores and distortions on the Bender-Gestalt, poor fine coordination, and defective finger schema. These perceptual defects also occurred significantly more often in the offspring of the schizophrenic mothers ($\chi^2, P < .05$), similar to the findings in Marcus'[61] much larger

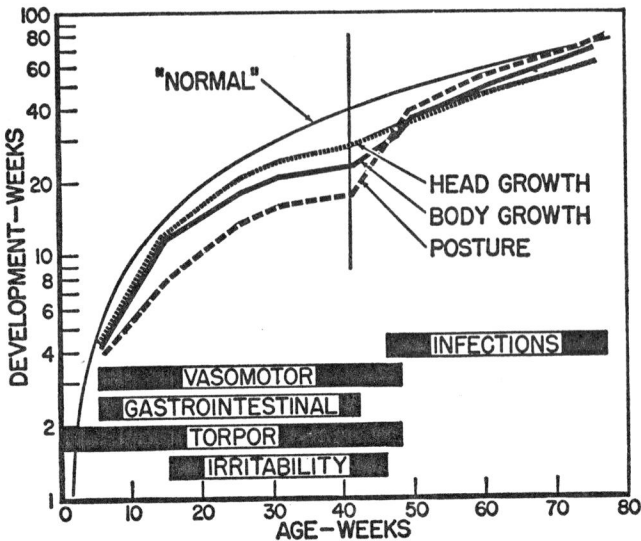

Fig 3.—Relationship between mean postural-motor development, physical growth, and clinical disturbances of schizophrenic child (Peter): Body Growth indicates auxodrome on Wetzel grid (from Fish[64]).

Table 6.—Severity of Pandevelopmental Retardation and Psychiatric Outcome at 10 Years

No. of Children (N = 21)*	Lowest Motor DQ Birth to 2 yr	No. Independently Diagnosed at 10 yr
Pandevelopmental retardation (with growth retardation)†		
1	<70	2 with
1	70-79	schizrenia
6	80-89	3 with severe, 3 with moderate personality disorder
Developmental lags with no growth retardation		
4	60-89	4 with moderate personality disorder
5	70-89	5 with mild or no symptoms
4	>90	4 with mild or no symptoms

*Conrad and two control infants were not examined between 2 and 10 months and are omitted from this table.
†Related to severe-moderate psychiatric disorders (χ^2: $P < .01$).

study. The infant data of Fish and Hagin[70] indicate that antecedents can be found before 2 years of age for the perceptual symptoms seen at 7 to 10 years. Failure on the block-design subtest of the WISC at 10 years correlated significantly with failure of form perception at 1½ to 2 years of age, as measured on the form board ($P < .05$, Fisher's test).[70]

None of the children with pandevelopmental retardation had had any pregnancy of birth complications. None of the children with pregnancy or birth complications showed regression of development or a peculiar pattern of scatter, and none had pandevelopmental retardation with an overall retardation of physical growth and postural motor development. Pregnancy and birth complications were followed in three of the infants by brief lags in early head control, of a mild degree, that then returned to normal.[65] Therefore, in individual infants, as well as in the group data in this study (Table 7), pandevelopmental retardation was significantly related to a genetic history for schizophrenia, but not to pregnancy and birth complications.

SPECTRUM OF NEUROLOGIC "VULNERABILITY" AND PSYCHIATRIC DISABILITY IN INFANT STUDIES AND OLDER PATIENTS

The relationship found in these infants between more severe disruption and retardation of early development, earlier onset of psychiatric symptoms, and more severe cognitive impairment in later childhood recalls the retrospective data in the large studies of schizophrenic children[31,45] and adults[55,58,59] described previously.

The infant data show a spectrum of severe to mild irregularity and retardation of physical growth, postural-motor, and visual-motor development that was followed by a corresponding spectrum of severity of psychiatric disorder, ranging from schizophrenia to moderately severe personality disorders. Perceptual and cognitive disorders were associated with the psychiatric disorders in many of the children. The pandevelopmental disorders and their sequelae were significantly related to being at genetic risk for schizophrenia and were not associated with pregnancy and birth complications.

Fish and colleagues[63,70,77] had hypothesized earlier that this poor integration of neurologic development in infancy was the analogue of the disorders of higher integrative functions seen in older schizophrenic children and adults, and that it constituted a "vulnerability to schizophrenia." Whether a particular vulnerable child became psychotic or developed a less severe personality disorder depended on the severity of his early deviations interacting with his particular environment.

Table 7.—Disorders in Offspring of Schizophrenic Mothers and Controls		
	No. of Mothers	
Disorders in Children	Schizophrenic (N = 12)	No Psychosis (N = 12)
Severe to moderate complications of pregnancy and birth	1	4
Pandevelopmental retardation	7*	1
Diagnosed schizophrenic or with severe to moderate personality disorder at 10 years	10†	3
Reading disability with perceptual dysfunction at 10 years	8*	2

*χ^2: $P < .05$.
†$P < .025$.

The relationship in the infant studies between more severe developmental impairment and more severe psychiatric disorder with an earlier onset resembles the spectrum of severity described earlier for the entire range of schizophrenia. The most severely disabled schizophrenics with the most chronic course have the highest frequency of early motor disorders,[58,59] the earliest onset, and the most severe cognitive impairment.[55] At the furthest extreme of this schizophrenia spectrum are the childhood schizophrenics with an onset before 2 years of age.[31,45]

Several large retrospective studies indicate that the spectrum of severity of early neurologic disorders paralleled the later severity of schizophrenia. Ricks and his coworkers[58,59] found more neurologic abnormalities in the childhood records of the more chronic adult schizophrenics. In childhood schizophrenics—the most severe of the chronic schizophrenics—more neurologic abnormalities[45] and more histories of severely retarded and irregular motor development[34,78] were found in the children who have the lowest verbal IQs and the poorest prognosis with the most chronic course.

There is some genetic evidence that this "schizophrenia spectrum," at its milder end, may also extend to severe schizoid and paranoid personality disorders. Kety et al[39] suggested from their adoption studies that borderline schizophrenia and possibly certain inadequate personality disorders may be milder variants of schizophrenia, occurring in the same genetically determined "schicophrenia spectrum" as chronic schizophrenia. Heston and Denney[79] found that "schizoid psychopaths" and certain emotionally labile neurotics clustered in the adopted offspring of schizophrenic mothers. They raised the possibilities that "a subcritical dose of the pathological genes produces or predisposes to disabilities other than schizophrenia," or that "schizophrenia as a biologic entity is broader than our present clinical entity, . . . the differing manifestations being due to modifying genes or life experiences." Shields et al[80] analyzed their own and others' genetic data and concluded that borderline schizophrenia, and some schizoid character disorders, occurring in the families of schizophrenics "can be construed as less specific manifestations of 'schizophrenic' genotypes," but good objective criteria are lacking to differentiate such disorders from nonspecific and environmental phenocopies that occur at an undetermined rate in the general population. The infant data parallel these observations of milder schizophrenic-like variants in adults. The infants whose pandevelopmental retardation was less severe than that in the preschizophrenic infants were diagnosed at 10 years of age as having severe personality disorders, with schizoid and paranoid features, similar to those described in the adult relatives of schizophrenics.

NEUROINTEGRATIVE DEFECT, "SCHIZOTAXIA," AND VULNERABILITY

Meehl[75,81] has formulated most clearly the necessarily indirect "causal chain from gene through biochemical endophenotype of neurophysiological endophenotype (e.g., synaptic slippage) to behavioral dispositions to the ultimate learned behavior."[81] " 'Clinical schizophrenia' as such cannot be inherited because it has behavioral and phenomenal contents which are learned."[75] He postulates that what is inherited is a *"subtle neuro-integrative* defect,"[81] which he termed "schizotaxia."[75] All schizotactic individuals develop a "schizotypic" personality organization. If the interpersonal regime is favorable and if the individual also has inherited certain constitutional strengths, he will remain a well-compensated schizotype, without symptoms of mental disease, but exhibiting faint signs of "cognitive slippage and other minimal neurological aberrations."[75]

The "endophenotype" will eventually be identified by the biochemical and neurophysiologic aberrations underlying "schizotaxia." Meehl suggested that research on the "exophenotype" should focus on "a refinement and objectification of the 'soft neurology', as seen in the longitudinal research of Barbara Fish and the ongoing study of Israeli Kibbutz children of schizophrenic mothers."[81]

Pandevelopmental retardation appears to serve as an early "marker" for the inherited neurointegrative defect in schizophrenia. Of the infants genetically at risk, those with the most severe pandevelopmental retardation became schizophrenic, and those with milder forms became "schizotypic" personality disorders, with varying degrees of decompensation in childhood and adolescence.

Changing Manifestations of Neurointegrative Defect with Maturation

The overt manifestations of the neurointegrative defect change with maturation. The age-specific defects are most readily detectable in their most severe form. In each age period, mild neurointegrative defects may be found in the entire population at risk, but only a smaller subgroup with severe psychiatric disorder shows extreme defects.

In the first year, pandevelopmental retardation occurred in about half of the schizophrenic offspring, often accompanied by disorders of state behavior, of the development of reaching and manipulation and of vestibular responsiveness, to be described subsequently. In the retrospective studies of disturbed children and adults, only the most severe motor retardation is recalled, and therefore these histories cluster in the most severe childhood schizophrenics[34,45,78] and the most chronically ill adult patients.[58,59]

Gross postural-motor retardation cannot be a "marker" once independent locomotion is achieved, but more subtle defects in motor integration can be found. These "soft neurologic" signs appear to identify the population at genetic risk up to 10 years of age, as they occurred in half of the schizophrenic offspring.[61] After 10 years, the milder defects in motor integration "mature" and "soft signs" no longer identify the entire population at risk.[61] However, certain schizophrenics continue to show "soft neurologic" signs as adolescents[82] and as adults, particularly those with thought disorders[83] or with a premorbid history of asociality.[84] It is conceivable that finer tests of motor integration might still identify a large adult population genetically at risk.[75] The disturbance in oculomotor tracking, which Holzman et al[85] found in schizophrenic patients with thought disorder and in their relatives, may be such a genetic "marker" in later life.

The spectrum of severe to mild disorders of visual-motor integration also changes its specific manifestations with maturation. The gross retardation of reaching and manipulation in the first year was succeeded by retarded form perception from 2 to 10 years of age.[70] Disorders of visual-motor and auditory-visual integration were among the "soft neurologic" signs that identified half of the 7 to 10-year-old schizophrenic offspring in Marcus' study.[61] These signs matured and were not detectable after 10 years of age in the group at genetic risk. However, severe visual-motor disorders on the Bender-Gestalt Test and other tasks still persist in many schizophrenics, particularly in the more chronic ones.[7]

Similarly, integrative disorders of language and cognitive function change in their manifestations with age. These functions appear to be more sensitive indicators of neurointegrative defect. When they are affected early, massive arrest or permanent retardation may result. The earliest and most severe disorders occur in the early childhood schizophrenics. In the most severely affected, speech begins late[31,34] and continues to be permeated by fragmented, stereotyped, and non-communicative utterances.[20,23] When this early defect is massive, it is reflected in a permanently retarded verbal IQ.[31] In later-onset schizophrenics, if retardation in IQ is present, it is much less severe and occurs predominantly in more severely chronically ill patients[3,55] However, more sensitive tests can detect subtler evidence of thought disorder in borderline schizophrenic patients who function normally on the WAIS,[86] and in many relatives of schizophrenics.[87] A "higher percentage" of disordered associations has also been found in the adolescent offspring of schizophrenics.[88]

All of these studies point to a neurointegrative defect that can be identified through measures of motor, perceptual, and cognitive integration in individuals genetically at risk for schizophrenia. Poor integration of these functions shows a continuity from birth to adulthood in affected individuals, although the manifestations change somewhat as these capacities mature. Neurointegrative defects can be identified in approximately half the offspring of schizophrenics and may represent an underlying biologic vulnerability to psychiatric disorder. The spectrum of severity of the neurointegrative defect, from infancy on, appears to be related to the spectrum of severity of later psychiatric disorder. The defect is most severe in schizophrenics; with increasing severity of the integrative defect, the psychotic disorder appears earlier and is associated with greater chronicity and cognitive and social disability. Milder defects are followed by severe to moderately severe personality disorders, often associated with perceptual and cognitive deficits.

The development of more refined quantitative measures for the specific motor, perceptual, and cognitive defects would enable us to identify the vulnerable individuals in populations at risk more precisely.[81] Such measures would also identify the symptoms that should be targets for early intervention.

DO PREGNANCY AND BIRTH COMPLICATIONS
CONTRIBUTE TO PANDEVELOPMENTAL RETARDATION
AND A SCHIZOPHRENIC OUTCOME?

Stabenau and Pollin,[89] in reviewing their own and other's studies of monozygotic twins discordant for schizophrenia, found that four times the number of the sick twins were differentiated from their co-twins by birth complications and CNS illness as children, twice as many were differentiated by lighter birth weight, but only 1.8 times as many by slower walking. In this series, paranatal and postnatal neurologic disability may have contributed to the development of more severe illness in 17 to 24 of the 100 monozygotic pairs.

However, Gottesman and Shields[33] doubted that "neurological deficiencies sufficient to account for much of the later psychopathology can be attributed to these differences in birth weight. . . ," which sometimes "represent only a trivial portion of the total weight." Furthermore, they pointed out that none of the "twin studies with representative sampling found lower birth weight to distinguish the future schizophrenic or the more severe of a concordant pair. Although there was a tendency for the twin with greater birth complications to be more at risk for schizophrenia in other studies, our evidence, when available, was inconclusive."

In 1968, Mednick and Schulzinger[88] reported a trend for the birth process to have been accompanied by more difficulties in the offspring of schizophrenic mothers compared to the controls. A reanalysis of these data in 1974[90] indicated that the excess in pregnancy complications characterized only first-born males. In 1971, Mednick et al[62] analyzed more detailed neonatal and developmental data on another group of infants born to schizophrenic parents and controls. In this "OB project," they analyzed perinatal and one-year follow-up records of 83 offspring of schizophrenics, and compared them to matched controls born to 83 character-disordered parents and 83 parents without recorded psychiatric illness. There were no differences in complications of pregnancy or delivery between the groups, except that more children of schizophrenics had low normal birth weights (2,550 to 3,000 gm). Despite this relative absence of increased trauma, the children of schizophrenics tended to have "retarded motor reflexes" at birth that persisted at 5 days of age, although the difficulties in the control infants usually had cleared up by the fifth day of life. Furthermore, the children of schizophrenics had retarded motor development compared to the controls, including delays in head control (after 4 months), sitting, standing, and walking. But these differences did not quite reach statistical significance.

Two recent studies also failed to replicate the conclusions of Mednick and Schulzinger 1968. McNeil and Kaij[91] found no differences between schizophrenics (n = 32) and controls, in the rates of obstetrical complications or the birth weights of the offspring. However, more of the schizophrenic offspring (21.9%) were light for gestational age. Hanson et al.[92] found no increase of obstetrical complications or of small-for-gestational-age babies among the offspring of schizophrenics (n = 29), even though 17% of their schizophrenic offspring showed abnormal behaviors at 4 and 7 years, which frequently are reported in the premorbid histories of schizophrenics.

Rieder et al[93] analyzed the larger pool of prospective data collected in Boston for the Collaborative Perinatal Study of the National Institute of Neurological Diseases and Stroke. They found a significant increase of deaths that were unexplained by complications of pregnancy among the 93 offspring of schizophrenics (7.5%), including some deaths with severe neurological malformations. The frequency of deaths paralleled the severity of schizophrenia in mothers or fathers. On the other hand, the involvement of only one of a pair of monozygotic twins did not fit a genetic causation.

Genetic or Traumatic Developmental Deviation?

In a discussion of the 1971 article by Mednick and colleagues,[62] Fish[94] commented on a number of features in the data that suggested genetically determined motor lags rather than retardation due to trauma. Decreased motor responses on the fifth-day examination differentiated the schizophrenic offspring more than did the immediate neonatal findings. The effects of preanesthetic medication and birth trauma, unless they are very severe, tend to subside after the second or third day, whereas genetically determined immaturity is more likely to persist, as happened in the schizophrenic offspring. In the schizophrenic offspring, the decrease in neonatal motor responses occurred in the presence of normal sucking responses, unlike the controls. This dissociation between different measures of "arousal" is like the dissociation seen in the "abnormally quiet" schizophrenic offspring reported by Fish,[67,68] but it is different from the more consistent underarousal that can occur with birth injury or severe retardation. A persistence of motor retardation during the first year of life generally follows only very severe birth injury, but it is frequent with genetically determined developmental lags.

In discussing the report of Mednick et al,[62] Heston[95] stated that it "adds critical data which supports the hypothesis that immaturity at birth is associated with schizophrenic genotypes in a direct relationship." He noted that "the schizophrenic fathers contributed immature infants in a proportion compatible with their total contribution of offspring," which would not have occurred had the intrauterine environment and the delivery process been the cause of the immaturity.

Although certain pregnancy complications appear to occur more often in the offspring of schizophrenic parents,[93] the evidence cited is not yet conclusive that such events increase the risk of the offspring developing schizophrenia as adults. Hanson et al[92] conclude that "if such complications are important, they appear to be no more important than any of a number of unpredictable, idiosyncratic life experiences that may lower a person's capacity to cope with stress."

On the other hand, such complications apparently add to the motor and cognitive impairments in early onset children schizophrenics. In Goldfarb's series,[47] severe complications of pregnancy occurred in 35% of the low-IQ "organic" childhood schizophrenics, compared to none in the "nonorganic" group. Also, in the series of 100 schizophrenic children described by Bender and Faretra,[31] abnormal pregnancies were most frequent in the most impaired group. The rate was highest (50%) in the 32 autistic schizophrenics, with onsets under 2 years of age, and was lowest (10%) in the 41 schizophrenics whose illness began after 3 years of age. Torrey et al[96] have now provided prospective data on 20 children with autism and childhood schizophrenia, identified in the entire nationwide sample (55,000) of the Collaborative Perinatal Study. The gestations of the psychotic children were marked by significantly more bleeding than the controls', especially in the second trimester. Rieder et al[97] found that a lower 7-year IQ in the child followed vaginal bleeding or edema of the face and hands during the pregnancies of chronic schizophrenic mothers, or of women married to such schizophrenics. This did not occur in the controls, which suggests that the offspring of the chronic schizophrenics had a greater genetic vulnerability, which made their IQs more susceptible to these complications.

Genetically Determined Developmental Deviation

An abnormal pregnancy or birth may add organic defect and increase the mental retardation of the young schizophrenic child, as in Bender's and Goldfarb's series, but it was not responsible for the irregular infant development observed by Fish. None of the infants with pandevelopmental retardation had had any pregnancy or birth complications. Pandevelopmental retardation was, however, significantly related to being a child of a schizophrenic mother. The schizophrenic children in Fish's series had onsets after 2 years of age and were not as severe as children with early infantile autism. Similarly, in Marcus' study,[61] the "soft" neurologic signs in 7- to 10-year-old children were significantly related to being born to a schizophrenic parent.

In the 7- to 10-year-old age group, it would be difficult, if not impossible, to distinguish on clinical grounds alone, these "soft" neurologic signs occurring in a population genetically at risk for schizophrenia, from those due to other causes. However, in infancy, repeated examinations disclosed peculiar regressions in physical growth, postural-motor, and visual-motor development that were distinctly different from the patterns seen following pregnancy and birth complications. A much greater number of infants genetically at risk for schizophrenia and infants with benign genetic histories would have to be matched for the presence or absence of pregnancy and birth complications, and then examined frequently from birth to 2 years of age, in order to determine how reliably regressions, retarded physical growth, and erratic patterning of development could differentiate the poor integration in schizophrenic offspring without birth complications from poor integration in infants at no genetic risk who had suffered brain damage.

DOES THE QUALITY OF MOTHERING CONTRIBUTE TO PANDEVELOPMENTAL RETARDATION AND A SCHIZOPHRENIC OUTCOME?

Certainly, in this study, a higher incidence of poorly integrated neurologic development, with the characteristics described previously, was related to a genetic history for schizophrenia. But it would be the height of naiveté to assume from this that the rates of neurologic maturation and the degree of disruption reflected only genetic programming, uninfluenced by environment. The severe sensory deprivation and impoverishment of early institutional care appear to be associated with developmental handicaps in some of the infants subjected to these conditions.[98] In that study, gross motor development was affected to a lesser degree than visual-motor, language, and social development.

However, one does not know the genetic histories of many abandoned infants, including those in the Provence and Lipton study.[98] It appears that the incidence of psychiatric pathology in such mothers is higher than in the general population. Horn et al[99] demonstrated that groups of unwed mothers who give their children up for adoption "contain substantial numbers of women who are *extremely* deviate on one or more of the clinical scales of the MMPI." Over 20% had abnormally high scores on the schizophrenia scale (T scores > 70). Provence and Lipton, as well as other authors, have not been able to explain why some infants are much more vulnerable than others to such institutional environments. It is probable that some of these infants were more vulnerable on a genetic basis, as in Fish's studies.

Interestingly, in the study of Heston and Denney,[79] in which the infants were matched for the duration of institutional care, no gross psychiatric sequelae depended on the extent of such deprivation. On the contrary, psychopathology in the offspring was related only to the presence or absence of schizophrenia in the biological mother. The authors are careful to state that they could not eliminate the possibility that more subtle emotional impairments existed that were not reflected in global ratings of disability or in the standard psychiatric diagnoses. Their findings add support to the notion that it is the genetically vulnerable infants who succumb most to severely impoverished environments. Similarly, in infants studied for "failure to thrive," it is not clear whether genetic factors increase their vulnerability, in addition to the emotional and physical neglect that seem to be implicated.

However, whatever the genetic background of such deprived populations, White and Held[100] demonstrated that the pace and sequence of visual-motor development can be altered significantly by providing specific patterns of early stimulation to the otherwise bleak institutional environment.

Obviously, it is much more complicated to assess the effects of environment in a heterogenous population when the constructive and deleterious factors are not under experimental control. One can therefore draw only the most tentative conclusions from Fish's infant data. These point to both genetic and environmental influences on development. Pandevelopmental retardation not only occurred significantly more often in the offspring of schizophrenic mothers, but it occurred in a severe form in some infants ("Rachel" and "Pia") reared in optimal environments by mothers who sensitively responded to the particular needs of these vulnerable infants.[101] This, as well as the clustering of these severe developmental disorders according to the genetic history, points to a genetic component in these deviations.

However, certain types of rearing experiences may exaggerate or mitigate the severity of particular developmental symptoms in the vulnerable group.[101] The most severe pandevelopmental retardation occurred in the two preschizophrenic infants. Both were reared in the most impoverished environments. Peter was reared by a dull, disorganized maternal grandmother, and Linda spent her first four years in a large foundling institution, as bleak as those described by Provence and Lipton. At 11 months, when Peter was unable to sit unsupported, he was able to perform manual tasks optimally "when cradled in the examiner's lap and physically supported. However, his grandmother was emotionally incapable of responding to his needs for special attention and it appeared that he could not practice his nascent skills when left unattended in his crib at home."[63] His spurt in development began in the month prior to his mother's return from the hospital. "The fact that he suddenly began to progress, despite the fact that he was still totally under his grandmother's care, indicates that there must have been an abrupt change in his inner resources."[63] Linda's acceleration in development also occurred spontaneously while she was still on the same large infant ward in the institution. It appears that genetic factors led to the initially poor neurologic integration in these infants and to their spontaneous remissions, but that their impoverished environments could well have added to their early neurologic retardation.

Later outcome appears to depend even more obviously on the child's life experiences interacting with his early developmental assets and impairments. The two preschizophrenic infants had the most severe early impairments and showed the least response to the environmental stimulation and support that they received after 7 years of age. Children with less severe deviations in infancy than this showed a greater capacity to respond to whatever stimulation and support was provided by the environment. Conrad was better integrated than Peter was at 9 years of age, although he had had a traumatic birth history and even much greater disruption of his relationships to parent figures than Peter.[65,66] Some children showed remarkably resilient adaptations to severe birth trauma and what are ordinarily considered to be pathogenic environments.[65] Rachel, whose early development and cognitive impairment at 10 years were worse than Pia's, is so far coping with her adolescent problems more successfully, apparently because she has been in a warm and continually supportive foster home. Pia has made several adolescent suicide attempts, having been rejected by her grandmother for the academic inadequacies she began to show in grade school. Whereas Conrad's greater competence compared to Peter appears related to his lesser early neurologic vulnerability, the fact that Rachel is coping better than Pia can only point to the positive effect of the environment on a very vulnerable child.

A genetically determined biologic vulnerability is just that—it can be exaggerated by a destructive or impoverished environment and can be compensated for by a constructive environment. The underlying neurobiologic disorder is the overriding determinant of outcome only when it is of devastating proportions. This appears to be true of the most severe of the early-onset childhood schizophrenics who are severely withdrawn and retarded from early infancy. Biologic disorder of this degree is virtually uninfluenced by variations in family environments, or by the most potent pharmacologic and educational measures currently available.[34]

The necessary influence of a genetic predisposition has been clearly demonstrated by the adoption studies[37,79] and the twin studies.[33] To go beyond this and attempt to evaluate the precise influences in the environment that cause one vulnerable "schizotypic" individual to decompensate and that help another to compensate presents enormous complications. The issues are still unclear, even in the studies of discordant monozygotic twins, when the genetic component can be held constant.[33,81] To study the effects of different rearing experiences in prospective studies of infants, when the genetic risk cannot be equated so precisely, one would need to match the infants according to their different profiles and the degrees of severity of early developmental impairments, and also for their compensating developmental assets.

If we are to match environments for their constructive and destructive effects on different types of infants, we need much more information regarding what effects specific differences in the environment can have on specific developmental symptoms. At the present time, we can rate only the most extreme differences in early mothering. The impact of different patterns of nurturing will be different on vulnerable infants with different degrees of vulnerability, and with different profiles of other developmental assets and liabilities. A depressed or withdrawn mother may have a more devastating effect on an apathetic infant than on an oversensitive, irritable one. An agitated, tense, or chaotic mother may be more disorganizing for the latter type of infant.[101]

The variables to be measured increase exponentially if we then want to compare the effects of subsequent life experiences on children with different early developmental assets and handicaps. One would need some understanding of the destructive or constructive meaning of these events for individual children, in the light of their own particular past experiences.[81]

Rather than embark on such enormously complicated studies of long-term outcome of infants at risk, I believe it is more appropriate and economical at the present stage of our knowledge to study first the nature of the biologic antecedents of schizophrenia in more detail in infants at risk. If we knew more about the mechanisms whereby the early motor, perceptual, and cognitive handicaps were produced, one could study the effects of specific early interventions on specific developmental impairments, as White and Held[100] have done in institutionalized infants.

If early interventions could be developed that could prevent, arrest, or compensate for the perceptual and cognitive impairments these infants often show before 2 years of age, one might interrupt the sequence of cumulative academic and vocational failure that makes for a more chronically disabled adult who retreats into "despair and apathy."[58]

OTHER FEATURES OF THE NEUROINTEGRATIVE DISORDER IN INFANTS AT RISK

"Abnormally Quiet" State

In addition to pandevelopmental retardation, three other abnormal patterns in the first months raise neurophysiologic questions. The first was an "abnormally quiet" state found in four offspring of schizophrenic mothers (Table 8). From birth to 4 weeks of age, these infants differed from the others in their ability to maintain an unbroken state of quiet visual alertness for up to one hour and 20 minutes, as early as 18 hours of age.[67,68] In contrast, the normally active infants spontaneously cried when awake and could remain alert only for two to five minutes without a pacifier, while under 2 months of age. The abnormally quiet infants did not cry in the first month, even with vigorous postural manipulation, unlike the others, although their responses to visual, auditory, and tactile stimuli were normal or increased.

These features were observed clinically in the first schizophrenic infant, Peter, in 1952.[63,64] In the 1959–1960 study, the difference in spontaneous activity and in responses to stimuli were measured under standard conditions.[67,68] These "quiet" infants also had extreme underactivity, flaccidity, and overextensibility of the joints. Their muscle tone was as doughy as that of infants with Down's syndrome. This hypotonia was apparently of central origin, as their deep tendon reflexes were 2+ to 3+, loose, and pendular.

The "quiet" infants also differed following caloric stimulation in the first month.[73] Their mean nystagmus when awake was only 0.5 seconds, compared to 37.2 seconds for the active infants. Decreased nystagmus is a very sensitive indicator of slight decreases in arousal.[102,103]

Table 8.—Other Features of the Neurointegrative Defect in Infancy
Abnormally "quiet" state: birth to 4 wk Continuous visual alertness: 15 to 80 min (vs 2 to 5 min) (without a pacifier) Marked decrease in spontaneous crying No crying with postural manipulation of body or extremities (decreased response to proprioceptive stimulation) Normal or increased responses to visual, auditory, and tactile stimuli Muscles "doughy" to palpation (as in Down's syndrome) Flaccid, overextensible at joints Deep tendon reflexes 2+ to 3+, loose, pendular Decreased caloric nystagmus when awake: 0.5 sec (vs 37.2 sec) Severe psychopathology at 10 yr in 3 of 4 "quiet" infants
Failure of midline bimanual skills ("hand-to-hand" items) Related to severe to moderate psychopathology at 10 yr (in all 8 infants; $P = .022$) Related to decreased caloric vestibular response (at 4 mo: $P = .008$; 7 mo: $P = .071$; 10 mo, random)
Decreased caloric nystagmus (0 to 10 sec) occurred with "Quiet" state (0 to 1 mo) Failure of midline bimanual skills (4 to 7 mo) Pandevelopmental retardation (0 to 24 mo)

But in these "abnormally quiet" infants, the decrease in nystagmus, spontaneous motor activity, and the response to manipulation all occurred in the presence of normal or increased visual fixation and following. The "abnormally quiet" state was characteristic of these infants between examinations, as well. It therefore appeared to be a sustained, but relatively "focal" depression of CNS functioning in the first month, limited to gross motor, proprioceptive, and vestibular systems.

In three of the four quiet infants, this abnormally quiet behavior was a precursor of severe psychopathology at 10 years. But Linda, who became grossly psychotic by 6 years of age, had appeared normally active in her first month. One should note here that all the abnormally "quiet" infants were white, whereas all of the black infants were active, including Linda.

Visual-Motor Disorders and Failures of Integrated Bimanual Skills

Visual-motor performance showed several severe disturbances that will not be reviewed in detail here.[63,66,70] These included delays in visual fixation on objects held in the infant's own hand, in contrast to normal attention to objects around him; severe delays in reaching and manipulation in the first year; apraxia and retarded form perception in the second year, as well as a variety of failures on perceptual tests at 10 years of age.

Gross irregularity, or "scatter," in integrative visual-motor tasks during infancy occurred only in children with severe to moderate psychiatric disorders at 10 years.[70] Only one item, failure of "hand-to-hand" integration, was similarly correlated with the presence of later severe to moderate psychiatric impairment ($P = .022$, Fisher's test).[104] This integrated functioning of one hand with the other at the midline normally begins with mutual fingering of one hand by the other at 16 weeks, followed by the transferring of objects from one hand to the other at 28 weeks, and finally at 40 weeks to the simultaneous grasp of one object in each hand and approximating them. Failure in these specific bimanual skills occurred in all eight of the children rated as having severe to moderate psychiatric impairment at 10 years, but they were not failed by either of the two children rated as having mild to no impairment.

There was also a significant relationship between the times when midline bimanual skills were failed and when vestibular response was reduced on one or both sides.[73] This relationship was significant at 16 weeks ($P = .008$, Fisher's test). It declined at 28 weeks ($P = .071$) and appeared at random at 40 weeks. The schizophrenic infant, Linda, had the most severe retardation in these "hand-to-hand" items[70] and in the associated vestibular hyporeactivity.[71] Although finger dexterity developed normally, her hands did not engage at the midline like a normal 16-week infant, even when she was 28 weeks old, and she did not transfer objects like a 28-week-old, even when she was 58 weeks of age.

Decreased Vestibular Responses

Absent or decreased (one- to ten-second nystagmus) vestibular responses were associated with the periods of pandevelopmental retardation between birth and 2 years of age, with the "abnormally quiet" state in the first month, and with the failures of bimanual skills in the fourth and seventh months.[73] The transitory nature of the absent responses rules out the possibility of an organic lesion of the vestibular system. Rather, it appeared to be a sensitive indicator of periods when several different CNS functions manifested integrative disorder. This suggests that transitory states of decreased CNS activity, which depressed gross motor, proprioceptive, and vestibular functions, but not vision, accompanied periods when CNS integration was disrupted.

On most of these occasions there were no overt behavioral changes to suggest the presence of a decreased arousal, which might have explained the failures in performance and the decreased nystagmus. The infants usually appeared visually intent and focused in their attention to the performance materials. The hypoactivity of the "abnormally quiet" babies in the first four weeks, which was accompanied by decreased nystagmus, has been discussed above. There were also four occasions when waking infants who had decreased nystagmus showed some degree of behavioral apathy. Although they were visually alert on these four occasions, three infants did not cry during the 60 seconds of cold air (10 C) stimulation that usually produced crying. They also showed complete absence of nystagmus on these occasions. This exceptional underresponsiveness occurred only in the three infants who were seriously disturbed at 10 years. Furthermore, these four instances occurred at the age when pandevelopmental retardation was most severe in these infants. The absence of the usual irritability with caloric stimulation suggests some covert state of decreased arousal. However, the association of this state with the periods of the worst pandevelopmental retardation, when physical growth was maximally retarded, testifies to a cumulative phenomenon that had begun one or more months before. This means that the poor central nervous system integration at these times was not a momentary phenomenon, but part of a continuing, profound process.

NEUROINTEGRATIVE DEFECT IN INFANTS AT RISK: A DYSREGULATION OF MATURATION AT ALL LEVELS

In summary, these infants had periods when several different CNS functions manifested integrative disorder. The biologic disorder during these periods disrupted the normal timing, sequences, and spatial organization of development. It was a disorder of the overall regulation and patterning of the orderly progress of maturation, not a disorder of isolated traits of responses. The normal temporal pattern was changed in a disorderly fashion, so that the rate alternated between being excessively slow and excessively fast, or even went into reverse. The spatial patterning was disrupted, as seen in the temporary reversal of the cephalocaudal gradient and the failures of midline integration of the hands. The peculiar "scatter" in functioning resulted in a profile of successes and failures on any single examination, unlike that seen in chronic brain syndromes (Table 9).

Finally, this integrative disorder affected many systems under control of the CNS, including physical growth, gross motor, visual-motor, vestibular functioning, and possibly arousal. The biologic disorder in preschizophrenic and vulnerable infants is a disorder of the total organism.

One could construct a theory of schizophrenia based on any one of

Table 9.—Neurointegrative Defect in Infancy: Signs of Dysregulation of Maturation in Many Systems

Periods of decreased CNS integration
Alternately retarded and accelerated development
Regression of development; loss of function
Reversed cephalocaudal gradient
Failure of integration of midline bimanual skills
Profile of failures unlike chronic brain syndromes

Involvement of many systems
Retarded physical growth with most severe, overall retardation
  (*pandevelopmental retardation*)
Decreased muscle tone, activity, crying ("quiet" state)
Decreased response to proprioceptive stimuli ("quiet" state)
Retarded postural-motor development
Decreased vestibular response to caloric stimulation (decreased
  "arousal"?)
Retarded visual-motor development
Retarded cognitive development

Severity of neurointegrative defect related to outcome
Pandevelopmental retardation (0 to 24 mo) related to schizophrenia and severe to moderate personality disorders (10 yr) (χ^2:
  $P < .01$)
Visual-motor retardation (form board, 18 to 24 mo) related to vi-
  sual-spatial deficit (block design, 10 yr) ($P < .05$, Fisher's test)

the disturbances that occur. Disorders of autonomic function, affect and "drive," proprioception and vestibular function, attention, perception, and cognition all occurred in the preschizophrenic infants, as they do in older schizophrenic children and adults. Each of these dysfunctions has been put forward at some time as "the" fundamental defect in schizophrenia. These early disturbances very likely predispose to particular schizophrenic symptoms.[63,70,77,105] The various developmental disorders also point to different aspects of brain function that should be studied, using neurophysiologic and biochemical methods. However, I do not believe that we will unlock the riddle of schizophrenia until we understand how the biologic disorder disrupts the *total* integrative functioning at *all* levels of central nervous system functioning, from physical growth and motor development up to perception and abstract reasoning.

STRATEGY FOR STUDYING NEUROPHYSIOLOGIC AND BIOCHEMICAL ABNORMALITIES IN INFANTS AT RISK

The infant data provide a strategy for studying the underlying neurophysiologic and biochemical abnormalities in infants at risk, using pandevelopmental retardation as a "marker" for the inherited neurointegrative defect in schizophrenia. If neurophysiologic or biochemical changes were studied longitudinally in infants genetically at risk, pandevelopmental retardation would identify the infants most vulnerable to later schizophrenia or severe personality disorders. Furthermore, the periods of severe retardation appear to reflect increased "activity" of the schizoprenic process. These measurable fluctuations in development would underscore the significance of any associated neurophysiologic or biochemical changes that occurred at these times. Without an external marker, the latter would be more difficult to distinguish from random variations. A series of two-year studies could screen the most promising measures to be used in later controlled, long-term studies of infants at risk.

Severe neurointegrative disorders in infancy delineate a biologic continuum of genetic vulnerability, extending from chronic schizophrenia to severe personality disorders in the "schizophrenia spectrum."[40] So far, no gross neurologic, psychologic, or behavioral disorders have been reported in the childhood histories of acute schizophrenics or manic depressives. Because developmental lags without growth retardation occur in many different conditions, ranging from no psychiatric disorder to moderately severe adult disorders (ie, "Carol"), I suspect that development alone is too gross and nonspecific a measure to delineate the more covert biologic antecedents of acute schizophrenia and manic-depressive disease. More specific biochemical or neurophysiologic measures will probably be required in order to identify the biologic antecedents of these disorders.

REFERENCES

1. Rosenthal, D.: *Genetic Theory and Abnormal Behavior*. New York, McGraw-Hill Book Co. Inc, 1970.
2. Redlich, F.C., & Freedman, D.X.: *The Theory and Practice of Psychiatry*. New York, Basic Books Inc, 1966.
3. Mason, C.F.: Pre-illness intelligence of mental hospital patients. *J. Consult. Clin. Psychol.* 20:297–300, 1956.
4. Robins, L.N.: *Deviant Children Grown Up*. Baltimore, Williams & Wilkins Co, 1966.
5. Bleuler, E.: *Dementia Praecox or the Group of Schizophrenias*, Zinken, J. (trans). New York, International Universities Press, 1950.
6. Kasanin, J.S., (Ed): *Language and Thought in Schizophrenia*. Berkeley, University of California Press, 1944.
7. Payne, R.W.: Cognitive abnormalities, In H.J. Eysenck (Ed): *Handbook of Abnormal Psychology*. New York, Basic Books Inc, 1961, Pp. 193–261.
8. Shakow, D.: Psychological deficit in schizophrenia. *Behav. Sci.* 8:275–305, 1963.
9. Salzinger, K., Portnoy, S., & Feldman, R.S.: Verbal behavior in schizophrenics and some comments toward a theory of schizophrenia, in P. Hoch, & J. Zubin, (Eds): *Psychopathology of Schizophrenia*. New York, Grune & Stratton Inc. 1966, Pp. 99–128.

10. Potter, H.W.: Schizophrenia in children. *Am. J. Psychiatry* 89:1253–1270, 1933.
11. Despert, J.L.: Schizophrenia in children. *Psychiatr. Q.* 12:366–371, 1938.
12. Despert, J.L.: Thinking and motility disorder in a schizophrenic child. *Psychiatr. Q.* 15:522–536, 1941.
13. Bender, L.: Child schizophrenia. *Nerv. Child* 1:138–140, 1942.
14. Bender, L.: Childhood schizophrenia. *Am. J. Orthopsychiatry* 17:40–56, 1947.
15. Kanner, L.: Autistic disturbances of affective contact. *Nerv. Child* 2:217–250, 1943.
16. Kanner, L.: Irrelevant and metaphorical language in early infantile autism. *Am. J. Psychiatry* 103:242–246, 1946.
17. Goldfarb, W.: Childhood psychosis, In P.H. Mussen, (Ed): *Carmichael's Manual of Child Psychology*, Ed. 3. New York, John Wiley & Sons Inc, 1970, vol. 2, Pp. 765–830.
18. Creak, M.: Schizophrenic syndrome in childhood: Report of a working party. *Br. Med. J.* 2:889–890, 1961.
19. Fish, B.: The "one child, one drug" myth of stimulants in hyperkinesis: Importance of diagnostic categories in evaluating treatment. *Arch. Gen. Psychiatry* 25:193–203, 1971.
20. Shapiro, T., & Fish, B.: A method to study language deviation as an aspect of ego organization in young schizophrenic children. *J. Am. Acad. Child Psychiatry* 8:36–56, 1969.
21. Shapiro, T., Roberts, A., & Fish, B.: Imitation and echoing in young schizophrenic children. *J. Am. Acad. Child Psychiatry* 9:548–567, 1970.
22. Shaprio, T., Fish, B., & Ginsberg, G.: The speech of a schizophrenic child from 2 to 6. *Am. J. Psychiatry* 128:1408–1413, 1972.
23. Shapiro, T., Chiarandini, I., & Fish, B.: Thirty severely disturbed children: Evaluation of their language development for classification and prognosis. *Arch. Gen. Psychiatry* 30:819–825, 1974.
24. Baltaxe, C.A.M., & Simmons, J.Q.: Language in childhood psychosis: A review. *J. Speech Hear. Disord.* 40:439–458, 1975.
25. Wing, J.K., Cooper, J.E., & Sartorius, N.: *Measurement and Classification of Psychiatric Symptoms: An Instruction Manual for the PSE and Catego Program.* London, Cambridge University Press, 1974.
26. Hermelin, B., & O'Connor, N.: *Psychological Experiments with Autistic Children.* New York, Pergamon Press, 1970.
27. Kanner, L.: General concept of schizophrenia at different ages. *Res. Publ. Assoc. Res. Nerv. Ment. Dis.* 34:451–453, 1954.
28. DesLauriers, A., & Halpern, F.: Psychological tests in childhood schizophrenia. *Am. J. Orthopsychiatry* 17:57–69, 1947.
29. Leitch, M., & Schafer, S.: A study of the thematic apperception tests of psychotic children. *Am. J. Orthopsychiatry* 17:337–342, 1947.
30. Kallman, F., & Roth, B.: Genetic aspects of preadolescent schizophrenia. *Am. J. Psychiatry* 112:599–606, 1956.
31. Bender, L., & Faretra, G.: The relationship between childhood schizophrenia and adult schizophrenia, In A.R. Kaplan, (Ed): *Genetic Factors in Schizophrenia.* Springfield, Ill, Charles C. Thomas Publisher, 1972, Pp. 28–64.
32. Kolvin, I., Ounsted, D., & Humphrey, M., et al: Six studies in the childhood psychoses. *Br. J. Psychiatry* 118:381–391, 1971.
33. Gottesman, I.I., & Shields, J.: *Schizophrenia and Genetics: A Twin Study Vantage Point,* New York, Academic Press Inc, 1972.
34. Fish, B., Shapiro, T., & Campbell, M., et al: A classification of schizophrenic chil-

dren under 5 years. *Am. J. Psychiatry* 124:1415–1423, 1968.

35. Kanner, L.: To what extent is early infantile autism determined by constitutional inadequacies? *Res. Publ. Assoc. Res. Nerv. Ment. Dis.* 33:378–385, 1953.

36. Kanner, L., & Eisenberg, L.: Notes on the follow-up studies of autistic children, In P.H. Hoch, & J. Zubin, (Eds): *Psychopathology of Childhood*. New York, Grune & Stratton, Inc, 1955, Pp. 227–239.

37. Meyers, D., & Goldfarb, W.: Psychiatric appraisals of parents and siblings of schizophrenic children. *Am. J. Psychiatry* 118:902–908, 1962.

38. Lotter, V.: Epidemiology of autistic conditions in young children: II. Some characteristics of the parents and children. *Soc. Psychiatry* 1:163–173, 1967.

39. Kety, S.S., Rosenthal, D., & Wender, P.H., et al: The types and prevalence of mental illness in the biological and adoptive families of adopted schizophrenics, in D. Rosenthal, & S.S. Kety, (Eds): *The Transmission of Schizophrenia*, London, Pergamon Press, 1968, Pp. 345–362.

40. Hanson, D.R., & Gottesman, I.I.: The genetics, if any, of infantile autism and childhood schizophrenia. *J. Austism Child. Schizo.* 6:209–234, 1976.

41. Rutter, M., & Lockyer, L.: A five to 15 year follow-up study of infantile psychosis: I. Description of the sample. *Br. J. Psychiatry* 113:1169–1182, 1967.

42. Rutter, M.: Autistic children—infancy to adulthood. *Semin. Psychiatry* 2:435–450, 1970.

43. Creak, M., & Ini, S.: Families of psychotic children. *J. Child Psychol. Psychiatry* 1:156–175, 1960.

44. Creak, M.: Childhood psychosis: A review of 100 cases. *Br. J. Psychiatry* 109:84–89, 1963.

45. Goldfarb, W.: The subclassification of psychotic children: Application to a study of longitudinal change. In D. Rosenthal, S.S. Kety, (Eds): *The Transmission of Schizophrenia*. London, Pergamon Press, 1968, Pp. 333–342.

46. Kohn, M.L.: Social class and schizophrenia: A critical review, In D. Rosenthal, S.S. Kety, (Eds): *The Transmission of Schizophrenia*. London, Pergamon Press, 1968, Pp. 155–173.

47. Goldfarb, W.: *Childhood Schizophrenia*. Cambridge, Mass, Harvard University Press, 1961.

48. Kanner, L.: Follow-up study of 11 autistic children originally reported in 1943, In L. Kanner, (Ed): *Childhood Psychosis: Initial Studies and New Insights*. New York, John Wiley & Sons Inc, 1973, Pp. 161–187.

49. Bennett, S., & Klein, H.R.: Childhood: Thirty years later. *Am. J. Psychiatry* 122:1121–1124, 1966.

50. Bender, I.: The life course of schizophrenic children. *Biol. Psychiatry* 2:165–172, 1970.

51. Annell, A.: The prognosis of psychotic syndromes in children: A follow-up of 115 cases. *Acta. Psychiatr. Scand.* 39:235–297, 1963.

52. Dahl, V.: A follow-up study of a child psychiatric clientele with special regard to the diagnosis of psychosis. *Acta. Psychiatr. Scand.* 54:106–112, 1976.

53. Garmezy, N., & Streitman, S.: Children at risk—the search for the antecedents of schizophrenia: I. Conceptual models and research methods. *Schizo. Bull.* 8:14–90, 1974.

54. Watt, N.F.: Longitudinal changes in the social behavior of children hospitalized for schizophrenia as adults. *J. Nerv. Ment. Dis.* 155:42–54, 1972.

55. Garmezy, N.: Process and reactive schizophrenia: Some conceptions and issues, In M.M. Katz, J.O. Cole, & W.E. Barton, (Eds): *The Role and Methodology of Classifica-*

tion in Psychiatry and Psychopathology. U.S. Government Printing Office, 1968, Pp. 419–466.

56. O'Neal, P., & Robins, L.N.: Childhood patterns predictive of adult schizophrenia: A 30-year follow-up study. *Am. J. Psychiatry* 115:385–391, 1958.

57. Watt, N.F.: Childhood and adolescent routes to schizophrenia, In D.F. Ricks, M. Thomas A. Roff, (Eds): *Life History Research in Psychopathology.* Minneapolis, University of Minnesota Press, 1974, vol 3, Pp. 194–211.

58. Ricks, D.F., & Nameche, G.: Symbiosis, sacrifice and schizophrenia. *Ment. Hyg.* 50:541–551, 1966.

59. Ricks, D.F., & Berry, J.C.: Family and symptom patterns that precede schizophrenia, In M. Roff, D.F. Ricks, (Eds): *Life History Research in Psychopathology.* Minneapolis, University of Minnesota Press, 1970, vol. 1, Pp. 31–50.

60. Kety, S.S., & Matthysse, S.: Prospects for research on schizophrenia. *Neurosci. Res. Program Bull.* 10:370–507, 1972.

61. Marcus, J.: Cerebral functioning in offspring of schizophrenics. A possible genetic factor. *Int. J. Ment. Health* 3:57–73, 1974.

62. Mednick, S.A., Mura, M., & Schulzinger, Z., et al: Perinatal conditions and infant development in children with schizophrenic parents. *Soc. Biol.* 18:S103–S113, 1971.

63. Fish, B.: The detection of schizophrenia in infancy. *J. Nerv. Ment. Dis.* 125:1-24, 1957.

64. Fish, B.: Longitudinal observations of biological deviations in a schizophrenic infant. *Am. J. Psychiatry* 116:25–31, 1959.

65. Fish, B., Shapiro, T., & Halpern, F., et al: The prediction of schizophrenia in infancy: III. A ten-year follow-up report of neurological and psychological development. *Am. J. Psychiatry* 121:768–775, 1965.

66. Fish, B., Shapiro, & T. Halpern, F., et al: The prediction of schizophrenia in infancy: II. A ten-year follow-up of predictions made at 1 month of age, In P. Hoch, J. Zubin, (Eds): *Psychopathology of Schizophrenia.* New York, Grune & Stratton Inc, 1966, Pp. 335–353.

67. Fish, P., & Alpert, M.: Abnormal states of consciousness and muscle tone in infants born to schizophrenic mothers. *Am. J. Psychiatry* 119:439–445, 1962.

68. Fish, B.: The maturation of arousal and attention in the first months of life: A study of variations in ego development. *J. Am. Acad. Child Psychiatry* 2:253–270, 1963.

69. Fish, P., & Alpert, M.: Patterns of neurological development in infants born to schizophrenic mothers, In J. Wortis, (Ed): *Recent Advances in Biological Psychiatry.* New York, Plenum Press Inc, 1963, vol 5, Pp. 37–42.

70. Fish, B., & Hagin, R.: Visual-motor disorders in infants at risk for schizophrenia. *Arch. Gen. Psychiatry* 28:900–904, 1973.

71. Wetzel, N.C.: The baby grid. *J. Pediatr.* 29:439–454, 1946.

72. Gesell, A.: *Developmental Diagnosis,* ed 2. New York, Paul B. Hoeber Inc., 1947.

73. Fish, B., & Dixon, W.F.: Vestibular hyporeactivity in infants at risk for schizophrenia: Its association with critical developmental disorders. *Arch. Gen. Psychiatry,* to be published.

74. McNally, W.J., & Stuart, E.A.: *Examination of the Labyrinth in Relation to its Physiology and Nonsuppurative Diseases.* Omaha, Douglas Printing Co., 1953.

75. Meehl, P.E.: Schizotaxia, schizotypy, schizophrenia. *Am. Psychol.* 17:827–838, 1962.

76. Paine, R.S., & Oppé, T.E.: *Neurological Examination of Children.* London, Spastics Society Medical and Information Unit—Heinemann Medical Books, 1966.

77. Fish, B.: Involvement of the central nervous system in infants with schizophrenia. *Arch. Neurol.* 2:115–121, 1960.
78. Fish, B.: The study of motor development in infancy and its relationship to psychological functioning. *Am. J. Psychiatry* 117:1113–1118, 1961.
79. Heston, L.L., & Denney, D.: Interaction between early life experience and biological factors in schizophrenia, In D. Rosenthal, & S.S. Kety, (Eds): *The Transmission of Schizophrenia*. London, Pergamon Press, 1968, Pp. 363–376.
80. Shields, J., Heston, L.I., & Gottesman, I.I.: Schizophrenia and' the schizoid: The problem of genetic analysis, In R.R. Fieve, D. Rosenthal, & H. Brill, (Eds): *Genetic Research in Psychiatry*. Baltimore, John Hopkins University Press, 1975, Pp. 167–197.
81. Meehl, P.E.: A critical afterword, In I.I. Gottesman, & J. Shields, (Eds): *Schizophrenia and Genetics: A Twin Study Vantage Point*. New York, Academic Press Inc., 1972, Pp. 367–415.
82. Hertzig, M.A., & Birch, M.G.: Neurologic organizations in psychiatrically disturbed adolescents. *Arch. Gen. Psychiatry* 19:528–537, 1968.
83. Tucker, G.J., Campion, E.W., & Silberfarb, P.M.: Sensorimotor functions and cognitive disturbance in psychiatric patients. *Am. J. Psychiatry* 132:17–21, 1975.
84. Quitkin, F., Rifkin, A., & Klein, D.F.: Neurologic soft signs in schizophrenia and character disorders: Organicity in schizophrenia with premorbid associality and emotionally unstable character disorders. *Arch. Gen. Psychiatry* 33:845–853, 1976.
85. Holzman, P.S., Proctor, L.R., & Levy, D.L., et al: Eye-tracking dysfunctions in schizophrenic patients and their relatives. *Arch. Gen. Psychiatry* 31:143–151, 1974.
86. Gunderson, J.G., & Singer, M.T.: Defining borderline patients: An overview. *Am. J. Psychiatry* 132:1–10, 1975.
87. Singer, M.T., & Wynne, L.C.: Differentiating characteristics of parents of childhood schizophrenics, childhood neurotics and young adult schizophrenics. *Am. J. Psychiatry* 120:234–243, 1963.
88. Mednick, S.A., & Schulzinger, F.: Some premorbid characteristics related to breakdown in children with schizophrenic mothers. *Psychiat. Res.*, suppl. 1, 1968, Pp. 267–291.
89. Stabenau, J.R., & Pollin, W.: Early characteristics of monozygotic twins discordant for schizophrenia. *Arch. Gen. Psychiatry* 17:723–734.
90. Mirdal, G.K.M., Mednick, S.A., & Schulzinger, F., et al: Perinatal complications in children of schizophrenic mothers. *Acta. Psychiatr. Scand.* 50:553–568, 1974.
91. McNeil, T.F., & Kaij, L.: Obstetric complications and physical size of offspring of schizophrenic, schizophrenic-like, and control mothers. *Br. J. Psychiatry* 123:341–438, 1973.
92. Hanson, D.R., Gottesman, I.I., & Heston, L.L.: Some possible childhood indicators of adult schizophrenia inferred from children of schizophrenics. *Br. J. Psychiatry* 129:142–154, 1976.
93. Rieder, R.O., Rosenthal, D., & Wender, P., et al: The offspring of schizophrenics: Fetal and neonatal deaths. *Arch. Gen. Psychiatry* 32:200–211, 1975.
94. Fish, B.: Genetic or traumatic developmental deviation? *Soc. Biol.* 18:S117–S119, 1971.
95. Heston, L.L.: Schizophrenia in infancy? *Soc. Biol.* 18:S114–S116, 1971.
96. Torrey, E.F., Hersh, S.P., & McCabe, K.D.: Early childhood psychosis and bleeding during pregnancy: A prospective study of gravid women and their offspring. *J. Autism Child. Schizo.* 5:287–297, 1975.
97. Rieder, R.O., Broman, S.H., & Rosenthal, D.: The offspring of schizophrenics: II.

Perinatal factors and IQ. *Arch. Gen. Psychiatry* 34:789–799, 1977.

98. Provence, S., & Lipton, R.C.: *Infants in Institutions.* New York, International Universities Press, 1962.

99. Horn, J.M., Green, M., & Carney, R., et al: Bias against genetic hypotheses in adoption studies. *Arch. Gen. Psychiatry* 32:1365–1367, 1975.

100. White, B.L., & Held, R.: Plasticity of sensori-motor development in the human infant, In J. Hellmuth, (Ed): *Exceptional Infant: The Normal Infant.* New York, Brunner/Mazel, Inc, 1967, vol. 1.

101. Fish, B.: An approach to prevention in infants at risk for schizophrenia: Developmental deviations from birth to 10 years. *J. Am. Acad. Child Psychiatry* 15:62–82, 1976.

102. Pendleton, M.E., & Paine, R.S.: Vestibular nystagmus in human infants. *Neurology* 11:450–458, 1961.

103. Collins, W.E.: Manipulation of arousal and its effects on human vestibular nystagmus induced by caloric irrigation and angular acceleration. *Aerosp. Med.* 54:124–129, 1963.

104. Dixon, W.J., & Massey, F.J., Jr.: *Introduction to Statistical Analyses,* ed 3. New York, McGraw-Hill Book Co., Inc., 1969.

105. Fish, B.: Contributions of developmental research to a theory of schizophrenia, In J. Hellmuth, (Ed): *Exceptional Infant: Studies in Abnormalities.* New York, Brunner/Mazel Inc, 1971, vol 2, Pp. 473–482.

24

FOLLOW-UP REPORT ON AUTISM IN CONGENITAL RUBELLA

Stella Chess

New York University Medical Center

A longitudinal study was conducted of 243 children with congenital rubella. In this sample a high rate of autism and a high rate of recovery were observed. Examination of the data suggested that the rubella virus was the primary etiologic agent. It is hypothesized that the course of autism was that of a chronic infection in which recovery, chronicity, improvement, worsening, and delayed appearance of the autistic syndrome all were found. Other rubella consequences such as blindness, deafness, and cardiac and neuromuscular defects remained present except as modified by operations and prostheses. Degree of mental retardation initially was related to the outcome of autism but shifts in mental retardation over time did not correlate significantly for the group with shift in the autistic symptoms.

In 1971 a strikingly high prevalence of autism was reported in a population of 243 children with congenital rubella (Chess, 1971). These children had been evaluated physically and neurologically and were also studied psychiatrically and tested psychologically. The children, who were 2.5 to 5 years old at the time, had a wide variety of physical defects and a high incidence of mental retardation and behavioral disorder, as is typically found in congenital rubella (Chess,

Reprinted with permission from *Journal of Autism and Childhood Schizophrenia*, Vol. 7, No. 1, 1977.

Korn, & Fernandez, 1971). Ten children showed a complete syndrome of infantile autism, using Kanner's strict criteria. Eight additional children had findings of a partial syndrome of autism. The judgment of partial rather than complete syndrome was based on the occurrence of transitory fleeting expressions of recognition of another person.

The prevalence rate for this group of children with congenital rubella was equivalent to a rate of 412 per 10,000 for the complete syndrome of autism and 329 for the partial syndrome, giving a combined rate of 741 per 10,000. This contrasts with the rate of 2.1 cases of autism per 10,000 child population in the Middlesex survey (Lotter, 1966) and .7 per 10,000 child population in the Wisconsin study (Treffert, 1970).

Outside of single fragmentary case reports, only the Baylor study had previously suggested a high prevalence of autism in congenital rubella (Desmond, Wilson, Melnick, et al., 1967). That report however, did not discuss the criteria of autism or provide behavioral details.

In the rubella sample, the parents of the autistic children were not found to be significantly different from the other parents. The socioeconomic status of the families was diversified. In the total rubella sample, the children with mental retardation and sensory handicaps showed a wide variety of behavioral characteristics and psychopathology. This appeared to rule out these conditions as the cause of the autistic syndrome.

These findings led to the conclusion that the high prevalence of autism was one consequence of the invasion of the central nervous system by the rubella virus. Other studies have documented the occurrence of viral infection of the central nervous system and panencephalitis in cases of congenital rubella (Desmond et al., 1967; Townsend, Baringer, Wolinsky, et al., 1975; Weil, Itabashi, & Cremer, 1975).

FOLLOW-UP

A follow-up of 205 of our congenital rubella cases was done when the children were 8–9 years of age. Physical evaluation, psychiatric study and psychological testing were repeated. The present report concentrates on the follow-up findings in 17 of the 18 cases with complete or partial autism syndrome originally (one mother refused follow-up with the statement "She cannot be helped with her problems"). It also includes a report of 4 additional children with autistic features who were not considered autistic in the earlier study.

DEFINITIONS

1. Psychiatric status, both originally and at follow-up, was determined by careful clinical evaluation of each child. This evaluation utilized detailed behavioral information obtained by research staff members from the parents or other primary caretakers and from teachers, psychological test data, supplementary questioning of the parents as indicated by the research staff child psychiatrist, and a standard clinical play interview with the child by this psychiatrist. The final diagnostic judgment in each case was made by the author, who also saw many of the children herself, through a review of all the data in research staff conferences.

2. Psychological status was determined by a combination of history of adaptive behavior obtained either from parents or from primary caretaker in an institution, plus the child's response to standardized tests to the extent that his attention could be elicited by the test material. In the first study the Stanford Binet and Catell tests were employed. For the follow-up, the Wechsler Intelligence Scale for Children was used. For those with hearing and speech deficiencies, the performance portion only was utilized for assessment. In the charts that follow, the term *retardation, unspecified* refers to a case in which intellectual functioning was clearly below age level but where the test and behavioral data could not specify exact level.

3. Hearing level was rated according to the categories developed by Mindel and Vernon (1971) with some modification. In young children accurate audiological assessment is often difficult and this is especially true in autistic youngsters. The ratings in this study were made from reports of parents, teachers and institutional caretakers of the child's auditory functioning in daily life experiences. For those children using hearing aids, level of functioning was rated with the use of such an aid.

4. Visual status was determined by the physical examination of The Rubella Birth Defect Evaluation Project, which had initially identified the group of children and continued to give many of them ongoing pediatric care. For those subjects whose pediatric care was being given by private or institutional physicians or whose visual status had been assessed by ophthalmologists elsewhere, reports of these examinations were utilized as the statement of the current visual status.

5. Speech was defined as oral language. Divisions were (a) no words, (b) single words, (c) phrases, (d) short sentences, (e) long sentences.

6. Language was defined as all means of communication including speech. This included actions indicating desires, intent and attitudes, gestures, facial expressive messages, pantomime, and the use of formal manual language or sign.

7. Unsual habits and rituals included such behaviors as twirling objects incessantly, light gazing, a ritual sequence of handling each new object, hand fluttering, and similar actions.

FINDINGS

Psychiatric evaluation of the 10 cases with the complete autism syndrome originally showed that 3 were recovered, 1 improved, and 6 unimproved as regards the autism on follow-up. Similar evaluation of the 7 cases with the partial autism syndrome showed that 3 were recovered and 4 were worse. One case with the partial syndrome refused follow-up. The criteria for improvement and recovery comprised the development of affective relatedness to people and communicative verbal or nonverbal language. Persistence of change in mental retardation or habits and rituals were not rated in and of themselves as evidence for or against the diagnosis of autism.

Four new cases, one of a full and three of the partial autism syndrome, were identified on follow-up. These four children had not exhibited behavior diagnostic of autism on the original psychiatric evaluation 4 years previously.

For each of these 22 children with autism, past or present, the findings were tabulated as to outcome, psychological status, hearing: level of functioning, visual status, speech, language, and unusual habits and rituals.

Tables I, II, and III will be discussed from the vantage point of the striking phenomena which have emerged from this study. Two findings have been unusual: (1) the extraordinarily high prevalence of autism in this population, 905 per 10,000 child population, (including the 4 new cases); and (2) the significant number of cases that recovered.

Tables I, II, and III permit a scrutiny of the possible relationship of both the high prevalence rate and recovery rate to a number of factors that have been linked to the autism syndrome. These include the presence and severity of mental retardation and the effect of sensory deprivation. A third factor, the influence of special parental characteristics, especially the so-called refrigerator parents, has been considered and found not to be evident in these rubella families.

Table I. Ten Subjects with Complete Autism Syndrome

		N	Recovered on follow-up (N = 3)			Improved on follow-up (N = 1)	Unimproved on follow-up (N = 6)					
			F102	F114	F302	M158	M402	M101	M334	M183	M224	M159
Psychological status												
Initial	Follow-up											
MR unspecified	MR profound	1	–	–	–	–	–	–	–	+	–	–
MR unspecified	MR severe	1	–	–	–	–	–	–	+	–	–	–
MR unspecified	MR mild	1	–	+	–	–	–	–	–	–	–	–
MR profound	MR profound	1	–	–	–	–	–	–	–	–	+	–
MR severe	MR severe	3	–	–	+	–	+	+	–	–	–	–
MR severe	MR unspecified	1	–	–	–	–	–	–	–	–	–	+
MR borderline	MR profound	1	–	–	–	+	–	–	–	–	–	–
MR borderline	Average intelligence	1	+	–	–	–	–	–	–	–	–	–
Hearing: level of functioning												
Uncertain		4	–	–	–	+	–	+	+	–	–	+
Rated 6 (profound loss)		3	–	+	–	–	+	–	–	–	+	–
Rated 4 (moderately severe loss)		2	+	–	+	–	–	–	–	–	–	–
Rated 3 (mild to moderate loss)		1	–	–	–	–	–	–	–	+	–	–
Visual status												
Cataract		2	R	R	–	–	–	–	–	–	–	–
Hyperopia		1	–	L	–	–	–	–	–	–	–	–
Aphakia		4	–	–	Bi	L	–	R	–	–	Bi	–
No pathology		4	–	–	–	–	+	–	+	+	–	+
Speech												
No words		8	–	–	+	+	+	+	+	+	+	+
Questionable single words		1	–	+	–	–	–	–	–	–	–	–
Single words		1	+	–	–	–	–	–	–	–	–	–
Language												
Points		4	–	+	+	+	–	–	+	–	–	–
Pulls		6	–	+	–	–	+	–	+	+	+	+
Signs		2	+	+	–	–	–	–	–	–	–	–
Facial expression		1	+	–	–	–	–	–	–	–	–	–
Responds to signs or gestures		2	–	–	+	–	–	–	–	–	+	–
Gestures		3	+	–	–	+	–	–	–	+	–	–
Pantomime		2	+	+	–	–	–	–	–	–	–	–
Imitates		1	–	–	–	+	–	–	–	–	–	–
Stands near or takes object		1	–	–	–	–	–	+	–	–	–	–
Unusual habits or rituals												
Severe		8	–	–	+	+	+	+	+	+	+	+
Mild, moderate		2	+	+	–	–	–	–	–	–	–	–
Cardiac or neuromuscular defects												
Patent ductus arter. IA		4	+	+	–	–	–	+	–	–	–	+
Pulmonic stenosis IA		3	–	–	+	–	+	+	–	–	–	–
None		4	–	–	–	+	–	–	+	+	+	–
Cerebral dysfunction												
Present		1	–	+	–	–	–	–	–	–	–	–
Absent		9	+	–	+	+	+	+	+	+	+	+

Autism and Mental Retardation

Table I details the relationship between the follow-up findings in the 10 subjects with a complete autism syndrome initially and psychological status, hearing level, visual status, speech, language, unusual habits and rituals, cardiac or neuromuscular defects, and cerebral dysfunction. Table II gives the same relationship for the 7 subjects with a partial autism syndrome initially, and Table III for the 4 subjects who showed a complete or partial autism syndrome for the first time on follow-up.

Of special interest are the findings with regard to mental retarda-

Table II. Seven Subjects[a] with Partial Autism Syndrome

		N	Recovered on follow-up (N = 3)			Worse (full autistic syndrome) on follow-up (N = 4)			
			F149	F260	M174	M148	M200	F152	F233
Psychological status									
Initial	Follow-up								
MR severe	MR unspecified	2	−	−	−	−	+	−	+
MR unspecified	MR unspecified	2	+	−	−	+	−	−	−
MR unspecified	MR severe	1	−	−	−	−	−	+	−
MR moderate	MR moderate	1	−	−	+	−	−	−	−
MR moderate	Average intelligence	1	−	+	−	−	−	−	−
Hearing: level of functioning									
Uncertain		1	+	−	−	−	−	−	+
Rated 6 (profound loss)		2	−	+	−	−	−	+	−
Rated 4 (moderately severe loss)		2	−	−	+	−	+	−	−
Rated 2 (slight loss)		1	−	−	−	+	−	−	−
Visual status									
Aphakia		2	−	R	−	−	−	L	−
Myopia		1	−	−	−	Bi	−	−	−
No pathology		4	+	−	+	−	+	−	+
Speech									
No words		6	+	+	+	+	+	−	+
Single words		1	−	−	−	−	−	+	−
Language									
Points		2	−	+	+	−	−	−	−
Pulls		4	−	+	+	−	+	−	+
Signs		4	+	+	−	+	−	+	−
Finger spelling		1	+	−	−	−	−	−	−
Imitates		1	−	−	+	−	−	−	−
Pantomimes		1	−	−	+	−	−	−	−
Echopraxic		1	−	−	−	−	−	+	−
Unusual habits or rituals									
Severe		4	+	−	−	+	+	−	+
Moderate		3	−	+	+	−	−	+	−
Cardiac or neuromuscular defect									
Stenosis, ventricular septal, or other defects		3	−	−	−	−	+	+	+
None		4	+	+	+	+	−	−	−
Cerebral dysfunction									
Present		3	+	+	+	−	−	−	−
Absent		4	−	−	−	+	+	+	+

[a]An eighth child was lost to follow-up.

Table III. Four Subjects with New Autism Syndrome

		Case that became full autistic syndrome	Case that became partial autistic syndrome (N = 3)		
	N	M151	M181	F180	F121
Psychological status					
Initial Follow-up					
MR moderate MR unspecified	1	+	−	−	−
MR moderate MR moderate	2	−	+	+	−
MR severe MR profound	1	−	−	−	+
Hearing: level of functioning					
Uncertain	4	+	+	+	+
Visual status					
Cataract	2	L	−	Bi	−
Aphakia	1	−	−	−	Bi
Glaucoma	1	−	−	L	−
No pathology	1	−	+	−	−
Speech					
No words	4	+	+	+	+
Language					
No communication	1	−	−	−	+
Pulls	3	+	+	+	−
Points	2	+	+	−	−
Echopraxic	1	+	−	−	−
Imitates	1	+	−	−	−
Leads	1	−	−	+	−
Unusual habits or rituals					
Severe	3	+	+	−	+
Moderate	1	−	−	+	−
Cardiac or neuromuscular defect					
Patent ductus arter. IA	1	+	−	−	−
Aortic and pulmonary	1	−	−	+	−
None	2	−	+	−	+

tion (Table IV) because of the common association between this in-tellectual deficit and autism. The comparisons in this sample are lim-ited by the substantial number of autistic children in whom in-tellectual retardation was evident, but in whom an IQ score could not be determined either initially, on follow-up, or both (MR unspecified). In addition, in some of the cases in whom an estimate of degree of retardation was made, the data for this determination were partially qualitative and impressionistic. Keeping these caveats in mind, three comparisons were made: (1) initial level of mental retardation and follow-up findings of autism, (2) initial level of mental retardation in the new cases of autism, and (3) change in degree of mental retarda-

Table IV. Initial Retardation Level and Outcome in Initial Complete and Partial Autism Cases

Initial level of mental retardation (N = 17)		Recovered or improved (N = 7)	Unimproved or worse (N = 10)
Unspecified	6	2	4
MR profound	1	0	1
MR severe	6	1	5
MR moderate	2	2	0
MR borderline	2	2	0

tion from initial to follow-up estimate and follow-up findings. In these comparisons the complete and partial autism cases are combined.

In the four cases in which autism was first diagnosed on follow-up, i.e., whose psychiatric status worsened during this period, one had severe and three had moderate mental retardation initially.

No cases of autims had average or higher IQ level initially, and only one (recovered) had average intelligence on follow-up.

The above findings indicate that lack of improvement or worsening of psychiatric status in cases of autism tended to be associated with a more severe degree of mental retardation initially than in those cases in which there was recovery or improvement. These data correspond with the findings in the autism literature in general (Rutter, 1974).

As can be seen from Table V, no impressive correlation between change in intellectual level and change in psychiatric status as regards autism is evident. It is true that the only two cases with definite improvement in intellectual status occurred in the recovered and improved group. On the other hand, positive change in psychiatric status was accompanied by worsening of intellectual status in one case and lack of change in two others. The three cases who were unimproved or became worse showed no change in intellectual level. The three new cases were either unchanged or worse.

Autism and Sensory Deprivation

With regard to sensory deprivation, the data are recorded as to hearing and vision. It is to be noted that these children did not have loss of touch, kinesthetic sense, or smell. Since the major differences in physical status between initial and follow-up evaluations was the removal of ripe cataracts in a few children (others had had this done prior to the first study) and possible slight worsening of hearing status, the data are given only as in the follow-up assessments. As Tables I, II, and III illustrate, the hearing categorizations for the total

Table V. Change in Intellectual Level and Follow-up Findings[a]

Change in intellectual level from initial to follow-up	Recovered and improved autism cases ($N = 5$)	Unimproved and worse ($N = 3$)	New autism cases on follow-up ($N = 3$)
Improved	2	0	0
Unchanged	2	3	2
Worse	1	0	1

[a]The cases with MR unspecified, either initially or on follow-up, are not included in Table V, inasmuch as it was not possible to determine their direction of change.

group range from 2 (slight loss) to 6 (profound loss), to seven children for whom the responses did not permit a judgment as to hearing ability. The visual status for the entire group included children with normal vision, some with pathology-mature cataracts or aphakia in one eye, and some bilateral visual pathology which consisted variously of hyperopia, severe myopia, bilateral cataracts or aphakia, or combinations of cataract and myopia or cataracts and glaucoma. The recovered group of six were in the hearing range of 4 (moderately severe loss) to 6 (profound loss), with one whose contradictory information did not permit identification of precise degree of hearing loss. Visual status similarly was variable, with three of the recovered children having no visual pathology while the others had cataracts or aphakia of one eye, or bilateral aphakia. The unimproved or worsened children showed essentially the same distribution of both hearing or visual status. Hearing levels were from 2 to 6, with several whose degree of loss was not able to be determined. The visual status included several with no pathology and others whose cataracts or aphakia were monocular or bilateral or who had severe myopia. Thus, the degree of sensory pathology bears no direct relationship to the movement of the autistic syndromes toward recovery or improvement, retaining some status, or worsening. In looking at the four new cases, no accurate hearing estimate was possible for all. Their visual status ranged from no pathology to a combination of bilateral mature cataracts together with glaucoma in one eye.

Most of the total group had no oral speech. The recovered child with normal intelligence used single words; two others, one in the recovered group and one who worsened, had questionable reports of use of single words. However, a clear trend relating autistic status and nonoral language was to be found. Gesture, facial expressiveness, pantomime, responding to requests, and use of sign was characteristic of the recovered children. Their skill in using these communication modalities was directly related to intelligence and, where sign was concerned, to the period of instructional time.

Recovery from the autism was replaced in one of the children who had initially been in the full syndrome group and the three in the partial syndrome group, by evidences of cerebral dysfunction. These subjects no longer showed effective unrelatedness, an essential feature of childhood autism. They differed in this respect from the others who remained classified as autistic. All four had positive neurologic findings. The nature of their perseverations and mood swings was consistent with those found in brain-damaged children and was in no way diagnostic of autism. For these reasons, a diagnosis of cerebral dysfunction was now given as an appropriate clinical designation of their behavioral characteristics.

Habits and Rituals

Ritualistic behavior of a wide range is one of the most prominent features of autism. Children with sensory defects are also prone to develop habits which look odd and some of which are considered socially inept or even disgusting. For affectively related sensorially handicapped youngsters, such rituals are so typical of the specific defect as to be defined by its name—as the term *blindisms*. Included in the roster of habits which such children employ, especially when they are not actively interacting with other people, are light gazing, head turning from side to side, eye pressing. One may postulate that these behaviors provide stimulation from the semicircular canals of the ear and exploit the meager residual reactive capacities of retina and optic nerve. Deaf children often heed vibrations and smell objects and people. Since in our society the socially sanctioned use of the olfactory sense is selective and complex, some of these children's use of this intact sense as an adjunct to their limited sensorial contact with their environment is considered undesirable.

It can be seen that there is considerable descriptive overlap in a sensorially handicapped group among rituals which replace human contact even when it is available to them, rituals which children put aside because human contact is preferable, and rituals which are used by the children in the service of interpersonal relatedness. The characteristic use of rituals by the autistic children of our study was a preferred activity. The instrusion of a person and interference with ongoing ritualistic occupation evoked characteristic shrieking, agitated motor activity, and persistent effort to regain the taken preferred object or to free self to return to the autistic actions.

Unusual habits and rituals by themselves are not pathognomonic for the autistic children. Similar behaviors were present in some of the nonautistic rubella children with blindness, deafness, and/or mental retardation. The difference is that the autistic children engaged in these unusual habits and rituals even when human contact was available to them, and even utilized them as one mechanism of avoiding interpersonal relationship. In the other children, by contrast, the same behaviors were put aside when human contact was available, and were even utilized to facilitate interpersonal relationships.

DISCUSSION

The two main observations in this study are (1) the high rate of autism in this population of rubella children and (2) the unexpectedly large proportion of children who recovered relatively quickly in childhood from their autistic symptoms, as compared to other follow-up reports on autistic children.

It seems likely that the autism was caused by the rubella virus. Alternative explanations, such as that the autism was derivative of the sensory deprivation or the mental retardation found in these children, are contraverted by several findings in the study of these autistic youngsters. Not only were there nonautistic children in our total sample with identical combination and severity of sensory defects as those who became autistic, but also the youngsters whose autism disappeared or improved retained their sensory pathology from the earlier to the later period. Furthermore, change in degree of retardation over time did not seem to correlate with the course of autism.

The unexpectedly large proportion of children who recovered from the autism would further indicate that, in these cases, the course has been that of a chronic infection in which recovery, chronicity, improvement, worsening, and delayed effects can all occur. There were no findings to suggest any other explanation for this high recovery and improvement rate. The child with the most dramatic recovery illustrates this clearly. This girl when first seen in the preschool period had a mature cataract in one eye with good vision in the other, moderate deafness, and a mild cardiac defect. From her physical appearance it was clear that she was well cared for and lovingly handled. Her reported behavior with objects and in routine functioning at home led to an estimate of borderline intelligence. Her observed behavior showed the classical findings of a complete autism syndrome of extreme degree. She sat and rocked with her thumb in her mouth and paid absolutely no attention to any of the people around her. All efforts to gain her interest and communicate with her were complete failures. When held she neither responded nor pulled away. She had no language, either oral or gestural (however, she was also deaf).

When seen on follow-up 4 years later, this girl's behavior had changed dramatically. She was alert, actively and appropriately responsive to the examiner, and cooperated actively with the examination procedures and played with the toys in a functional way. When the examiner involved herself in the play, the child was actively responsive and pleased. Her ability to dress herself was age-appropriate. Reports from her school for the deaf indicated that she was now functioning at an average intellectual level. Figure drawing was age-appropriate. She could say single words and lipread these words, and language, both receptive and expressive, further included pantomime, gesture, facial expressiveness, and sign.

This dramatic recovery had occurred in spite of a severely traumatic family situation. Her mother had died a month previously of cancer after a long illness with several hospitalizations. Death had actually occurred at home in the girl's presence. Her father was an alcoholic, as observed on the three occasions of our direct contact with him. The neighbors had reported this to the Child Abuse Agency to request that the child be placed in a residential school for the deaf rather than remain at home. Her only stabilizing influence in the immediate family was a normal sister 2 years older. Under these adverse environmental circumstances, and with the continuing presence of both cataract and deafness, it would indeed be difficult to explain this child's recovery as due to any psychological cause.

That a viral infection of the central nervous system can cause severe behavioral disturbance is well-known from the time of the sequelae of the epidemic of Von Economo's encephalitis in 1914 (Barr, 1974). Many afflicted children showed a wide range of diversity and severity of pathological behavior. In some cases the symptoms appeared years after the initial acute stage of the illness.

There is no intention here to advance any hypothesis that all cases of autism are caused by a viral infection of the brain. Quite the contrary, the hypothesis that appears most reasonable is that autism may be the final behavioral consequence of many different causes. It is, however, of great theoretical interest to find that a viral invasion of the central nervous system may produce the severe and complex psychopathology that we identify as childhood autism.

It is generally accepted that the diagnosis of childhood autism can only be made if the onset has occurred prior to the age of 30 months. In general clinical experience this criterion appears valid. However, in this study it would appear not always to be an appropriate limitation.

The four new cases whose diagnoses were first made at the school age examination completely met Kanner's criteria for autism, either full or a partial syndrome. At the preschool evaluation, although none of them had behaved in a manner completely appropriate to mental age and physical defects, they had not fulfilled the criteria for either full or partial autism. Using the concept of a chronic viral encephalitis, this late onset could be an example of a "slow virus" effect.

REFERENCES

Barr, D. G. D. Infections. In F. Cockburn & C. Drillien (Eds.), *Neonatal medicine*, London: Blackwell Scientific Publications, 1974. Pp. 656–659.

Chess, S. Autism in children with congenital rubella. *Journal of Autism and Childhood Schizophrenia*, 1971, *1*, 33–47.

Chess, S., Korn, S. J., & Fernandez, P. *Psychiatric disorders of children with congenital rubella*. New York: Brunner/Mazel, 1971.

Desmond, M., Wilson, G. S., Melnick, J. L., et al. Congenital rubella encephalitis. *Journal of Pediatrics*, 1967, *71*, 311–331.

Lotter, V. Services for a group of autistic children in Middlesex. In J. K. Wing (Ed.), *Early childhood autism*. Oxford: Pergamon Press, 1966. Pp. 241–256.

Mindel, E., & Vernon, M. *They grow in silence*. Silver Springs, Maryland: National Association of the Deaf, 1971.

Rutter, M. The development of infantile autism. *Psychological Medicine*, 1974, *4*, 147–163.

Townsend, J. J., Baringer, J. R., Wolinsky, J. S., et al. Progressive rubella panencephalitis: Late onset after congenital rubella. *New England Journal of Medicine*, 1975, *292*, 990–993.

Treffert, D. A. Epidemiology of infantile autism. *Archives of General Psychiatry*, 1970, *22*, 431–438.

Weil, M. L., Itabashi, H., & Cremer, N. E. Chronic progressive panencephalitis due to rubella virus simulating subacute sclerosing panencephalitis. *New England Journal of Medicine*, 1975 *292*, 994–998.

Part IX

CLINICAL ISSUES

In the past, the identification of behavior disorders associated with brain damage was limited primarily to instances of gross neuropathology—chronic encephalitis, epilepsy, cerebral palsy, serious head trauma, etc. In recent years, however, there has been a radical swing of the pendulum. A clinical syndrome labeled as minimal brain dysfunction has been described, reported to be a frequent cause of childhood behavior disorder, and diagnosed even in the total absence of evidence of neurological abnormality. The concept of a typical behavioral syndrome due to cerebral damage, whatever the etiology, has also been widely advocated.

These formulations clearly have great importance for diagnosis and treatment, as well as for public health policies. Rutter, with his usual incisiveness and analytic clarity, reviews the actual state of our knowledge of the "brain damage syndrome." His summation is authoritative, and indicates pointers for treatment as well as directions for further research.

Schowalter's survey emphasizes the consequences that debilitating physical illness can have on psychological development in adolescence. The reciprocal interactive influence of the physical and psychological during this special developmental stage is emphasized—a far cry from earlier one-sided psychogenic views in the psychosomatic literature. A psychoanalytic approach is combined with practical supportive measures and medical treatment, and shaped to the specific needs of each individual case.

25

BRAIN DAMAGE SYNDROMES IN CHILDHOOD: CONCEPTS AND FINDINGS

Michael Rutter

Institute of Psychiatry, London

Concepts with snappy titles tend to catch the interest of professional and lay people alike, and once established they are remarkably difficult to shift. The history of medicine and of psychology is replete with examples of concepts reified by catch phrases which persist in spite of a mounting volume of contrary evidence. If these concepts were confined to academic papers they might not do much harm, but they are far from the property of the academic ivory tower. The distinctive feature of catch phrase concepts is that they become part of everyday language and so tend to have a widespread influence on practical policy and on the treatment of individual patients. Therein lies the danger if the concept is misleading. One such concept is that of the "brain damage syndrome" or "brain damaged child".

Although it seems as if the concept should apply to a collection of neurological features, in fact it is usually used to refer to a supposedly characteristic syndrome of behaviour which has been thought to be due to some form of damage or disease of the brain. There have been many variations in the ways in which the concept has been expressed, and it would be misleading to consider all views as interchangeable.

Reprinted with permission from the *Journal of Child Psychology and Psychiatry*, Vol. 18, 1977, 1–21.
Hargreaves Memorial Lecture given in Leeds on October 17, 1975.

Nevertheless, certain common features appear in most of the statements about the brain damage or minimal brain dysfunction syndrome. These are best outlined by quoting from some of the leading writers on the topic.

The first point concerns the frequency with which brain damage leads to psychiatric disorder in children. Wender (1971), in his book on *Minimal Brain Dysfunction in Children* has asserted that it is "probably the most common single diagnostic entity seen in Child Guidance Clinics". He goes on to state that in his personal experience 50 per cent of pre-adolescent children at a psychiatric clinic suffer from minimal brain dysfunction, and that the frequency of this syndrome is so high that a child in this age-group should be presumed to have the diagnosis until proved otherwise.

The second point concerns the neurological evidence for brain damage. Paradoxically, there is general agreement that the usual signs of neurological abnormality are absent. Thus Wender (1971) claims that the "prevalance of 'hard' (classical) neurological signs is approximately normal". Similarly, Wedell (quoted by MacKeith, 1973) starts his definition by specifying "a condition in which there is little or no evidence of neurological abnormality". These statements of course, necessitate bringing in the concept of so-called "soft" neurological signs which are said to be more common. However, even these are not universal. Wender is quite explicit that "it is important to emphasize that many minimal brain dysfunction children—approximately half—are neurologically intact. There is no doubt that the syndrome can appear with total absence of neurological signs or symptoms or EEG abnormality". We need not dwell on the logical problems implicit in such a statement.

Instead, let us turn to the third point, namely the allegedly distinctive nature of the behavioural characteristics of brain damaged children. Bakwin and Bakwin (1966) stated "The behavioural manifestations of cerebral damage, whatever the etiology, are fairly uniform and characteristic". Similarly, Wender (1971) claimed that "the behavioural pattern associated with minimal brain dysfunction is rather distinct and is easily identified", although he went on to add that there were several variations of the syndrome. Fourthly and lastly, there is the question of treatment. Wender (1971) stated "the treatment of choice in virtually all instances consists first of medication".

Thus, it is postulated that there is a distinctive and characteristic syndrome which results fairly directly from damage to the brain, which is very common and which requires treatment by drugs. Although usually supposed to be due to brain damage, the syndrome frequently occurs in the complete absence of any kind of neurological abnormality. Of course such assertations have lead to equally vigorous denials. Pond (1960, 1961) has argued that "chronic disorders following brain damage are largely the result of handing or mis-handling of the handicapped child by parents and society generally". He urged that "it is time this idea of a brain damaged syndrome was scotched before it gets too firmly entrenched in the literature".

This appears a very confusing state of affairs, and in this paper we critically examine these concepts by reference to a series of studies undertaken with colleagues over the last ten years. Our strategy is best outlined by means of the questions which we have tried to answer. The first is: What associations can be found between brain pathology and psychiatric disorder? To answer that question it seemed best to start with a group of children with overt and indisputable neurological conditions, in order to determine whether their rate of psychiatric disorder exceeded that in the general population. However, that strategy raised a second question, namely: How commonly is brain damage the cause of psychiatric disorder in children and how many brain damage be recognised if the neurological examination is normal? The third question is: If the rate of psychiatric disorder is raised in children with brain damage, do the disorders constitute a uniform and characteristic clinical picture? That leads on to the fourth question: By what means does brain damage lead to psychiatric disorder; what mechanisms are involved? Hopefully the answers to that question may give a lead to the fifth and last question. How should psychiatric disorders in neurologically impaired or brain damaged children be treated? The evidence on each of these questions will be given, in turn.

DOES BRAIN DAMAGE LEAD TO AN INCREASED RISK OF PSYCHIATRIC DISORDER?

Let us start with the first question concerning the rate of psychiatric disorder in children with brain damage. Because children referred to hospitals or clinics tend to be a highly selected group, the question requires a systematic study of children in the general population. For this purpose we utilised the Isle of Wight epidemiological studies of school age children (Rutter et al., 1970a; Rutter et al., 1970b). The total population was first studied by means of multiple screening procedures. Then, on the basis of those results, various groups were selected for intensive study by means of neurological examination, psychological testing, psychiatric interviews with the child, teacher reports, and psychiatric interviews with the children. In this way it was possible to obtain accurately diagnosed groups of children with different handicapping conditions. For present purposes we need to be concerned with only three of these groups—the neuro-epileptic group, the other physical handicap group, and the psychiatric disorder group. The neuro-epileptic group consisted of all children aged 5–14 year with cerebral palsy, epilepsy or some other overt disorder above the brain stem. The other physical handicap group consisted of 10–12 year old children with a chronic handicapping physical condition which did not involve the brain; disorders such as asthma, diabetes, heart disease, orthopaedic deformities, and diseases of the spinal cord or peripheral nervous system (e.g. polio). The psychiatric disorder group included all 10–11 year old children with an emotional or behavioural disorder which involved some type of persisting disability or social impairment. In other words it did not include merely odd children or those with mild or transient problems.

Because these groups were studied in the same way with the same standardized diagnostic instruments, it was possible to look at the overlap between groups. In short, the data allowed accurate estimate of how many neuro-epileptic children also had a psychiatric disorder, together with an appraisal of whether this rate was above or below that in the general population or in any other handicapped group. That, of course, is just what was needed to answer the first question.

It was found that about 6 to 7% of the general population had psychiatric disorders (see Table 1). The rate in the group of children with chronic physical handicaps not involving the brain was nearly twice that. But the rate was very much higher still in the neuro-epileptic group, where as many as a third of the children had psychiatric disorder.

These findings suggested that brain damage was associated with a particularly high rate of psychiatric disorder. But before we could draw that conclusion with confidence a number of methodological checks were needed. First, there was the question of whether the differences might be due to rater bias. We were able to exclude this possibility because the ratings were made blind to which group the children were in. It was also noticeable that the differences between the groups were much the same according to each of the different sources of information: parents' questionnaire, teachers' questionnaire, and interview with parents. Secondly, the differences between the groups could be an artefact of I.Q. differences, as the mean level of I.Q. was much lower in the neuro-epileptic group and low I.Q. is known to be

TABLE 1. PREVALENCE OF PSYCHIATRIC DISORDER IN NEURO-EPILEPTIC CHILDREN AGED 5–14 yr ATTENDING SCHOOL

	With psychiatric disorder	Total
General population 10 and 11 yr old children	144 (6·6%)	189
Physical disorders not involving the brain	16 (11·5%)	139
Brain disorder	34 (34·3%)	99

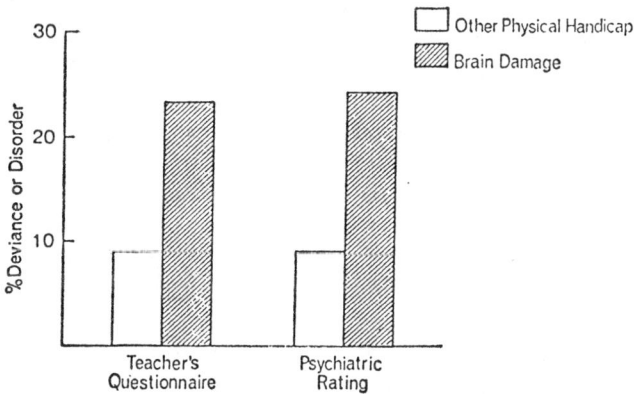

(Rutter, Graham and Yule, 1970)

FIG. 1. Brain damage and psychiatric disorder (children I.Q. 86 or more).

associated with an increased risk of psychiatric disorder (Rutter, Graham and Yule, 1970). In order to control this possible bias we repeated the comparison for the sub-groups of children who had an I.Q. of 86 or more (Fig. 1). There was still a twofold difference in the rate of psychiatric disorder between the neuro-epileptic group and the "other physical handicap" group. Accordingly, low I.Q. could not account for the high rate of psychiatric disorder in brain damaged children.

On the other hand, it was possible that the results were being biased by age differences between the groups; the age range was greater in the neuro-epileptic group. The findings suggested that this was not the case because there was still a high rate of psychiatric disorder in the neuro-epileptic group even when comparisons were restricted to the much narrower age range of the chronic physical handicap group.

It was also possible that the findings could be a consequence of the nature of the child's physical disability. The rate of psychiatric disorder was not systematically related to the *severity* of physical handicap. But, the *pattern* of physical handicaps in the two groups was rather different. The neuro-epileptic group included visibly crippled children with cerebral palsy and epileptic children whose condition is sometimes associated with stigma. Neither obvious crippling nor stigma was common in the "other physical handicap" group. It was not possible to control entirely satisfactorily for these differences in pattern of physical handicap, so there was a need for a further sample.

For this purpose, together with Dr. U. P. Seidel, we carried out a systematic study in North London of children aged 5–15 year with an I.Q. in the normal range (i.e. 70 or more) and all of whom had a visibly crippling condition (Seidel *et al.*, 1975). Thirty-three of these children had cerebral disorders (mostly cerebral palsy) and 42 had noncerebral or peripheral conditions (consisting of muscular dystrophy, polio, or spina bifida). The groups were well matched in terms of age, sex, psychosocial circumstances and degree of physical disability.

The rate of behavioural deviance on the teachers' questionnaire and of psychiatric disorder was twice as high in the brain damaged group. The groups were well matched in all respects except the presence of brain damage. Accordingly we may conclude that brain damage is indeed accompanied by a much increased rate of psychiatric disorder. Furthermore, the increased psychiatric risk is due to brain damage as such, because it was not found in children with crippling disorders due to lesions outside the brain.

However, this suggestion may be tested more rigorously by determining if there were differences in the rate of psychiatric disorder *within* the brain damaged group according to neurological features, such as severity, nature or locus of the damage. This was examined in the Isle of Wight study (Rutter *et al.*, 1970a) where we found that psychiatric disorder was significantly commoner in children with bilateral brain lesions than in those with strictly unilateral conditions. Thus, it seemed that the extent of brain damage was relevant.

Other neurological features were also important (see Figs. 3 and 4). For example in the cerebral palsy group, psychiatric disorder was commoner in those with strabismus, retarded language, or specific reading difficulties. In the epileptic children psychiatric disorder was more frequent in children with low I.Q. and also in those with psycho-motor fits rather than with other types of epilepsy. The frequency of fits was not related to psychiatric disorder, but on the other

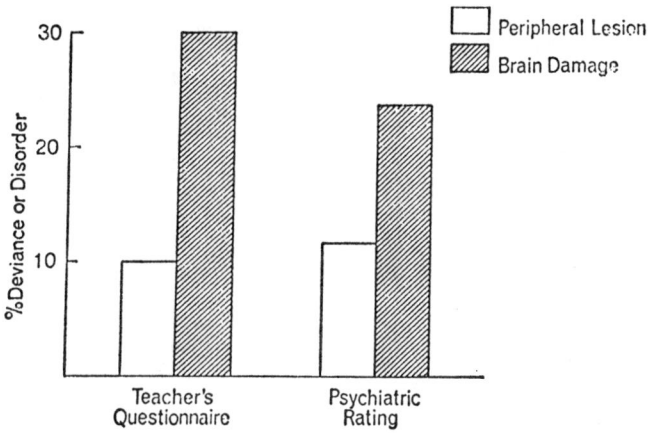

(Seidel et al,1975)

FIG. 2. Brain damage and psychiatric disorder.

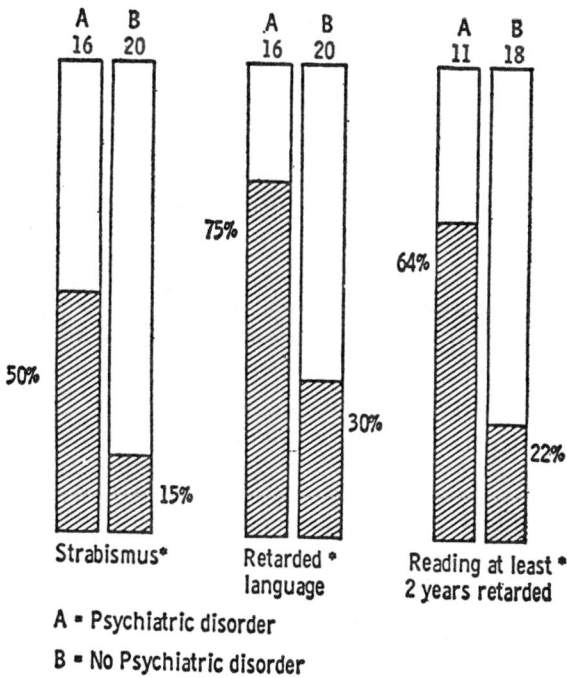

A = Psychiatric disorder

B = No Psychiatric disorder

FIG. 3. Factors associated with psychiatric disorders in 5–14 yr old children with brain disorder attending school.

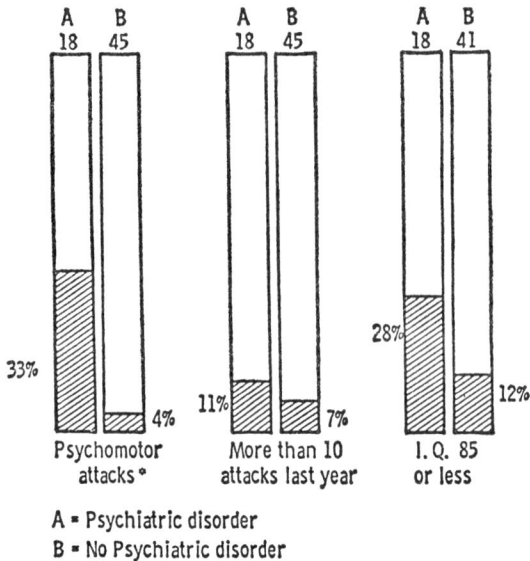

FIG. 4. Factors associated with psychiatric disorders in 5–14 yr old epileptic
children attending school.

hand there were very few children with frequent fits. The evidence is
circumstantial, but it seems that both the severity and nature of the
neurological condition influence the risk of psychiatric disorder.

Psychiatric disorder was also more frequent in cerebral palsied children with fits, although the difference fell short of statistical significance. Nevertheless, the difference may be meaningful in that evidence from other studies suggests that psychiatric problems are more
likely when there is physiological disturbance of brain function rather
than just loss of brain function. For example, psychiatric disorder in
adults is more likely to follow head injury when epileptic fits occur
(Lishman, 1968). Also in childhood the notion that active disturbance
of brain function has a greater effect than loss of function is supported by the finding that there may be a striking improvement in
behaviour following the operation of hemispherectomy when it is carried out in well selected cases (Griffith and Davidson, 1966; Wilson,
1970). Children may be better off with only one hemisphere, than
with two, one of which is producing active electrical disturbance. Further evidence comes from studies of temporal lobectomy in adults
where there is a close relationship between reduction in number
of fits and a decrease in aggressive behaviour (Falconer and

Serafetinides, 1963; James, 1960). Less is known about temporal lobectomy in children although beneficial effects from the operation have been claimed (Davidson and Falconer, 1975).

Very little is known, however, regarding the effects of the locus of the lesion. Generalised brain damage is present in most cerebral palsied children, so this was not a suitable group to study for this purpose. Accordingly, in order to investigate this question*, we chose to examine a group of school age children with head injuries in which there was a unilateral, compound, depressed fracture of the skull, with an associated dural tear, and gross damage to the brain substance which had been confirmed at operation. The children were studied at least two years after the accident by means of neurological and psychiatric examination of the child, interviews with the parents, and psychological testing. The rate of behavioural deviance assessed by teachers' questionnaire was compared with a control group of children in the same school classes. As in previous studies, the rate of behavioural deviance was significantly greater in the brain damaged children, being twice as high as in the control group. But the main interest lies in the findings *within* the brain damage or head injury group, according to the locus of lesion and other neurological variables. In fact, no associations with psychiatric disorder were found. The age of the child at the time of injury, the duration of unconsciousness, the side of the damage, and the locus of the lesion were all unassociated with psychiatric disorder.

Before assuming by this means that it is of no significance which part of the brain is injured various methodological issues must be considered. First, there is the question of whether there was sufficient damage of the brain to provide a valid test. All the children had obvious brain trauma confirmed at operation, and over a quarter needed a later cranioplasty because of the severity of skull damage. However, half the children never lost consciousness, and there was an average level of I.Q. at follow-up. So, although there was gross local trauma the lesions did not necessarily go deep into the brain substance and there was little general damage to the brain. Secondly, although locus of lesion may not be important in relation to emotional and conduct disorders, it may be crucial with respect to some of the rarer conditions associated with brain damage (such as psychosis). Thirdly it may be that local effects are less often found in childhood than in adult life simply because of the greater plasticity of brain function during the developmental phase.

---

*Together with Drs. D. Shaffer and O. P. D. Chadwick.

It is not possible to be sure that there are not psychiatric effects of locus of injury as these might have been evident with deeper injuries. But certainly no effects specific to locus of cortical injury were found in this sample of quite severely injured children. In that the rate of psychiatric disorder was very high in spite of relatively minor neurological sequelae, it seems likely that psychiatric disorder was not usually *directly* due to brain damage. Nevertheless, putting all the findings together, we must conclude that brain damage is associated with a very marked increase in the rate of psychiatric disorder, and that this increase is due to some aspect of brain damage and not just to physical handicap.

HOW COMMONLY IS BRAIN DAMAGE A CAUSE OF CHILD PSYCHIATRIC DISORDER?

The second question is: How commonly is brain damage a cause of psychiatric disorder in children? And how may brain damage be recognised if the neurological examination is normal? We need to start with the second part of that question. Firstly, it is quite clear that it is possible to have organic brain damage in spite of a normal neurological examination. This is shown, for example, by the normal neurological findings in most of the children in the head injury study, and by the similar normal findings in many children who have experienced encephalitis, and by the findings regarding children with epilepsy. The problem is how to diagnose brain damage when the neurological examination reveals no clear abnormality.

So-called "soft" neurological signs have usually been used in this situation (Hertzig *et al.*, 1969; Kennard, 1960; Wolff and Hurwitz, 1973). Such signs fall into three rather different groups, the pooling of which can only lead to confusion (Rutter *et al.*, 1970a). The first group consists of indications of developmental delay in functions such as speech, motor coordination, right–left differentiation or perception. These are not minor signs and most can be observed with a high degree of reliability so they are not soft in that sense. The problem lies in their interpretation. Lack of skill in these developmental functions is normal in young children and the clinical meaning of developmental delay depends on the degree of impairment in relation to the child's chronological and mental age. Furthermore, delay may be due to intellectual retardation, specific maturational disorders, brain damage, or a combination of these. Unfortunately, there are no satisfactory ways of determining in an individual child whether or not the soft signs are indicative of brain injury or some other condition not due to structural damage to the brain.

The second group of soft signs includes those which may be due to either neurological or non-neurological causes. Nystagmus and strabismus both fall into this category. In many cases, with careful examination, it should be possible to determine the nature of the aetiology but unfortunately this is not always the case.

The third group of signs consists of slight abnormalities which are difficult to detect. These are often minor examples of classical neurological signs such as slight asymmetries of tone or reflexes. The softness of these signs resides in the demonstrated unreliability of judgements concerning their presence. If there is doubt as to whether the abnormality is truly present there will be corresponding doubt as to the significance of the supposed abnormality.

Evidently the notion of soft signs is not a very satisfactory one. Certainly there are statistical associations between such signs and brain damage but so also are there with mental age and with other features. In short, they are an unsatisfactory guide to the presence of brain damage in the *individual* patient, although they are of some value in the study of groups. They are also of considerable value as reflections of current function (in speech, perception, etc.). This is sufficient justification for their inclusion in the standard neurological examination of children (Touwen and Prechtl, 1970) even though the concept of soft signs of brain damage is invalid.

A history of some illness or injury of the brain (such as encephalitis) is another way to diagnose brain damage, but this accounts for very few cases. Other historical items such as low birth weight or neo-natal difficulties are also sometimes used as possible indicators. The difficulty with this approach is that there is only a very weak association between these background factors and any kind of pathological outcome; behavioural, cognitive or other (Rogers et al., 1955; Wolff, 1967; Davie et al., 1972; Broman et al., 1975; Shaffer, 1976a). The same applies to psychological test findings and EEG abnormalities (Herbert, 1964; Rutter et al., 1970a; Werry, 1972). None of these items in isolation is of much use in diagnosing brain damage although, in combination, a probability of brain abnormality may be built up through a process of "increasing suspicion" (Ingram, 1969). Nevertheless, it must be concluded that at present, there are no really reliable and valid means of diagnosing brain damage when the neurological examination is normal, and when there is no history of clear cut brain injury or disease.

That leaves the first part of the question: How commonly is brain damage a cause of psychiatric disorder in children? Impossible to answer with any accuracy. Certainly psychiatric disorder is associated with various developmental and cognitive abnormalities which may be associated with brain damage. For example, our own studies in both the Isle of Wight and in London showed the higher frequency with which conduct disorders are associated with specific reading retardation (Rutter *et al.*, 1970b); Sturge, 1972). Similarly, Stevenson and Richman (1976) have observed a strong association between language delay and behavioural problems in 3 year olds. These associations could reflect underlying brain damage, but equally they could reflect maturational delays or psycho-social influences. It seems very likely that cognitive and developmental impairments play a role in the genesis of child psychiatric disorder. But it may well be, that this is so regardless of whether the impairments are due to brain damage.

In summary, it is highly likely that in addition to those children with cerebral palsy and obvious neurological conditions, there are many others with some degree of damage or dysfunction of the brain. The numbers remain rather uncertain but if estimates are made for the proportion of children with clumsiness, speech delay, mental retardation and the like, whose disorders are probably associated with brain damage a figure in the region of 5% or so is obtained. Circumstantial evidence suggests that these less easily diagnosed forms of brain damage are probably also associated with an increased psychiatric risk, but at present there are no reliable means of assessing the strength of the association or the proportion of cases of psychiatric disorder in which minor brain damage plays a part.

IS THERE A CHARACTERISTIC BEHAVIOURAL SYNDROME OF BRAIN DAMAGE?

Let us then turn to the third question: Do the psychiatric disorders associated with brain damage constitute a uniform characteristic clinical picture? To answer that question, we may turn first to the Isle of Wight findings (Rutter *et al.*, 1970a).

Most neuro-epileptic children showed the usual mixture of emotional and conduct behaviour disorders found in children without brain damage, and clearly there was no stereotyped psychiatric syndrome. However, it was notable that a few children showed the rarer syndromes of hyperkinesis and psychosis, and the proportion of neuro-epileptic children with these rarer syndromes was above that in non-brain damaged children with psychiatric disorder (see Table 2). The frequency of the hyperkinetic syndrome or psychosis is, however, related to I.Q. so that these diagnoses are made much more often in mentally retarded children with brain damage. Conversely, they are quite infrequent in brain damaged children of normal intelligence.

TABLE 2. PSYCHIATRIC DIAGNOSIS

Diagnosis	No brain damage (%)	'Neuro-epileptic' (%)
Conduct/mixed	38	35
Neurotic/emotional	60	47
Other	2	17

Thus, none of the cerebral palsied children in the North London study (Seidel et al., 1975) were either hyperkinetic or psychotic and very few of the head injury group (Shaffer et al., 1975) had either diagnosis and none were psychotic. Thus it seems, that much of the association between brain damage and these rarer diagnoses may be a result of the cognitive impairment which follows from the brain damage, rather than a direct effect of the brain damage as such. Of course, there are a few psychiatric conditions consistently associated with organic brain dysfunction such as, acute confusional states, dementia and ictal disorders such as *petit mal* status. These are very important in their own right, but they constitute a tiny proportion of cases of child psychiatric disorder, and no examples are included in any of the studies mentioned.

Of course, it might be that although the overall diagnoses of brain damaged children are similar to those of other children with psychiatric disorder, there could still be differences in individual symptoms. We have looked at this systematically in each of the studies and the results are fairly consistent; that is, brain damaged children show an excess of most types of symptomatology but that, if like is compared with like, there is nothing characteristic about the symptoms. In other words the symptoms of brain damaged children without psychiatric disorder are similar to those of children in the general population. The symptoms of brain damaged children with psychiatric disorder are similar to those of non-brain damaged children with psychiatric disorder. The usual pattern is illustrated by the Isle of Wight findings (Rutter et al., 1970a) for "restlessness", a symptom often thought to be associated with brain damage (see Fig. 5). There may be a slight tendency (even after appropriate controls have been introduced) for disorders of attention and of activity level (both an increase and a decrease of activity) to be minimally more frequent in brain damaged children but the differences are slight and of little, if any, practical importance.

However, our symptom assessments consisted of relatively crude ratings, so that it was necessary to go on to make finer more objective

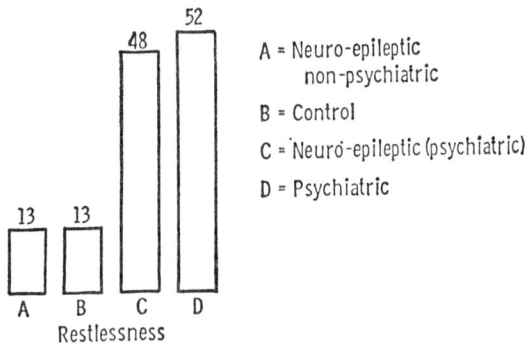

FIG. 5. Behaviour as judged from teachers' questionnaires (9–12 yr old group).

TABLE 3. SUBJECT GROUPS

1. No neurological disease.	Normal conduct	(PNC)	(N : 8)
2. No neurological disease	Deviant conduct	(PDC)	(N : 13)
3. Neurological abnormality	Deviant conduct	(NDC)	(N : 13)
4. Neurological abnormality	Normal conduct	(NNC)	(N : 7)

measures. This was done in a study of children attending pediatric and neurological clinics undertaken by Shaffer *et al.* (1974). Four groups of children were studied (see Table 3); a control group and three groups with conduct disorders or neurological abnormalities present either in isolation or in combination. By making suitable combinations of these groups it is possible to determine which behavioural features are a function of neurological abnormality and which are a function of conduct disorder. Actometers (modified watches) were used to measure limb movement in the free-play situation; a stabilimeter was used to assess the amount of wriggling when the child was seated during testing, and various special tests were carried out to assess impulsivity and attention. The pattern of results may be illustrated by considering arm movements and impulsivity (the findings for other measures were broadly similar).

As shown in Fig. 6, impulsiveness showed no association with neurological abnormality but it was significantly commoner in children with conduct disorders. The arm actometer findings showed the same pattern (see Fig. 7). Activity level was higher in the children with conduct disorder, but was not significantly higher in those with neurological abnormality. It seems that most of the features, such as impulsiveness and over-activity, which are reputed to be indicators of brain

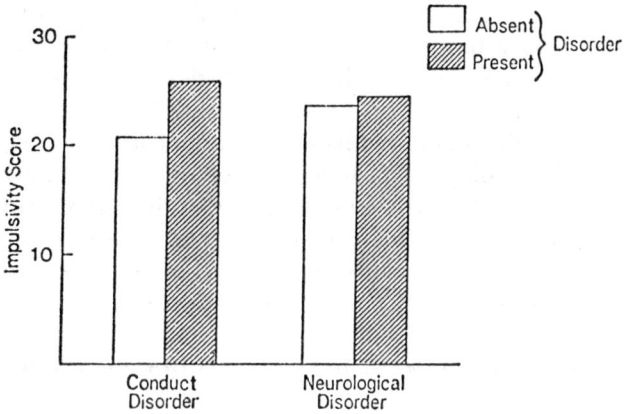

(Shaffer et al, 1974)

FIG. 6. Impulsivity, conduct disorder and neurological abnormality.

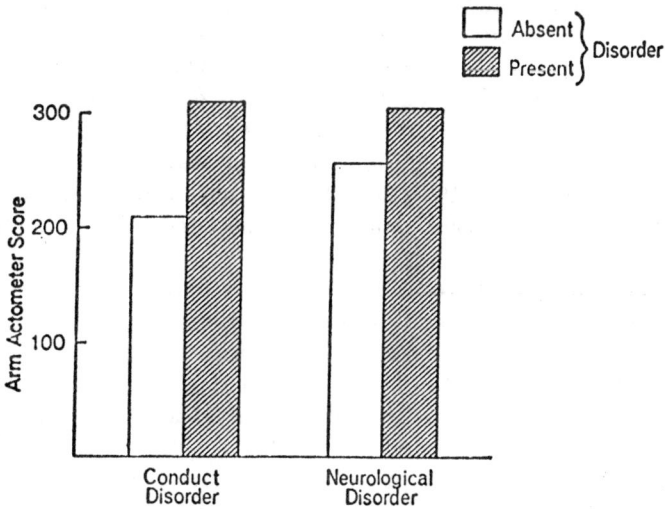

(Shaffer et al, 1974)

FIG. 7. Arm actometer score, conduct disorder and neurological abnormality.

damage are in fact merely very common features of psychiatric disorder regardless of the presence of neurological abnormality. The findings from other studies are all closely similar (see Rutter *et al.*, 1970a; Werry, 1972).

It may be concluded that the behavioural stereotype of the brain damaged child must be firmly rejected. Brain damaged children show a heterogeneous range of psychiatric disorders without specific features, except in the case of certain rarer conditions. Where does that leave the hyperactive child syndrome? It is not a syndrome of brain damage although biological factors probably often play an important part in its aetiology. Nevertheless there are studies which suggest that it has sufficient distinctive features to warrant its isolation as a separate psychiatric condition (Cantwell, 1975). The main problem is how far it differs from the broader range of conduct disorders.*

HOW DOES BRAIN DAMAGE LEAD TO PSYCHIATRIC DISORDER?

The fourth question is: By what means does brain damage lead to psychiatric disorder—what mechanisms are involved? The important biological factors have already been mentioned; namely that active physiological disturbance of the brain probably has more adverse behavioural sequelae than loss of brain function. There are also the strong cognitive effects of brain damage. Table 4 shows the I.Q. distribution of children with cerebral palsy on the Isle of Wight, compared with the general population (Rutter et al., 1970a). It is obvious that mental retardation is very much commoner in children with cerebral palsy, as also found in numerous other studies. The North London study (Seidel et al., 1975) also showed that even within the normal range of intelligence brain damage is associated with a lowering of I.Q.

However, quite apart from low I.Q., brain damage is also associated with specific reading difficulties. This was found in the Isle of Wight study of children with neuro-epileptic disorders (Rutter et al., 1970a), and again in the North London study (Seidel et al., 1975). Half the cerebral palsied children in the latter study had severe reading difficulties compared with only 15% of children with other crippling disorders not involving brain pathology. Similarly, in the head injury study, 38% of the children (whose mean I.Q. was 97) were at least 2 years backward in reading (Chadwick and Shaffer, 1975). As shown in several studies (see Rutter et al., 1970b; Rutter et al., 1970b) both low I.Q. and reading difficulties are associated with an increased risk of behavioural deviance at school and, to a lesser extent, with psychiatric disorder as shown at home. Thus, the cognitive sequelae of brain

---

*That question is currently being investigated by our colleagues Dr. Eric Taylor and Dr. Seija Sandberg.

TABLE 4. I.Q. DISTRIBUTION IN CHILDREN WITH CEREBRAL PALSY (ISLE OF WIGHT STUDY)

I.Q.	% in C.P.	% in Gen. Population
100+	24	50
70–99	21	47
50–69	18	2·5
Below 50	36	0·5

damage are one of the important mechanisms leading to psychiatric disorder.

However, psychosocial influences are also very important. Family and social disadvantage are not more frequent in brain damaged children than in the general population*, but when present they much increase the risk of psychiatric disorder. For example, in the Isle of Wight study (Rutter et al., 1970a) within the group of brain damaged children, neurotic disturbance in the mother and "broken homes" were both strongly associated with psychiatric problems in the children. Within the epileptic group the same applied, as did also low social status. In the North London study (Seidel et al., 1975) overcrowding, anomalous family situations (i.e. the child was not living with both natural parents), marital discord, and psychiatric disorder in the mother were all significantly associated with child psychiatric disorder. These were combined into a family adversity index in order to examine how these lead to disorder in association with brain damage. The same was done in the head injury study (see Table 5) where a broader range of psychosocial variables were associated with psychiatric disorder (Shaffer et al., 1975).

ADDITIVE OR INTERACTIVE EFFECT?

In considering how brain damage and psychosocial disadvantage might together lead to psychiatric disorder, it is important to differentiate between *additive* and *interactive* effects. An additive effect means that both factors play a part in causation and that the overall effect of the two in combination is simply a sum of the two when they occur in isolation. In short, the two influences do not interact or potentiate each other. An interactive effect, on the other hand, means that the combination of adverse influences (e.g. brain damage plus

---

*Whereas this is true in general there are, of course, subgroups of brain damaged children (such as those injured in repeated accidents or those damaged by battering) who do come from families which are disadvantaged in various ways.

TABLE 5. FAMILY ADVERSITY INDEX

1. Father: unskilled/semiskilled job
2. Overcrowding or large family size
3. Marital discord and/or broken home
4. Mother: depression/neurosis (questionnaire score/interview rating)
5. Child ever 'in care'
6. Father: Any offence against law

psychosocial disadvantage) has a *greater* effect than simple summation because of an interactive or potentiating effect. In this instance, an interactive effect would mean that brain damage increases a child's vulnerability to psychosocial stresses so that he is *more* likely to be affected than is a normal child.

These alternatives may be examined in relation to the teacher questionnaire findings in the North London study (Seidel *et al.*, 1975). The bottom line of Fig. 8 indicates that the rate of behavioural deviance in crippled children without brain damage is very low when there is no psychosocial disadvantage. Moving to the right along the bottom line it may be seen that proportion of children with behavioural deviance in those with psychosocial disadvantage is much higher. The upper line shows the same phenomenon for the cerebral palsied children. The slope of the line for the two groups is much the same. This means that there has not been any interaction but only an additive effect. In short, both the brain damage and the psychosocial disadvantage acted independently to lead to psychiatric disorder, so that the combined effect of the two was additive *without* any extra risk due to brain damage sensitizing children to psychosocial risk factors. Figure 9 shows the same thing for the interview rating of psychiatric disorder in the North London study. Again it may be observed that the lines are parallel indicating an additive rather than an interactive effect. The head injury findings (Shaffer *et al.*, 1975) show the same when comparison is made with a London general population sample of children without brain damage (Rutter *et al.*, 1975). The rate of behavioural deviance in the head injury children was above that in the control group, and in both cases the rate of psychiatric disorder was higher when there was psychosocial disadvantage (see Fig. 10). But the relationship between psychiatric disorder and psychosocial disadvantage was exactly the same in both groups. In other words the two factors acted independently. So rather surprisingly, there does not seem to be any interaction. The findings mean that brain damage is associated with a much increased risk of psychiatric disorder even in

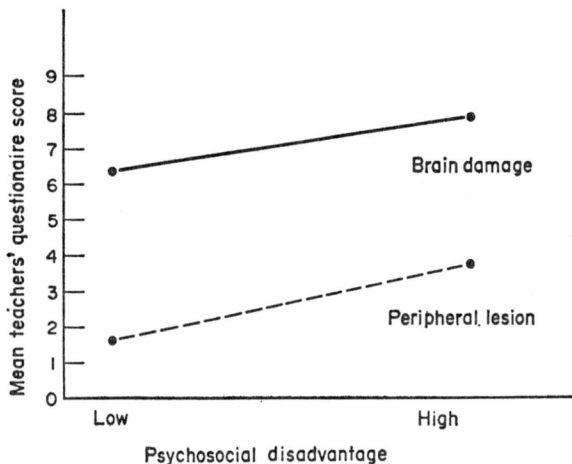

FIG. 8. Behavioral deviance and psychosocial disadvantage (North London Study).

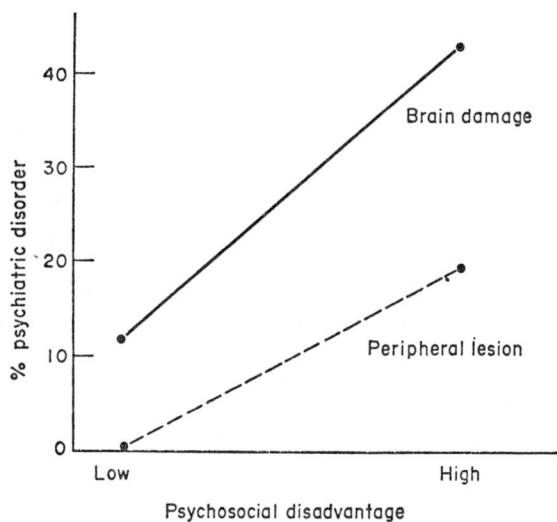

FIG. 9. Psychiatric disorder and psychosocial disadvantage (North London Study).

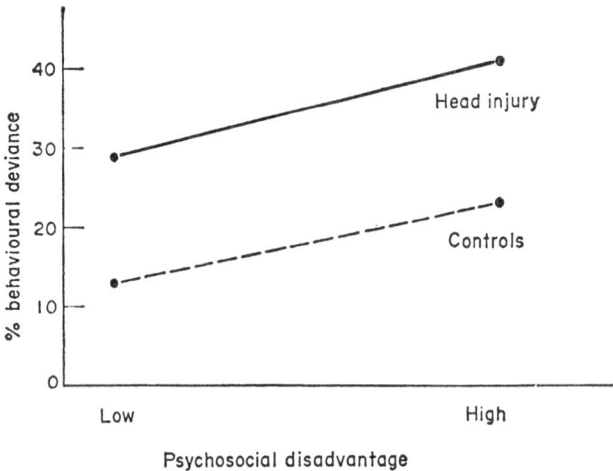

FIG. 10. Behavioural deviance and psychosocial disadvantage (Head Injury Study).

the *absence* of psychosocial disadvantage. Furthermore, the main explanation for the high rate of psychiatric disorder in brain damaged children can *not* lie in any effect on susceptibility to psychosocial stress.

TRANSACTIONAL EFFECT?

It is necessary also to consider the possibility of a *transactional* effect, namely that brain damage may increase the *likelihood* of a child experiencing adverse environmental influences. This was not the case so far as overall psychosocial or family disadvantage was concerned, but we were unable to examine differences *within* families. Studies of temperament (Graham *et al.*, 1973; Rutter *et al.*, 1977) have shown that children with adverse temperamental characteristics are more likely than other children to be the subject of parental criticism and scapegoating. That is, when parents are depressed and irritable they do not "pick on" all their children to the same extent; they are more likely to take it out on the child with "difficult" temperamental features. This represents a *transactional* effect in which the presence of a personal characteristic increased the frequency or *amount* of psychosocial stress experienced (rather than an increase in susceptibility as in an interactive effect).

There is some limited circumstantial evidence to suggest that the same phenomenon may occur with brain-damaged or otherwise handicapped children. Thus, Lynch (1975) showed that children battered by their parents differed systematically from their sibs in terms of perinatal complications, physical illness and separations during infancy. It appeared that the least healthy children were the ones most likely to experience physical abuse. Similarly, Gallagher (1975) suggested that the impulsive behaviour of some brain damaged children generated feelings of hostility towards them; and Knobloch and Pasamanick (1962) showed that neurologically abnormal infants were more likely than other infants to have mothers who behaved tensely towards them. The matter requires further study but there are possible pointers that children with brain damage may be more likely than other children to be the focus or target of psychosocial disturbance.

MECHANISMS IN THE GENESIS OF PSYCHIATRIC DISORDER

The mechanisms by which brain damage might lead to psychiatric disorder may be summarised as follows: first, there is the behavioural disruption due to abnormal brain activity. This may be especially important in epileptic children with gross generalised disturbance on the EEG, but the question has been little investigated up to now and very little is known on how far it is in fact an important factor. Second, there are the crucial cognitive effects due to both general intellectual impairment and also specific reading retardation. These may be important because educational failure often leads to social opprobrium and stigma at school; so that in part it is society's response to poor scholastic attainment which puts the child at psychiatric risk as much as the direct problems stemming from cognitive deficits (Rutter et al., 1970b). Third, there are the probable effects of brain damage on temperament and personality. There have been very few attempts to study these directly. The three brain damaged children in the New York longitudinal study varied in temperament (Birch et al., 1964) but follow-up suggested that this variation was important in terms of whether or not there were later psychiatric difficulties (Thomas and Chess, 1975). Prechtl (Prechtl, 1960; Prechtl and Dijkstra, 1960) has reported that children with neurological abnormalities following perinatal complications show an increased rate of adverse behavioural attributes during the preschool period and Ucko (1965) found that boys who suffered neonatal anoxia tended to be more difficult temperamentally than other children (although some had positive and adaptive temperamental characteristics). Other studies (e.g. Gallagher, 1957; Ernhart et al., 1963; Schulman et al., 1965) have also produced findings compatible with the suggestion that brain damage is associated with wide temperamental variation but also with an increased rate of "difficult" or poorly adaptive characteristics. Evidence is meagre but it may be that brain damage especially tends to increase difficulties in the areas of attention, adaptability and frustration tolerance.

Fourth, there are the adverse secondary effects of treatment. Problems may sometimes stem from the side-effects of drugs (Stores, 1975), from recurrent admission to hospital (Douglas, 1975; Quinton and Rutter, 1976), and from the restriction of physical activities. While probably none of these constitutes a major influence each may contribute to the development of psychiatric problems.

Fifth, there are family responses to the brain damaged child. Little is known about how these may influence children's adaptation to their handicaps but it is likely that in rather different ways, both scapegoating (see above) and overprotection (Levy, 1943) may predispose to psychiatric disorder. The matter is currently being investigated in connection with children's recovery from severe head injury.* Finally, there is the way in which the individual brain damaged child responds to his handicap. Clinically, this appears very important although adequate research data are lacking. Nevertheless, there is a suggestion of its importance in the repeated finding that psychiatric disorder is more likely in the child with mild or moderate physical disabilities than in the severely crippled child (Rutter *et al.*, 1970; Seidel *et al.*, 1975). This may be because the severely crippled child has adjusted to the fact that he obviously cannot compete in the ordinary world, whereas the mildly handicapped child has not. He can compete, but not very well, and paradoxically this makes it more difficult for him than if he were not able to compete at all.

TREATMENT

Clearly, much has still to be learned about the mechanisms by which brain damage leads to psychiatric disorder, but there is a strong indication that most of the effects are indirect, and this offers hope for treatment. That brings us to the last question: How should psychiatric disorders in neurologically impaired or brain damaged children be treated? First, the importance of psychosocial influences and the very heterogeneity of psychiatric disorders associated with brain damage demands a broad based approach. We must try to ameliorate the

---

*In an investigation being undertaken with colleagues Dr. D. Shaffer and O. P. D. Chadwick and Mrs. G. Brown.

psychosocial stresses, as in any other child with psychiatric disorder. This requires environmental manipulation, counselling and casework with parents, and a variety of other available techniques. With the individual child, there is a need for the usual range of treatments; psychotherapy, behaviour therapy and counselling techniques. The frequency of educational problems, of course, makes remedial teaching and work with the schools more than usually important.

But are there any specific treatments which arise because of the presence of brain damage? This question tends to be associated with the use of stimulant drugs. There is good evidence that these provide short term gains for children with hyperactivity or attentional problems, although little is known regarding their value over longer periods (Shaffer, 1976b). But their benefit is not a function of brain damage. Indeed, what very little evidence there is suggests that the outcome may be worse in children with overt neurological abnormalities (Ounsted, 1955), although possibly slightly better in those with so-called soft signs (Satterfield, 1973). Medication is useful in some children but its use is not specific to brain damage.

However, there are special concerns regarding the psychiatric implications of cognitive disabilities. Obviously, the first need is to ameliorate these and to aid scholastic progress as far as possible by skilled remedial teaching geared to the needs of the individual child (see Rutter and Yule, 1976). But also it is very important to ensure that there are no unnecessary secondary consequences of educational difficulties. In some circumstances it seems that handicapped children may respond better in the more protected and accepting environment of a special school which recognises the realities of specific and general cognitive disabilities. Thus, Griffiths' (1969) study suggested that children with severe language disorders tended to show poor adjustment following transfer to ordinary schools. Similarly, in the North London study (Seidel et al., 1975) we found that the association between low I.Q. or reading difficulties and psychiatric disorder was less marked in the case of youngsters with cerebral palsy attending special schools than that usually found with children at ordinary schools. Of course, special school placement has its own problems and it is not suggested that this provides any kind of general answer. But it is suggested that there is every reason to help the ordinary schools become more accepting of the child who is falling behind in his school work and better able to provide rewards for the unintelligent as well as the intelligent children (see Hargreaves (1967) for a discussion of the ways in which bottom stream children tend to be disadvantaged in the secondary schools).

There is also a great need to help both the family and the brain damaged child himself to adapt and respond positively to whatever cognitive, physical or behavioural handicaps may be present. The particular difficulties of the mildly handicapped child who compares himself unfavourably with his normal peers have already been mentioned. He needs to be helped to see the positive side of himself and to recognise his accomplishments as well as to accept his limitations. Counselling and psychotherapy, in their special focus on the special problems of handicapped children have an important place in this connection. Families, too, need assistance in their adjustment to a child who is different. Counselling and casework may aid them in this process and help them to avoid the contrasting dangers of overprotection or oversolicitude (which may inhibit autonomy and social adjustment) on the one hand, and on the other excessive criticism or scapegoating.

Lastly, there is the matter of how to deal with temperamentally difficult children. Temperamental features are not fixed and immutable and there is a need to help children increase their adaptability and improve their approach to learning. However, in addition it is also important to guide parents and teachers in how best to respond to children with different temperamental characteristics. Chess *et al.* (1965) have given a valuable lead in this connection.

SUMMARY

A great deal has still to be learned on the various ways in which brain damage predisposes children to psychiatric disorder. Research has shown that many of the stereotypes of "the brain damaged child" were mistaken and misleading. But, equally, studies have clearly shown the major importance of brain damage as a factor contributing in a substantial way to the genesis of child psychiatric disorder. Treatment methods have still to be evaluated but already there are pointers as to how psychiatric disorders in neurologically impaired or brain damaged children should be treated. In dismissing over simplified catch phrase concepts concerning brain damage syndromes it is important not to overlook the reality of the problems to which they refer.

REFERENCES

Bakwin, H. and Bakwin, R. M. (1966) *Clinical Management of Behavior Disorders in Children*, 3rd Edn. Saunders, Philadelphia.
Birch, H., Thomas, A. and Chess S. (1964) Behavioral development in brain-damaged children. *Arch. gen. Psychiat.* **11**, 596–603.

Broman, S. H., Nichols, P. L. and Kennedy, W. A. (1975) *Preschool I.Q.: Prenatal and Early Developmental Correlates.* Erlbaun, Hillsdale, N.J.

Cantwell, D. (Ed.) (1975) *The Hyperactive Child: Diagnosis, Management, Current Research.* Spectrum, New York.

Chadwick, O. F. D. and Shaffer, D. (1975) Personal communication.

Chess, S., Thomas, A. and Birch, H. (1965) *Your Child is a Person.* Viking Press, New York.

Davidson, S. and Falconer, M. A. (1975) Outcome of surgery in 40 children with temporal-lobe epilepsy. *Lancet* i 1260–1263.

Davie, R., Butler, N. and Goldstein, H. (1972) *From Birth to Seven.* Longman, London.

Douglas, J. W. B. (1975) Early hospital admissions and later disturbances of behaviour and learning. *Develop. Med. Child Neurol.* **17**, 456–480.

Ernhart, C., Graham, F., Eichman, P., Marshall, J. and Thurston, D. (1963) Brain injury in the pre-school child: some developmental considerations—II. Comparison of brain injured and normal children. *Psychol. Monogr.* **77**, 17–33.

Falconer, M. A. and Serafetinides, E. A. (1963) A follow-up study of surgery in temporal lobe epilepsy. *J. Neurol. Neurosurg. Psychiat.* **26**, 154–165.

Gallagher, J. A. (1957) A comparison of brain injured and non-brain injured children on several psychological variables. *Monogr. Soc. Res. Child Develop.* No. 65, Vol. 22.

Graham, P., Rutter, M. and George, S. (1973) Temperamental characteristics as predictors of behaviour disorders in children. *Am. J. Orthopsychiat.* **43**, 328–339.

Griffith, H. and Davidson, M. (1966) Long-term changes in intellect and behaviour after hemispherectomy. *J. Neurol. Neurosurg. Psychiat.* **29**, 571–576.

Griffiths, C. P. (1969) A follow-up study of children with disorders of speech. *Br. J. Dis. Commun.*, **4**, 46–56.

Hargreaves, D. H. (1967) *Social Relations in a Secondary School.* Routledge & Kegan Paul, London.

Herbert, M. (1964) The concept and testing of brain-damage in children: a review. *J. Child Psychol. Psychiat.* **5**, 197–216.

Hertzig, M., Bortner, M. and Birch, H. (1969) Neurologic findings in Children Educationally designated as 'brain damaged'. *Am. J. Orthopsychiat.* **39**, 437–466.

Ingram, T. T. S. (1969) The new approach to early diagnosis of handicaps in childhood. *Develop. Med. Child Neurol.* **11**, 279–290.

James, I. P. (1960) Temporal lobectomy for psychomotor epilepsy. *J. ment. Sci.* **106**, 543–558.

Kennard, M. (1960) Value of equivocal signs in neurologic diagnosis. *Neurology* **10**, 753–764.

Knobloch, H. and Pasamanick, B. (1962) The developmental behavioral approach to the neurologic examination in infancy. *Child Develop.* **33**, 181–198.

Levy, D. (1943) *Maternal Overprotection.* University of Chicago Press, Chicago.

Lishman, W. A. (1968) Brain damage in relation to psychiatric disability after head injury. *Br. J. Psychiat.* **114**, 373–410.

Lynch, M. A. (1975) Ill-health and child abuse. *Lancet* ii, 317–319.

Mac Keith, R. (1963) Defining the concept of 'minimal brain damage'. In *Minimal Cerebral Dysfunction* (Edited by Mac Keith, R. and Bax, M.). Clinics in Develop. Med. No. 10 SIMP/Heinemann, London.

Ounsted, C. (1955) The hyperkinetic syndrome in epileptic children. *Lancet* ii, 303–311.

Pond, D. (1960) Is there a syndrome of 'brain damage' in children? *Cerebral Palsy Bull.* **2**, 296–297.

Pond, D. (1961) Psychiatric aspects of epileptic and brain-damaged children. *Br. med. J.*

2, 1377–1382; 1454–1459.

Prechtl, H. (1960) The long-term value of the neurological examination of the newborn infant. *Develop. Med. Child Neurol.* **2**, 69–74.

Prechtl, H. and Dijkstra, J. (1960) Neurological diagnosis of cerebral injury in the new born. In *Prenatal Care* (Edited by Len Berge, B.). Noordhoft, Groningen.

Quinton, D. and Rutter, M. (1976) Hospital admissions and child psychiatric disorder (in preparation).

Rogers, M., Lilienfeld, A. and Pasamanick, B. (1955) Pre- and para-natal factors in the development of childhood behavior disorders. *Acta Neurol. Psychiat. Scand.* Suppl. 102), 56–66.

Rutter, M. and Yule, W. (1976) Reading difficulties. In *Child Psychiatry: Modern Approaches* (Edited by Rutter, M. and Hersov, L.). Blackwell Scientific, London. (In press).

Rutter, M., Graham, P. and Yule, W. (1970a) *A Neuropsychiatric Study in Childhood.* Clinics in Develop. Med., Nos. 35/36, SIMP/Heinemann, London.

Rutter, M., Quinton, D. and Yule, B. (1977) *Family Pathology and Child Psychiatric Disorder.* Wiley, London. (In preparation).

Rutter, M., Tizard, J. and Whitmore, K. (Editors) (1970b) *Education, Health and Behaviour.* Longman, London.

Rutter, M., Cox, A., Tupling, C., Berger, M. and Yule, W. (1975) Attainment and adjustment in two geographical areas.—I. The prevalence of psychiatric disorder. *Br. J. Psychiat.* **126**, 493–509.

Satterfield, J. H., Cantwell, D. P., Saul, R. E., Lesser, L. I. and Podosin, R. L. (1973) Response to stimulant drug treatment in hyperactive children: Predictions from EEG and neurological findings. *J. Autism Childh. Schiz.* **3**, 36–48.

Schulman, J., Kaspar, J. and Throne, F. (1965) *Brain Damage and Behavior: A Clinical-Experimental Study.* Thomas, Springfield.

Seidel, U. P., Chadwick, O. F. D. and Rutter, M. (1975) Psychological disorders in crippled children. A comparative study of children with and without brain damage. *Develop. Med. Child Neurol.* **17**, 563–573.

Shaffer, D. (1976a) Brain injury and behavior disturbance in childhood. In *Child Psychiatry: Modern Approaches* (Edited by Rutter, M. and Hersov, L.). Blackwell Scientific, London (In press).

Shaffer, D. (1976b) Drug treatment. In *Child Psychiatry: Modern Approaches* (Edited by Rutter, M. and Hersov, L.). Blackwell Scientific, London. (In press).

Shaffer, D., Chadwick, O. and Rutter, M. (1975) Psychiatric outcome of localized head injury in children. In *Outcome of Severe Damage to the Central Nervous System* (Edited by Porter, R. and FitzSimons, D.). Ciba Foundation Symp. 34 (new series). Elsevier, Excerpta Medica, N. Holland, Amsterdam.

Shaffer, D., McNamara, N. and Pincus, J. H. (1974) Controlled observations on patterns of activity, attention and impulsivity in brain-damaged and psychiatrically disturbed boys. *Psychol. Med.* **4**, 4–18.

Stevenson, J. and Richman, N. (1976) Behaviour, language and development in three year old children (submitted for publication).

Stores, G. (1975) Behavioural effects of anti-epileptic drugs. *Develop. Med. Child Neurol.* **17**, 647–658.

Sturge, C. (1972) Reading retardation and antisocial behaviour. M. Phil. Thesis, University of London.

Thomas, A. and Chess, S. (1975) A longitudinal study of three brain damaged children. *Arch. gen. Psychiat.* **32**, 457–462.

Touwen, B. C. L. and Prechtl, H. F. R. (1970) *The Neurological Examination of the Child with Minor Dysfunction.* Clinics in Develop. Med. No. 38. SIMP/ Heinemann, London.

Ucko, L. E. (1965) A comparative study of asphyxiated and non-asphyxiated boys from birth to five years. *Develop. Med. Child Neurol.* **7**, 643–657.

Wender, P. H. (1971) *Minimal Brain Dysfunction in Children.* Wiley, New York.

Werry, J. S. (1972) Organic factors in childhood psychopathology. In *Psychopathological Disorders of Childhood* (Edited by Quay, H. C. and Werry, J. S.). Wiley, New York.

Wilson, P. J. (1970) Cerebral hemispherectomy for infantile hemiplegia. *Brain* **93**, 147–180.

Wolff, P. H. and Hurwitz, I. (1973) Functional implications of the minimal brain damage syndrome. *Sem. Psychiat.* **5**, 105–115.

Wolff, S. (1967) The contribution of obstetric complications to the etiology of behaviour disorders in childhood. *J. Child Psychol. Psychiat.* **8**, 57–66.

26

PSYCHOLOGICAL REACTIONS TO PHYSICAL ILLNESS AND HOSPITALIZATION IN ADOLESCENCE

John E. Schowalter
Yale University School of Medicine

This paper surveys some of the psychoanalytic and psychosomatic literature which comments on the developmental aspects of adolescence and on the impact of bodily illness. Special attention is paid to the influence of debilitation on an adolescent patient's self-esteem and ego-ideal formation. It is suggested that the encouragement of self-care, the facilitation of the appropriate use of signal anxiety, anticipatory mourning and/or denial, as well as education in adaptive skills, are specific measures which are psychologically felicitous for the care of physically ill adolescents.

In spite of the importance of adolescence as a developmental stage and of physical illness as a threat to body intactness, there is surprisingly scanty psychoanalytic literature concerning the impact of bodily illness on the mental life of adolescents (Schowalter and Lord, 1973).

Reprinted with permission from *Journal of the American Academy of Child Psychiatry*, Vol. 16, 500–516, 1977.

This work was supported by the Maternal and Child Health Division of the Health Services and Mental Health Administration of the U.S. Department of Health, Education and Welfare, the Connecticut Department of Health, and U.S. Public Health Service Grant No. 5T1 MH-5442-20.

Although the literature on adolescence as a developmental stage is voluminous and much is written about the impact of medical illness at this age, there has been little, if any, attempt to synthesize the two sets of findings.

Freud (1939) noted that the weakening of the ego resulting in diminished anticathexis, the strengthening of the drives, and the awakening by current events of similarly repressed impulses were three conditions which promoted the return of the repressed; and he used illness and puberty as examples for the first two conditions. The intent in this paper is to survey and integrate the pediatric and psychosomatic literature with some of the psychoanalytic writings about bodily development and functioning in adolescence. I shall focus on the effects of illness upon self-esteem and ego-ideal formation during adolescence. Short clinical vignettes from experiences as a consultant to the Adolescent Inpatient and Outpatient Services of the Yale-New Haven Hospital will be used occasionally to note useful therapeutic approaches.

Experience suggests that once a disease process has become established, the symbolic meanings given that process and the ego defenses raised in response to it differ little, whether the etiology was more somatopsychic or psychosomatic. Therefore, no strict differentiation will be attempted in the paper between disorders in regard to their "cause."

PUBERTY AND ADOLESCENT CHANGES

With puberty, momentous changes take place in the body and even when these changes progress uneventfully, it is usual for adolescents to express considerable concern about whether their body indeed is normal. As Fraiberg (1955) has noted, the body is felt as a stranger to the adolescent, and "Who am I?" is a perpetual question. The fact that with each generation pubertal changes occur earlier (Dubos, 1967), while society does not always adjust accordingly (Solnit, 1971), may incur added stresses for today's adolescents.

Geleerd (1961) has called attention to how puberty heightens cathexis of perception of stimuli from inside and outside the body and how the bodily changes interfere with the prepubertal sense of identity and self. Others have recently commented on the importance of bodily sensations in giving rise to emotions (Tyrer, 1973), and Jones (1922) wrote that adolescence is the time when control over emotions as well as motor outflow must be accomplished. The disruption of the psychic structures caused by physical changes is enhanced by the psychological separation of adolescents from their closest personal objects, their parents. This latter accomplishment is described by Freud (1905) as one of man's most significant and painful psychic achievements. One interaction between these two occurrences has been pointed out by Anna Freud (1958) when she remarked that the withdrawal of libido from the parental objects to the self could give rise to a hypochondriacal outcome.

The importance of adolescence as the time for a second individuation process (Blos, 1967), for the establishment of identity (Erikson, 1956), and for the development of the self (Jacobson, 1964) is well documented. As with other popular terms, "self" is a concept which is not always easily agreed upon (Marcus, 1973). In this paper self-esteem will refer to the appreciation or opinion of oneself. Jacobson's work (1961) especially has emphasized the importance of the interplay during adolescence of changes in psychic structure in regard to the body and in regard to feelings about the self.

PHYSICAL ILLNESS

Adolescence is a time of relatively good physical health; however, health concerns are common in this age group (Deisher and Mills, 1963). For present purposes I shall focus on the most common disorders.

Body-Image Manifestations

The most direct way the bodily changes of illness can affect the adolescent's psychological development is through postponed physical growth and sexual maturation. Retardation of growth and sexual development may be the first presenting complaint in regional ileitis (Crohn and Yarnis, 1958) and may be a later manifestation with cystic fibrosis, malabsorption syndrome, renal failure, hypopituitarism, hypothyroidism, or with the prolonged and severe hypoxemia of cyanotic congenital heart disease.

Some disorders during adolescence seem to give rise to more body-self problems than others. Two examples of conditions which are especially known for this difficulty are diabetes and anorexia nervosa.

The requirements for treatment of diabetes with daily self-administered injections heighten and elaborate conflicts raised by sexual and aggressive fears associated with penetration and the threat of disaster if the injections are not accomplished. Conflict over insulin administration plus the usual severity of juvenile diabetes has led most workers to find relatively poor psychological adjustment in these patients (Koski, 1969). Poor adjustment, however, has been shown to be least pronounced in diabetics who are most able to acknowledge that their bodies are not like those of everyone else (Swift et al., 1967). Most diabetics can begin assuming total responsibility for their bodies and their care by age 12 and take over completely by age 15 (Partridge et al., 1972). When bodily self-care by diabetics is accomplished, their psychological adjustment usually improves.

Anna Freud (1958) has written of the distortions and fears of oral impregnation in adolescents with anorexia nervosa. Bruch (1962) has suggested a distorted body image in the etiology of this sometimes fatal illness of adolescence. Galdston's (1974) review of his findings emphasizes the frequency of the "60 pound ego ideal" in patients he has studied. Adolescent inpatient facilities usually have a number of patients with diabetes and anorexia nervosa who periodically use their bodies to express simultaneously their rebellious independence by not following the prescribed treatment and their dependence by forcing physicians to hospitalize and care for them. Asthma patients also do this. For many of these patients their vulnerable bodies represent a shameful weakness but are also powerful vehicles of influence over their family, friends, and physicians.

Our experience on a ward for adolescents is that expressions of sexuality are rare. This may be due to physical or psychological reasons. Hospitalized adolescents act more like latency-aged children, each sex staying chiefly with its own, and there is much shyness, especially about one's body. Occasional patient suggestions to mix sexes in multibed rooms are met with horror by the large majority of other patients. Boys are often put off by the necessary physical care given by nurses, and it was found that although all patients upon admission are informed that they may call nurses by their first names, boys are to a statistically significant degree more likely than girls to suppress or repress this fact (Schowalter and Anyan, 1973). Because delayed sexual development hampers the adolescent's social life and acceptance by peers, and since it has been postulated that the onset of orgasm in the boy (Eissler, 1958) and of menstruation in the girl (Kestenberg, 1961) are crucially important events for identifying formation and intrapsychic organization, the understanding of the meanings of these physical delays of maturation for each patient is necessary for good care.

The order of appearance of physical immaturity and the use of regression are often difficult to decide. For example, although it is difficult to speak of primary gain in terms of most physical illness, it is true that illness often follows psychic strain (Mutter and Schleifer,

1966), thus representing either a response to the individual's weakened state or to a need for expiation. The problem of the quantity and quality of primary or secondary gain is often a difficult one. Katz (1963) observed that for psychological illness the distinction between the two concepts is less obvious than often assumed. This is also true for physical illness. For some patients who are unable to face the libidinal and aggressive demands of adulthood, maintaining their symptoms becomes an acceptable course to avoid the unfolding of adolescence and its stresses.

Ann, a 17-year-old girl, was brought to the clinic because of asthma attacks. Her history indicated that her asthma was not severe, but she used the diagnosis as an excuse to withdraw from the increasingly intimate social life of her peers. Being a pretty girl, she was often asked for dates, but she would reply to these requests, "No, I can't. I've got asthma." With the uncovering and clarification of her fears about becoming pregnant and angering her somewhat seductive and overly protective father, her asthma did not improve, but she was able to begin to show appropriate sexual interest in boys her own age.

The assaults on the body, both from the illness and from its subsequent treatment, cause the usual adolescent conflicts between dependence and independence and between regressive and progressive forces to be further complicated. Regression is the rule, and expressions of helplessness are ubiquitous for those hospitalized (Schowalter and Lord, 1970). There is the feeling that everything, especially the body, is out of control. For example, Blom (1958) found that older children's greatest fear with tonsillectomy was losing control while under anesthesia.

The fear of loss of control is often a castration equivalent during adolescence (Fountain, 1961). From many discussions and observations with patients on our ward, it has become clear that the fantasies involved in the fear of losing control usually concern the fear of body disintegration or of becoming insane. These fantasies are often more anxiety-provoking for adolescents than actual loss of control; and, not infrequently, after a patient has had an anxiety attack or a temper outburst, he or she feels more at ease.

Although fantasies may promote anxiety and regression in the physically ill patient, fantasies may also prove remedial. Geleerd (1964) has stressed the importance of fantasies as an avenue for trial actions by adolescents in order to reach adaptation. The types of fantasies and the degree of regression by ill adolescents are crucial to the patient's type of adaption. While regression can be in the service of the ego (Kris, 1934), Freud (1939) made clear that stress may either promote and encourage mastery or lead to inhibition and avoidance. Unfortunately, we are not as good at predicting as we are at explaining why a particular outcome is chosen. In Janis's careful attempt to calibrate physically ill patients' "work of worrying" (1958), he has shown that too much or too little anxiety can be maladaptive. He also concludes that it remains unclear how to get the correct dosage of fear and worry. In our experience an optimal amount of signal anxiety seems to lead to adaptive fantasies, while no worry is associated with a stifling of fantasy production. Extreme worry tends to conjure up cataclysmic scenes which feed a vicious cycle.

Probably at no other age is illness as shameful as it is during adolescence, when body strength and looks are so important for self-esteem. This is a feeling not only of the patient but one felt by others as well. Winkler (see Calef, 1959) showed people pictures of handicapped and normal children and found the former erroneously described as more vicious, suspicious, and hostile. It is common for adolescent patients to juxtapose this feeling of shame with questions about why they become ill. Anna Freud (1949) has described that preadolescents are often intrigued with the idea of being dirty, and some patients voice suspicion that their "dirty" or sexual thoughts influenced their becoming ill.

Bob, a 16-year-old boy with idiopathic scoliosis, was hospitalized for spinal fusion. He was shy and embarrassed about his body to an extreme which caused the staff to ask for a psychiatric consultation. Because of complications following surgery, he remained in the hospital for more than two months. During that time, I saw him three times a week. What emerged was his belief that the curvature of his spine was perhaps due to the erections he began having about the time that the curvature was first noticed. A crookedness seemed to him an apt punishment for the masturbation urges he experienced since he also believed his erect penis was more crooked than it should be.

While for most patients shame, guilt, and shyness are the legacy of their physical malady, there are adolescents who respond like those described by Freud as the "exceptions" (1916). As Freud (1940, p. 179) pointed out, and Engel (1959) elaborated, some patients' physical symptoms are necessary to expiate their feelings of shame and guilt. In the case of these "exceptional" patients, usually those who have been ill for some time, however, the adolescents act and do exactly as they please, especially in relation to authority, and make it clear that they have suffered enough and therefore are or should be exempt from the normal expectations of people and life. This independence often causes further debilitation and sometimes proves fatal, but it is interesting to note that occasionally patients who earn the label of "too mean to die" live up to this prediction by surviving against all medical odds (Seligman, 1974).

The Impact of Illness and Hospitalization on Behavior and Object Relations

Just as Bernfeld (1938) divided adolescents into rebellious and compliant types, hospital staffs sometimes categorize patients as "bad" and "good." The "good" patient is often the one who uses denial, repression, and reaction formation, while the patient labeled as "bad" or rebellious is more likely to use projection, regression, and counterphobic defenses.

One puzzling type of "good" patient is the withdrawn patient described by Seligman (1974). While some very ill patients who withdraw psychologically do well, others show this behavior as a prelude to rapid deterioration and death. Although both types of patients resemble each other phenomenologically, one group uses withdrawal for the conserving and husbanding of strength, while the other uses it for expressing feelings of hopelessness and of giving up. It is clear that similar behavior expresses different meanings, but it is not so clear whether the similar behavior expresses similar or different types of self-esteem or ego ideals. Although not studied systematically, my impression is that adolescents who give up under the impact of serious illness have developed the belief that destruction is their destiny and those who lie dormant but with a fierce will to survive have the conviction that they must live to fulfill some accomplishment, usually one believed set down for them by their parents.

Carl, a 14-year-old boy, was admitted to the hospital after a freak accident in which a gasoline can exploded and caused severe burns over his back and legs. Following the acute period of shock, he became extremely withdrawn, and I was asked to see him because the staff feared he was deeply depressed. At first the boy parried my advances, but after a time he became comfortable talking to me. What came out was that he was less depressed than determined to conserve the energy he believed he needed to survive. Survival above all meant that he could fulfill his mother's wish that he become a Catholic priest like her brother.

While some ill adolescents choose to withdraw and become quiescent, for the majority the enforced inactivity and passivity are difficult and run counter to adolescent developmental needs. Mittelmann (1954) has written of a basic motor urge which if frustrated can lead to pathology; Spiegel (1958) has commented on how action is a common defense for adolescents; and a recent panel noted how frequently adolescents use external factors to express internal changes (Sklansky, 1972). Most at risk are patients who must be immobilized for long periods in traction or body casts. These adolescents often have grave psychological difficulties (Blake, 1969). In economic terms, narcissistic libido replaces object libido, and possibilities to discharge tensions are reduced. In addition, privacy is lost since one cannot keep others away, the self and body images are changed, and there is a feeling of inability to protect onself from real or imagined dangers. If the aspects of sensory deprivation are not combatted successfully, hallucinations may occur, and it is imperative that these patients be given human companionship as well as physical stimulation. As Bergmann and Anna Freud (1965) found with younger children, there is often a rush of activity, sometimes destructive, after the patient is released from the immobilization. When talked to during or following immobilization, these patients frequently describe two primary anxiety-provoking feelings. One was the fear that they could not get away if something threatened them from the outside; and the second, derived from the internal pressures of embarrassment and shame which were accompanied by the wish to get away and hide.

Another aspect of the impact of illness is how it is used by the adolescent in his relations with his parents and doctors. Balint (1957) has commented on the way in which symptoms, whether or not of consequence, are often used as a way to establish a legitimate relationship between patient and doctor. Although, as Anthony (1969) has pointed out, adolescents' resistance to psychiatrists have given them a bad name in most psychotherapeutic circles, pediatricians and internists are elevated into "superparent" status by some sick teen-agers who seek them out to become the self-chosen parent replacement (A. Freud, 1969). In addition, the utilization of doctors as models often has more than a touch of identification with the aggressor (A. Freud, 1936). Physicians are not only viewed as being able to intimidate the adolescent's parents, but "doing operations" and "giving shots" are goals frequently stated by what appears to be a disproportionately large group of chronically ill adolescents who want to become doctors.

Just as symptoms gain the patient a closer relationship with a physician, they become a legitimate way to ask for and obtain care and concern from others (Mechanic, 1972). Expanded caretaking usually includes parents, and this is especially important during adolescence when there are great social and developmental pressures not to need help or be cared for by anyone, especially not by parents. It has been shown that adolescents who have a history of illness admit to pretending to be ill more frequently than adolescents without such a history

(Peterson, 1972). Mothers in particular may also encourage prolongation of symptoms, since illness often gives the mother a last opportunity to "baby" her adolescent before she loses him or her to maturity and, in the case of a son, to another woman. Care therefore must be taken during hospitalization to encourage the patient to maintain as much autonomy as is realistic and comfortable (Schowalter, 1971).

Separation and Threat of Death

Finally, hospitalization separates the adolescent physically from his family and friends. Although for some patients separation from family comes as a relief, for most it is a cause of loneliness. Separation from peers, who are important supporting attachments at this age, also creates a significant loss for many patients. This was emphasized in one survey which showed that more than a quarter of the hospitalized adolescents preferred peers to parents as visitors (Schowalter and Lord, 1969).

The ultimate ravage of illness is death, and since adolescence is a time for physical and sexual fulfillment, the possibility of death is perhaps more poignant at this age than at any other (Schowalter, 1970). Most adolescents who are dying seem to know it without being told, and some make it clear they do not want to be told. Freud (1915) wrote that "in the unconscious every one of us is convinced of his own immortality" (p. 289). Perhaps immortality is part of most people's ego ideal, and many dying adolescents who know their fate still do not want to talk about it. In our experience, those who believe in reincarnation or an afterlife tend to talk more freely than those who believe in nothing after death. This is similar to the findings of the large study by McIntire et al. (1972) which showed that adolescents who frequently contemplated suicide were those who tended to have a view of death as not final. It seems easier to face death if one does not fully believe in it. Actually, although it is often noted that suicide is relatively common in robust adults struck with a serious or disabling illness (Roth and Kerr, 1970), one seldom sees suicides in chronically or even fatally ill adolescents. In most of these patients there seems to be an innate push toward fulfillment. Solnit and Green (1963) have described the dying child's fear of death before fulfillment, and this seems especially intense during adolescence. As if to illustrate this point to me, a 17-year-old boy dying of leukemia once paraphrased about himself the popular quote of Vince Lombardi, a well-known football coach at the time: "I'm not going to lose," he said, "but maybe the clock will run out before I win." Occasionally (Schowalter et al.,

1973) a severely ill adolescent decides that death rather than life is being prolonged and asks that treatment be stopped. Although many moral and psychological issues must be faced in each such situation, with a particular patient I saw it was clear that for her such a decision was congruent with a realistic view of herself and of her situation. Perhaps for most people it is not true that "what we are left with is the fact that the organism wishes to die only in its own fashion" (Freud, 1920, p. 39), but this girl died with almost unbelievable speed and ease once her decision was made. Of course, such "self-willed" deaths have been well known in many cultures for many years (Milton, 1973). What seems to occur is that the individual's death becomes part of a self-image, and the body concurs.

EGO IDEAL AND SELF-ESTEEM

As with many psychoanalytic terms, the meaning of ego ideal and self-esteem has evolved and is still evolving. Sandler et al. (1963) and, most recently, Blos (1974) have provided useful reviews of the peregrinations of these concepts. In his early writings (1914, p. 94; 1916–17, p. 429) Freud viewed the ego ideal as the individual's narcissistic ideal of the self. He later saw ego ideal and conscience (1921, p. 110) and ego ideal and superego (1923, p. 28) as synonymous. Finally in the *New Introductory Lectures* (1933, pp. 64–65), he separated the functions of the ego ideal from the superego, but viewed the superego structurally as the "vehicle" for the ego ideal. Opinions continue to differ as to whether the ego ideal is part of the ego, the superego, or an entity by itself. Schafer (1967) has noted that to add to the confusion the term is often used not to represent a psychic structure, but rather the internalized ideals of others (especially parents) or the ideals of the self.

The ego ideal arises as the infant's "rescue operation for narcissism" (Hartmann and Loewenstein, 1962). New ideal objects, both to take the place of those of the rejected parents and as a new measure for the approaching adult self, are often chosen with the recrudescence of narcissism during adolescence (Blos, 1972; Hartmann et al., 1946). It is also usual during adolescence for the ego ideal to become more realistic (Lampl-de Groot, 1962) and take over some of the functions previously held by the superego (Blos, 1962). Indeed, it is during adolescence that Blos (1974) believes the structuralization of the ego ideal takes place.

How the view of one's self is changed under the impact of physical illness is of more interest here than is the adolescent's idealized images of others. Jacobson (1964) has commented on the problem all adolescents face in continually having to reassess their constantly changing psychic and bodily reality. There is some evidence that females have more difficulty than males with this view of themselves (Clifford, 1971; Rothchild, 1967), but, in any event, illness compounds the difficulties. In 1935 Schilder elaborated on the impact which organic changes always have on the body image, and Greenacre (1958) has emphasized how important the body image is in identity formation and how identity formation may be influenced at the time of sickness.

Ill adolescents usually have more difficulty understanding their bodies than normal adolescents. Kaufman (1972), for example, found that even teen-agers who understood their illness quite well intellectually were often bizarre when they tried to depict what was actually happening inside them. Secondly, adolescent patients' views of themselves are usually worsened. Body image and self-esteem seem inexorably connected. Pless and Roghmann (1971) reviewed the findings of the English National Survey of Health and Development (Douglas, 1964), the Isle of Wight Survey (Rutter et al., 1970), and the Rochester (New York) Child Health Survey (Roghmann and Haggerty, 1970) of chronically ill children and adolescents. The reviews shows that all three surveys found more psychiatric illness and academic problems in the physically ill patients than in the controls and concludes that the psychological maladjustment of the young chronically ill patient is probably due to his evolving perception of himself as a person of diminished value and worth. This conclusion is supported by another study which shows that with their low self-esteem, adolescents having a history of chronic illness are twice as likely as controls to report that they are not as happy as their peers (Peterson, 1972). Annie Reich (1960) has noted that self-esteem depends on the nature of the inner image against which we measure ourselves as well as the ways and means at our disposal to live up to it. Therefore, it is not surprising that for the ill adolescent, self-esteem may also suffer.

In the last century, William James (1890) formulated an equation in which self-esteem equaled success divided by pretension. Jacobson (1954) has described self-esteem as the expression of discrepancy or harmony between self-representation and the wishful concept of the self. Ill adolescents are more likely than others either to be unable, or fear they will be unable, to fulfill the ambitions usual for this developmental period. The illness and the adolescent's reaction to it tend to feed on one another in a vicious circle. That "healthy narcissism" which Eissler (1971) finds essential to keep us from being crushed by the fear of death is sorely bruised in those who are seriously or chronically ill. Shame resulting from an ego—ego-ideal discrepancy (Piers and Singer, 1953) can lead to emotional problems which further distort and damage the self-image (Hauser and Shapiro, 1973). Closing the circle, low self-esteem can increase the likelihood of an adolescent having physical symptoms. Indeed, in a very careful study of a large group of adolescents, Rosenberg (1965) found "without exception, each step down the self-esteem scale finds a larger proportion of respondents with many psychosomatic symptoms" (p. 23).

CLINICAL CORRELATES

Practically speaking, a lesson we have learned in clinical work with sick adolescents is that by strengthening the patient's self-image one can often bring about an increased desire to get well, which in turn brings about a more positive self-image. One method we have found successful on an adolescent ward is to provide positive models which at times become ideal objects for the patients. This utilizes the aspect of the ego ideal associated with identifications. Ritvo (1972) has recently reemphasized the breaking of old object ties in adolescence as a cause of increased narcissistic libido and occasionally the cause of bodily preoccupation and hypochrondriacal concerns. By stressing continuity of care through the use of a single doctor and relatively few nurses and by encouraging positive peer attachments, we strive to provide replacement objects to the patient for new identifications. As mentioned earlier and as has been written about by Easson (1966), the doctor often becomes an ideal object of the adolescent patient. This is true in physical as well as emotional illness.

It is most common for adolescents to use peers, especially those a little older or who possess some special talent, as an ideal to model themselves after. What is strived for is a sort of doppelgänger effect. Many people who have worked with sick children have discovered the advantage gained by a patient, especially one who is chronically ill or who is undergoing mutilating surgery, to associate with an older patient who survived and coped with the ordeal successfully (Mattsson, 1972). Such exposure often helps replace massive denial or exaggerated fears with realistic expectations and appropriate amounts of signal anxiety. In our work on a number of occasions, and a few times spectacularly, the use of this technique has profoundly changed the newer patient's view of the future and of self. In some cases the switching of emphasis of psychological attachment from a parent to a patient who successfully coped with a malady like that of the patient seemed similar to Katan's concept of "removal" (1937), although the process was seldom as complete or nonincestuous as originally defined.

Debra, a fearful 16-year-old girl with ulcerative colitis and an overly dependent relationship with her parents, was hospitalized prior to surgery. A colectomy with colostomy was planned. A 17-year-old boy who had undergone the same surgical procedure almost a year earlier and who had subsequently adjusted well was asked to talk to the girl about what to expect. A friendship developed. Not only did these meetings reassure the girl and help her through the pre- and post-operative period, but the self-respect and confidence she gained from this relationship and from her own successful physical adjustment aided her to loosen appropriately her emotional ties to her parents.

Finally, adolescent patients should be encouraged to become involved as much as is appropriate in their own care. By participating in these responsibilities, the adolescent retains a sense of his or her body as personal property and becomes an active partner in the outcome rather than only a passive victim. Anna Freud (1952) once stated she wished to "stress how serious a measure hospitalization is, separating the child from the rightful owner of his body at the very moment when this body is threatened by dangers from inside as well as from the environment" (p. 80), and for the adolescent assistance in minimizing these threatening aspects of passivity and regression is especially important.

Although no large-scale studies exist which prove the long-term impact of the above-mentioned approaches on later adult development, the results of our experience with adolescent patients during hospitalization and outpatient clinic follow-ups, as well as through direct psychoanalytic treatment of adolescents and reconstructions in adult analyses, suggest that these provisions are important in enhancing self-esteem and in allowing the ego ideal to progress appropriately in its development.

CONCLUSIONS

This paper joins together a brief summary of the literature regarding the impact of physical illness on the adolescent with that of some of the psychoanalytic thinking about psychological changes which occur during this developmental stage. Observation and theory corroborate the debilitating illness during adolescence puts the patient at considerable risk in terms of the various physical and psychological transitions which define puberty and adolescence.

There is substantial literature which propounds that bodily illness in general and certain specific disorders especially lower adolescents' self-esteem and place in jeopardy the formation of a positive and productive ego ideal. In addition, there are data to suggest that loss of self-esteem may foster or promote illness.

It is clear from our experience and from that presented in the literature that the encouragement of self-care, the facilitation of the appropriate use of signal anxiety, anticipatory mourning and/or denial, as well as education in adaptive skills are specific measures which are psychoanalytically sound and which are of great help to the adolescent in maintaining his identity, in acquiring new objects who will be useful models for adjustment to his particular condition, and in successfully combating the regressive invitation to passivity so often inherent in illness and hospitalization.

REFERENCES

Anthony, E. J. (1969), The reactions of adults to adolescents and their behavior. In: *Adolescence*, ed. G. Caplan & S. Lebovici. New York: Basic Books, pp. 54–78.

Balint, M. (1957), *The Doctor, His Patient and the Illness*. New York: International Universities Press.

Bergmann, T. & Freud, A. (1965), *Children in the Hospital*. New York: International Universities Press.

Bernfeld, S. (1938), Types of adolescence. *Psychoanal. Quart.*, 7:243–253.

Blake, F. G. (1969), Immobilized youth. *Amer. J. Nurs.*, 69:2364–2369.

Blom, G. E. (1958), The reactions of hospitalized children to illness. *Pediatrics*, 22:590–600.

Blos, P. (1962), *On Adolescence*. New York: Free Press.

—— (1967), The second individuation process of adolescence. *The Psychoanalytic Study of the Child*, 22:162–186.

—— (1972), The function of the ego ideal in late adolescence. *The Psychoanalytic Study of the Child*, 27:93–97.

—— (1974), The genealogy of the ego ideal. *The Psychoanalytic Study of the Child*, 29:43–88.

Bruch, H. (1962), Perceptual and conceptual disturbances in anorexia nervosa. *Psychosom. Med.*, 24:187–194.

Calef, V. (1959), Report on panel: Psychological consequences of physical illness in childhood. *J. Amer. Psychoanal. Assn.*, 7:155–162.

Clifford, E. (1971), Body satisfaction in adolescence. *Percept. Mot. Skills*, 31:119–125.

Crohn, B. B. & Yarnis, H. (1958), *Regional Ileitis*, 2nd ed. New York: Grune & Stratton.

Deisher, R. W. & Mills, C. A. (1963), The adolescent looks at his health and medical care. *Amer. J. Publ. Hlth*, 53:1928–1936.

Douglas, J. W. B. (1964), *The Home and the School*. London: Mackgibbon & Kee.

Dubos, R. J. (1967), Biological remembrance of things past. *Bull. Phila. Assn. Psychoanal.*, 17:133–148.

Easson, W. M. (1966), The ego-ideal in the treatment of children and adolescents. *Arch. Gen. Psychiat.*, 15:288–292.

Eissler, K. R. (1958), Notes on problems of technique in the psychoanalytic treatment of adolescents. *The Psychoanalytic Study of the Child*, 13:223–254.

―――― (1971), Death drive, ambivalence, and narcissism. *The Psychoanalytic Study of the Child*, 26:25–78.

Engel, G. L. (1959), "Psychogenic" pain and the pain-prone patient. *Amer. J. Med.*, 26:899–918.

Erikson, E. H. (1956), The problem of ego identity. *J. Amer. Psychoanal. Assn.*, 4:56–121.

Fountain, G. (1961), Adolescent into adult. *J. Amer. Psychoanal. Assn.*, 9:417–433.

Fraiberg, S. (1955), Some considerations in the introduction to therapy in puberty. *The Psychoanalytic Study of the Child*, 10:264–286.

Freud, A. (1936), *The Ego and the Mechanism of Defense*. New York: International Universities Press, 1946.

―――― (1949), On certain difficulties in the preadolescent's relation to his parents. In: *The Writings of Anna Freud*, 4:95–106. New York: International Universities Press, 1968.

―――― (1952), The role of bodily illness in the mental life of children. *The Psychoanalytic Study of the Child*, 7:69–81.

―――― (1958), Adolescence. *The Psychoanalytic Study of the Child*, 13:255–278.

―――― (1969), Adolescence as a developmental disturbance. In: *Adolescence*, ed. G. Caplan & S. Lebovici. New York: Basic Books, pp. 5–10.

Freud, S. (1905), Three essays on the theory of sexuality. *Standard Edition*, 7:125–243. London: Hogarth Press, 1953.

―――― (1914), On narcissism. *Standard Edition*, 14:73–102. London: Hogarth Press, 1957.

―――― (1915), Thoughts for the times on war and death. *Standard Edition*, 14:275–300. London: Hogarth Press, 1957.

―――― (1916), Some character-types met with in psychoanalytic work. *Standard Edition*, 14:311–315. London: Hogarth Press, 1957.

―――― (1916–17), Introductory lectures on psycho-analysis. *Standard Edition*, 15 & 16. London: Hogarth Press, 1963.

―――― (1920), Beyond the pleasure principle. *Standard Edition*, 18:7–64. London: Hogarth Press, 1955.

―――― (1921), Group psychology and the analysis of the ego. *Standard Edition*, 18:69–143. London: Hogarth Press, 1955.

―――― (1923), The ego and the id. *Standard Edition*, 19:12–66. London: Hogarth Press, 1961.

―――― (1933), New introductory lectures on psycho-analysis. *Standard Edition*, 22:5–182. London: Hogarth Press, 1964.

―――― (1939), Moses and monotheism. *Standard Edition*, 23:7–137. London: Hogarth Press, 1964.

―――― (1940), An outline of psycho-analysis. *Standard Edition*, 23:144–207. London: Hogarth Press, 1964.

Galdston, R. (1974), Mind over matter. *This Journal*, 13:246–263.

Geleerd, E. R. (1961), Some aspects of ego vicissitudes in adolescence. *J. Amer. Psychoanal. Assn.*, 9:394–405.

―――― (1964), Adolescence and adaptive regression. *Bull. Menninger Clin.*, 28:302–308.

Greenacre, P. (1958), Early physical determinants in the development of the sense of identity. *J. Amer. Psychoanal. Assn.*, 6:612–627.

Hartmann, H., Kris, E., & Loewenstein, R. M. (1946), Comments on the formation of psychic structure. *The Psychoanalytic Study of the Child*, 2:11–38.

―――― & Loewenstein, R. M. (1962), Notes on the superego. *The Psychoanalytic Study of the Child*, 17:42–81.

Hauser, S. T. & Shapiro, R. L. (1973), Differentiation of adolescent self-images. *Arch. Gen. Psychiat.*, 29:63–68.

Jacobson, E. (1954), The self and the object world. *The Psychoanalytic Study of the Child*, 9:75–127.

——— (1961), Adolescent moods and the remodeling of psychic structure in adolescence. *The Psychoanalytic Study of the Child*, 16:164–183.

——— (1964), *The Self and the Object World*. New York: International Universities Press.

James, W. (1890), *The Principles of Psychology*. New York: Dover, 1950.

Janis, I. L. (1958), Emotional inoculation. In: *Psychoanalysis and the Social Sciences*, ed. W. Muensterberger & S. Axelrad. New York: International Universities Press, pp. 119–154.

Jones, E. (1922), Some problems of adolescence. In: *Papers on Psycho-Analysis*. London: Balliere & Cox, 1950, pp. 389–406.

Katan, A. (1937), The role of "displacement" in agoraphobia. *Int. J. Psycho-Anal.*, 32:41–50, 1951.

Katz, J. (1963), On primary gain and secondary gain. *The Psychoanalytic Study of the Child*, 18:9–50.

Kaufman, R. V. (1972), Body image changes in physically ill teen-agers. *This Journal*, 11:157–170.

Kestenberg, J. S. (1961), Menarche. In: *Adolescents*, ed. S. Lorand & H. I. Schneer. New York: Hoeber, pp. 19–50.

Koski, M. (1969), The coping processes in childhood diabetes. *ACTA Paed. Scand.*, Suppl. #198.

Kris, E. (1934), The psychology of caricature. In: *Psychoanalytic Explorations in Art*. New York: International Universities Press, 1952, pp. 173–188.

Lampl-de Groot, J. (1962), Ego ideal and superego. *The Psychoanalytic Study of the Child*, 17:94–106.

McIntire, M. S., Angle, C. R., & Struempler, L. J. (1972), The concept of death in midwestern children and youth. *Amer. J. Dis. Child.*, 123:527–532.

Marcus, I. M. (1973), Report on panel: The experience of separation-individuation in infancy and its reverberations through the course of life. *J. Amer. Psychoanal. Assn.*, 21:155–167.

Mattsson, A. (1972), Long-term physical illness in childhood. *Pediatrics*, 50:801–811.

Mechanic, D. (1972), Social psychologic factors affecting the presentation of bodily complaints. *New Eng. J. Med.*, 286:1132–1139.

Milton, G. W. (1973), Self-willed death or the bone-pointing syndrome. *Lancet*, 1:1435–1436.

Mittelmann, B. (1954), Motility in infants, children, and adults. *The Psychoanalytic Study of the Child*, 9:142–177.

Mutter, A. Z. & Schleifer, M. J. (1966), The role of psychological and social factors in the onset of somatic illness in children. *Psychosom. Med.*, 28:333–343.

Partridge, J. W., Garner, A. M., Thompson, C. W., & Cherry, J. (1972), Attitudes of adolescents toward their diabetes. *Amer. J. Dis. Child.*, 124:226–229.

Peterson, E. T. (1972), The impact of adolescent illness on parental relationships. *J. Hlth Soc. Behav.*, 13:429–437.

Piers, G. & Singer, M. (1953), *Shame and Guilt*, Springfield: Thomas.

Pless, I. B. & Roghmann, K. J. (1971), Chronic illness and its consequences. *J. Pediat.*, 79:351–359.

Reich, A. (1960), Pathologic forms of self-esteem regulation. In: *Psychoanalytic Contributions*. New York: International Universities Press, 1973, pp. 288–311.

Ritvo, S. (1972), Late adolescence. *The Psychoanalytic Study of the Child*, 26:241–263.

Roghmann, K. J. & Haggerty, R. J. (1970), Rochester child health surveys: I. *Med. Care*, 8:47–59.

Rosenberg, M. (1965), *Society and the Adolescent Self-Image*. Princeton: Princeton University Press.

Roth, M. & Kerr, T. A. (1970), Diagnosis of the reactive depressive illnesses. In: *Modern Trends in Psychological Medicine*, ed. J. H. Price. New York: Appleton-Century Crofts, pp. 165–199.

Rothchild, E. (1967), "Anatomy is destiny." *Pediatrics*, 39:532–538.

Rutter, M., Tizard, J., & Whitmore, K. (1970), *Education, Health and Behavior*. London: Longmans, Green.

Sandler, J., Holder, A., & Meers, D. (1963), The ego ideal and the ideal self. *The Psychoanalytic Study of the Child*, 18:139–158.

Schafer, R. (1967), Ideals, the ego ideal, and the ideal self. In: *Motives and Thought*, ed. R. R. Holt. *Psychol. Issues*, 18/19:131–174. New York: International Universities Press.

Schilder, P. (1935), *The Image and Appearance of the Human Body*. New York: International Universities Press, 1950.

Schowalter, J. E. (1970), The child's reaction to his own terminal illness. In: *Loss and Grief*, ed. B. Schoenberg, A. Carr, D. Peretz, & A. Kutscher. New York: Columbia University Press, pp. 51–69.

——— (1971). The utilization of child psychiatry on a pediatric adolescent ward. *Journal of the American Acad. of Child Psychiatry*, 10:684–699.

——— & Anyan, W. R. (1973), Experience on an adolescent inpatient division. *Amer. J. Dis. Child.*, 125:212–215.

——— Ferholt, J. B., & Mann, N. M. (1973), The adolescent patient's decision to die. *Pediatrics*, 51:97–103.

——— & Lord, R. D. (1969), Admission to an adolescent ward. *Pediatrics*, 44:1009–1011.

——— ——— (1970), Utilization of patient meetings on an adolescent ward. *Psychiat. in Med.*, 1:197–206.

——— ——— (1973), On the writings of adolescents in a general hospital ward. *The Psychoanalytic Study of the Child*, 27:181–200.

Seligman, R. (1974), A psychiatric classification system for burned children. *Amer. J. Psychiat.*, 131:41–46.

Sklansky, M. A. (1972), Report on panel: Indications and contraindications for the psychoanalysis of the adolescent. *J. Amer. Psychoanal. Assn.*, 20:134–144.

Solnit, A. J. (1971), Adolescence and the changing reality. In: *Currents in Psychoanalysis*, ed. I. M. Marcus. New York: International Universities Press, pp. 98–110.

——— & Green, M. (1963), The pediatric management of the dying child: Part II. In: *Modern Perspectives in Child Development*, ed. A. J. Solnit & S. Provence. New York: International Universities Press, pp. 217–228.

Spiegel, L. A. (1958), Psychoanalytic psychology of adolescence. *The Psychoanalytic Study of the Child*, 13:296–308.

Swift, C. R., Seidman, F., & Stein, H. (1967), Adjustment problems in juvenile diabetes. *Psychosom. Med.*, 29:555–571.

Tyrer, P. J. (1973), Relevance of bodily feelings in emotion. *Lancet*, 1:915–916.

Part X

CHILD ABUSE

The phenomenon of child abuse, when first identified, appeared to be relatively clear-cut and simple, albeit tragic and shocking. As with so many psychosocial issues, however, experience has shown increasingly that the problems involved in the causation, prevention and management of child abuse are deep-seated, complex and multifaceted. The solutions are not only far from simple, but frequently bring new problems and contradictions to the fore.

The three papers in this year's selection illustrate the difficulties and dilemmas facing the committed professional in the child abuse field. At the same time, each project presents promising approaches and recommendations, arising out of practical experience and thoughtful analysis, for dealing with this vast and tragic psychosocial problem.

Rosenfeld and Newberger define the two major professional approaches, defined as "compassion" and "control," and discuss the contradictions that often arise between these two philosophies. The contradictions are real and not apparent and often pose painful dilemmas for the helping professional. The authors define these dilemmas clearly and recommend approaches to resolve them.

Derdeyn, in his paper "Child Abuse and Neglect" reviews the trends in treatment and in legal decisions with respect to custody of abused and neglected children. The complex psychological and legal issues are summarized succinctly, and the implications and consequences of an initial decision to remove the child from the home are emphasized.

In the third article, Derdeyn reviews the issues involved in foster care placement of neglected and abused children. He highlights the reality that foster care for many children is interminable and may involve a number of different placements, which is in sad and tragic contrast to the all too prevalent myth that foster care readily terminates in return home or adoption. Permanent foster placement is then examined in the light of the reality rather than the myth.

PART X: CHILD ABUSE

27

COMPASSION VS CONTROL

Conceptual and Practical Pitfalls in the Broadened Definition of Child Abuse

Alvin A. Rosenfeld

Stanford University Medical Center

and

Eli H. Newberger

Harvard Medical School and Children's Hospital, Boston

*A broadened understanding of child abuse has enabled practition-
ers to think of the parents of abused children not as evil murderers
but as human beings caught in a complex web of social isolation
and deprivation. Concomitantly, child abuse laws have changed
dramatically in the last decade to include virtually all childhood
physical symptoms of family crisis; physical, sexual, and emotional
abuse and child neglect are now reportable by nearly all profes-*

Reprinted with permission from *Journal of the American Medical Association*, Vol. 237,
2086–2088, 1977. Copyright 1977, American Medical Association.

Read in part before the 28th annual meeting of the American Association of
Psychiatric Services for Children, San Francisco, Nov 12, 1976.

This study was supported in part by grant OCD-CB-141 from the Office of Child
Development, U.S. Department of Health, Education, and Welfare.

*sionals who have contact with children. There has been a dramatic
increase in case reports, but the services for which families become
eligible do not approach the humane rhetoric and intent of child
abuse legislation. Society and the helping professions are caught in
a dilemma that we characterize and address clinically as compassion vs control.*

For more than a century, child welfare agencies have undertaken to
assure the safety and well-being of children. This important work
began as a concern to provide basic life supports for the children of
the immigrant poor and focused on providing homes for the homeless.[1] More recently, it has progressed to a legally mandated intervention on behalf of children who are suffering from physical, sexual, or
emotional traumatization in their homes.[2] As the statutory basis for
this protection has rapidly evolved in the last two decades, there have
developed neither clear-cut legal guidelines for family intervention
nor a scientific foundation for protective service work.[3-6] The lack of a
rigorous practical and theoretical framework for law and for clinical
practice has created a muddled and perplexing situation for professionals concerned with the health and welfare of children.

HISTORICAL BACKGROUND

In 1962, Kempe and his co-workers[7] dramatized the problem of
child abuse with the term "the battered child syndrome" in a paper
that precipitated public outrage and deep professional concern. Although the phenomenon was hardly new[8] and the existing clinical
studies of child abuse were mostly of dubious quality,[9] the time was
ripe for action. The concern led to the passage of a child abuse reporting statute in every state. In retrospect, it is of note that these
laws were enacted in the 1960s, an era of concern for the rights of the
disadvantaged. As they have developed (and broadened) to the present day, these statutes oblige all professionals in contact with children
to report any symptoms or serious suspicions of physical, sexual, or
emotional abuse. Most laws also require signs of neglect to be reported. In 1974, the passage of a national child abuse act (PL 93-247)
that makes available to states modest support for protective service
work has, through the establishment and administration of federal
regulations, effectively expanded the list of reportable conditions.
Since nearly all of the statutes are worded imprecisely, they give the
reporter wide latitude in addition to legal immunity. Usually, the department of public welfare or the police are designated to receive the

report. Once a report is filed, an investigation may begin to determine whether the child is at risk in his parents' care, and appropriate steps may be taken.

The child abuse statutes are intended to protect children whose lives are in danger and for whom other statutes do not afford protection. They spell out state and professional responsibility toward families who have problems in protecting their children, and state that helpful services (such as counseling, provision of a homemaker, day care, and temporary foster-home care) shall be provided to strengthen family life. Few anticipated the number and variety of cases that would be reported under the child abuse laws. Where in 1967 fewer than 7,000 cases of child abuse came to the attention of the authorities,[10] in 1974 there were more than 200,000 (V. De Francis, JD, personal communication, Feb 13, 1976). No child welfare office had resources remotely adequate to deal with this deluge. For example, when Florida introduced a state-wide hot line for child abuse reporting as the centerpiece of its strategy to deal with the problem, the state was overwhelmed with calls. This led to a rapid deterioration of the method of screening cases for service.[11]

Moreover, the social workers who man these departments, which tender mainly to impoverished children and families, are overworked, underpaid, and poorly supervised, and they have insufficient access to psychiatric, psychological, and medical consultation and treatment.[12,13] Staff turnover in welfare departments is enormous, and the prospects of continuing service to troubled families is small. With few clear-cut guidelines for decisions, action can be taken on the basis of exhaustion, emotionalism, or personal values about child rearing, rather than from attention to statutory or administrative guidelines or to commonly understood standards of sound professional practice. At present, services do not approach the humane rhetoric and intent of child abuse legislation. The system may mete out punishment in the guise of help.

CHILD ABUSE AND LATER DEVIANT BEHAVIOR

It has been noted that child abuse has a multi-generational pattern: the parents of abused children may themselves have been abused and neglected in childhood.[14] Violent criminals seem often to have suffered abuse as children; for this reason, Schmitt and Kempe[15] strongly suggest that action on the problem of child abuse will prevent crime. The data that form the basis for these conclusions can be accounted for in large part by insufficiently rigorous study design. The studies share a prominent bias that favors poor people. Of the few studies that have comparison groups, nearly none match cases and controls adequately.[5] The single controlled follow-up study that matches cases and controls on social class suggests that the developmental consequences of child abuse can be accounted for on the basis of low social class.[16] Finally, foster-home care, a common protective service intervention, is associated with an unfortunate and predictable psychiatric morbidity of its own.[17]

COMPASSION VS CONTROL

As laws have been passed broadening the list of conditions mandated to be reported as child abuse, a humane philosophy of clinical treatment has evolved.

Newer knowledge has shown social isolation, illness, and parental psychologic symptoms to be associated with child abuse, and our present orientation also acknowledges current life stresses, including unemployment, marital conflict, crises associated with drugs and alcohol, and inadequate access to essential resources and services.[18]

This broadened understanding of the setting of child abuse enables practitioners to see abusing parents not as evil murderers but as human beings caught in a complex web of personal and social deprivation that inhibits the normal loving relationships between parents and their children. The philosophy of practice has become assertedly humane: Kempe and Helfer's second book[19] is entitled *Helping the Battered Child and His Family*. Behavior that might be characterized by an outside observer as destructive or criminal has come to be seen and interpreted by those involved in its identification and treatment in terms of the psychosocial economy of the family.

The more compassionate understanding of the family has changed expectations of the clinician. He or she is expected to approach each case with both an abundance of human kindness and a nonpunitive outlook on intervention, which should be aimed at strengthening the entire family. Compassionate intervention has created a commonly understood language of child abuse treatment, one in which the abusing parents are frequently seen as victims themselves. They may effectively be relieved of responsibility for their actions by a professional who perceives the social and developmental origins of their behavior.

The clinician may find incompatible the dual role suggested by the two models of intervention that we identify as a consequence of our broadened concept of child abuse and call "compassion" and "control."

The compassionate model derives from the need for insight and the formation of a helpful professional-parent relationship to understand and to improve the functioning of abusing families. In practice, when the abusing parents are seen as sad, deprived, and needy human beings (rather than as cold, cruel murderers), one sympathizes with their plight and may proffer help in the form of counseling and other services, such as provision of a homemaker, health and child care, and other supports. One may contemplate with dread strong intervention on behalf of the child, such as court action on his or her behalf, with or without foster-home placement.

The danger implicit in the compassionate approach is that over-identification with an abusive parent can be paralyzing. We have seen injuries and fatalities that are traceable to a physician's, nurse's, social worker's, or judge's inability to act on perceived danger for want of alienating the parents. Fused with utopian notions about the curative power of love and genuine concern, the compassionate model may also demoralize professionals when the treatment relationship proves hopeless.

One may take it as a personal failure to love sufficiently or appropriately. "Perhaps one more week" or "This time I'm sure she won't do it again. We had a really good talk . . ." are familiar refrains of the professional who has become attached, involved, and overidentified with the family as victim. When an interdisciplinary team approaches a case, there may be reluctance to assume the role of the "bad guy" who will tamper with the therapeutic relationship by taking the drastic step of signing a care and protection petition in the juvenile or family court.

The control model refers to the aggressive use of intervention to limit and, if necessary, to punish deviant behavior. It assumes that an individual must take full responsibility for his actions and the State will hold him accountable.

For several reasons, the human service community may reject the notion of control. First, it is perceived as being in direct conflict with the model of compassion and the ethical mandate to be humane and to refrain from a judgmental posture in one's work. Any threat of force against abusing parents may be seen as cruel. The compassionate approach requires the behaviors of physician and friend, while control requires the action of the not-so-friendly policeman who may blow the whistle on an intolerable situation.

Second, child-care professionals are reluctant to set limits for adults, even if the situation screams for action. Third, the philosophy of helping the family carries in it an implicit standard of professional deportment that does not allow the expression (and for many, we fear, the acknowledged experience) of strong negative feelings towards their clients or patients. The rage that a conscientious professional may feel in a child abuse case cannot be expressed directly. It may be translated to a displacement of anger, so that judges and police who impose criminal sanctions on parents (whose behavior would undoubtedly yield them a long jail sentence if done against an adult) become the villains. Another manifestation on this displacement is the anger that sometimes develops between physicians and social workers on these cases. This can grow so intense that communication and intelligent problem-solving cease. Another way to deflect the rage without acknowledging it is to rationalize it. Thus, under the guise of looking out for the child's best interests, a harsh and punitive approach may be used in all cases, with the unspoken motive of punishing the bad parents.

GIVING COMPASSION AND CONTROL

In all cases, there is a need for a balance and coordination of compassion and control, and we suggest that because it is not always humanly possible to maintain objective judgment during intensive work with abusive families, we might assign the functions separately. The assessment of a family referred for child abuse might be done by someone expert in deciding whether the case warrants a therapeutic trial, or whether strict legal intervention, such as a care and protection petition, is required. If a primarily compassionate treatment approach is attempted, the person working with the family would not be the one deciding if, when, or what legal intervention is necessary. A professional who has no interest in forming a helping relationship with the family (an administrator, as opposed to a therapist, in the psychiatric model) would be assigned to the case. The administrator's function would be to make the practical decisions about protective intervention on behalf of a child. Were the administrator an experienced and senior person, one would reasonably anticipate in him or her the maturity to decide calmly and to help the clinician define the relative balance of compassion and control. Furthermore, at times, only the authority and oversight of a court may give sufficient leverage (eg, the threat of a child's being taken away) to make possible a compassionate relationship (or any relationship) between professional and family.

STANDARD FOR DECISION-MAKING

There is need for a standard that would guide the choice of the intervention model. While there is no body of empirical data with which to finalize such a standard, we propose six measurements in the form of dualisms to inform professional decisions. No one measurement is sufficient for a decision.

1. Acute vs chronic injury: If the injury is an isolated experience that occurs during situational stress, a more compassionate model might be applicable, whereas recurrent severe injuries might call for intervention more weighted on the side of control.

2. The abusive incident acceptable or unacceptable: A parent who continues to manifest guilt and concern after an isolated episode may be more likely to respond to a more compassionate intervention model, whereas the parent who shows lack of concern about the injury may well require control. Prolonged observation may be necessary accurately to assess a parent's reaction. We warn against casual impressions.

3. Social vs dissocial: This measurement addresses the parent's pattern of behavior in reference to the norms of the culture or subculture. In suggesting it, we acknowledge the inability and reluctance of professionals to make such judgments. The greater the degree of social deviance (isolation, alcoholism, drug abuse, criminality), the more likely the need for control.

4. Love vs hate for the child: Of the various symbolic meanings of a child to a parent, the most pertinent to this discussion is valence, or the subjective parental attitude towards the child. If the child is seen as good, a compassionate approach may be more likely to succeed, whereas a child seen as intrinsically bad may need to be protected by a model that emphasizes control of the parent.

5. The child seen as separate from or fused to the parent: This measurement addresses the parent's ability to conceive of the child as a separate entity with needs of its own. A capacity for empathy and appropriate parental behavior is supported by this ability, and a more compassionate model may be apt in a case of abuse. A fused perception of parent and child may support a control intervention.

6. Integrated or disintegrated parental ego: A person with demonstrated (or potential) personality strength sufficient to inhibit destructive impulses may more likely respond to a compassionate approach. The desire to quiet a crying child is universal. The impulse to harm the child if necessary to quiet him is prevalent, if not universal.[20] The lack of sufficient ego strength to deflect that impulse into a channel

other than abuse may reflect either transient disturbance or serious ego pathology. If it means the latter, at least one aspect of intervention will have to be control.

Obviously there is a great deal of overlap in these measurements, and none provides the answer when or how to employ compassion and control. Child abuse, like other clinical problems, calls for sound clinical judgment. The identification of assumptions implicit in present child protective work and the establishment of a rational basis for future thinking about child abuse will promote the development of a more effective and humane practice.

REFERENCES

1. Kadushin, A.: *Child Welfare Services*. New York, Macmillan Publishers, 1967, pp. 36–65.
2. Wald, M.S.: State intervention on behalf of "neglected" children: A search for realistic standards. *Stanford Law. Rev.* 27:985–1040, 1975.
3. Gelles, R.J.: Child abuse as psychopathology: A sociological critique. *Am. J. Orthopsych.* 43:611–621, 1973.
4. Newberger, F. H., & Hyde, J.N.: Child abuse: Principles and implications of current pediatric practice. *Ped. Clin. North Am.* 22:695–715, 1975.
5. Newberger, F. H., & Daniel, J.H.: Knowledge and epidemiology of child abuse: A critical review of concepts. *Ped. Ann.* 5:15–25, 1976.
6. Bourne, R.D., & Newberger, E.H.: "Family autonomy" or "coercive intervention?" Ambiguity and conflict in a proposed juvenile justice standard on child protection. *Boston University Law. Rev.*, to be published.
7. Kempe, C.H., Silverman, F.N., Steele, B.F., et al: The battered child syndrome. *JAMA* 181:17–24, 1962.
8. DeMause, L.: Our forbears made childhood a nightmare. *Psychol. Today* 8:85–88, 1975.
9. Polansky, N.A., & Polansky, N.E.: The current status of child abuse and child neglect in this country, in *Report of Task Force 1*. Joint Commission on the Mental Health of Children, Washington, D.C., 1968.
10. Gil, D.G.: *Violence Against Children*. Cambridge, Mass, Harvard University Press, 1970.
11. Price, M.: *Child Protection Report*, Washington, D.C. March 13, 1975.
12. Nagi, S.Z.: *Child Maltreatment in the United States: A Cry for Help and Organizational Response*. Columbus, Ohio, Ohio State University Publications, 1976.
13. Jenkins, S.: Child welfare as a class system, in A.L. Schorr (Ed): *Children and Decent People*. New York, Basic Books Inc. Publishers, 1974, pp 3–23.
14. Steele, B.F., & Pollock, C.B.: A psychiatric study of parents who abuse infants and small children, In R.E. Helfer, & G.H. Kempe, (Eds): *The Battered Child*, ed 2. Chicago, University of Chicago Press, 1974, pp 89–133.
15. Schmitt, B.D., & Kempe, C.H.: Neglect and abuse of children, In V.C. Vaughn, & R.J. McKay (Eds): *Nelson Textbook of Pediatrics*, ed 10. Philadelphia, W.B. Saunders Co., 1975, pp 107–111.
16. Elmer, E.: A followup study of traumatized children. *Pediatrics* 59:273–274, 1977.
17. Fanschel, D., & Schinn, E.B.: *Dollars and Sense in the Foster Care of Children: A Look at Cost Factors*. New York, Child Welfare League of America, 1972.

18. Newberger, E.H., Reed, R.B. Daniel, J.H. et al: Pediatric social illness: Toward an etiologic classification. *Pediatrics,* to be published.
19. Kempe, C.H., & Helfer, R.E.: *Helping the Battered Child and His Family.* Philadelphia, J.B. Lippincott Co., 1972.
20. Chase, N.F.: *A Child Is Being Beaten.* New York, Holt Rinehart & Winston Inc., 1975.

28

CHILD ABUSE AND NEGLECT: THE RIGHTS OF PARENTS AND THE NEEDS OF THEIR CHILDREN

Andre P. Derdeyn

University of Virginia Medical Center, Charlottesville

The trends in treatment and in legal decisions with respect to custody of abused and neglected children are reviewed. Parental rights, including a familial right to treatment, are discussed in terms of the needs of children for their parents and for a safe home environment. It is argued that the critical point for the assertion of parents' rights is not the ultimate custody hearing but the initial decision to remove the child from its home.

Many of the profound social changes that have occurred in this society are reflected in family law. General laws for adoption and divorce first appeared in the mid-nineteenth century, and reflected new attitudes towards children and towards the marital relationship. The legal process for divorce has recently become more humane through no-fault divorce laws. In the early United States, custody contests between parents were settled in favor of the father; later the mother developed the superior right to custody as against the father.[11] One area that has seen little change, however, is that of the basic parental right to custody. With regard to third parties, either father or mother has had a right overwhelmingly superior to any intervenor, and this continues with little change up to the present time.[13]

Reprinted with permission from *American Journal of Orthopsychiatry*, Vol. 47, 377–387, 1977. Copyright 1977, the American Orthopsychiatric Association, Inc.

In response to the growing awareness of the extent of child abuse and neglect, every state has enacted legislation to facilitate the protection of abused and neglected children.[33] In spite of some protests to the contrary, however, the basic right of biological parents to the custody of their children has not appreciably diminished. The termination of residual parental rights so that the child is made free for adoption continues to be done only with great reluctance. In response to the challenge of increasing public concern with the welfare and rights of children, the rights of parents have taken some new forms.

Reports of the efficacy of treatment and rehabilitative efforts with abusing and neglecting families will be reviewed, and the current status of the rights of parents with regard to the custody of their children in Supreme Court and in other legal developments will be discussed. It is felt that a thoughtful integration of the needs and rights of parents and the needs of their children suggests some changes in public policy in the area of child abuse and neglect.

TREATMENT OF CHILD ABUSE AND NEGLECT

Once any medical emergencies have been dealt with, the treatment of child abuse and neglect has generally consisted of intervention with the parents, with the child either remaining in the home or being placed in foster care. Recently, the child's need for psychiatric treatment has also been recognized,[24] but the greatest change has been in the broadening of the original concern regarding physical abuse to include the much more common (and much more nebulous) varieties of neglect.[16] There has been some shift in emphasis away from a strictly psychodynamic and psychopathological model associated exclusively with abuse to a concern about social and economic stress factors associated with abuse and other forms of maltreatment.[3,18,19] This increased appreciation of environmental stress has led to the understanding that underlying many instances of maltreatment is an "inability of a parent to nurture [his or her] offspring,"[43] or a "deficit in parenting"[17] related to early emotional deprivation and current environmental stress. The necessity for comprehensive and compassionate treatment to nurture emotionally deprived adults in difficult social and economic situations is generally recognized,[34] but the availability of these types of services remains limited in many areas.

Treatment Results

Treatment programs which can provide a broad variety of supportive and therapeutic services report good results in a high percentage of cases. Fontana[17] reported on a program including live-in facilities which was successful in preventing separation of mother and child in 65% of their cases. The remaining 35%, or 22 children, experienced a "long-term separation" from the mother and were removed from the parental home. Steele and Pollack[61] reported that "all but a few" of 60 families who abused infants in their treated group showed significant improvement, defined minimally as elimination of "dangerously severe physical attack on the infant."

A project whose objective was minimizing short-term disruptions for children and their families demonstrates the effectiveness a comprehensive protective service program can have. Funding by the US Children's Bureau allowed local welfare departments to provide effective additional service functions on a 24-hour basis. Emergency caretakers could stay with children in their homes in situations of temporary abandonment or parental emergencies, and homemakers could come to the homes on a daily basis when parents could not adequately care for their children themselves. If children could not be maintained in their homes by a homemaker, or if there was a breakdown at the regular foster home placement, emergency foster homes were made available for immediate temporary placement. This program was markedly effective in achieving the target goals of reducing the number of children removed precipitously from their homes, and reducing the number of children going through the legal system.[5]

In another report,[44] a carefully integrated program involving an academic pediatric hospital and local social service agencies was effective in reducing markedly the risk of reinjury subsequent to the diagnosis of child abuse. The improvement in the reinjury rate, furthermore, was not attributable to foster placement, which was infrequent.

Reports from other than comprehensive, demonstration-type programs reveal that the effects of intervention may not be so positive as the ones reported above. In their two-year follow-up of ten battered children, Terr and Watson[63] found that

> ... confusion, delays, poorly coordinated efforts and failure by agencies and individuals to assume responsibility ... produced serious emotional stresses to already traumatized youngsters.

The authors of a study of 112 child homicides felt that their work did "not tend to support the belief that severely abusing parents are receptive to counseling or psychotherapy."[32]

A child care agency reviewed the records of 28 abused or severely neglected children, 24 of whom had been placed in foster care. The authors estimated that fourteen of the 24 children would need long-term care, indicating that adoption was not planned and return home was not deemed possible.[4]

In a New York City study regarding 624 children who had spent at least 90 days in foster care, abuse and neglect accounted for the placement of nineteen percent of them. Although only 36% of all the children were still in foster care at five years, 48% of the abused and neglected children remained in foster care at the end of five years.[15]

The efficacy of treatment of child abuse and neglect varies tremendously: small, well-organized, demonstration-type programs may be quite effective in avoiding parent-child separations and in preventing subsequent abuse and neglect. For the majority of abused children and their families, however, available rehabilitative or treatment services are at a low level, and family disruption and long-term foster care too often follow intervention. Even at best, the results of rehabilitative efforts cannot provide the sole rationale for the current emphasis upon treatment of abusing and neglecting families. A review of various legal areas relating to the family will facilitate an understanding of existing policy.

PARENT AND CHILD IN THE LAW

Rights of Parents vis a vis Children

The Tenth Amendment reserves to the states the area of family domestic relations law. As in many other areas of family law, however, the area of dependency, neglect, and abuse of children has increasingly become affected by Supreme Court decisions based on the due process and equal protection clauses of the Fourteenth Amendment.[45] Although the constitution does not mention the family or the raising of children, parental rights with regard to their children have been substantially developed in Supreme Court decisions on the bases of individual liberty and family privacy.

In 1922, in a Nebraska case involving a law forbidding the teaching of foreign languages in public schools, the court stated that the liberty protected by the Fourteenth Amendment includes the right "to marry, establish a home, and bring up children."[40] An Oregon law requiring all children to be sent to public primary schools was overturned in 1925 because it "unreasonably interferes with the liberty of parents and guardians to direct the upbringing and education of children under their control."[49] In 1943, the Court wrote that, "It is cardinal with us that the custody, care, and nurture of the child reside in the parents."[51] A 1953 opinion referred to parental custody of a child as

"Rights more precious . . . than property rights,"[39] and held that Four-teenth Amendment liberties included the "immediate right to the care, custody, management, and companionship of . . . minor chil-dren,"[39] In a 1968 pornography case, the Court wrote that

> . . . constitutional interpretation has consistently recognized
> that the parents' claim to authority in their own household
> to direct the rearing of their children is basic in the struc-
> ture of our society.[20]

Family relationships have been recognized as parental interests enti-tled to due process protection. In 1965, it was held that a parent could not be deprived of the custody of his child without formal notice and a hearing regarding the issue.[1] In 1972, in *Stanley v. Il-linois*, the rights to notice and a hearing were extended to the fathers of illegitimate children.[59] In that opinion, a parent's interests in the "companionship, care, custody, and management of his or her chil-dren" were considered to be rights protected under the due process clause. Fourteenth Amendment rights were also important in recent abortion decisions,[50,55] which will not be discussed in this paper.

It should be noted that all these opinions cited either support the rights of parents to have custody or control over their child, or con-sider the family as a unit, with the implicit assumption that honoring the rights of parents will not have any ill effect upon their children. In *Stanley v. Illinois*, the issue resolved was one of sex discrimination among adults. The impact upon children of extending greater rights to the unwed fathers was not considered by the court. Although un-doubtedly some children have benefitted from the greater legal rec-ognition of the rights of the putative father, the delays and confusion in adoption of young children occasioned by this decision have been considerable.[2,14,53,56]

In the 1972 *Wisconsin v. Yoder* decision, the Supreme Court upheld parental religious objections to compulsory public education of Amish children beyond the eighth grade.[66] The questions of the children's preferences, or of the effect upon young people of leaving the Amish community with only an eighth-grade education were not considered by the court in the majority opinion. These issues were, however, ad-dressed by Justice Douglas, who wrote in a dissenting opinion that he did not think the case could be decided properly unless all three chil-dren involved testified on their own behalf. He wrote:

> It is the future of the student, not the future of the par-
> ents, that is imperiled by today's decision. If a parent

> keeps his child out of school beyond the grade school, then the child will be forever barred from entry into the new and amazing world of diversity that we have today.... It is the student's judgment, not his parents' that is essential if we are to give full meaning to...the Bill of Rights.... If [the child] is harnessed to the Amish way of life by those in authority over him and if his education is truncated, his entire life may be stunted and deformed.[66] (p. 245–246)

The majority opinion stated that it was not necessary to consider the children's preferences because the children were not parties in the case. In this case, the interests of parents and their children were not necessarily identical, but this was not recognized in the majority opinion.

In contrast to these cases assuming an identity of interest between parents and their children, *Wyman v. James* in 1971 distinguished the interests of a child from those of a parent.[67] A mother receiving AFDC payments refused to permit a home visit by a welfare department worker. The court took into account that the child's interest in the home visit was separate from the mother's in that the visit "enables the State to determine that the intended objects of its assistance benefit from its aid." It was felt that the admitted infringement upon the mother's constitutional right to privacy was not unreasonable. The court noted that the focus of the visit is upon the child, and stated:

> The dependent child's needs are paramount, and only with hesitancy would we relegate those needs, in the scale of comparative values, to a position secondary to what the mother claims as her rights.[67] (p. 318)

Thus, in this particular instance the Court recognized that the interests of parent and child were not identical. In *Kremens v. Bartley*, soon to be decided by the Supreme Court, the issue is between the rights of parents to make commitment decisions for children and the right of children to due process and counsel in commitment proceedings. It is to be expected that situations involving conflicts of interest between parent and child will increasingly come before the Supreme Court.

Due Process and Right to Counsel

Representation for the child. The 1967 *Gault* case held that constitutional due process protections applied to children as well as adults.[28]

In *Gault*, an adolescent faced a long term of incarceration at a state training school. The Supreme Court reasoned that the potential loss of liberty required due process safeguards, the most important of which was counsel for the child, at state expense if necessary. Thus, for the older child before a court because of misbehavior, *Gault* established that a system based only upon the *parens patriae*[10] doctrine of "best interests of the child" was not sufficient to guarantee him fair treatment. However, due process rights have not generally been extended to children involved in the various situations where the custody of the child is an issue, such as in abuse, neglect, dependency, or termination of parental right procedures where the rather amorphous "best interests of the child" rule is inconsistently applied.[31,46]

Representation for the parent. The right to counsel, at state expense, for indigent parents involved in neglect and termination proceedings is increasingly being recognized. The rationale for assigned counsel involves four major issues: 1) the parental right to have custody and to care for a child are "inherent constitutionally protected liberties"[62] as developed in the Supreme Court decisions cited above; 2) the sanctions against the parent of either loss of custody or termination of parental rights are serious and warrant protection of due process;[49] 3) due process and equal protection of the law require appointed counsel to avoid discriminating against the indigent;[6] and 4) as the parents' adversary has increasingly become a governmental rather than a private agency, the state is the parents' adversary in neglect proceedings, and the citizen is at a great disadvantage if not represented by counsel.[9,27,48] Recently, a number of state courts have ruled that constitutional due process requires that counsel be supplied to indigent parents in neglect cases.[18,30,60] Another parental right of recent appearance is the right for a transcript of the court record at state expense for purposes of appeal.[7,26]

It can be seen that, as our tradition of parental rights encounters a somewhat changed climate of opinion regarding children, existing rights of parents become refined and new rights develop. One that may be in the process of development is a familial right to treatment in child abuse and neglect.

A Familial Right to Treatment

It has been held by many authors that any state intervention in family affairs be kept to a minimum, and that children be removed from homes only after extensive efforts have been made to ameliorate the situation.[41,54,64,65] The concept of a state responsibility to rehabilitate is a growing one, and it has recently been formalized by the idea that statutes for termination of parental right include a "familial right to treatment"[35] philosophy.

A legal basis of the familial right to treatment is derived directly from the Social Security Act of 1935, which states its purpose as

> ... encouraging the care of dependent children in their own homes or in the homes of relatives by enabling each State to furnish financial assistance and rehabilitation and other services ... to needy dependent children and the parents ... with whom they are living to help maintain and strengthen family life.[58]

State governments dispensing federal AFDC funds to a parent involved in an abuse, neglect, or termination of parental rights action are starting to be held by defense attorneys to the language of the purpose clause. The state responsibility to rehabilitate is increasingly being used as a defense by parents in custody and termination actions, and the situation may be approaching where due process assumes a trial of treatment.

A few recent cases will help illustrate the influence of this concept. In a 1975 Arizona case of a chronically abused child, involvement of the welfare department had included removal of the child from the home, return of the child to the home under supervision, psychiatric evaluation of the family, and eventually a petition to terminate parental rights. In the opinion terminating parental rights, the court wrote that "termination [of parental rights] was not violative of due process when undertaken only after significant efforts at rehabilitation."[23] Presumably, due process required those "significant efforts at rehabilitation."

In recent years, the New York State legislature, realizing that impediments to terminating parental rights were preventing a great number of otherwise eligible children from being available for adoption, has developed a permanent neglect statute to facilitate termination of the rights of parents so that adoption of their children is made possible.[22] The "permanently neglected child" is defined as a child

> ... in the care of an authorized agency, either in an institution or in a foster home, and whose parents or custodian has failed for a period of more than one year ... substan-

tially and continuously or repeatedly to maintain contact with or plan for the future of the child, although physically and financially able to do so.[36] (p. 1112)

But in conjunction with the relative ease with which parental rights regarding children who have been in foster care at least a year can at least theoretically be terminated in New York, the law requires "diligent efforts" to encourage and strengthen the parental relationship when such efforts will not be detrimental to the moral and temporal welfare of the child. Rhode Island is another American jurisdiction specifically requiring proof of agency efforts in proceedings to terminate parental rights.[53]

Recent New York opinions require two findings in order to terminate parental rights: 1) the parent must have fulfilled the criteria for permanent neglect, and 2) the agency must have not failed in its duty to encourage and strengthen the relationship between mother and child.[37,38] When a mother failed to visit her placed child for six months, but the court found that the agency was "dilatory" in the performance of its duty to strengthen the parental relationship, the court determined that parental rights should not be terminated.[25] In another New York case, an adoption attempt by foster parents who had cared for a child for ten years was turned down because of the agency's lack of effort in enforcing visitation with the biologic mother after the child objected to the visits. The opinion stated:

> The court can terminate parental rights only when the parent has failed to maintain contact or plan for the child despite the agency's diligent efforts in accordance with the law. More is needed than has been shown in this case before the court will take this extreme and drastic step.[29] (p. 2430)

It is the author's opinion that a court's refusal to recognize what appears to be a committed relationship between foster parents and foster child of ten years' duration is pretty drastic in itself. A reconsideration of the rights of parents in the light of the needs of their children is in order.

PARENTS' RIGHTS AND CHILDREN'S NEEDS

The unity of interest between parent and child that is assumed in law is in large part an accurate reflection of the emotional realities of family living. While the "children as chattel" idea has come to be recognized as excessive in the 1970s, a parental sense of "ownership" may bespeak healthy identification with the child as a family member, a positive emotional bonding with the child, and a healthy commitment. Also, abusing and neglecting parents may be of great positive emotional value to a child, in spite of their maltreatment of the child.

Children are usually quite adequately taken care of by their parents, and questions of the rights of children relative to the rights of their parents do not normally arise. When these kinds of questions do arise, invariably the children involved are at considerable risk. The impact of the rights of parents upon the welfare of abused and neglected children may become an issue of importance.

The rights of young children in the various types of disputes in which the custody of the child is an issue have but one purpose: to help insure that the child has the opportunity to grow up in a fairly healthy parent-child relationship. Due to the child's immaturity, the rights of children in such predicaments are an abstraction, a vehicle to facilitate his or her remaining or being placed in a situation where the child's needs for adequate care and a committed relationship can be met.

The emphasis in public policy in recent years has been to provide protective services while the child remains in the home,[57] and the latest available statistics indicate that the child remains in the home in 83% of protective service cases.[42] From the child's point of view, the emphasis upon parental rights, including a familial right to treatment, can be rationalized up to a point. This point occurs when remaining at home becomes so dangerous physically or destructive emotionally that the child must be removed from the home for all but short-term and carefully managed separations.

When services have not been successful in helping parents to function adequately, the accustomed next step is to remove the child to foster care and continue to engage the parent or parents in rehabilitative services in the absence of the stresses of raising their child. This frequently leads to reunions followed by repeated removals to foster care and eventually to the child remaining in foster care indefinitely. Although the initial protective order is issued by a court, and the court must issue a removal order, the most hotly contested court involvement at the present time occurs when the child welfare agency petitions for termination of parental rights. Usually, as stated above, protective services have failed to alleviate the situation and the child has already been removed from the home. The court, at the time of such a termination of parental rights hearing, is in many ways not faced with what appears to be a momentous problem: the parents are not currently abusing or neglecting their child, and the child is apparently being adequately cared for in a foster placement. A frequent response of the court is to find that termination of parental rights is not warranted, but that the child requires continued foster care.[12]

The truly momentous decision is the removal of the child from the home in the first place, and this juncture needs to be recognized as the critical moment it is for the child, the family, the agency, and for the decision-making process itself. To the child, removal is very disruptive, for it entails a discontinuity with his or her parents, siblings, home, and school, and the child is usually plagued with feelings of helplessness, devaluation, and responsibility for the disruption. The parents are faced with a sense of loss and failure, but also may feel relief at being absolved of responsibility of caring for the child who has been removed from the home. With the child out of the home, rehabilitative or treatment activities related to parenting skills or interactions with the child tend to lose their immediacy. For the agency also, any sense of urgency regarding the child tends to diminish greatly when the child is placed. As has been eloquently articulated elsewhere, the child's sense of time in such situations is vastly different from that of any of the adults involved,[21] and at this time when the adults' levels of concern have diminished, the child may become increasingly at risk to his or her development.

The decision to remove the child for all but brief and carefully planned separations has important implications for the child's emotional life, for the level of motivation for rehabilitation of abusing and neglectful parents, and for the effective functioning of agencies and individuals attempting to help these parents. The decision to remove a child should be the critical decision, and the one in which the burden should properly rest on the state to prove that removal is absolutely necessary for the well-being of the child. Once the child is removed, however, the burden should shift to the parent or parents to establish that their rights should not be terminated or that they are capable of caring for the child. In the latter case, the child should, as soon as possible, be returned to the home and be followed under careful supervision. If there is little potential for rehabilitation of parents, or if the child's timely return home is not possible, then a permanent placement with a person willing to make a long-term commitment to the child must be secured with minimum delay.

CONCLUSION

As child abuse and neglect have become the subjects of legislation and governmental activity, concern for adequate legal protection of parents, particularly the indigent ones most often implicated, has understandably become greater. The parental right to custody has increasingly become defined as a "liberty" or a "freedom," and its protection has progressively become considered in terms of the constitutional guarantees of due process and equal protection of the laws. The law continues to assume a unity of interest of parent and child. Even for abused and neglected children, there is in a sense a convergence of the legal rights of parents with the emotional needs of children up to the point of removal of the child. Vigorous efforts to rehabilitate and any familial right to treatment are clearly warranted up to the time of child removal, which is the most critical point in the entire child care system. It is at the time of removal that the weight of parental rights should be exerted, in order to allow the parents to keep their child if the state cannot establish that they cannot care for their child adequately. Once past the time of removal, except in cases where the separation is time-limited and carefully carried out, parental rights and children's needs may diverge widely. After the point of removal of a child, due process and any familial right to treatment appear to be a new constitutional garb on the traditional essentially unqualified parental right to possession of a child.

REFERENCES

1. *Armstrong v. Manzo.* 1965. 380 U.S. 545.
2. Barron, J. 1975. Notice to the unwed father and termination of parental rights: implementing Stanley v. Illinois. Fam. Law Quart. 9:527–546.
3. Brown, R. 1976. The battered child syndrome. J. Forensic Sci. 21:65–70.
4. Burland, J., Andrews, R. and Headsten, S. 1973. Child abuse: one tree in the forest. Child Welfare 52:585–592.
5. Burt, M. and Balyeat, R. 1974. A new system for improving the care of neglected and abused children. Child Welfare 53:167–179.
6. Catz, R. and Kuelbs, J. 1974–75. The requirement of appointment of counsel for indigent parents in neglect or termination proceedings: a developing area. J. Fam. Law 12:223–244.
7. *Chambers v. District Court of Dubuque County.* 1967. 152 N.W. 2d 818.
8. *Danforth v. State Department of Health and Welfare.* 1973. 303 A. 2d 794.
9. De Francis, V. 1972. The status of child protective services. *In* Helping the Battered Child and His Family, C. Kempe and R. Helfer, eds. Lippincott, Philadelphia.
10. Derdeyn, A. 1975. Child custody consultation. Amer. J. Orthopsychiat. 45:791–801.
11. Derdeyn, A. 1976. Child custody contests in historical perspective. Amer. J. Psychiat. 133:1369–1376.

12. Derdeyn, A. 1977. Dependent, neglected and abused children: a case for permanent foster placement. Amer. J. Orthopsychiat. (in press)
13. Derdeyn, A. and Wadlington, W. Adoption: the rights of parents versus the best interests of their children. J. Amer. Acad. Child Psychiat. (in press)
14. Dukette, R. and Stevenson, N. 1973. The legal rights of unmarried fathers: the impact of recent court decisions. Soc. Serv. Rev. 47:1–15.
15. Fanshell, D. 1976. Status changes of children in foster care: final results of the Columbia University longitudinal study. Child Welfare 55:143–171.
16. Fontana, V. 1973. Somewhere a Child is Crying: Maltreatment—Causes and Prevention. Macmillan, New York.
17. Fontana, V. and Robison, E. 1976. A multidisciplinary approach to the treatment of child abuse. Pediatrics 57:760–764.
18. Gelles, R. 1973. Child abuse as psychopathology: a sociological critique and reformulation. Amer. J. Orthopsychiat. 43:611–621.
19. Gil, D. 1975. Unraveling child abuse. Amer. J. Orthopsychiat. 45:346–356.
20. Ginsberg v. New York. 1969. 390 U.S. 629.
21. Goldstein, J., Freud, A. and Solnit, A. 1973. Beyond the Best Interests of the Child. Free Press, New York.
22. Gordon, H. 1971. Terminal placements of children and permanent termination of parental rights: the New York permanent neglect statute. St. John's Law Rev. 46:215–263.
23. Hernandez v. State ex rel Arizona Department of Economic Security. 1975. 530 P. 2d 389.
24. In, P. and McDermott, J. 1976. The treatment of child abuse: play therapy with a 4-year-old child. J. Amer. Acad. Child Psychiat. 15:430–440.
25. In re Anonymous. 1975. 368 NYS 2d 372.
26. In re Appeal in Pima County. 1976. 540 P. 2d 642.
27. In re B. 1972. 30 N.Y. 2d 352.
28. In re Gault. 1967. 387 U.S. 1.
29. In re Plowden. 1976. 2 Family Law Reporter 2428.
30. In the Matter of B. 1972. 334 NYS 2d 133.
31. Isaacs, J. 1972. The role of the lawyer in child abuse cases. In Helping the Battered Child and His Family, C. Kempe and R. Helfer, eds. Lippincott, Philadelphia.
32. Kaplun, D. and Reich, R. 1976. The murdered child and his killers. Amer. J. Psychiat. 133:809–813.
33. Katz, S., Howe, R. and McGrath, M. 1975. Child neglect laws in America. Fam. Law Quart. 9:1–362.
34. Kempe, C. and Helfer, R., eds. 1972. Helping the Battered Child and His Family. Lippincott, Philadelphia.
35. Levine, R. 1975. Foundations for drafting a model statute to terminate parental rights: a select bibliography. Juvenile Justice 26(3):42–56.
36. McKinney's 1975 Session Laws of New York, 198th Session. 1975. West Publishing Co., St. Paul.
37. Matter of Orzo. 1975. 374 NYS 2d 554.
38. Matter of Ray AM. 1975. 376 NYS 2d 431.
39. May v. Anderson. 1953. 345 U.S. 528.
40. Meyer v. Nebraska. 1922. 262 U.S. 390.
41. Mnookin, R. 1973. Foster care—in whose best interest? Harvard Ed. Rev. 43:599–638.
42. National Center for Social Statistics. 1974. Children served by public welfare agencies and voluntary child welfare agencies and institutions—March 1972. US Department of Health, Education and Welfare, Washington, D.C.

43. Newberger, E. 1973. The myth of the battered child syndrome. Current Med. Dialogue 40:327–334.
44. Newberger, E., Hagenbuch, J. and Ebeling, N. 1973. Reducing the literal and human cost of child abuse: impact of a new hospital management system. Pediatrics 51:840–848.
45. Noonan, J. 1973. The family and the supreme court. Catholic Univ. Law Rev. 23:255–274.
46. *Note.* 1974. Due process for children: a right to counsel in custody proceedings. New York Univ. Rev. Law and Soc. Change 4:177–189.
47. *Note.* 1972. In the Matter of Ella B., A test for the right to assigned counsel in family court cases. Columbia Human Rights Law Rev. 4:451–459.
48. Paulsen, M. 1966. The legal framework for child protection. Columbia Law Rev. 66:679–717.
49. *Pierce v. Society of Sisters.* 1925. 268 U.S. 510.
50. *Planned Parenthood v. Danforth.* 1976. 44 United States Law Week 5197, July 1, 1976.
51. *Prince v. Massachusetts.* 1943. 321 U.S. 158.
52. Reeves, B. 1973–74. Protecting the putative father's rights after Stanley v. Illinois: problems in implementation. J. Fam. Law 13:115–152.
53. *Rhode Island Gen. Laws Ann.* 15-7-7, Supp. 1974.
54. Rodham, H. 1973. Children under the law. Harvard Ed. Rev. 43:487–514.
55. *Roe v Wade.* 1973. 410 U.S. 113.
56. Schafrick, F. 1973. The emerging constitutional protection of the putative father's parental rights. Fam. Law Quart. 7:75–111.
57. Shepherd, R. 1974. Solomon's sword: adjudication of child custody questions. Univ. Richmond Law Rev. 8:151–200.
58. *Social Security Act of 1935.* 42 U.S.C. ¶ 601.
59. *Stanley v. Illinois.* 1972. 405 U.S. 645.
60. *State v. Jamison.* 1968. 444 P. 2d 15.
61. Steele, B. and Pollock, C. 1968. A psychiatric study of parents who abuse infants and small children. *In* The Battered Child, R. Helfer and C. Kempe, eds. University of Chicago Press, Chicago.
62. *Stubbs v. Hammond*, 1965. 135 N.W. 2d 540.
63. Terr, L. and Watson, A. 1968. The battered child rebrutalized: ten cases of medical-legal confusion. Amer. J. Psychiat. 124:1432–1439.
64. Wald, M. 1975. State intervention on behalf of "neglected" children: a search for realistic standards. Stanford Law Rev. 27:985–1040.
65. Wald, M. 1976. State intervention on behalf of "neglected" children: standards for removal of children from their homes, monitoring the status of children in foster care and termination of parental rights. Stanford Law Rev. 28:623–706.
66. *Wisconsin v. Yoder.* 1972. 406 U.S. 205.
67. *Wyman v. James.* 1971. 400 U.S. 309.

29

A CASE FOR PERMANENT FOSTER PLACEMENT OF DEPENDENT, NEGLECTED, AND ABUSED CHILDREN

Andre P. Derdeyn

University of Virginia Medical Center, Charlottesville

The number of children entering foster care continues to rise. Despite efforts to rehabilitate families and to place children for adoption, for many children foster care tends to be interminable. Return to the home is often impeded by a paucity of parental resources; adoption is often blocked by the courts' reluctance to terminate parental rights. Permanent foster placement is suggested as an alternative arrangement for better meeting the needs of some of these children.

Concern for dependent, neglected, and abused children has increased substantially since identification of the "battered child syndrome" in 1962.[27] The new awareness of child abuse has stimulated increasing attention among members of the mental health, medical, and legal professions for the broad group of dependent, neglected, or abused children whose care at home may be less than adequate. Previously, such children tended to be almost exclusively the concern of child welfare agencies. Mental health clinicians are now increasingly

---

Reprinted with permission from *American Journal of Orthopsychiatry*, Vol. 47, 604–614, 1977. Copyright 1977, the American Orthopsychiatric Association, Inc.

involved as primary therapists and as consultants to courts and welfare departments. As a result of these activities, clinicians are becoming familiar with the practices of child care agencies and courts, and are beginning to develop ideas as to how these systems might better conform to the emotional needs and realities of these children and their families.

SOME ASPECTS OF FOSTER CARE

The number of children in foster care has increased dramatically over the last decade. In 1965, there were 287,000 children in foster care.[26] By 1975, the number has reached an estimated 364,000 children.[17]

Ideally, foster care is a temporary expedient designed to provide care for children at a time when their families cannot do so. If the family cannot be reunited, then adoption is the alternative generally sought in order to provide the child with continuity and stability of relationship with a parenting person. However, we know that for many children foster care is by no means temporary. Maas and Engler,[30] in their study involving over 4000 children, predicted that more than half would remain in foster care for most of their childhoods. A recent cross-sectional study[20] of all the children in foster care in the state of Massachusetts revealed that 60% had been in care between four and eight years, with the average being over five years. Recent approaches to counter the excessive duration of foster care have centered upon schemes for review of cases in care. The purpose of review is to stimulate planning and activity in order to return the child to the parental home or make him available for adoption. The idea of regular review of agency caseloads has achieved considerable attention and legislative action.[5] In New York state, such review has been shown to be quite effective in stimulating adoption but has had much less impact upon discharging children to their parents.[15]

In order to appreciate the problems of moving children out of foster care, some of the issues impeding the child's returning home or being placed for adoption require discussion. The first of these is the paucity of financial and emotional resources of the families of foster children.

Factors Impeding Return

The Columbia University longitudinal study of children in foster care in New York City has provided information regarding 467 families with one or more children entering foster care. The children were under twelve years of age and were entering foster care for the first time.[25]

Poverty of the mothers was extreme. Forty-eight percent received public assistance, and thirteen percent of those not receiving it had incomes of less than $75 per week. Only twenty percent lived with a spouse.[25]

Mental illness of the child-caring person was associated with more children entering foster care than any other category.[13] Where mental illness of the child-caring person was the prime factor leading to foster placement, there was a dramatic difference between children who were born out of wedlock and those who were born in wedlock. Almost 56% of the out-of-wedlock children of mentally ill mothers were still in care at the end of 3½ years, while only 33% of the wedlock children of mentally ill mothers remained in foster care.[12]

Thirty-six percent of the original study sample of 624 children remained in foster care at the end of five years.[14] Of this group remaining in care five years, 46% had experienced three or more placements. About two-thirds of the children remaining in care five years had lost contact with their parents.

It is evident that the biological families of foster children are particularly vulnerable to disruption due to poverty, mental illness, and one-parent status. Problems in reintegrating these families, often complicated by the overwhelming environmental factors associated with poverty, are also exacerbated by the agencies themselves being poorly funded, poorly staffed, and having an extremely high rate of turnover among child welfare workers.[39]

Adoption

While many persons may be unable or may lack the desire to care for their children, relatively few parents whose children are placed in foster care are willing voluntarily to surrender their children for adoption. Therefore, when agencies come to the decision that adoption is the best course for a child, they frequently must petition the court for termination of parental rights, usually on the basis of unfitness or abandonment by the parents. The courts are very respectful of the rights of biological parents and terminate such rights with reluctance.[11]

The following cases serve to illustrate the continuing power of the traditional rights of parents.

> Grandparents attempted to adopt a boy for whom they had cared for four years. In those four years, the child's father

had sent several cards but had had no other contact with him. The court, in maintaining the right of the biological father to the custody of his child, made it clear that the major issue was whether the father had forfeited his right and not what would be best for the child. The opinion stated: "The mere fact that there is evidence of the relationship's destruction is of no consequence if it cannot be established that there was parental conduct which caused it. Therefore, evidence relating solely to the question of what disposition may be in the child's best interest—evidence pertinent primarily to an inquiry into the present vitality, strength and stability of the parent-child relationship—is ultimately inconsequential"[1] (p. 795).

In a similar situation, a court in an abandonment case held that, "Even where the flame of parental interest is reduced to a flicker the court may not properly intervene to dissolve the parentage"[45] (p. 38).

It is evident that, with regard to termination of parental rights, the strength of the rights of parents is such that the parental claim tends to be dispensed with only by the justification that the biological parent was somehow at fault or indicated some clear intent to abandon the child.

Not only have courts been reluctant to interfere with parental rights, but those rights have recently been extended. In *Stanley v. Illinois*, the U.S. Supreme Court ruled that unmarried fathers are entitled to a hearing on their fitness as parents before custody or guardianship can be awarded to anyone else.[15] In this way an issue of sex discrimination between the adults—the unwed mother and the putative father—was resolved, but in some situations this new procedure has added an important impediment to the adoption of illegitimate children whose fathers frequently have little interest in them or who use this new power in ways hostile to the unwed mother and destructive to the child.[2,19]

An approach to increasing the opportunity for children with special needs has been developed by the United States Department of Health, Education, and Welfare.[16,48] This model statute for subsidized adoption has been emulated by a number of states, including Virginia.[4] The Virginia law defines eligible children to include

. . . any child who has special needs because of a handicap to placement for adoption by reason of his physical, mental, or emotional condition, race, or membership in a sibling group.[49] (p. 62)

The special needs include medical care, educational and mental health services, and legal services for effecting adoption. Subsidized adoption appears to be one mode of better serving a group of children who have tended to remain in long-term foster care. However, this type of adoption entails the same difficulties in terminating the rights of biological parents as does any other adoption.

The Continuing Need for Foster Care

For a great number of children, foster care is not a temporary state but a way of life. A number of factors work to maintain the status quo in foster care—the large and growing number of children, the lack of resources of their biological families, and the power of parental rights. Maas and Engler[30] showed not only that many children would live out their childhoods in foster care but also that many of these children would live in multiple foster homes. The more recent data cited in this paper indicate little change in that situation. New approaches, such as subsidized adoption and review of foster care, will be helpful but by no means capable of vastly reducing the number of children currently placed in or destined to enter foster care. It is apparent that foster care is likely to remain as a pragmatic solution in many situations, and that great numbers of children will be in long-term placement for many years to come.

PERMANENT FOSTER PLACEMENT

Between the myth (foster care readily terminates in return home or in adoption) and the reality (foster care for many children is interminable and may involve a number of different placements), there may be an alternative warranting serious consideration. Long-term foster care, which for many children may be inevitable, might with certain changes be made much more desirable. Permanent foster placement should be considered in those situations where strong emotional bonds have developed between foster parents and foster child. Such a legal arrangement would ensure the stability and continuity of the foster parent-foster child relationship. In addition to serving families where there is an established good relationship between foster parents and foster child, permanent foster care would be applicable to some unadoptable children. Children currently in long-term foster care for whom adoption is of diminishing likelihood are those who are older, of minority race, or suffering from some handicap. Others are not free for adoption due to agency inertia or judicial maintenance of parental rights. In addition, some children continue to have important emotional ties to biological parents who can never take care of them, and the termination of the relationship with biological parents required by adoption would be undesirable for them.[34,47]

The Concept

The author of a 1962 legal study[41] regarding unfit parents was impressed by the extremes of abuse and neglect which the courts would tolerate and still refuse to terminate the rights of parents. She concluded that the welfare of the children required a new type of legal relationship, that of permanent custody in a foster parent. The parental rights of the biologic parents would be severed, but the foster parent and the child would be assured a permanent relationship. The biologic parent would be allowed visitation, similar to the noncustodial parent in divorce.[41] This idea that custody might be placed in foster parents appeared in the social work literature about the same time[29] and has continued to be discussed both in the social work[31,40] and the legal literature.[3,7,44,46] Recently, the concept of permanent custody in the foster parents has been introduced in the psychiatric literature as "foster care with tenure."[18]

This concept of permanent foster placement appears to be a feasible one. Due to a combination of current attitudes of some courts and of recent developments in the rights of foster parents to children in their care, it appears that permanent foster placement can become a viable alternative to meeting the needs of some children.

Long-Term Foster Placement in the Courts

Courts not uncommonly devise solutions to custody problems which approach the concept of permanent foster care. In these cases the courts achieve a compromise between the right of "ownership" of the biological parent and the needs of the child by maintaining custody in the foster parent without disturbing the legal relationship between biological parent and child. Case examples may help to illustrate how this comes about.

A three-year-old boy had been in and out of the custody and the protective services of a child care agency several times because of adjudicated neglect since the age of eleven months. At age two, he was again placed in foster care. A year later the lower court terminated the rights of the biological parents as part of the child care agency's plan to find an adoptive placement. The parents appealed and the case came before the Maryland Supreme Court when the boy was almost five. The court conceded that the relationship between the biological parents was "extremely unstable" and cited numerous changes of address, separations, and warrants sworn by the parents against each other. The court decided that while it was clear that "[the boy's] best interest would be served by his remaining in the foster home for the present time . . . the record . . . falls far short of justifying the drastic result of permanently terminating the appellants' parental rights"[19] (p. 647). Continued foster care was thought to be warranted, but termination of parental rights was not found to be justified.

Three children were placed in the same foster home when they were ages six, three, and one. Ten years later the foster parents intended to leave the state and take the children with them. Up to that time the biological mother had telephoned the children several times a year and had visited them occasionally. The foster parents, upon their move, had provided plans for the children to visit their biological mother. The biological mother objected and petitioned the court to return the children to her custody. The lower court decided that the children should remain with the foster parents and, upon appeal, the Illinois Supreme Court upheld that decision. The court reasoned that the major issue was the welfare of the children, which would be advanced by their remaining with their foster parents.[24]

A 1975 New York case points up the flexibility that would be possible were permanent custody in a foster parent an available alternative.

A six-year-old girl was declared to be permanently neglected, and the parental rights of her mother were terminated. The mother appealed and the decision was affirmed, terminating irrevocably the relationship between this mother and child. A justice, in a dissenting opinion, noted that the mother had no intention of abandoning her child, and, in fact, visited her regularly twice a month. He observed that the mother had a "generally inadequate and defeatist attitude towards life," suffered a very ingrained "generalized lassitude," and noted that "any change of life style [was] fraught with fears and tension"[23] (p. 674). However, he had reservations about terminating the mother's rights on grounds that she might possibly be helped to function at such a level that she could regain custody of her child.

From the record, it does not appear very likely that the mother would indeed have become able to care for the child. However, given this child's age of six and her mother's demonstrated interest in her, one can assume that the relationship with her mother was of considerable importance to the child. The decision that a continuing relationship between a child of this age and her mother should be permanently severed may not necessarily be the best one for the development of the child. In this case, an alternative of permanent foster care with visitation by the biological mother might have been the optimum arrangement. In this way the child and the foster family would have the stability of their home situation and their relationship assured, as would be the continuity of the relationship between the child and her biological mother.

When the courts can deal with the more limited issue of custody disputes between biological parents and foster parents, the interests of the child may sometimes determine the outcome. In these situations, courts are relatively free to recognize the importance of an established, positive relationship shared by the child and the foster parents. In custody, unlike adoption, residual parental rights are not disturbed. A disadvantage in the cases described is that the biological parents may at any time attempt to regain custody of the child.[6] In at least some circumstances, permanent custody rather than adoption might actually be preferable. When there are important family ties, permanent foster care could steer a course between the instability of the usual foster care situation and the harsh "either-or" choices in adoption of older children where, typically, one set of adult contenders legally banishes the other from the child's life.

The courts' increased awareness of the importance to children's development of nurturing relationships has led to a greater likelihood of maintaining custody in foster parents. This has in part caused and has in part resulted from the development of some legal rights of foster parents. These new rights of foster parents will be discussed next.

The Developing Rights of Foster Parents

Foster parents have long been considered to have a number of duties, few rights, and to be essentially employees of the agency with which they contract.[26] Typically, when a foster parent attempts to contest removal of a child by the responsible welfare agency or attempts to adopt a child against agency wishes, courts have upheld the rights of biological parents and the sanctity of the placement contract between foster parents and the agency.[35] These contracts generally stipulate that the making of any plans for the child, including plans for adoption, be left to the agency. Traditionally, foster parents have not been considered to have a legally-recognizable interest in their foster child. Recently, courts have begun to acknowledge some rights of foster parents. The traditional status of foster parents is reflected in the following two cases.

A boy who had been with foster parents since the age of three days was removed from the foster parents' home eight years later and placed in the home of prospective adoptive parents. The Court of Appeals simply upheld the statute prohibiting anyone but prospective adoptive parents selected by the agency from adopting children relinquished to the agency. The foster parents were not even able to obtain a hearing on their petition for adoption, and removal of that child was final.[22]

In another situation, a biological mother sought to gain custody of her child. The foster parents who had cared for the child from age three months to five years attempted to terminate the biological mother's rights preparatory to their adopting the child. The court found that the foster parents "were bound by their agreement with the Department of Public Welfare," and that the "Department . . . was entitled to the possession of the . . . child"[21] (p. 1087–88). The foster parents, therefore, had no legal standing, and the child was given to the custody of her biological mother.

Change in the legal status of foster parents is evident in the two cases to follow.

An agency worker with eleven months' experience thought a foster mother appeared nervous, and it was the worker's impression that the home atmosphere was detrimental to the foster child who had lived with this family from age three weeks to nine years. The foster parents contested the agency order for removal of the child, but the lower court upheld the agency's action. The superior court reversed the award, retaining custody of the child in the foster parents. The opinion noted the emotionally devastating effect of separating the child from its foster parents and that determination of custody should focus on the best interests of the child and not on the rights claimed by the child placement organization.[8]

A similar case involved a five-year-old boy who had spent his last four years with a foster family. The child care agency ordered return of the child to the biological parents, and this was enforced by the lower court. Upon appeal, the superior court felt that in spite of the contract under which the foster parents cared for the child, the foster parents, as the *de facto* parents for four years, had the legal standing to file a petition raising the issue of who should have custody of the child. The contract they had signed with the child care service was, therefore, unenforceable.[43]

The right to a part in decision-making regarding children in their care has been increasingly sought by foster parents and foster parent organizations.[28,38] In 1976, a United States District Court held unconstitutional a provision of New York law which authorized the state to remove children from foster homes without affording a prior hearing to either the foster child or its foster parents.[36] This case has been heard by the United States Supreme Court but the decision has not been made public at the time of this writing.

In some states, laws are being developed to give foster parents the right to notice and participation in any hearing regarding their foster child.[7] In addition, legislation is developing to make foster parents who have had a child in their custody for two years legal parties in proceedings regarding that child[35] and to allow foster parents to petition the courts to revoke custody of the child care agency and place the guardianship of the child in themselves.[37] In New York, persons who have been foster parents for two years are given first consideration if the child is available for adoption.[34] It is apparent that foster parents are beginning to achieve a voice in decisions regarding children in their care.

CONCLUSION

Currently, long-term foster placements exist as an occasional and sometimes accidental compromise between the rights of biological parents and the needs of their children. The concept of permanent foster placement is itself a compromise, one that is both feasible legally and, for many children, more sound for them emotionally than is the current temporary custody in foster parents. In the legal arena, superimposed upon the essentially immutable tradition of a biological parent's proprietary interest in his children, there is a growing awareness of the emotional needs of children. Established foster parent-foster child relationships are being accorded some importance as to custody, but much less so in adoption disputes.

It is apparent that the parental right issue is and will remain a major block to adoption. When a dispute between a biological parent and a third party involves termination of parental rights preparatory to adoption, parental right is very often the determining factor. If parental rights are not directly confronted by means of an attempt to terminate those rights, however, custody may be determined by what the court decides is best for the child's welfare. The weakness of this arrangement with regard to continuity of the child's relationship with the foster parents is that the biological parents may continue to challenge the foster parents' custody of the child.

With the advent of increased rights of foster parents, it appears possible that in certain circumstances, the foster parents' rights to custody might be made a permanent one. Legislation might allow permanent foster placement for children whose relationship with foster parents is of such length and quality that the children should not be removed from the foster home, even if parental rights are terminated and the child is thus eligible for adoption. Where foster parents are financially dependent upon foster care payments and wish to make a long-term commitment but not to adopt the child, permanent foster placement could help to assure a stable living situation. Subsidized adoption can also meet the needs of some of these foster child-foster parent families if the children are available for adoption or if the rights of biologic parents can be terminated.

There are several other situations in which permanent foster placement could optimally meet the needs of some children. When there are unbroken emotional or unbreakable legal ties to biological parents and a child might thereby remain unavailable for adoption, permanent foster placement could provide stability for a child if the foster parents are able to make a long-term commitment. When an older child's ties to a biological family that is incapable of caring for him are strong, permanent foster placement could provide the optimum situation for stability for the child in his foster home and continuity of his relationship with the biological family. Permanent foster placement would require that custody be placed in foster parents rather than in agencies, for agencies may pose the same threat to the stability and continuity of foster parent-foster child relationships as do biological parents.

Permanent foster care, like adoption, the last major social and legal innovation regarding children and their families, would have no clear legal tradition in the common law of England. Similar to adoption cases, courts would be inclined to interpret permanent foster care statutes narrowly, particularly when the interests of biological parents might be in opposition to those of foster parents. In order to achieve the desired ends, legislation would have to be detailed and comprehensive.

In *Stanley v. Illinois*,[43] which expanded the rights of putative fathers with regard to their children, the Supreme Court wrote:

> ... [illegitimate] children cannot be denied the right of other children because familial bonds in such cases [are] often as warm, enduring, and important as those arising within a more formally organized family unit. (p. 652)

If this were written about foster children, it would be even more accurate, for this description would surely describe a much greater proportion of foster parent-foster child relationships than it does putative father-illegitimate child relationships.

Permanent foster care with adequate legal protection can assume a useful place in the existing system that attempts to serve children in need of adequate parenting. The increasing rights of foster parents with regard to children in their care augurs well for the development of permanent foster care. It appears to be inevitable that, in questions of custody, young children will be bystanders in struggles between concerned adults,[10,34] and it is appropriate that foster parents, sometimes the only adults who have an ongoing relationship with a child, are becoming able to join biological parents and child care agencies in the struggle for custody.

REFERENCES

1. *Adoption of VMC.* 1974. 528 P. 2d 788.
2. Barron, J. 1975. Notice to the unwed father and termination of parental rights: implementing Stanley v. Illinois. Fam. Law Quart. 9:527–546.
3. Bodenheimer, B. 1975. New trends and requirements in adoption law and propos-

als for legislative change. Southern Calif. Law Rev. 49:10–109.

4. Browder, J. 1975. Adoption and foster care of handicapped children in the United States. Develpm. Med. Child Neurol. 17:614–620.

5. Chappell, B. 1975. Organizing periodic review in foster care: the South Carolina story. Child Welfare 54:477–586.

6. Clark, H. 1968. The Law of Domestic Relations in the United States. West Publishing Co., St. Paul, Minn.

7. *Comment.* 1974. The foster parents' dilemma "who can I turn to when somebody needs me?" San Diego Law Rev. 11:376–414.

8. *Commonwealth v. Children's Services.* 1973. 307 A. 2d 411.

9. *Commonwealth v. Hayes,* 1974. 215 Va. 49.

10. Derdeyn, A. 1976. Child custody contests in historical perspective. Amer. J. Psychiat. 133:1369–1376.

11. Derdeyn, A. and Wadlington, W. 1977. Adoption: the rights of parents versus the best interests of their children. J. Amer. Acad. Child Psychiat. 16:238–255.

12. Fanshell, D. 1971. The exit of children from foster care: an interim research report. Child Welfare 50:65–81.

13. Fanshell, D. 1975. Parental visiting of children in foster care: key to discharge? Soc. Serv. Rev. 49:493–514.

14. Fanshell, D. 1976. Status changes of children in foster care: final results of the Columbia University longitudinal study. Child Welfare 55:143–171.

15. Festinger, T. 1975. The New York review of children in foster care. Child Welfare 54:211–245.

16. Gallagher, U. and Katz, S. 1975. The model state subsidized adoption act. Child. Today 4:8–10.

17. Geiser, R. 1974. The shuffled child and foster care. Trial 10(3):27–35.

18. Goldstein, J. 1975. Why foster care—for whom for how long? Psychoanal. Study Child 30:647–662.

19. *Goodyear v. Cecil County Department of Social Services.* 1971. 273 A 2d 644.

20. Gruber, A. 1973. Foster Home Care in Massachusetts. Commonwealth of Massachusetts Governor's Commission on Adoption and Foster Care.

21. *Huey v. Lente.* 1973. 514 P. 2d 1081.

22. *In re adoption of Runyon.* 1969. 74 Cal. Rptr. 514.

23. *In the Matter of "Female" B. v. Little Flower Children's Services.* 1975. 370 NYS 2d 672.

24. *Interest of Martin.* 1975. 333 N.E. 2d 711.

25. Jenkins, S. and Norman, M. 1975. Beyond Placement: Mothers View Foster Care. Columbia University Press, New York.

26. Katz, S. 1971. Legal aspects of foster care. Fam. Law Quart. 5:283–302.

27. Kempe, C. et al. 1962. The battered child syndrome. JAMA 181:17–24.

28. *Kurtis v. Ballou.* 1970. 308 NYS 2d 770.

29. Lewis, M. 1964. Foster family care: has it fulfilled its promise? Annals Amer. Acad. Polit. Soc. Sci. 335:31–39.

30. Maas, H. and Engler, R. 1959. Children in Need of Parents. Columbia University Press, New York.

31. Madison, B. and Schapiro, M. 1970. Permanent and long-term foster family care as a planned service. Child Welfare 49:131–136.

32. *Matter of Crabtree.* 1975. 541 P 2d 1311.

33. Mnookin, R. 1975. Foreword. *In* Children and the Law, M. Shimm, ed. Law and Contemporary Problems 39:1–7.

34. *New York State Social Welfare Law.* 1973. 383.3 (McKinney Supplement).

35. *Note.* 1973. The rights of foster parents to the children in their care. Chicago-Kent Law Rev. 50:86–102.
36. *Organization of Foster Families for Equality and Reform v. Dumpson, March 22, 1976.* U.S. District Court for the Southern District of New York.
37. Pearlman, M. 1972. Foster parents' rights in Connecticut. Conn. Law Rev. 5:36–59.
38. Reistroffer, M. 1972. Participation of foster parents in decision making: the concept of collegiality. Child Welfare 51:25–29.
39. Shapiro, D. 1974. Occupational mobility and child welfare workers: an exploratory study. Child Welfare 53:5–13.
40. Shyne, A., Sherman, E. and Phillips, M. 1972. Filling a gap in child welfare research: service for children in their own homes. Child Welfare 51:562–573.
41. Simpson, H. 1962. The unfit parent: conditions under which a child may be adopted without the consent of his parent. Univ. Detroit Law J. 39:347–392.
42. *Stanley v. Illinois.* 1972. 405 US 645.
43. *Stapleton v. Dauphin County Child Care Service.* 1974. 324 A. 2d 562.
44. Taylor, H. 1966. Guardianship or "permanent placement" of children. Calif. Law Rev. 54:741–747.
45. *W. v. G. 1974.* 356 NYS 2d 24.
46. Wald, M. 1976. State intervention on behalf of "neglected" children: standards for removal of children from their homes, monitoring the status of children in foster care, and termination of parental rights. Stanford Law Rev. 28:623–706.
47. Watson, K. 1958. Long-term foster care: default of design? the voluntary agency responsibility. Child Welfare 47:331–364.
48. Watson, K. 1972. Subsidized adoption: a crucial investment. Child Welfare 51:220–230.
49. *Virginia Code Annotated.* 1975. Vol. 9A, 63.1–238.1 and 63.1–238.5. Michie Co., Charlottesville, Va.

Part XI

CHILD ADVOCACY ISSUES

All will agree that the prime responsibility of the child mental health professional is to act as the advocate for the needs and rights of children. Unless translated into specific principles and programs of action, to which the professionals give their full commitment, this generalization becomes empty and meaningless.

Polier raises this challenge directly and forcefully. She formulates the issues out of a lifetime of commitment to the needs and rights of underprivileged children. In this paper, she spells out the contradictions and conflicts among professionals arising from different ideological, cultural and religious approaches, and from struggles for power and resources. She makes a plea for hard day-to-day efforts combined with humility instead of "generalities that assume wisdom on all questions affecting children."

The other three articles in this section examine specific important issues relevant to child advocacy. Gordon provides an authoritative review of the problems and questions the appropriateness and use of standardized academic achievement tests for minority and disadvantaged children. Cohen and Zigler focus on the need to develop explicit, enforceable and realistic federal standards for day care for young children. Swire and Kavaler report a study of the health care and needs of foster children, which details the almost incredible prevalence of serious physical, mental and developmental problems in this disadvantaged group.

30

EXTERNAL AND INTERNAL ROADBLOCKS TO EFFECTIVE CHILD ADVOCACY

Justine Wise Polier

Former Judge, New York State Family Court

Child advocacy has rightly been defined as an effort to challenge and change systems that are injurious to children, that are inadequate to prevent harm, or that provide inappropriate help to children [7]. Advocacy is thus distinguished from an effort on behalf of a single child. On the basis of this definition, the need for child advocacy has become ever more evident during the last decade.

But child advocacy in the United States has had to confront a tradition of rugged individualism and the active opposition of powerful forces that see it as one more costly extension of the dreaded "welfare state." And its development has also been subjected to strains and stresses due to conflicts and contradictions among advocates of the new "child advocacy."

HISTORY OF NONINTERVENTION

Child advocacy from its renascence has been forced to confront the American philosophy translated into systems that assume each family is responsible for its children (barring some disaster) without the aid of public intervention. The rugged individualism of the American

---

Reprinted with permission from *Child Welfare*, Vol. 56, 497–508, 1977.

tradition, adherence to the concept of natural rights of parents, and minimal public action to protect children in their own homes dominated the child welfare scene all but completely until the Great Depression. Abbott wrote in 1938: "All children are dependent, but only a relatively small number are dependent on the state [1]." Almost 40 years later (1976) Steiner finds that "that description of governmental reticence remains valid [11]." There has been steady resistance to governmental aid to children beyond corporal or physical protection, and to any comprehensive planning to support the development of children within their own families.

It is only 8 years since the Joint Commission on Mental Health of Children proposed a national system of child advocacy. Unhappily, the early enthusiasm that met this proposal has been dissipated. Instead of moving forward, the Nixon and Ford administrations reduced federal responsibility for human welfare and sought to transfer responsibility to states and communities by various devices, including grants and undesignated revenue sharing, little of which went to benefit children, and by purchase of services for children from profit-making and nonprofit groups without supervision. The federal government moved toward abdicating responsibility for minimum standards and away from effective monitoring of existing standards.

As the economic recession deepened, chasms in the network of aid programs to families widened while unemployment struck 8 million men, women and youths. Half the states failed to include in their programs needy families with unemployed fathers. Only 24 states took advantage of the limited provisions for emergency assistance allowable through AFDC. Voluntary agencies found they could not meet even the dire necessities of poor families and their children, as levels of public assistance went down and eligibility requirements were tightened unmercifully [12].

> There are still . . . some 6 million Americans making less than $3000 a year who either do not know about or can't afford food stamps. There are more than 7 million needy children in family day care homes who could be receiving three federally supported nutritious meals a day and yet only some 15,000 do so. Fewer than 2 million out of a potential 12 million needy school children are receiving school breakfasts. The children of the working poor are almost entirely ignored.*

---

*Letter by Barbara Bode of the Children's Foundation to the Field Foundation, Jan. 14, 1977.

Traditional resistance to governmental planning for children and inbred opposition to governmental intervention thus constitute one major roadblock to child advocacy.

ORGANIZED ATTACKS ON CHILD ADVOCACY

In addition to traditional resistance to change, there is growing evidence of concerted attacks on child advocacy. Some of the important sources of such attacks are the easiest to identify, yet so powerful and widespread that they are the most difficult to counter. Growing determination and substantial financing on the part of business and industrial interests are now directed toward forcing government to cut funds for services to people at both federal and state levels. This is part of the planned opposition to what is loosely called a "welfare state." Inevitably, child advocacy has become a target for such attacks, since the consequences, when advocacy is effective, are more services to children and families. One also finds among these opponents anxiety, if not fear, that poor people are responding to government largesse as a matter of right, rather than with "gratitude."

Too many persons of good will, including some child advocates, have been overly impressed by slogans emanating from such groups. Warnings that to throw money at people does no good, that more dollars are no answer to social problems, that the poverty program of the Great Society failed, have been made believable by skillful repetition. It is only since the recent election that a study by the independent Congressional Budget Office reported findings that, contrary to the myth of failure, the Great Society programs had been effective in combating and reducing poverty. This study found that federal social welfare programs, *including* in-kind assistance, had reduced the rate of poverty by 60% in the last decade [9]. To what extent such findings cheer or depress right-wing opponents of child advocacy, I do not attempt to say. It is, however, significant that this study has already been harshly criticized by Harrington, an eminent advocate for the poor, as expressing false optimism [6]. He points to the omission of any mention of the undercounting of the poor by the census and to the inflation of in-kind benefits based on the federal dollar cost. He finds a failure to recognize the demoralization that welfare dependency brings to people. And he underscores that 25% of all families, now as in 1965, continue to live below the poverty level, if in-kind transfers are excluded.

To child advocates it is significant that both the Congressional study and Harrington's critique are in agreement that widespread poverty remains a core problem for both people and government.

Whether the dominant figures of previous federal administrations initiated the erosion of social welfare programs for children and families or acted in response to the demands of opponents of such programs is a critical issue for child advocates only as it reflects the strength of a determined opposition. The hard reality is that there has been an awesome and awful reduction in human services of all kinds that affect millions of children in programs for school lunches, for day care and for maternal health programs during the very period in which child advocacy is said to have been "born again." No matter how acceptable to the opponents of child advocacy, such widespread poverty among families presents a central challenge to child advocacy. Certainly, lasting benefits for children can be built only on programs that assure entitlements to basic necessities as a matter of right under law.

GAINS AND LOSSES IN CHILD ADVOCACY

Despite overwhelming obstructions, some important gains in child advocacy have been achieved. In a few states, official programs for child advocacy have taken hold, although in other states (such as New York) such programs have quickly disappeared. In smaller geographical areas citizen groups have become active in general advocacy programs or have focused on specific problems. The intellectual ferment stemming from child advocacy has also touched both professional and citizen groups. Unfortunately, in the absence of reliable data (in this as in all areas concerning the welfare of children), there is as yet no way to evaluate how successful the unofficial groups have been, but they may have outstripped official achievements. Important benefits have come from professional groups that ask whether traditional ways cf making decisions *for* rather than *with* those who need services are sound or right [10].

In significant ways, the rights of children subject to courts and administrative agencies have been recognized in the federal courts. Thanks to public law groups that have been advocates for children in class actions, the Bill of Rights is no longer regarded as applicable only to adults; children have been held to be entitled to its protections.

Unhappily, the present (Burger) Supreme Court has moved relentlessly to make the federal courts less and less responsive to the claims of children and adults when misconduct or mistreatment is charged against governmental or private agencies. This is in direct contrast to actions of the Warren court, which affirmed that federal courts are the protectors of rights guaranteed by the Constitution and U.S. laws. As a result of the Burger court decisions, public law groups are now far more hesitant to bring actions as advocates for children than they were a few years ago. The loss of this form of advocacy, both new and important, is indeed tragic, and only time and a change in the personnel of the Supreme Court can restore the promise for child advocacy advanced by the Warren court [2].

One other significant and positive byproduct of the child advocacy ferment stems from recent efforts to get facts, to learn where children are and what is happening to them. It is all but incredible that in this computer age so little is known about children whose lives are being molded by educational, health and welfare institutions, as well as by courts and administrative agencies. It has become clear that child advocacy, except as an abstraction, can become effective only as facts are learned on which to base judgments on what needs to be done. Even then there will be sharp differences in viewpoint, but only then will there be even a basis for honest, serious differences.

The absence of data has forced the Children's Defense Fund, for example, to undertake its own studies on education [4;5], juvenile justice [3] and children without homes. In each of these areas— education, juvenile justice and social welfare—where the facts showed conditions injurious to large groups of children, the realities for children required that child advocates take legal action to end abuses; to halt suspensions and expulsions; to enjoin the placement of children in jails and obtain damages for injuries to jailed children; and to end the irresponsible out-of-state banishment of handicapped children by state agencies without regard to how children were treated.

Without the discovery of what is actually happening to children, child advocacy has a hollow ring. The reasons are twofold: first, advocacy in any field requires in-depth knowledge of a subject if it is to be sound and command respectful consideration; second, in each area where serious fact finding has been done on the conditions of children, communities and even child experts were found to be unaware of what was happening to children in their own communities. When facts are presented, individuals, community groups, professionals and, in some instances, political figures become sufficiently concerned to join together to meet problems they had not previously faced.

But facts and figures will never be sufficient by themselves. They must be interpreted by people who have gained understanding from day-to-day work with children of what children need and where they are hurting as individuals. Otherwise, theories gained from figures are likely to remain abstract, not relevant to the realities for children. Professional workers have a unique opportunity to construct what their special knowledge and experience show to be needed in the wider areas of programming and funding.

LIMITATION AND INNER CONTRADICTIONS WITHIN CHILD ADVOCACY

That child advocacy has always been confronted by external opposition was to be expected. But it has also faced increasing differences among child advocates. These conflicts, like those within a family, are often bitter. There is a personal accent, at times a sense of betrayal, and uncertainty of purpose between colleagues. This is understandable, since it is always far easier to take on "the enemy" than those one regards as allies.

Like a general affirmation of "the true and the beautiful," child advocacy was initially hailed as a splendid concept. The going began to get rough when it moved into the field of action. Contradictions and conflicts inevitably arose from differences as to sound ideological goals for children and families in American society, varying approaches to cultural and religious problems, different perceptions about what is in the best interest of children, and even struggles for power and resources. Attempts to hammer out single or certain answers accentuated differences. Thus, insistence that general principles can guide decisions on whether or when the rights of individual children take priority over the rights of biological parents created dissension. Part of the dissension caused by some advocates' insistence on general principles arose from the failure to take cognizance of the uniqueness of each child, the family context of which the child is a part, or of how any generalization, when applied, may help or injure individual children and their families.

In daily problems that arise for advocates as for children and families, there is great need of sensitivity and humility in searching for the strengths, the special frailties, the needs of all parties. No matter how good the intentions, there can be no justification for using children to support an advocacy theory, rather than building an advocacy case that is focused on the needs of children. Biological parents have been declared eager to maintain rights to their children, although many would, in fact, be relieved if the children were placed in permanent homes through adoption, if this did not require their being labeled as bad parents. Repeatedly, young women who are unable to sign surrenders of their children show relief when a court terminates their rights and obligations.

Perhaps most difficult are the underlying differences between child advocates committed to reducing intervention by the state in the lives of citizens and those who support far greater acceptance of governmental responsibility for the well-being of all individuals. And, even among those who support far wider social programs for education, health and welfare, there are those who would minimize government intervention as threatening when it seeks to control the conduct of parents or children through institutions such as the juvenile court. Unfortunately, other forms of coercion, as through denial of assistance or appropriate care by administrative agencies, have thus far received less attention of advocates, though such controls may affect even more children.

Difficult, concrete problems also arise from conflicts as to what is right for individual children and families in our changing society, especially when decisions involve plans for the well-being of a child. These differences illustrate how illusory theoretical principles are when invoked to solve the complex and ever-varying problems that confront child advocates.

Custody Issues. For years in this country in custody controversies, the natural rights of parents (first the father, then the mother, now both) were given priority in any decision on custody, excluding consideration of the best interest of the child. When the formula of "the best interest of the child" was applied, it remained a vessel whose content was determined by the attitudes of social workers, probation officers, judges and community mores.

However, as between parents and nonparents, the doctrine of natural rights was construed so that courts in fact considered the interests of the child only when the evidence first established unfitness of parents.

More recently, new understanding of the importance of permanence and a sense of family for a child once removed from home has shaken earlier doctrines. The psychological family has become more important, and foster parents who have been the only family a child has known are receiving more recognition. However, a seesaw continues to operate even among child advocates as to whether to press for the rights of parents or for the importance to a child of belonging within a psychological family.

At any one time or place, child advocates may focus on the right of a child to be freed permanently so that adoption may become possible, despite objections by a parent who has been a parent in name only. At another time or place it has been urged that where parents are poor, uneducated or members of a minority group, they should not be expected to visit or keep appointments with a child in foster

care, and that such conduct should not deprive parents of legal custody of a child.

Such differences have been further compounded by the recent position that biological fathers, even though absent and nonsupporting (in
many cases not acknowledging paternity), are entitled to receive notice
and be heard before a child can be freed for adoption. It is contended
that knowledge of the biological father is important to the child's
sense of identity. In contrast, other child advocates for children of
single mothers on welfare have taken strong exception to new federal
and state requirements that mothers who receive public assistance
identify and prosecute absent fathers, with little regard to what this
will mean to the mothers or their children.

Neglected Children. Among child advocates there is a strong drive to
reduce intervention, or at least removal of children, by juvenile courts,
to those cases in which serious physical injury has been perpetrated
against a child or there is imminent danger of serious physical injury.
The argument grows as evidence mounts that removal of a child leads
all too often to an endless limbo in foster care, with separations that
deny continuity in the life of a child and impair a child's sense of belonging. It is also contended that evaluation of emotional neglect is
beyond the competence of courts and should be eliminated from their
jurisdiction, except in extreme cases. This position is buttressed by the
recent concentration on physical abuse, which is more universally recognized as unacceptable.

These ideas are challenged by other child advocates on two scores.
First, those working with children have found that emotional neglect,
the continuing absence of nurturing by parents, is frequently far more
devastating to a child than occasional physical abuse. Second, there is
concern that the narrowing of jurisdiction for intervention on behalf
of neglected children leads to one more area in which there will be a
growing avoidance of the pains and hurts suffered by children that
impair their growth. And there is little reason to believe that voluntary alternative services will be made available to or used by emotionally neglecting parents.

Status Offenders. The central concern of many reformers in the
juvenile justice field has been to remove from the jurisdiction of
courts children who are charged with offenses that would not constitute crimes if committed by adults. They point to the inadequacy of
juvenile courts rendering appropriate services, and raise questions as

to when children should be subjected to intervention not invoked against adults who engage in similar conduct.

Other advocates regard the underlying problems as more complex. Proposals to remove jurisdiction from the juvenile courts fail to recognize that those working in the courts have found a higher proportion of deeply disturbed children among incorrigible (or PINS) youngsters than among the children charged with what would be criminal acts if committed by adults. In some cases, conflicts between parents and children have often become so severe and persistent that the children are no longer part of the family in any true sense. There is also reason for concern that proposals for diversion on a voluntary basis become meaningless, both by reason of the unavailability of alternatives and by the inability of many parents or children to use alternatives.

Also forgotten is the historical fact that the juvenile court was initially intended to treat all children before it as status offenders, and that the concept of focusing on the whole child and his needs is one that should not be lightly discarded.

Delinquent Children. Child advocates have justifiably become frustrated by the limitations of the juvenile courts and the abuse of discretionary sentencing. Beginning with Gault, concentration on the introduction of due process into the juvenile courts brought significant gains (at least on the books) in assuring fair fact-finding hearings for children charged with delinquent acts. Dissatisfied with the continuing dispositional procedures and unequal punishments, many child advocates now propose that the court be limited to dispositional orders within fixed schedules of punishment for specific violations set by state legislatures. Having lost confidence in the ability to assure appropriate rehabilitative services, they have concluded that the concept of treatment is little more than a cover for punishment.

Other advocates see little reason to expect legislative bodies to be less subject to political pressures and community anger than the courts.* They fear legislators will yield to demands for protection to the community, for more secure facilities and longer incarceration. They note the rising hostility to the violent delinquent and see his rights and welfare being traded off in bargaining for the removal of

---

*Recent legislative action in many states to waive younger delinquents to the criminal courts, to require longer sentences for children, to lower juvenile court age jurisdiction, provide examples of causes for such concern.

status offenders and limitations on court jurisdiction. They also see the growing use of waivers of juveniles to the criminal justice system for children charged with violent offenses. Some advocates continue to believe that children and adolescents should receive different as well as separate treatment from adults in view of their capacity for growth and change.

The Medical Model. Many child advocates have increasingly questioned the use of psychiatric help for the rehabilitation of juvenile delinquents. They cite correctly the pretension of mental health diagnostic and treatment services both in courts and in institutions to which children have been committed for treatment. They argue that there is no evidence of effectiveness and that the promise of treatment has been used to justify incarceration in custodial institutions. They hold that less damage will be done to children if dispositions are based on the offense only, and not on the evaluation of the offender.

Other child advocates have pointed to the widespread physical, emotional and mental disabilities that burden many delinquent children. The all-too-few physicians who have examined delinquent children carefully have shown that the failure to identify medical problems, regardless of whether a child is a first offender or recidivist, has committed a minor offense or a violent offense, deprives children of diagnostic and treatment services for underlying problems [8]. There is concern that rejection of the medical model will weaken the search for better methods of treatment.

Even within the opposition to using treatment modalities, one finds a contradiction among child advocates that is far from resolution. While the medical model is denigrated to reduce its role at the level of court diagnostic and dispositional decisions, it is at the same time contended that where a child is deprived of freedom in the name of treatment, the child is entitled to treatment in accordance with the best knowledge and skills available.

CONCLUSION

Despite the problems cited, great hope for the potential of the child advocacy movement remains, although it is challenged by counterforces that seek to reduce its role, and by serious conflicts within the world of child advocacy.

What of the future? The question is not whether advocates for children are needed. The answer to that is an unqualified "yes." There is, however, a second, more difficult, question concerning how far child advocacy should rely on legislatures or administrative agencies to effect significant improvements in laws, organizational structures, procedures, and in the delivery of better services to children both within and outside their homes. Here, the answer is less certain, since economic and political factors affect what resources and personnel will be provided to make new structures and services more responsive to the needs of children than the old structures.

The third, and possibly most pertinent question is how advocacy can be developed into an ongoing process, informed by growing knowledge and a constant search for better ways to meet the needs of children. The answer will depend not on generalities that assume wisdom on all questions affecting children, but on rare combinations or hard day-to-day efforts and humility in regard to the complex and special needs of children.

Child advocates, then, must be ready to put their fingers in the dike when they discover wrongs perpetrated against children. They must also develop a broader perspective built on their knowledge of holes in the dike and the consequences of limiting choices to one kind of response as against others. This means the development of new kinds of engineering in human affairs at an ever more informed level, so that child advocates will be willing and able to reexamine theories, practices and even achievements in specific areas in terms of the consequences to children.

REFERENCES

1. Abbott, Grace. "The Child and the State," introduction to Organizing for Administration of Child Welfare Services, Vol. 2. Chicago: University of Chicago Press, 1938.
2. Board of Governors, Society of American Law Teachers. "The Burger Court's Efforts to Close the Federal Courthouse to Public Interest Litigation." Oct. 10, 1976.
3. Children's Defense Fund of the Washington Research Project. Children in Adult Jails. December 1976. (States visited: Florida, Georgia, Indiana, Maryland, New Jersey, Ohio, South Carolina, Texas, Virginia.)
4. ———. Children Out of School in America. October 1974.
5. ———. School Suspensions: Are They Helping Children? September 1975.
6. Harrington, Michael. "Hiding the Other America," New Republic, Feb. 25, 1977.
7. Knitzer, Jane. "Child Advocacy: A Perspective," American Journal of Orthopsychiatry (April 1976).
8. Lewis, Dorothy Otnow, and Balla, David. Delinquency and Psychopathology. New York: Grune and Stratton, 1976.
9. New York Times. Jan. 18, 1977.
10. Polier, Justine Wise. "Professional Abuse of Children," American Journal of Orthopsychiatry (April 1975).
11. Steiner, Gilbert Y. The Children's Cause. Washington, D.C.: Brookings Institute, 1976.
12. Wickenden, Elizabeth. Introduction to "People in Trouble," National Voluntary Health and Social Welfare Organizations, December 1976.

31

HUMAN DIVERSITY, PROGRAM EVALUATION AND PUPIL ASSESSMENT

Edmund W. Gordon

Columbia University

Considerable static has been raised over the past several years about two related but distinct problems. I say static because the disturbance signals have been fairly constant and loud, but not very clear. We know some things are not right, but we are not quite sure what they are and are even less certain about what ought to be done. The two related problems have to do with the following:

1. the appropriateness of existing standardized tests of achievement for the assessment of academic function in minority and disadvantaged group member students; and
2. the appropriateness of such instruments for the assessment of the impact of large-scale educational programs.

Let us turn our attention first to the problems that arise when we try to apply normative approaches to assessment to the appraisal of

Reprinted with permission from *IRCD Bulletin*, Vol. XII, No. 1, Winter, 1977, 1–7.

This paper was originally presented at the Office of Education Invitational Conference on Achievement Testing of Disadvantaged and Minority Students, Reston, Va., in May 1976. It will be published with the other conference papers in Wargo, M. J. and Green, D. R. eds., *Achievement Testing of the Disadvantaged and Minority Students for Educational Program Evaluation*. Monterey, Cal.: CTB/McGraw-Hill, in press.

educational achievement in disadvantaged and low-status minority populations. Concern with this problem dates back at least to the forties when Davis and Eells sought approaches to assessment that were free of cultural loadings. As they discovered the futility of their efforts at developing tests that were culture free, they directed their search at the development of tests that were culture fair. These efforts, as you may recall, were more successful, but the instruments resulting from their work had low predictive value when subsequent achievement in academic settings was the referent.

As the civil and human rights movements of the fifties and sixties advanced, additional attention was focused on the inappropriateness of standardized tests for the assessment of minority group members. In this period, it was not unusual for psychometricians to add five to fifteen points to the scores of minority subjects to compensate for the assumed artificial depression in test scores resulting from the inappropriateness of the test. However, these added points were arrived at arbitrarily and reflected an assumed common and uniform depression in scores despite known differentials in the minority subjects' exposure to and involvement in the majority culture. The practice subsided as its illogic and its patronizing character became better recognized.

Other efforts have been directed at insuring the inclusion of minority group members in the populations on which the instruments are normed. This procedure, however, only slightly reduces the impact of the majority group's dominance in the norming procedure. A more sensitive accommodation, of course, is the development of population-specific norms and the use of such norms in the interpretation of the data. However, this practice has been questioned since the reality standard is performance in competitive academic and work situations with majority group members. This is also the criticism raised against population-specific instrumentation. The speaker who follows me, Brother Bob Williams, has done pioneering work in the development of a test of "black intelligence," or rather an achievement test, with black culture as the referent. I think Bob's data lead in to the same problem we have with population-specific norms. Unless and until the curricula and the criteria for mastery are made more congruent with the purposes and values of the target populations, the changed foci of assessment will continue to have low predictive value. Or, to be more accurate, the traditional curricula will continue to be inappropriate to the assessed behavior and potentials of the target groups. With all of these efforts proving to be somewhat unsuccessful, it is not surprising that by the early 1970's some of us are calling for a moratorium on the use of standardized tests with minority group members.

One could argue that what we have here is a political rather than a psychometric problem. This is especially likely to be the case so long as it appears that the objection to the standardized tests is based on the fact that minority group members tend to score less well than do majority group members. It is not so much the differential in minority group-majority group scores that leads me to question the appropriateness of standardized achievement tests and the normative approach to their interpretation. Increasingly, I am persuaded not only that such instruments and procedures are inappropriate for the assessment of achievement in minority and disadvantaged populations, but also that traditional standardized tests and normative approaches to assessment are dysfunctional and counterproductive to the purposes of pedagogy whenever we are confronted with the problems of educating populations with diverse characteristics.

When we first turned to the problems of educating educationally and socially disadvantaged children, a great deal of attention was given to the special characteristics of this population. The notions that dominated this new field were largely determined by conceptions of this population as homogeneous with respect to conditions of life and behavioral characteristics. We assumed a pervasive "culture of poverty." The population was largely identified by its deficits in comparison with characteristics assumed to be typical of the white middle class. Subsequent work and more careful study reveal that minority and disadvantaged children are not a homogeneous mass. In fact, there appears to be as much variation within populations so designated as there is between disadvantaged and more privileged groups. Diversity and heterogeneity, rather than deficiency and homogeneity, are now recognized as presenting the challenge. And, it is not only a challenge presented by children of low-status peoples; diversity in human characteristics increasingly is recognized as the central problem in pedagogical design for all peoples.

Learners differ in interests, in cognitive style, in rate of learning, in patterns of developed abilities, in motivation, in work habits, and in temperament, as well as in ethnicity, sex, and social class. In fact, it may well be that our preoccupation with such status and indicator variables as SES, sex, and ethnicity have retarded the scientific development of pedagogy. The differences associated with these status groups may have much less relevance for the design of educational treatments than do differences in behavioral function. When we refer to SES, we are using an indicator variable to imply the presence or absence of certain functional characteristics or circumstances that are presumed to influence learning and development. But the exchange of socialization strategies across SES designations makes social class a much less reliable indicator than we used to think. As sex roles change and are interchanged, and as ethnicity is confounded by social class, the specific characteristics of conditional and behavioral individuality provide better levers for, or guides to, educational planning. It is these characteristics of conditional and behavioral individuality that make for the pedagogically relevant dimensions of human diversity. It is these educationally relevant dimensions of diversity to which education must be responsive. Yet, it is conditional and behavioral individuality and diversity that normative and standardized approaches to assessment ignore and, in large measure, are designed to avoid. For example, test items are selected with a view toward their capacity to tap stable functions, and by stable we usually mean those functions less likely to be influenced by situational or personalistic variability. We demand that the items be presented in standardized and uniform conditions that are insensitive to differential response tendencies. The data of these tests are analyzed to reflect one's position in relation to a group norm rather than to reflect one's mastery of the task or the process by which one engages the task. It almost looks as if our tests were designed to be of no use to teachers since it is these processes of engagement, these differential response tendencies, these situational and personalistic variables that are of crucial importance in the design and management of teaching and learning transactions. I, therefore, assert that normative and standardized approaches to assessment are not only inappropriate for the assessment of achievement in minority and disadvantaged populations, but are also dysfunctional and counterproductive to pedagogy.

Glaser (1976) identified several reasons for the current dissatisfaction with standardized testing. He referred more specifically to tests of intelligence, but his argument is relevant here, particularly since I view intelligence tests as slightly more refined tests of achievement. Glaser wrote:

1. The present operational definition of intelligence (achievement) measures seems to have reached a plateau or asymptote of efficiency with our present technology. The predictive validity of tests has not increased for some time.

2. Since tests essentially measure general scholastic aptitude, they have not adequately recognized the discontinuity between the backgrounds and cultures of certain groups in our society and the requirements for succeeding in the conventional education system.

3. Tests reflect a restrictive overselective view of intelligence

(achievement) that limits the educational system in adapting to students in order to maximize their achievement. In essence, the tests give go/no-go selective decisions but do not provide much deeper diagnosis for the conduct of education.

4. There is recognition that test theory and technique have not made contact with modern psychological theories of learning and cognition, and that test development should be influenced by new developments in these areas. Modern theory brings us close to understanding the components of cognitive functioning and can help us succeed in analyzing and understanding the detailed processes underlying intellectual abilities—the initial task that Binet set for himself, but had to abandon.

Why has the circumstance come about and why does it persist? Much of the impetus for the development of a technology of assessment related to intellective function and achievement resulted from, and has been maintained by, a supply-and-demand approach to access to education and the distribution of educational opportunities. Prior to the twentieth century, access to a limited supply of educational opportunities was guarded by selection procedures based upon the prospective student's social status—in the pre-Reformation period, access was limited to the political and religious nobility, later it was limited to other privileged classes. Twentieth-century selection procedures have come to be dominated by the student's demonstrated or predicted intellectual status. Where the supply of opportunities has been limited, great emphasis has been placed on the selection of students and the prediction of their performance when exposed to those opportunities. Binet's work in intelligence test development was directed toward the creation of an instrument that could be used to identify those pupils who were likely to benefit from schooling. His admonitions that we also turn to treatment of those expected not to succeed were generally ignored. In a period of scarce educational opportunities, Binet's concern for the educability of intelligence did not gain favor. Society found greater utility in the promise of the predictive and selective validity of his new test.

This emphasis on selection and prediction has continued even though the social conditions that gave rise to it have changed. In recent years, we have seen in the U.S.A. a growing concern with universal access to education. The educational product requirements of the nation are more frequently coming to be defined in terms of our capability to provide postsecondary educational opportunities for the majority of our youth and a continued program of learning for most of our citizens. If this trend continues, selection and prediction can no longer be allowed to dominate the technology of psycho-educational appraisal; rather, the stage must be shared with an emphasis on *description* and *prescription* (i.e., the qualitative description of intellective function, leading *not* to the selection of those most likely to succeed but to the prescription of the learning experiences required to insure more adequately that academic success is possible).

The position being advanced here is that psychological testing obviously can be used to measure achieved development. Using those measurements, we can predict, with reasonable validity, subsequent achievement in the same dimensions of behavior under similar learning experience conditions. Thus, persons who have learned an average amount during one learning period (high school) may be expected to learn an average amount in the next learning period (college). However, we have not given adequate attention to the fact that psychological testing can be used for the following purposes: (a) to describe and qualitatively analyze behavior function in order to gain a better understanding of the processes by which achievement is developed, (b) to describe nonstandard achievements that may be equally as functional in subsequent situations requiring adaptation, or (c) to specify the conditions in the interaction between learner and learning experience that may be necessary to change the quality of future achievements.

If we are to approach such goals in achievement testing, we will need to redress the imbalance made more obvious by the growing recognition of individual and group differences in function, on the one hand, contrasted with a fairly undifferentiated measurement technology on the other. Until such progress is made, the logic of my position forces me to endorse the call for a moratorium on the traditional usages of standardized achievement testing and its normative interpretation as not in the best educational interests of minority and disadvantaged populations.

Let me turn quickly to the second issue, that is, the appropriateness of the use of standardized and normative approaches to testing in the assessment of the impact of large-scale educational programs. There are several interrelated problems here. Before discussing them, I need to make certain that the record shows that I am consistent. Since I have argued that these tests should not be used in traditional ways with minority and disadvantaged populations, I must also argue that they not be used to assess large-scale educational programs directed at these populations. In his academic lecture at the 1973 American Psychological Association annual meeting, Donald Hebb quoted one of his favorite admonitions. "If something is not worth doing, it is also not worth doing *well!*" To paraphrase, if these tests are not worth using, they are also not worth using on a large scale to make decisions about children's lives and to inform public policy. But the problems of the evaluation of these programs are much bigger than the question of whether to test or not to test, or what tests to use.

I estimate that we have invested since 1965 between one-half and three-fourths of a billion dollars in evaluations of educational programs for the disadvantaged. There are currently two major studies underway—a five-million-dollar NIE study and an Office of Education study that I once heard estimated as possibly costing twenty-one million dollars over a seven-year period. Those are big sums of money even in periods of inflation. Yet, having examined the RFP for the OE study and having been rather close to the NIE study, I am not at all confident that either will provide the kind of guidance for the relevant policy decisions that is needed or expected. Like their predecessor studies, they are likely to produce equivocal findings. It is not because we don't have good and intelligent people designing and conducting these studies. When I went to Washington in 1965 to provide leadership in the development of the research and evaluation program for Project Head Start, a friend who is one of our most distinguished authorities in educational measurement and research declined to assist me. He indicated that he would not touch such an evaluation as Head Start or Title I with a fifty-foot pole because it was an impossible task in view of the absence of better agreement on what the treatment is, the conditions under which it is delivered, and the absence of assessment instruments appropriate to the treatment, the conditions, and the populations served. Nonetheless, I went ahead and found good people to advise and to help, but no single one of us was, nor together were, good enough to overcome the constraining problems to which my friend called my attention as he sympathetically refused to join me in my folly. You know, it is my belief that if I were to ask him again today, he would still refuse because we have not adequately addressed the problems he raised. Yet, we continue large-scale evaluations and continue to make the same errors and continue to produce negative or confusing results. One wonders if there is a conspiracy to prove that such programs cannot succeed, that minority and disadvantaged people cannot be educated, that it is poor policy to continue heavy investments of public funds in efforts at equalizing educational opportunity. When one puts these evaluations together with the race and genetics debate and with the "schooling doesn't make a difference" pronouncements, it is exceedingly difficult to keep the faith.

I know that this meeting was not called to discuss the problem of large-scale evaluation, but it is important for us to understand that the problem is larger than one of what kind of achievement tests to use. It may be that we could endure the problems related to the tests if we were better able to deal with such problems as the following:

1. the nebulousness and variability of treatments
2. the complex economic, political, and social context in which the treatments are set
3. the diversity of populations served and goals sought
4. the reconciliation of necessary and sufficient conditions for change and growth
5. such limitations of evaluative research technology as:
    a. program and population specification
    b. program and population sampling
    c. interchangeable and dialectical nature of the dependent and independent variables
    d. inappropriateness of extant statistical analyses for the study of the dynamic blending of variables by which effects may be explained
    e. the policy of the best generic treatment
    f. normative approaches to aggregate data in search of relationships that may be idiosyncratically expressed.

It may be that some of these problems will be the focus of our next conference. For the present, let us return to achievement testing. What are the limitations of these tests for educational program evaluation? Suchman described five levels of evaluation research (Suchman, 1967).

1. Evaluation should answer questions as to quantity and quality of treatment. Was treatment delivered, how much, and how good?
2. Evaluation should answer questions relative to performance or impact. Did any change occur that can be inferred to have resulted from the treatment? What are the intended as well as unintended consequences?
3. Evaluation should address the question of adequacy. To what degree are the results adequate to relieve the problem to which the treatment was applied?
4. Evaluation should address questions of efficiency. Is there a better way to achieve equivalent results?
5. Evaluation should address questions of process and explanation. How and why did the treatment work or fail?

Obviously, questions as to the nature and quantity of treatment or its efficiency cannot be addressed directly by achievement test data. However, questions of performance/impact, of adequacy, and of process/explanation could and should be addressed by achievement data. The problem is that standardized norm-based tests contribute very little to these questions. In their present state, these tests tell us something about performance in relation to some reference group. They enable us to make crude go/no-go decisions. They provide data that in the aggregate inform us with respect to positive, zero, or negative impact. We may infer adequacy of treatment from the relative position of the respondents, but since the tests tend not to be specifically related to the criteria of competence, they tell us little about the adequacy of the performance or treatment in relation to need. Similarly, these tests are not directed at illuminating aspects of process. Although underlying processes can be inferred from the analysis of some of the items, assessment of the process variables by which performance-treatment interactions can be judged is not the current purpose of capability of these tests. In fact, the very processes by which we develop them are counterproductive as far as data that speak to questions of adequacy, process, and explanation are concerned. As we strive to achieve reliability and validity, we are forced to eliminate items sensitive to situational and personalistic variance, or otherwise unstable. What we look for are items that are least influenced by variations in instruction or in pupils. In sum, I am asserting that if good evaluation data are needed to inform policy decision-making, then good evaluation procedures and instrumentation must be applied. Since the achievement tests available to us fail to address crucial evaluation questions, they are inadequate to the task at hand. In commenting on a related point, Calfee (1976) wrote: "If a principal, superintendent or program director (or legislator) is to make informed, rational decisions about the strengths and weaknesses of the teaching and learning that take place under his supervision, something more than a gross characterization of success or failure is necessary." I think I cannot be accused of overstating the case when I claim that traditional approaches to norm-based standardized testing fail to provide more than gross characterizations of success and failure. This is true of their use with all children. When we use them to assess achievement in the programs for the poor, the disadvantaged, and the discriminated against, the problem is compounded.

Given this low estimate of the utility of normative and standardized approaches to achievement testing and the equally low likelihood that the call for a moratorium will be heeded, what can be done to improve upon the current state of the arts?

Despite my criticisms of the extant standardized instruments, they need not be immediately discarded. A great deal of work has gone into the development of item pools that tap a variety of intellective functions. The problem is that these items have been grouped, presented, scored, and analyzed with a view toward gross classification with respect to success or failure, with a view toward distributing the examinee population over the bell-shaped curve, and with a view toward predicting who will succeed. These same instruments can, however, be analyzed for the following purposes:

1. To identify the dimensional or categorical functional demands of selected standardized tests. What dimensions of function appear to be tapped by the instrument as these can be conceptualized from a surface examination of item content?

2. To determine the rationale utilized in the development of each of several tests in order to identify the conceptual categories for which items were written and into which item-response consistencies might cluster empirically.

3. To determine the learning-task demands represented by the items of selected tests and the classification of those demands into functional categories. The extent to which selected tests provide adequate coverage of the typical learning-task demands found in educational settings might also be appraised. Are the tests measuring the processes required by important learning tasks? What types of learning-task demands correspond to the processes ostensibly measured by the test?

4. To utilize the categories produced by any or all of the above strategies in the metric and nonmetric factorial analysis of test data in order to uncover empirical dimensions of test responses. These dimensions could be interpreted in the context of item clusters derived from the conceptual and task analytic strategies described above to ascertain the context to which they provide an empirical foundation for those clusters or require a reconceptualization of response processes. The empirical dimensions could then be used to produce individual and group profiles reflecting across the several categories or factors.

Numbers 1, 2, and 3 above are intended to unbundle existing standardized tests and to reveal their factorial demand structure. They are basic to number 4, which involves the analysis of performance data to reveal diagnostic patterns that become the basis for the profiles suggested in number four.

In addition, with these same instruments we could do the following:

1. Explore possibilities for adding to their quantitative reports on the performance of students, reports descriptive of the patterns of achievement and function derived from the qualitative analysis of existing tests. Existing instruments should be examined with a view to categorization, factorial analysis, and interpretation to determine whether the data of these instruments can be reported in descriptive and qualitative ways, in addition to the traditional quantitative report. For example, reresponse patterns might be prepared differentially for:

    a. Information recall
      (1) Rote recall
      (2) Associative recall
      (3) Derivative recall
    b. Vocabulary
      (1) Absolute
      (2) Contextual

2. Move away from existing instruments and explore the development of test items and procedures that lend themselves to descriptive and qualitative analyses of cognitive and affective adaptive functions, in addition to wider specific achievements.

    a. In the development of new tests, attention should be given to the appraisal of
      (1) Adaptation in new learning situations
      (2) Problem solving in situations that require varied cognitive skills and styles
      (3) Analysis, search, and synthesis behaviors
      (4) Information management, processing, and utilization skills
      (5) Nonstandard information pools
    b. In the development of new procedures, attention should be given to the appraisal of
      (1) Comprehension through experiences, listening, and looking, as well as reading
      (2) Expression through artistic, oral, nonverbal, and graphic, as well as written symbolization

      (3) Characteristics of temperament

      (4) Sources and status of motivation

      (5) Habits of work and task involvement under varying conditions of demand

  c. In the development of tests and procedures designed to get at specific achievements, attention should be given to

      (1) Broadening the varieties of subject matter, competencies, and the skills assessed

      (2) Examining the achievements in a variety of contexts

      (3) Open-ended and unstructured probes of achievement to allow for atypical patterns and varieties of achievement

      (4) Assessing nonacademic achievements such as social competence, coping skills, avocational skills, and artistic, athletic, political, or mechanical skills

Calfee and others have been experimenting with some alternative approaches to prediction based on "all-or-none tests." They assert that there are some indicator skills the mastery of which is essential to next steps in learning. Knowledge of the alphabet is an example of such a skill. It is known to be predictive of subsequent performance on reading achievement tests. Calfee asserts that "alphabet knowledge is an indicator, not a cause, or reading success and failure." On the basis of empirical data, one can determine "cut-off points" by which we can predict success or failure in reading mastery. It is basically a criterion-referenced test procedure in which the criterion is based upon specific skills or competencies known to be indicative of readiness for the next level of work. The procedure can be used as a diagnostic screening device, as a tool of pupil evaluation, as an instrument of program evaluation, or in needs assessment. It does not identify process, but is an indicator of success or failure in a crucial element in process.

Another alternative is represented by Project TORQUE, which claims to develop tests that help teachers help students. TORQUE can also be used to evaluate large groups of students or to assess the impact of particular curriculum materials. The developers of the test claim that their instrument is diagnostic, that it identifies what children know and do well, as well as pinpointing children's problems closely enough to help guide further instruction. The claim sensitivity to children's varied characteristics. All of this is made available through a criterion-referenced model easily administered by teachers.

Obviously, criterion-referenced testing is one of the alternatives available to us. Since there is a session scheduled on this subject, I will not discuss the approach further except for a cautionary note.

Tradition weighs heavily on all of us. We tend to try to legitimatize the new by reference to the old. In a number of instances, we try to demonstrate the goodness or validity of a criterion-referenced test by showing that it correlates well with an achievement or intelligence test. That may be necessary to gain respectability or acceptance, but it can defeat the purpose behind our movement away from norm-based standardized testing. For example, when we were selecting instruments with which to assess the impact of the early Head Start efforts, we asked Bettye Caldwell to develop an idea she had for a criterion-referenced test of mastery of those developmental and preliteracy skills judged to be associated with successful school entry. The Caldwell Preschool Inventory was the result. However, in an effort to gain credibility for the Inventory and later for the impact data generated therefrom, we added standardized tests of intelligence and achievement to the battery. As the pressure to demonstrate Head Start's effectiveness mounted, the criterion-referenced test was dropped and the standardized test remained, even though it was the Caldwell Inventory that best addressed the growth in skills that was the goal of the special program. Else Haeussermann went into retirement regretting that her excellent procedures for assessing learning processes in children with cerebral damage had not been standardized and age-group norms established. So heavily did tradition weigh on her conception of what she was doing that she never was convinced that her criterion-referenced techniques derived a great part of their value from the fact that they were not constrained by standardization and the interpretation of the data was not limited by norm-based scoring.

One final example. In a highly diagnostic mode, Glaser described a performance analytic approach to the assessment of memory function. Drawing upon a conceptualization of the processes involved in short-term memory for sequences of items, he suggested that analyses of performance based upon such conceptualizations may have implications for assessing individual differences as well as for improving performance. Glaser wrote:

> A young or mentally retarded child might fail the test because of insufficient familiarity with the sequence or ordinal numbers, or because of inexperience in using the number sequence to order other materials. An individual may not perform well because he has not developed the grouping

and chunking strategy characteristic of his age level, although he might utilize grouping when prompted by the examiner. Another individual may not be able to accomplish the coding process necessary to take advantage of chunking. Others might lack the capacity for holding back their working memory storage long enough to order their output properly. With the advantage of this kind of added theoretical insight to augment the conventional intelligence test digit span sub-test, it might be possible to localize the source of difficulty for an individual who fails under the standard procedure. This could be of considerable help in indicating how deficient performance in this and related tasks might be remedied.

Studies like those just described raise the possibility that measures of intelligence and aptitude, analyzed in terms of cognitive processes, will move intelligence and aptitude test predictions from static statements about the probability of success to dynamic statements about what can be done to increase the likelihood of school success. Hopefully, this viewpoint will lead to measuring instruments which are diagnostic, in the sense that they tell us how educational institutions should adjust to the person, instead of simply telling us, as most intelligence tests do, which people already are adjusted to the institution.

Educational assessment of individuals and programs greatly influences what happens in the delivery of educational services. Whether we like it or not, whether we intend it or not, what teachers teach and the way they teach are in large measure determined by the characteristics of the assessment instruments and programs. In addition, the results of what we do in evaluation no longer remain hidden away in dusty files. Our findings are more and more frequently used to support the biases and purposes of public policy makers. Thus, what we measure and the way we measure it impinge heavily on the lives of individuals and on the society in general. These observations seem to suggest that the problems we face are not only technical, but also involve philosophical and moral issues:

What is it that we want education to be?
What are the behaviors and goals of educators and learners that we are willing to encourage?

What priorities in public policy are we willing to support?
What is the contribution of our work to the achievement of
social justice?

REFERENCES

Calfee, Robert. "Practical Uses of Assessment for Individualized Reading Instruction." Unpublished proceedings of the Conference on Beginning Reading Instruction. University of Pittsburgh, LRDC, May, 1976.

Glaser, Robert. "On Intelligence and Aptitudes." Unpublished paper read at the Work Conference on Exploring Alternatives to Current Standardized Tests. University of Pittsburgh, May, 1976.

Haeussermann, Else. *Developmental potential of preschool children*. New York: Grune and Stratton, 1958.

Hayden, Robert C. *Project Torque: a new approach to the assessment of children's mathematical competence*. Newton, Mass: Educational Development Center, 1976.

Hebb, Donald. "What Psychology is About." *American Psychologist*, February, 1974, 71.

Suchman, Edward A. *Evaluative research: principles and practice in public service and social action programs*. New York: Russell Sage, 1967.

Williams, Robert L. "The BITCH-100: A Culture Specific Test." *The Journal of Afro American Issues* 3, No. 1 (Winter 1975): 103.

32

FEDERAL DAY CARE STANDARDS: RATIONALE AND RECOMMENDATIONS

Donald J. Cohen and Edward Zigler

Yale Child Study Center, New Haven

Day care for young children is an increasingly popular and needed resource. However, there is no consistent federal policy for assuring quality. This paper argues that fiscal and monitoring responsibilities should be based in a federal agency committed to children and families, and standards should be explicit, enforceable, and economically realistic.

What quality day care is the federal government buying? Over one million preschool children are in day care, and hundreds of thousands of children spend their most active hours, week in and week out, in federally subsidized day care settings. The annual federal bill for day care approaches $2 billion. Yet, despite its increasing involvement in funding day care, the federal government has been reluctant to enforce standards for day care quality. This essay reviews the history and the reasons for that reluctance. We argue that, at the least, the federal government must assure that the day care it subsidizes is not detrimental to children. And we suggest revisions in the existing Fed-

Reprinted with permission from *American Journal of Orthopsychiatry*, Vol. 47, 456–465, 1977. Copyright 1977, the American Orthopsychiatric Association, Inc.

The study was supported in part by USPHS grant HD-03008.

eral Interagency Day Care Requirements and the mechanisms for enforcing them.

HISTORY

Although day care has existed in America for over 100 years, the idea of government responsibility for day care quality is relatively recent. The first day care centers, or day nurseries, opened in the 1850s as informal rescue programs for the children of the poor.[18] These private charitable efforts were intended to be no more than temporary aids to families until the mother was able to stay home.[3,5] It is remarkable that, even with the advent of large numbers of working mothers and substantial public funding, this conception of day care as a social welfare tool has endured. Day care has remained suspect—at worst, family-undermining; at best, an inferior alternative to mothers staying at home. Thus, politicians rarely advocate day care simply for the sake of children; rather, they feel compelled to justify day care as a device to achieve some other social goals, such as freeing women to join the mobilization for war, or helping to reduce public welfare rolls.

To the extent that a sense of public responsibility has developed toward day care, it has more often taken the form of protecting children from all day care than from bad day care. In the early 1900s, when the number of immigrant children in day nurseries began to swell, charitable agencies established strict eligibility requirements for day care. Even the families who used day care usually looked forward to the time when the mother could return full time to the care of children. Similarly, although World War I increased the ranks of working women, the nation still saw day care as a temporary solution to an emergency situation. As soon as the war ended, progressive reformers proposed mother's pensions and other measures designed to enable mothers to stay at home. The working women never really did return home in the expected numbers, but the government continued its hands-off policy toward day care, as if any move to protect the quality would be viewed as an endorsement of mothers working.[5]

Even when the Depression and World War II vastly increased the federal expenditure on day care, the government was careful to underline day care's temporary status. Federal administration was not vested in the Children's Bureau, and most likely champion of day care quality. Instead, during the Depression, when day care was advanced as a source of public employment, administration was placed in the Works Progress Administration (WPA).[1] Then, during World War II, when work became a patriotic as well as a financial necessity for many mothers, the Children's Bureau was again relegated to the sidelines of federally subsidized programs. Day care administration fell to the Office of Defense, Health and Welfare Services.[32] The nearly 3000 wartime day care facilities were virtually exempt from specific federal and state child care regulation. As soon as the war ended, the nation quickly disassembled the day care system, even though the large numbers of mothers in the work force and the need for day care continued.

CURRENT FEDERAL STANCE

Despite the increasing federal government involvement in day care in the last decade, the principle of federal responsibility for day care quality has yet to be firmly established.[11] At least twelve different federal agencies, ranging from the Department of Agriculture to the Small Business Administration, have invested in day care.[2,10] But, despite the existence of the Children's Bureau and the creation in 1969 of the Office of Child Development, no single federal agency has been granted the economic power necessary to coordinate this maze of day care, much less enforce standards of quality. In a recent example, control of the largest federally funded day care program, under Title XX of the Social Security Act, was not vested in the OCD but rather in the Community Services Administration of HEW. Although the Children's Bureau personnel in the Office of Child Development are theoretically charged with guaranteeing the quality of Title XX day care, OCD does not have the power to make such review meaningful. Once again, the United States has repeated the mistake of previous day care efforts, placing control of day care in an agency not primarily committed to the welfare of children.

Just as Title XX day care finds its administrative home in an agency not specifically devoted to children, so too its primary political justification is to reduce welfare rolls, not help children. Yet, there is no convincing evidence that day care helps welfare parents become working parents. And, even if it did, is it wise economic policy for the federal government to buy day care for more than one or two children in a poverty-level family in order to move a mother into the work force at near poverty wages?[29] Shrinking job markets make this strategy of using day care as a tool of welfare reform still less likely to succeed.

Questions of day care strategy and fiscal control are closely related to day care standards. If the commitment to day care is based on some other social goal than the welfare of children, and if the fiscal power is distributed accordingly, the quality of the programs suffers. Compare, for example, the differences between Title XX day care and the day care component of the Head Start program, which is under the fiscal as well as theoretical jurisdiction of OCD. Although both day care programs serve children of the economically disadvantaged, the two groups of children are often treated quite differently.

Head Start has, from its inception, been viewed as a quality program to benefit children; it represents an oasis of concern about children in many communities. Head Start's education and health components are specifically designed to meet the needs of the children it serves. In addition, Head Start has served as a national model of developmental programming for children.[24,28]

By contrast, the quality of Title XX day care varies considerably. Title XX day care was originally supposed to comply with the 1968 Federal Interagency Day Care Requirements, which we will discuss later. But the states legitimately feared that the federal government would not provide the money necessary to comply. As a 1973 HEW audit revealed, the states would have a lot of catching up to do: four-fifths of the 552 facilities sampled did not meet federal requirements even in basic health and safety areas.[14] In view of this problem, Congress placed a moratorium on Title XX compliance with the FIDCR. As of this writing, day care facilities need only follow state licensing laws in order to receive Title XX funds. Furthermore, Title XX makes day care compete for funds with other social services, such as those for the aged and the handicapped. How well children fare in the various states depends upon the effectiveness with which their case can be made to state legislators, and children cannot lobby in their own behalf.

RATIONALE FOR FEDERAL STANDARDS

Federal day care regulation is needed in addition to state day care licensing laws for several critical reasons. Licensing laws vary from state to state and even between localities in a single state. In many instances, they have become so intricate that they primarily constitute a barrier to creating new day care facilities that are clearly needed. Furthermore, day care licensing laws typically concern themselves with the physical safety of children (e.g., does the center have enough protection against fire; are the caregivers free of communicable diseases?). Other crucial criteria of day care quality, such as the child-staff ratio and the competency of the caregivers, tend to be neglected or are beyond the scope of many state licensing laws.

Some states are, of course, just as enlightened about day care standards as are day care spokespeople at the federal level. But if a state is willing to have 25 preschoolers cared for by a single caregiver, the federal government should not commit itself to such standards, much less help pay for the services delivered in this way. Standards can probably more effectively be monitored at the state than at the federal level, but the issue is not a constitutional one dealing with the proper division between state and federal prerogatives. Rather, the issue is what kind of lives children will experience in day care settings during their formative years.[19]

Even if a nation commits itself to the need for day care standards, however, there remains the pragmatic problem of determining just what those standards should be. Clearly, there is a paucity of experimentally-controlled, rigorous data to guide social policy concerning children. But it is the responsibility of policy makers to navigate the most reasonable course of action based on the considerable evidence and experience to date. In charting their course, their overriding concern should be the medical dictum, "First of all, do no harm." In the absence of "hard" evidence, we must endorse the program least likely to be detrimental to children and families.

In the day care quality debate, which reached a peak in the early 1970s, "custodial" and "comprehensive" have been rallying cries. The cost-effectiveness stalwarts were said to favor limited, custodial day care, satisfying only the most basic psychological and physical needs, while the quality-at-any price advocates, who thought all children should have a broad array of health, educational, psychological, parent involvement, and social services, were said to favor comprehensive day care. These extreme positions left a large middle ground which some, including the authors, attempted to fill by advocating "developmental" day care. This meant providing the services necessary to guarantee the healthy social, emotional, intellectual, and physical development of the child. In the end, however, all of these terms may have contributed more to semantic confusion than to the elucidation of day care quality. Wisely, these terms were largely ignored by parents, who were simply looking for a caregiver and a day care setting in which their children would be at least moderately content and happy.[26]

Misleading rhetoric has also plagued discussion of the 1968 Federal Interagency Day Care Requirements, often cited as the manifesto of quality day care. Since they are supposed to govern all federally supported day care and are written into several major bills, these requirements deserve far closer analysis than they usually receive.

FEDERAL INTERAGENCY DAY CARE REQUIREMENTS

Hastily written in 1968, the Federal Interagency Day Care Requirements (FIDCR) reflect the state of the day care art at the time. Based largely on the Head Start experience, they were deliberately unspecific, more guidelines than clearly defined standards. Yet, the FIDCR contain many problems, even for day care advocates. First, their lack of specificity has made them difficult to enforce. In fact, the FIDCR have received the same treatment as the goal-setting statements issued by the old Children's Bureau: Enforcement has never even been attempted. Second, the 1968 FIDCR were primarily concerned with center-based day care, which serves only a small proportion of the children in day care. Third, the FIDCR did not clearly define the responsibilities of the day care provider and the various administering agencies, and they were vague on the requirements for care givers. Finally, the 1968 FIDCR were not sufficiently age-specific; that is, they did not provide for the special day care needs of infants and toddlers, as contrasted with those of preschool and school-age children.

Interestingly, despite these obvious deficiencies, the 1968 FIDCR ratio of one caregiver for each five children ages 3–4 years has attained near-sacred status. No figure recurs more frequently in Congressional testimony as the hallmark of quality child care. And yet, this ratio, sound enough for the preschool children in the Head Start program from which it was probably derived, would make no sense at all for infants: It is doubtful whether one caregiver could carry five infants to physical safety, in the event of a fire or disaster, much less provide them with adequate daily attention. As for school-age children, a 1:5 ratio may be unnecessarily protective. Those close to day care have long recognized the deficiencies of the high-minded 1968 standards. However, there has been an unwillingness to challenge them for fear that nothing better would be substituted and that the outcome would be far worse.

1972 FIDCR Proposals. In 1970, while serving in the Office of Child Development, we began an attempt to revise and strengthen the 1968 FIDCR as a foundation for the day care component of the Welfare Reform Plan. (The implicit assumption was that, even if the reform plan did not go through, new day care regulations were needed for the federal day care program already being funded through the Social Security Act.) This revision process began at the Airlie House Conference of 1970, at which a cross section of one thousand individuals concerned with day care, including providers, parents of children in day care, and professionals, met together. They developed a statement of principles concerning day care, as well as the basis for a series of manuals with guidelines for infant care, preschool day care, and school age day care.[8,9,15,23] Following the Airlie House Conference, OCD worked for two years to develop a final set of day care standards. Cost analyses were assessed; the day care state licensing laws of every state were examined. Finally, HEW Secretary Elliot Richardson approved the revisions and set them to the Office of Management of the Budget (OMB), whose approval was necessary before the new standards could be implemented. Sadly, the 1972 revisions disappeared in OMB, blocked by federal unwillingness to enact enforceable standards.

The 1971 proposed standards[12] are more appropriate and enforceable than the 1968 FIDCR.[13] First, the 1972 revisions are less center-based; they reflect the fact that most day care is conducted in homes, not centers. Second, the 1972 revisions are more age-specific, providing for the special needs of infants and toddlers. Third, the 1972 standards are much more precise on staff competency and the responsibilities of administering agencies and day care providers to the families they are supposed to be serving. Table 1, which compares the two sets of standards, reveals some of the major differences and suggests issues that must be considered in defining any set of standards.

It is too simplistic to argue that the 1972 proposed standards are more lenient than the 1968 FIDCR. The revisions would allow one caregiver to care for seven children in the 3-to-4½ year age range, while the 1968 standards would allow no more than a 1:5 ratio for this age group. Experience since 1968 suggests that this is generally possible if the caregiver is not burdened with other responsibilities, and the children have no extraordinary needs. The 1972 revisions are, however, more stringent than the 1968 FIDCR in that they allow one caregiver to care for no more than three infants. How did we decide on this figure, and why did the 1968 drafters not specify any ratio for infant day care?

INFANT DAY CARE CONTROVERSY

As early as 1944, a Children's Bureau conference concluded that children under three did not, in general, benefit from group experience. Most child development experts would probably still suggest extreme caution in group care for very young children. Yet, more and more parents are placing children under three in day care; indeed,

Table I

COMPARISON OF FEDERAL DAY CARE REQUIREMENTS

1972 PROPOSED FEDERAL DAY CARE REQUIREMENTS (FDCR)	1968 FEDERAL INTERAGENCY DAY CARE REQUIREMENTS (FIDCR)
CARE SETTINGS. Applies to all federally supported day care, including in-home care, family day care, group day care homes and centers; contains specific requirements for each type of care.	CARE SETTINGS. Covers only centers and family and group day care; contains no requirements pertaining to in-home care; developed primarily with center care in mind; vague on the different requirements for different settings.
AGE-SPECIFICITY. Recommends child-staff ratios according to age of child and type of day care; distinguishes among seven age groups for centers and three age groups for day care homes, recognizes the special needs of infants and toddlers. One caregiver is allowed to attend no more than three infants or four toddlers.	AGE-SPECIFICITY. Only distinguishes among three age groups for both center and family day care; sets no required ratio for center care for children under three, specifying only that state standards be followed (average ratio of adults to children under three is 1:7 in states where such ratios have been established).
RATIO FOR CENTERS. One caregiver per 3 infants (0–1½ yrs); per 4 toddlers (1½–3 yrs); per 7 children (3–4½ yrs); per 10 children (4½–6 yrs); per 13 children (6–8 yrs); per 16 children (9–11 yrs); per 20 children (12–14 yrs).	RATIO FOR CENTERS. One caregiver per 5 children (3–4 yrs); per 7 children (4–6 yrs); per 10 children (6–14 yrs). No requirement established for children under three years.
RATIO FOR FAMILY DAY CARE. One caregiver per six children, provided at least half the group is over three; in no case may one adult care for more than three toddlers or two infants.	RATIO FOR FAMILY DAY CARE. One caregiver per six children; permits one adult to serve as many as five toddlers.
STAFF COMPETENCY. All caregivers required to possess specified competencies and be able to provide children with appropriate developmental activities according to a written plan or schedule; requires at least one staff member with specified educational or experience qualifications in each center serving 39 or more children.	STAFF COMPETENCY. Does not require a written plan or schedule of activities; does not specify minimum training or experience qualifications for any staff member.
ACCOUNTABILITY. Sets forth specific requirements to ensure accountability of day care operators: in providing programs that meet federal requirements; for supervision of staff; for keeping financial and other records; etc.	ACCOUNTABILITY. Unique and specific requirements for operators not clearly identified; no clear distinction between requirements pertaining to caregivers, operators, and administering agencies.
PARENT PARTICIPATION. Requires each facility serving 15 or more children to have a policy advisory council, consisting of 50% parents; requires administering agencies to evaluate and act upon complaints from policy advisory councils and parents in general.	PARENT PARTICIPATION. Requires each facility or agency serving 40 or more children to have a policy advisory council, consisting of at least 50% parents or representatives; does not directly address the responsibility of administering agencies to investigate or act upon parent complaints.

this sector shows the fastest rise in day care utilization. While we are far from sanguine about this increase, there is no clear evidence that infant day care, of adequate quality, harms children. Outstanding psychologists have concluded that infant day care is not associated with any marked deleterious consequences.[7,17] While other studies[4,20,27] report possible negative effects, they are perhaps too subtle to guide the policy maker. Most important, none of these studies takes into account the real-life alternatives—*e.g.*, the effects of day care vs. the effects of being parked at home in front of the TV all day, or the effects of generously staffed vs. understaffed day care on children. In evaluating the impact of day care, many factors concerning children's lives, not simply short-term programmatic effects, must be considered.[6,22,25]

Based on existing research and our own best judgment, we decided on the 1:3 ratio for infants under eighteen months. One has only to think of the burdens of the mother of twins or triplets to wonder how one caregiver could regularly care for four hungry babies or curious toddlers. And what would happen in the event of a fire or other crisis? One caregiver for two children below age two would probably best approximate what most parents want for their children. However, such a ratio would be so prohibitively expensive that it would only discourage compliance. In finally deciding on the ratio of 1:3 for infants, we had to satisfy many interests—those of the mother who needs a place for her infant, the provider who must operate without losing money and perhaps with a profit, and the young child who needs a special kind of caring.

LESSONS TO GUIDE ENFORCEMENT

In restructuring federal day care requirements, it is important to remember the practical lessons of day care regulation at the state and local level. Locally, regulation has perhaps done as much to prevent good day care as to exclude bad. Complying with complex fire, building, zoning, and other codes that were not specifically designed for day care has often made licensed day care prohibitively expensive in centers and impossible to provide in homes.[21,30] Model state licensing codes, developed by the Office of Child Development, are making inroads against these antiquated procedures.[31] However, action involving so many overlapping state bodies is inevitably slow. Experts in state day care regulation generally hope for licensing procedures that will help day care facilities to comply, not just order them to close, thereby removing the present incentive to go underground.[21]

Several lessons emerge from the state and local experience. First, drafters of any new federal standards must be careful to analyze the cost implications of day care dictated by the standards (as was done for the 1972 revision).[16,33] The agency that sets the standards must have some fiscal power to assure that the states get sufficient funds to comply. Second, standards are meaningless without a national monitoring system to enforce them. Since a system of sufficient federal personnel to personally inspect day care would add considerable cost to the day care, and would be more distant from the actual day care operations, we should promote monitoring by parent users of day care and volunteer consumer advisory groups, as well as by state and local government agencies monitored by the federal government. Finally, as former HEW Secretary Wilbur Cohen suggests, it is unrealistic to expect hundreds of thousands of American day care settings to meet any agreed-upon set of standards overnight. There must be a grace period, up to a year on all but the most serious deficiencies, during which standards are not used to drive day care settings out of existence, but rather to aid them in upgrading their services. When day care does not meet federal standards, the providers should be given a list of necessary modifications, indicating the priorities and granting a reasonable time frame for implementation.

Most discussions of day care standards include recommendations on who should administer or deliver day care at the state and local level. Some advocates feel that the public school system, with its history of administrative and educational sophistication, could best guarantee the delivery of quality day care under the supervision of local boards of education; others feel that the school system is already overburdened, often educationally unsuccessful, and too insulated from community forces to be entrusted with day care. Some child advocates feel that for-profit day care is incompatible with humane care and high quality and should be excluded from receiving federal funds; others, that private enterprise is basic to the American system and that business expertise should be able to deliver economically viable, high quality day care responsive to consumer demands.

This very pluralism of day care underscores the importance of federal standards for quality. Until more definite knowledge is available, the federal stance should be as neutral as possible on day care delivery, allowing day care to be administered by schools, as well as by community organizations. Similarly, with respect to profit-making day care, the central issue does not seem to be whether for-profit day care should benefit from federal funds, but rather whether day care, non-profit or for-profit, will comply with quality standards. If realistic federal day care standards were set and enforced, we think many of the current battles about the appropriate role of the schools and profit-making day care would be resolved satisfactorily.

CONCLUSIONS

The safety and welfare of children in day care make it crucial that our nation commit itself to some federal standards for the care purchased with federal money or encouraged by federal policy. The standards must be realistic, explicit, operationally definable, and enforceable; sensitive to the individual needs of children and families and to differences during development; appropriate for day care provided in different types of settings; and carefully analyzed for cost. Sufficient funding and consultation should be available to assist providers in complying with standards within a defined, finite "grace" period. And the federal agency that sets the standards should have the real economic power to assure that standards are respected in practice.

Formal evaluations of implemented federal standards and increasing experience with the impact of day care on children and families will, no doubt, clarify areas in which there has been continuing disagreement—e.g., the role of private enterprise in providing day care or the benefits and dangers in day care for infants and toddlers. These and other areas of legitimate concern indicate the need for thoughtful, longitudinal studies that are sensitive to the real options that face families. Emerging experience, research, and evaluations will also suggest revisions in standards for day care. However, available knowledge already delineates broad areas of consensus about the basic, minimal characteristics of the care that a nation such as ours should offer its children. During the past decade, discussion among child care advocates has often highlighted differences in emphasis and ideology. The more fundamental, broader areas of agreement have tended to become obscured. Individuals and groups concerned with day care should be cautious that the goal of an ideal child care system available to all children in the future does not lead to inaction on behalf of those children who are in day care today and tomorrow.

REFERENCES

1. Alschuler, R. 1942. Children's Centers. William Morrow, New York.
2. Auerbach, S. 1973. Federally sponsored child care. *In* Child Care—Who Cares? P. Roby, ed. Basic Books, New York.
3. Beer, E. 1970. Working Mothers and the Day Nursery. Lawrence Verry, Mystic, Conn.
4. Blehar, M. 1975. Anxious attachment and defensive reactions associated with day care. *In* Influences on human development. U. Bronfenbrenner and M. Mahoney, eds. Dryden Press, Hinsdale, Ill.
5. Bremner, R. 1974. Children and Youth in America: A Documentary History, Vol.

III: 1933–1973, Parts 1–4. Harvard University Press, Cambridge, Mass.

6. Bronfenbrenner, U. 1974. A Report on Longitudinal Evaluations of Preschool Programs, Vol. II: Is Early Intervention Effective? US Department of Health, Education and Welfare, DHEW Pub. No. (OHD) 74–25.

7. Caldwell, B. et al. 1970. Infant care and attachment. Amer. J. Orthopsychiat. 40:397–412.

8. Cohen, D. and Brandegee, A. 1974. Day Care: Serving Preschool Children. US Department of Health, Education and Welfare, Office of Human Development, Office of Child Development, DHEW Pub. No. (OHD) 74–1057.

9. Cohen, D. et al. 1972. Day Care (4): Serving School-Age Children. US Department of Health, Education and Welfare, Office of Child Development, DHEW Pub. No. (OCD) 72–34.

10. Committee on Finance, United States Senate. 1974. Child Care: Data and Materials. US Government Printing Office, Washington, D.C.

11. Committee on Labor and Public Welfare, United States Senate. 1975. Child and Family Services Act, Parts 1–5. S. 626 and H.R. 2966.

12. Federal Day Care Requirements (FDCR). 1972. Revisions prepared by the Office of Child Development, Department of Health, Education and Welfare.

13. Federal Interagency Day Care Requirements (FIDCR). 1968. US Department of Health, Education, and Welfare; US Department of Economic Opportunity; US Department of Labor. Pursuant to Sec 522 (d) of the Economic Opportunity Act. US Government Printing Office, Washington, D.C. (reprinted 1970).

14. HEW Audit Agency. 1973. Survey of Child Care Services Provided Under Title IV of the Social Security Act, November 1973.

15. Huntington, D., Provence, S. and Parker, R., eds. 1972. Day Care (2): Serving Infants. US Department of Health, Education and Welfare, Office of Child Development, DHEW Pub. No. (OCD) 72–8.

16. Inner City Fund. 1972. Estimated Cost of the Federal Day Care Requirements. Submitted to the Office of Child Development.

17. Kagan, J. Kearsley, R. and Zelazo, P. 1976. The Effects of Infant Day Care on Psychological Development. Presented to the AAAS, Boston.

18. Kerr, V. 1973. One step forward—two steps back: child care's long American history. In Child Care—Who Cares? P. Roby, ed. Basic Books, New York.

19. Keyserling, M. 1972. Windows on Day Care. National Council of Jewish Women, New York.

20. Lippman, M. and Grote, B. 1974. Socioemotional efects of day care: final project report. Western Washington State College, Bellinham, Wash.

21. Morgan, G. 1972. Regulation of Early Childhood Programs. Day Care and Child Development Council of America, Washington, D.C.

22. National Research Council. 1976. Toward a National Policy for Children and Families. National Academy of Sciences, Washington, D.C.

23. Office of Child Development. 1971. Day Care (1): A Statement of Principles, US Department of Health, Education and Welfare, Office of Child Development, DHEW Publ. No. (OCD) 73–2.

24. Parker, R., ed. 1972. The Preschool in Action: Exploring Early Childhood Programs. Allyn and Bacon, Boston.

25. Ryan, S., ed. 1974. A Report on Longitudinal Evaluations of Preschool Programs, Vol. I: Longitudinal Evaluations. US Department of Health, Education and Welfare, DHEW Pub. No. (OHD) 74–24.

26. Rodes, T. and Moore, J. 1975. National Childcare Consumer Study, Vol. I: Basic

Tabulations. Office of Child Development, US Department of Health, Education and Welfare.

27. Schwarz, J., Krolick, G. and Strickland, R. 1973. Effects of early day care experience on adjustment to a new environment. Amer. J. Orthopsychiat. 43:340–346.

28. Stanley, J., ed. 1972. Preschool Programs for the Disadvantaged: Five Experimental Approaches to Early Childhood Education. Johns Hopkins University Press, Baltimore.

29. Steiner, G. 1971. The State of Welfare. Brookings Institution, Washington, D.C.

30. US Department of Health, Education and Welfare (Office of Child Development). 1971. Abstracts of State Day Care Licensing Requirements, Part 1: Family Day Care Homes and Group Homes; Part 2: Day Care Centers. DHEW Pub. Nos. (OCD) 72–11; 72–12.

31. US Department of Health, Education and Welfare (Office of Child Development). 1972 (and later versions). Models for Day Care Licensing.

32. US Department of Labor (Children's Bureau). 1942. Defense of Children Series. Nos. 1–11. Washington, D.C.

33. Young, D. and Nelson, R. 1973. Public Policy for Day Care of Young Children: Organization, Finance, and Planning. D.C. Health, Lexington, Mass.

33

THE HEALTH STATUS OF FOSTER CHILDREN

Margaret R. Swire and Florence Kavaler

Foster Care Evaluation Study

A study of the health care and needs of foster children in the New York City area indicated a prevalence of serious physical, mental and developmental problems. The level of pathology was roughly comparable to that of other disadvantaged child populations.

The last several years have been characterized by increased concern over the effectiveness and efficiency of present methods of both delivering and paying for various types of health care. In the United States, legislation enacted in the last decade has reduced some of the financial barriers to the adequate provision of health services, especially for children. Conceptual schemes and theoretical frameworks have been developed and empirical studies have been designed to examine various aspects of medical care assessment. Despite these developments, there are many indications that millions of needy youngsters eligible for free health care in this country have failed to receive adequate preventive or specialty services. Of particular concern are those children who are medically indigent, who are without

Reprinted with permission from *Child Welfare*, Vol. 56, 635–653, 1977.

The study was supported by Grant No. MC-R-360032, "Evaluation of Health Services for Foster Children," Maternal and Child Health Service, H.S.M.H.A., U.S. Department of Health, Education and Welfare. Progress reports on earlier stages of the research appeared in *Child Welfare* in November 1972 and March 1974.

homes of their own, and who are currently receiving various forms of foster care services.

There are more than 300,000 youngsters in this category in the U.S. today, with a continuing upward trend in the number of children so placed [1]. Although little is known about the health needs of this special population, the data available indicate that the public cost of providing health care to these youngsters is vast. During the fiscal year 1973–74 Medicaid funds expended by federal, state and local governments for health services for these children exceeded $200 million [2]. In New York City alone, costs have annually exceeded $22 million for the 28,000 children so placed [3]. Such an enormous infusion of public money requires accountability, surveillance and appraisal of the services rendered. For this reason and because children entering foster care exhibit the precise characteristics long associated with the greatest unmet needs [4;5;6;7], the New York City Department of Health, supported by funds from the Maternal and Child Health Services of the U.S. Department of Health, Education and Welfare, initiated an evaluative study of health services for foster children. The first phase of this study, carried out in 1971 and 1972, documented current health delivery systems in New York City social agencies and provided a basis for their evaluation. Two earlier papers resulted from this initial research. One dealt with standards of health care for foster children [8] and the second provided preliminary information on the medical care programs of 14 New York City child care agencies [9]. The present report focuses on selected findings of phase 2 of the study.

This research, conducted in 1973–74, assessed the health status and medical care needs of children in foster care homes in New York City and examined the relationship between the cost of care, the health needs of the youngsters, and the structure and functioning of existing medical care programs provided by the agencies that assume responsibility for the children. In all, 668 youngsters from eight New York City child care agencies were included in the study. They were clinically examined, their medical records were reviewed and their sociodemographic profiles ascertained. This report presents the results of the health examinations performed for this study. The main objective was to describe quantitatively the range of problems among the sample group. The paper also makes a number of comparisons between the sample children and youngsters from different social and economic strata, and analyzes health differentials by selected demographic and socioeconomic characteristics.

SAMPLE AND DATA COLLECTION

In New York City a network of over 70 administratively autonomous agencies provides care, mostly through purchase-of-service
agreements with the city Bureau of Child Welfare, to more than
28,000 foster care children. From this universe of agencies a sample of
eight was selected for inclusion in the study. There were two agencies
that administered the city's Direct Care Program for 4000 children,
and six agencies drawn from the pool of 14 voluntary child care agencies studied during the phase 1 survey [10].

Agency selection was dictated by: a) cost and logistical considerations; b) statistical factors,* and c) the need to represent the salient
and differing characteristics of all the agencies caring for the children
in respect to the religious auspices under which they operate, the
amount spent for health services (per capita costs among the agencies
ranged from $733 to $83), how the service was supplied (whether by
the agency itself as a centralized service or a decentralized one), the
size of the foster boarding home caseload for which the agency assumed responsibility, and social and demographic characteristics of
the population served.

CHILD SAMPLE

The child study sample was drawn from the population of the eight
agencies selected. Included were children who were New York City
public charges as of July 1, 1972, residing in foster home care; who
were between the ages of 1 and 15 inclusive; and who lived in households in the five boroughs of New York City and the westernmost
part of Nassau County, adjacent to New York City.

The sample was drawn in several stages. The first stage, performed
in November 1972, involved obtaining each agency's roster of children. Each list identified the names and ages of children in care as of
July 1, 1972. These rosters were used as the base from which 130
names were drawn from each agency. The names were then classified
into four equal strata by sex and age group (under 6, and 6 and
over). Cases that did not meet the study's criteria for age and geo-
graphic acceptability were deleted and resampling was performed as

---

*It was determined that no less than 80 cases per agency were required, since a small-
er number would seriously reduce the chances of describing and analyzing differences
that might have significance for the provision of health services for this group of children.

needed. Although it was planned to use only the primary sample, it was recognized that additional reserve segments would be needed to avoid the risk of insufficient numbers of examinees and to account for the vagaries of sample mobility and response rate. Accordingly, an element of flexibility was introduced into the design and a second sample of 130 names was similarly drawn and stratified for each agency. The yield of eligible children in any given agency became the basis for a decision to sample further. This approach, which was dictated by cost and logistical considerations, featured disproportionate sampling within each agency (i.e., an agency with a smaller child care caseload would have a larger part of its population in the study). The sampling process yielded a total of 1257 names. Of these, 795 met the study's eligibility criteria for participation in the clinical examinations. In all, 84% of the sample group received such evaluations. Among those not examined, the primary reason for nonparticipation (for 78 out of 127 nonparticipants, or 61%) was the foster mother's refusal to cooperate; other reasons, which were numerically insignificant, included such factors as the child's being away or ill, transportation problems, and a range of miscellaneous reasons. These patterns did not vary significantly across the agencies.

Of the 462 children (42%) who did not meet eligibility criteria for inclusion in the project, 21% were not within the study's age range, 19% could not be contacted, 12% were in the process of being removed from foster care, and 10% lived outside the survey area. Thus, noneligibility was in part a function of population mobility and turnover as these children returned to their own families or became adopted. These factors were evenly distributed across the agencies.*

The extent of potential bias resulting from the 425 cases of children not examined was ascertained for four key variables on which comparable data were available. These were: sex, ethnicity, chronic medical problem at entry, and health status upon admission to the foster care agency. Such comparisons, although not conclusive, suggest that the children examined closely approximate the known characteristics of those who were not examined.

It is important to note that although the original plan called for selection of a representative group of foster home children, self-

---

*Overall, it appears that sample erosion due to unavailability of one kind of another was evenly distributed across the agencies, and does not affect the representation of any one facility. However, the loss of 42% of the original sample selected within a relatively short time is an important confounding variable, and a factor of which studies of this type of population must take note.

selection factors (as detailed earlier) resulted in a biased study group. It is not possible, therefore, to generalize that the health status of the typical foster home child in New York City is similar to that of the typical child who participated in this study. It may be better or worse. What is possible is a rather insightful description of the level of health of the children who did participate. And to the degree to which this description has meaning for improving the quality of health services that should be available to all foster children, this survey will have been worthwhile.

METHOD

The health examinations performed were designed to provide a comprehensive picture of the physical, dental and mental health status and needs of the study children. The assumption underlying this approach was that direct clinical evaluations would offer a mechanism for viewing health and care. In effect, the findings of this survey would gauge the health of the study group and provide: a) measures of the end result of medical care rendered; b) information not only about diagnosed conditions, but about previously unattended or undiagnosed conditions; and c) baseline data on the physical, dental and psychiatric status of these children.

The basic elements of the health assessment consisted of a complete and careful medical history and a physical examination of all systems; vision, audiometric, dental screening tests and a laboratory workup; a developmental examination for infants and children under 6; psychological testing for school-age children; and psychiatric evaluations for a randomly selected subsample of children over 6.

The tests were carried out by a team of pediatricians* and other health professionals at the pediatric outpatient center of New York Hospital—Cornell Medical School. Guidelines prepared with the assistance of consultants described recording procedures and defined the clinical terms used in the study. In addition, the group to be examined was equally distributed among the survey examiners to minimize the interexaminer bias. At the end of each appraisal, a decision was made concerning the child's general health and need for subsequent treatment. The results of the examinations and recommendations were reported to each child's agency.

---

*Resident and attending pediatricians.

RESULTS

Six hundred and sixty-eight children, or 84% of those eligible for testing, were screened at the New York Hospital Pediatric Clinic, with specific procedures administered in accordance with age-group differentials. The findings presented here "describe" the general health levels of the children evaluated along the dimensions of physical, developmental, psychiatric and dental health.

PHYSICAL

Physician's Impression of Health Status

Four hundred and ninety-seven children (26%) showed some significant physical abnormality upon examination and received the classification "other-than-well" by survey pediatricians. Boys showed slightly higher levels of problems than girls, as did children under 2 years old when compared with those over 2. Ethnically, Puerto Rican children appeared to have somewhat poorer health (33%) than whites (24%) or blacks (24%), but differences fell just short of statistical significance.

Several previous studies have sought to explore the health levels of children by means of direct clinical appraisals. Perhaps the most comprehensive and widely known is that conducted by the Division of Health Examination Statistics of the National Center for Health Statistics. This program, known as the Health Examination Survey (HES), comprises a probability sample of the nation's noninstitutionalized child population and provides data on the prevalence of illness and other health-related measures. Since the HES clinical examination protocols served as the principal prototype for the design of this survey, the appraisals performed in both these investigations should be roughly comparable. Thus, in each survey the examining pediatrician recorded a diagnostic impression of the child's general health status* and assigned a rating of "well" or "other-than-well," i.e., having some significant abnormality.

Survey evidence suggests that children in the present study were generally less healthy than those of comparable ages from the HEW

---

*Excluded from the assessment were acute conditions, minor skin problems, caries, defective vision and hearing, abnormal laboratory test results or other procedures not requiring the professional time and skill of a physician.

sample: among the 6–11-year-olds, one child in five had some significant finding, compared with one child in nine in the HES group [11].
Relevant comparative data for low income populations are supplied by
Head Start clinical studies of preschool children and by Job Corps appraisals of high school youngsters. For the former, rates of 17% and
20% were reported for samples in California and Boston [12:382–
387;13], as against a rate of 30% for our preschool group. The Job
Corps figures were considerably higher, ranging from 24% to 62% for
adolescents in various different cities [14:40–43;15;16:64–65]. The
corresponding rate for comparably aged youngsters in our survey was
24%.

Referral for Specialty Care

Two hundred and forty-four children (37%) were found to have
343 potentially adverse conditions requiring recommendation for referral for specialty treatment: 26% were referred for specialty care for
a single problem, 7% for two problems and 4% for three or more
problems. The overall proportion of children referred for specialty
treatment did not vary significantly by sex, age or ethnic group, nor
did it vary by such parameters as education of the natural mother, reason for placement, education of the foster mother, foster family income or foster family occupational status. It should be noted that, although not strictly comparable, data reported by other researchers of
disadvantaged groups are in accord with these findings. Thus, treatment need rates ranged from 35% to 49% for samples of low income
children in Texas, Harlem and Boston [17;18;19:241–249].

Chronic Conditions

In respect to chronic illness, survey pediatricians identified 442
chronic conditions among the 668 examinees.* Almost half the children examined (45%) were found to have at least one chronic problem; of these 25% showed evidence of a single condition, and 20%
exhibited multiple disabilities. The distribution of these conditions indicates musculoskeletal (23%), congenital (15%), speech (13%) and

---

*Chronic illnesses were defined in the instructions to study pediatricians as "serious
medical illnesses of a chronic nature which may impair the child's current and future
functioning." Rate includes relatively minor conditions and more serious ailments.

cardiovascular (12%) constituted the major conditions diagnosed.†
Within the sample, boys averaged .71 problems, somewhat more than
girls, who averaged .58, a difference significant at the .05 level of confidence. Ethnically, variations were also detected, with whites exhibiting significantly more problems (.80) than blacks (.62) or Puerto Ri-
cans (.57). With respect to age, younger children were distinguishable
from others by their higher level of problems (.76 for those under 6
years, .57 for those between 6 and 11, and .50 for those 12 to 15),
possibly indicating that such conditions were corrected for the older
group.

Although varying methodologies and field techniques preclude
rigorous comparisons, it is interesting to contrast these results with
evidence from previous studies. Thus, the chronic illness rate (23%)‡
for comparably aged "average" children from the nation's general
pediatric population was only half that of our study group (45%) [20].
Moreover, figures furnished by other researchers as far apart as
Rochester, New York [21], Alamance County, North Carolina [22],
and Great Britain [23], though not totally consistent, generally fall
within the range of 10% to 20% for samples drawn from a wide
socioeconomic spectrum.

Height and Weight Levels

Measurements performed on study children showed their growth
levels to be considerably below normative expectancies [24]: 8% of the
total group, or twice the expected number, fell below the 5th percentile for heights, and also for weights. Moreover, one-third, as compared with an expected one-quarter, fell below the lower quartile. Although such shifts were consistent across sex and age groups up to 11
years, those children most affected were under 6. Within this age
range, almost three times the predicted number (11%) fell below the
5th percentile. Older children in the sample more closely approxi-

---

†All disabilities and impairments identified by survey pediatricians were coded according to the *Eighth Revision, International Classification of Disease, Adopted for Use in the
United States*, P.H.S. Pub. No. 1693, Public Health Service, Washington, 1967. Chronic
conditions were defined and categorized to comply with the guidelines established by
the National Center for Health Statistics, P.H.S., Pub. No. 80, Series 10. Public Health
Service, 1973.

‡Chronic illness was broadly defined (mild, moderate and severe ailments) in the HES
study, the Rochester, New York, survey, and the Great Britain investigation. The North
Carolina chronic illness rate includes only moderate to severe conditions.

mated the published norms. Apparently, although the growth rates of our preschool group were considerably below those of youngsters from more advantaged segments of society, those of our school-age sample showed a fairly normal pattern of acceleration. Birch and other investigators pointed to nutritional inadequacy as the single most important factor contributing to abnormal growth rates [25:184]. This suggests that our study children had somewhat deficient diets early in their lives. Later in their childhood they seemed to attain more adequate levels of nutrition.

Vision and Hearing

The screening tests revealed that about one in four children aged 6–11 and more than one in three youngsters aged 12–15 had poor visual acuity (20/40 or worse) when tested without correction. There were no striking differences by sex or ethnicity, but defective vision increased significantly with age. Our sample had a higher incidence of visual defects than a representative group of comparably aged children that were similarly screened in the nationwide HES program: 11% of the 6–11-year-olds and 22% of the 12–17-year-olds tested in that study were found to have poor visual acuity [26;27]. Surveys of disadvantaged populations are, however, more consistent with our findings [28;29].

Among the children questioned as to their vision correction status, 111 (23%) reported that they wore glasses, but information on the adequacy of correction was limited to 66 examinees who brought their glasses to the testing center. Of these, 61%, a disturbingly high proportion, were found to have inadequate correction. Data analyzed to ascertain acuity levels among children who reported that they wore glasses showed that more than 29% had normal acuity levels and thus did not require corrective lenses.

Audiometric screening tests were administered to the study children with the following results: 85% passed; 15% were referred for further testing. Differences were not significant by age or sex, but hearing test results varied markedly by ethnicity: fewer Puerto Rican children (75%) passed the screening test than their white (82%) or black (88%) counterparts, perhaps indicating a language difficulty during the testing sessions.

In general, hearing problems appeared to be more prevalent in our survey group than in the general pediatric population. Examinees aged 6–11 were three times more likely to have hearing losses in the speech range than youngsters of the same age from the broad-based

HES sample that were similarly screened (3% as compared with 1%) [30]. Positive findings, however, fell within the range reported for other low income populations (2.2%–3%) [31;32].

Developmental Levels

Survey psychologists tested 279 preschool children on the Denver Developmental Screening Test (DDST) and found 10% to be "abnormal,"* 19% "questionable" and 71% "normal" in their physical, motor, perceptual and cognitive skills. There were some differences by sex and ethnicity in the distribution of "abnormal" and "questionable" ratings, but none according to age. Thus, male, Puerto Rican and black children were overrepresented in the "questionable" category, and whites in the "abnormal" category, though differences fell just short of statistical significance. Further analysis showed that the prevalence of developmental problems appears related to the ethnic group of the natural mother; more children with white mothers than children with black or Puerto Rican mothers were classified as "abnormal," and more children with Puerto Rican mothers received "questionable" ratings. Differences were consistently significant. "Normal" ratings were more likely to be assigned to children with black mothers (76%) than those with white (60%) or Puerto Rican (64%) mothers.

These findings deviate considerably from previously reported developmental data: one child in 33 in the DDST middle class standardization population [33] and in a sample of culturally deprived Philadelphia children [34] were classified as "abnormal," compared with one child in 10 in our sample group. Comparative figures for "normal" and "questionable" ratings, on the other hand, were rather similar for all three study groups.

Serious developmental delays appear far more prevalent among this preschool foster care population than among children living in either a middle class or low income environment. This finding may be related to the fact that the previous studies were based on populations that excluded as "high risk" children who were adopted, had been born prematurely, were breech deliveries, had serious physical handicapping conditions, or were twins. In our sample, however, such serious developmental delays appear ethnically related, with white chil-

---

*Abnormal ratings, according to the test developers, have a referral criterion designed to correspond to IQs or DQs of 70 or below: Frankenburg, W. K., et al. "Development of Preschool-aged-children—Racial-Ethnic and Social Class Comparisons," paper presented at SRCD Meeting, Philadelphia, March 1973.

dren far more deviant developmentally (one in four) than their black or Puerto Rican peers (one in 14). The differences may also be an artifact of the study's procedure. That is, the DDST manual states that "abnormal" and "questionable" results may be related to a number of factors in the administration of the examination (e.g., lack of active cooperation of the children), and suggests that such findings be verified in 2 or 3 weeks [35]. Unfortunately, repeat testing was beyond the scope of this study; all testing consisted of a single encounter with examiners.

PSYCHIATRIC IMPAIRMENT

Survey evidence showed that only 4% of those tested (a subgroup of 179 school-age children) were unimpaired mentally; 35% were judged to have "moderate" impairment and another 35% "marked-to-severe" levels of impairment. The mental health status of the study group did not vary by age, sex, ethnic group, educational level of the natural mother, household composition, or public assistance status of the natural parents. However, children placed in foster care for reasons of "severe neglect or abuse" were evaluated as significantly more impaired (49%) than children placed for any other reason. The least impaired children appear to be those placed because of physical illness or incapacity of the child-caring person (26%). Mental health status also showed a relationship to the number of different foster care placements that each child had since admission to the agency; just under two-fifths (37%) of the children having had one placement were classified in the "marked-to-severe" category, compared with 50% of those with three or more placements. Differences were significant to the .05 probability level. It appears that three or more placements are strongly associated with higher levels of impairment. Although the reasons for this relationship are not clear, one might expect psychological symptoms to occur more frequently in children having had a series of placements.

Previous studies that used similar standardized evaluations have generally reported lower levels of psychiatric impairment among children than was observed in this survey. Thus, the rate of "moderate-to-severe" psychiatric impairment for our sample (35%) was 50% greater than that of the Langner New York City welfare sample (23% and about triple that of his New York City cross-sectional group (12%) [36]. Langner also reported that 20% of the children who had not been in their mother's care since birth were impaired, against only 12% of those who had been constantly in her care. A clinical study of children from Manhattan's lower East Side by Silver and Hagan produced a figure comparable to Langner's [37:645–674]. However, Rutter, Tizard and Whitmore reported a distinctly lower prevalence rate of 7% for clinically significant conditions among 10–11-year-old children from the Isle of Wight [38].*

Since most of the research on the behavioral adjustment of children has been based on parent, teacher or self-ratings, published data are not strictly comparable to those of the present survey. Nonetheless, to the extent that these studies provide rough estimates of the level of maladjustment in other populations, they are useful and instructive for comparisons. Leighton, using a self-administered questionnaire, found 22% of a Chapel Hill, North Carolina, elementary school group and 17% of a junior-senior high school sample to be maladjusted [39]. Similar rates were reported by Lapouse for her "representative" Buffalo study group [40:1130–1141], and by Pless and Roghmann in a Rochester sample of average 6–10-year-olds [41]. However, Rutter, Tizard and Whitmore, using parent and teacher ratings, screened the entire 10–11-year-old population of the Isle of Wight and produced a rate of only 7%, and Britain's National Child Development Study [43] showed a similar figure (9%) for its sample of "ordinary" children. Not surprisingly, "disadvantaged" youngsters in this same British study were three times more likely than their "ordinary" counterparts to be classified as maladjusted (26% as against 9%).

Although past work offers little in the way of comparative data for other foster care populations, a recent Massachusetts study [44] found behavioral/emotional disorders to be the leading single cause of illness among 5862 foster home children, accounting for one-third of all disabilities as reported by social workers. These various figures tend to suggest that children in our urban foster care sample are far more likely to experience behavioral maladjustments than those drawn from a wider socioeconomic spectrum.

Dental

Survey data showed that 38% of the children screened (a subgroup of 473 youngsters between 3 and 15 years) were in need of treatment for one or more dental problems. Need levels increased significantly

---

*The Langner samples (1972) were 6–18-year-olds, a Manhattan cross-section of 1034 and a Manhattan welfare group of 1000. The Silver and Hagan sample (1970–71) consisted of 168 6–7-year-olds from Manhattan's lower East Side, 79% white, 12% black, 9% Puerto Rican. The Rutter-Tizard-Whitmore sample (1970) was the entire 10–11-year-old population of the Isle of Wight.

with advancing age, rising from 21% for the 3–5-year-olds to 61% for the 12–15-year-olds, but no differences occurred by sex or ethnic group. By contrast, a study of typical high school students from a Pittsburgh suburb produced a rate of only 30% for referable dental disease [45:572–600]. Other investigators studying low income populations have reported figures ranging from 60% to 90%. In the summer of 1966, for example, 65% of 1276 preschool children enrolled in a Boston Head Start program were referred for dental care [46], and more recently 85% of a sample of Harlem adolescents were found to be in need of treatment [47].

Regarding the prevalence of dental decay, over half of the children examined were found to have one or more decayed teeth, with the level of decay rising sharply and consistently with age. Thus, one-third of the 3–5-year-olds, two-thirds of the 6–11-year-olds and three quarters of the 12–15-year-olds had one or more instances of caries. An earlier study of low income preschool Head Start youngsters reported decay levels ranging from 40% to 90% [48:191–194] and a Chicago survey of school-age indigent children produced the strikingly high decay rate of 97% [49]. By contrast, evidence from the broad-based HES investigation revealed that one in four children between 6 and 11 years and one in two children between 12 and 17 had one or more decayed teeth [50;51].

In sum, comparisons with other populations consistently place the dental needs of our sample at levels comparable to those of other disadvantaged groups, and significantly above the levels of more socially and economically representative samples. The widespread prevalence of dental decay among the examinees seems to indicate that dental care has been neither promptly, consistently nor adequately provided. This is supported by data from our record survey, which show that nearly half (47%) of the children classified as "in need of dental treatment" had not been to a dentist in the last 5 years. Apparently the removal of economic barriers, at least for the sample studied, was not sufficient in itself to ensure adequate utilization of preventive or therapeutic dental services.

CONCLUSION AND SUMMARY

The data reported in this paper were derived from a survey carried out in 1973–74 by the New York City Department of Health, with the technical assistance of the pediatric outpatient evaluation clinic of New York Hospital—Cornell Medical School. Using direct clinical examinations, information was gathered on the physical, mental and dental health status of 668 children from eight New York City child caring agencies. Although much in-depth data were obtained, self-selection factors resulted in a biased study sample. Therefore, as pointed out earlier, it is not possible to generalize that the health status of the typical foster child is similar to that of the typical child that participated in this survey.

What has been possible is a description of the level of health of the children who did participate. And to the degree to which this description has meaning for improving the quality of health services that should be made available to all foster children, the study will have been worthwhile. Mindful of these limitations, we report the principal findings that follow.

SUBSTANTIAL LEVELS OF HEALTH PROBLEMS

Physical

● Almost half (45%) the sample children were found to have at least one chronic problem. Of these, one in four showed evidence of a single condition, and one in five exhibited multiple disabilities.

● More than a third (37%) of the study group were found to have one or more adverse conditions requiring medical attention.

● About one in four sample children aged 6–11 and more than one in three youngsters aged 12–15 were found to have poor visual acuity (20/40 or worse) when screened without correction; among this group 11% had moderately to severely defective vision (20/70 or worse) and 4% had severe impairment (20/200 or blind). Sixty-one percent of the children tested with their glasses were found to have inadequate correction, and 29% of those who reportedly wore glasses had normal acuity levels when tested without corrections.

Developmental

● More than one-fourth (29%) of the preschool children tested for developmental delays were judged to be "abnormal" or "questionable" in the areas of personal-social, language, and fine or gross motor abilities. Among this group, one in three were classified as "abnormal" in development.

Mental

● Only 4% of the children screened by survey psychiatrists were found to be unimpaired mentally. By contrast, the rate for "moderate-severe" impairment was 70%

Dental

● Nearly two out of 3 (63%) sample children aged 6–11 had one or more decayed teeth; about two-fifths of those aged 6–11 and four-fifths of those aged 12–15 were judged to be in need of dental treatment.

COMPARISON WITH OTHER SAMPLES

Children in our sample group of all ages were found to be less healthy than youngsters from other pediatric populations representing different social, cultural and economic strata. They were more likely to exhibit physical, emotional and dental pathology than children drawn from broader based samples, and, perhaps not surprisingly, their needs were at levels roughly comparable to those of other disadvantaged populations.

In short, the greater health risks associated with poor, inner-city minority group children are characteristic of our sample. Even bearing in mind the words of Fanshel [52:66] that "the one-time cross-sectional investigation tends to be biased in the direction of finding severe pathology," it nevertheless remains true that children who stay in the foster care system continue to have significant medical and psychiatric problems that social agencies must meet.

REFERENCES

1. U.S. Department of Health, Education and Welfare. Child Welfare Statistics, Pub. No. (SRS) 73-03258, NCSS Report E-9, April 27, 1973.
2. U.S. Department of Health, Education and Welfare. Medical Assistance (Medicaid), financed under Title XIX of the Social Security Act, Pub. No. (SRS) 75-03150, January 1974.
3. New York State Department of Social Services Statistical Report on Vendor Medical Care, 1974. (Schedules "D" and "E" State Claims Div.). This figure includes payments to physicians, dentists, podiatrists, clinical laboratories.
4. Maas, Henry S., and Engler, Richard E. Children in Need of Parents. New York: Columbia University Press, 1959.
5. Grow, Lucille J., and Shyne, Ann W. Requests for Child Welfare Service. New York: Child Welfare League of America, 1969.
6. Jenkins, Shirley, and Norman, Elaine. "Families of Children in Foster Care," Children, XVI, 4 (1969).
7. Sauber, Mignon. "Preplacement Situations of Families: Data for Planning Services," Child Welfare, XLVI, 10 (October 1967).
8. Kavaler, Florence, and Swire, Margaret R. "Health Services for Foster Children: An Approach to Evaluation," Child Welfare, LI, 9 (November 1972).
9. ———. "Health Services for Foster Children: An Evaluation of Agency Programs," Child Welfare, LII, 3 (March 1974).

10. Ibid.
11. National Center for Health Statistics. Examination and Health History Findings Among Children and Youth, 6–17 Years—United States. Vital and Health Statistics, Series 11, No. 129. DHEW Pub. No. (HRA). Washington, D.C.: Health Resources Administration, November, 1973.
12. Gilbert, A., Lewis, A., and Day, R. W. "Project Head Start: An Evaluation of Medical Components in California," California Medicine, CVI (May 1967). (Sample: preschool children primarily, but not exclusively, underprivileged.)
13. Mico, R. "A Look at the Health of Boston's Head Start Children," Journal of School Health, XXXVI (1966). Sample: 1467 underprivileged school children.
14. Eisner, V.; Goodlett, C. B., and Driver, M. B. "Health of Enrollees in Neighborhood Youth Corps," Pediatrics, XXXVIII (1966).
15. Bernstein, Betty J. "Examination of Health Aspects in the Early Planning of the Poverty Program in New York City," paper presented at annual meeting APHA, Chicago 1965.
16. Medical World News. Major Ailments Affect One-Third of Poor Children. Nov. 5, 1965.
17. New York Times. Welfare Youth Get Health Tests. September 1974.
18. Brunswick, A. F., and Josephson, E. Adolescent Health in Harlem, American Journal of Public Health (October 1972 supplement).
19. Mico, R.: op. cit.
20. National Center for Health Statistics. Children and Youth, Selected Health Characteristics—United States. Vital and Health Statistics, Series 10, No. 62, Washington, D.C., February 1971.
21. Pless, I. B., and Roghmann, K. J. "Chronic Illness and Its Consequences: Observations Based on Three Epidemiologic Surveys," Journal of Pediatrics, LXXIX, 3 (September 1971).
22. Richardson, W. P.; Higgins, A. C., and Ames, R. C. The Handicapped Children of Alamance County, North Carolina: A Medical and Sociological Study. Wilmington, Del.: Nemours Foundation, 1965.
23. Douglas, J. W. B. The Home and the School. London: Mackgibbon and Kee, 1964.
24. Stuart, Harold C., et al. Anthropometric charts, based on "repeated measurements of children under comprehensive studies of health and development." Children's Medical Center, Boston, Department of Maternal and Child Health, Harvard School of Public Health.
25. Birch, H. G., and Gussow, J. D. Disadvantaged Children: Health Nutrition and School Failure. New York: Harcourt, Brace and World, and Grune and Stratton, 1970.
26. National Center for Health Statistics Binocular Visual Acuity of Children: Demographic and Socioeconomic Characteristics—United States. Vital and Health Statistics. Series 11, No. 112, Public Health Service. Washington, D.C.: Government Printing Office, 1972.
27. National Center for Health Statistics. Visual Acuity of Youths 12–17 years—United States. Vital and Health Statistics, Series 11, No. 127. Public Health Service. Washington, D.C.: Government Printing Office, May 1973.
28. Kessner, D. M.; Snow, C. K., and Singer, J. Assessment of Medical Care for Children: Contrasts in Health Status, Vol. 3. Washington, D.C.: National Academy of Sciences, 1974.
29. Brunswick and Josephson, op. cit.
30. National Center for Health Statistics: Hearing Levels of Children by Age and

Sex—United States. Vital and Health Statistics, Series 11, No. 102. Public Health Service. Washington, D.C.: Government Printing Office. February 1970.
31. Kessner, et al., op. cit.
32. Wedge, Peter, and Prosser, Hilary. Born to Fail. London: Arrow Books, 1973.
33. Frankenburg, W. K., et al. "The Revised Denver Developmental Screening Test: Its Accuracy as a Screening Instrument," Journal of Pediatrics, LIX, 6 (December 1971).
34. Sandler, L., et al. Developmental Test Performance and Behavioral Styles of Disadvantaged Nursery School Children. Philadelphia. Hahnemann Medical College, 1971.
35. Frankenburg, W. K.: Dodds, J. B., and Fandal, W. W. Denver Developmental Screening Test Manual, revised edition. Denver: University of Colorado Medical Center, 1970.
36. Langner, T. Psychiatric Impairment in Urban Children Over Time. Summary of work on project, unpublished, May 1972.
37. Silver, A., and Hagan, R. "Profile of a First Grade: A Basis for Preventive Psychiatry," Journal of the American Academy of Child Psychiatry, XI (October 1972).
38. Rutter, M.; Tizard, J., and Whitmore, K. Education, Health and Behavior. London: Longmans, Green, 1970.
39. Leighton, D., et al. Measuring Stress Levels of School Children as a Program Monitoring Device: Three Years' Experience in a Single School System (1969, 1971, 1972). Unpublished study.
40. Lapouse, R. "Relationship of Behavior to Adjustment in a Representative Sample of Children," American Journal of Public Health, LV (1965). Also, "Epidemiology of Behavior Disorders in Children," American Journal of Diseases of Children (1966), 594–599.
41. Pless and Roghmann, op. cit.
42. Rutter, Tizard and Whitmore, op. cit.
43. Wedge and Prosser, op. cit.
44. Gruber, A. R. Foster Care in Massachusetts. Governor's Commission on Foster Care, 1973.
45. Rogers, K. D., and Reese, G. "Health Studies of Presumably Normal High School Students," American Journal of Diseases of Children, LVIII (December 1964).
46. Mico, op. cit.
47. Brunswick and Josephson, op. cit.
48. North, A. F. "Project Head Start and the Pediatrician," Clinical Pediatrics, VI (April 1967).
49. Chicago Indigent Dental Survey, 1960. Reported in Chicago Board of Health Preliminary Report on Patterns of Medical and Health Care in Poverty Areas of Chicago and Proposed Health Programs for the Medically Indigent, Chicago, 1965.
50. National Center for Health Statistics. Decayed, Missing and Filled Teeth Among Children—United States. Vital and Health Statistics. Series II, No. 106. Health Services and Mental Health Administration. Washington, D.C.: Government Printing Office, August 1971.
51. National Center for Health Statistics. Decayed, Missing and Filled Teeth Among Youths 12-17 Years—United States. Vital and Health Statistics, Series II, No. 144. Health Resources Administration. Washington, D.C.: Government Printing Office, October 1974.
52. Fanshel, David. "The Exit of Children From Foster Care," Child Welfare L, 2 (February 1971).